CALIFORNIA VOL 1

Experience Chemistry

in the Earth System

We are excited and proud to partner with Flinn Scientific in the development of this highly innovative program. Flinn Scientific supports science educators in opening young minds to the challenges and joys of scientific discovery.

The cover shows bismuth, a commonly used, naturally occurring metal that has some unique properties. The layered, hollowed-out shape of crystallized bismuth is typical of "hopper crystals." The multiple colors of a bismuth crystal are caused by differences in the oxide layer that forms on its surface. Sebastian Janicki/Shutterstock; Bkgd: Sylverarts Vectors/Shutterstock

---

Savvas Learning Company LLC, 15 East Midland Avenue, Paramus, NJ 07652

ISBN-13: 978-1-4183-0680-9
ISBN-10: 1-4183-0680-0

4 20

PROGRAM AUTHORS

Christopher Moore, Ph.D. is the Dr. George F. Haddix Community Chair in Physical Science at the University of Nebraska Omaha, where he directs programs for pre- and in-service secondary chemistry and physics teachers. Holding a M.S. in applied physics and a Ph.D. in chemistry from Virginia Commonwealth University, Dr. Moore has worked as a physical science teacher at several secondary schools in Virginia, as a professional materials scientist, and as a scholar of and consultant on science education. His education research focuses on the development of scientific reasoning and expert-like science practice abilities, and his materials science research focuses on electronic materials for devices. He is the author of the books *Teaching Science Thinking: Using Scientific Reasoning in the Classroom* and *Creating Scientists: Teaching and Assessing Science Practice for the NGSS.*

Michael Wysession, Ph.D. is a Professor of Earth and Planetary Sciences at Washington University in St. Louis and Executive Director of The Teaching Center. Author of more than 100 science and science education publications, Dr. Wysession was awarded the prestigious National Science Foundation Presidential Faculty Fellowship and Packard Foundation Fellowship for his research in geophysics, primarily focused on using seismic tomography to determine the forces driving plate tectonics. Dr. Wysession is also a leader in geoscience literacy and education; he is the chair of the Earth Science Literacy Initiative, author of several popular video lectures on geoscience in The Great Courses series, and a lead writer of the Next Generation Science Standards*.

Consulting Author

Bryn Lutes, Ph.D. is a chemist, technology translator, and educator. Holding a Ph.D. in Organometallic Chemistry, Dr. Lutes has worked both in and out of the classroom to help faculty incorporate active-learning techniques and technology to support student learning. She currently teaches General Chemistry for post-baccalaureate premedical students, Quantitative Reasoning, and Inorganic Chemistry Laboratory, where she continues to explore and incorporate active-learning and technology-assisted pedagogies.

CONSULTANT AND REVIEWERS

Program Consultant

Tanya Katovich is a chemistry educator and consultant. In 2015, she received the Davidson Award, presented annually by the Chemical Industry Council of Illinois to the outstanding chemistry teacher in Illinois. In 2017, Tanya became an Illinois finalist for the Presidential Award for Excellence in Mathematics and Science Teaching (PAEMST). She currently serves as the Vice-President and a member of the board of directors for the nonprofit organization Northern Illinois Science Educators (NISE).

Academic Reviewers

Aida Awad
Adjunct Instructor
American InterContinental University
Buckeye, AZ

Nicole Bouvier-Brown, Ph.D.
Associate Professor of Chemistry & Biochemistry
Loyola Marymount University
Los Angeles, CA

Drew Budner, Ph.D.
Assistant Professor of Chemistry
Coastal Carolina University
Conway, SC

Thomas Bussey, Ph.D.
Assistant Teacher Professor
Department of Chemistry & Biochemistry
University of California, San Diego
La Jolla, CA

Stephen Contakes, Ph.D.
Associate Professor of Chemistry
Westmont College
Santa Barbara, CA

Michael Everest, Ph.D.
Professor of Chemistry
Westmont College
Santa Barbara, CA

Alison J. Frontier, Ph.D.
Professor of Chemistry
University of Rochester
Rochester, NY

Hasan Palandoken, Ph.D.
Associate Professor
Department of Chemistry & Biochemistry
California Polytechnic University
San Luis Obispo, CA

Robert Senter, Ph.D.
Instructor of Chemistry
Loyola Marymount University
Los Angeles, CA

Amanda Silberstein, Ph.D.
Assistant Professor of Chemistry
Westmont College
Santa Barbara, CA

Shanju Zhang, Ph.D.
Associate Assistant Professor
Department of Chemistry & Biochemistry
California Polytechnic University
San Luis Obispo, CA

Teacher Reviewers

California

Gregory Aniol
Chemistry Teacher
Riverside Unified School District
Riverside, CA

Manny Colon
Science Department Chair/
Science and Engineering
Teacher
University Preparatory School
Victorville, CA

Stephanie Farmer
Chemistry Teacher
Dougherty Valley High School
San Ramon, CA

Rhonda Frohn
Chemistry Teacher
Conejo Valley Unified School
District
Thousand Oaks, CA

Sean Gilbert
Chemistry Teacher
Leuzinger High School
Lawndale, CA

Rodger Golgart
Chemistry Teacher
Grand Terrace High School
Grand Terrace, CA

Ricardo Gutierrez
Biology/Earth Science Teacher
Temescal Canyon High School
Lake Elsinore, CA

Brittney Kang
Science Teacher
Portola High School
Irvine, CA

Katie Keeler
Chemistry Teacher
Newbury Park High School
Newbury Park, CA

Jeralyn Helnick Newton
Science Teacher
Portola High School
Irvine, CA

Ayanna Pantallion
Chemistry Teacher
Santa Monica-Malibu Unified
School District
Santa Monica, CA

Michael Tang
Science Teacher
Portola High School
Irvine, CA

Dawn Toth
Chemistry Teacher
Redlands Unified School District
Redlands, CA

Amanda Waterfield
Chemistry Teacher
Victor Valley Unified School
District
Victorville, CA

National

Jodi Fertoli
Chemistry Teacher
Staten Island Technical High
School
Staten Island, NY

Martin Goldman
Chemistry Teacher
Edison High School
Edison, NJ

Jessica Johnson
Chemistry Teacher
Jackson Public Schools
Jackson, MS

Kurt Rogers
Chemistry Teacher
Northern Highlands High School
Allendale, NJ

Michelle Tindall
K-12 Curriculum Coordinator
Birmingham Public Schools
Birmingham, MI

Susan Todd
Chemistry Teacher
Claxton High School
Claxton, GA

Lab Review

All labs in the program were developed and tested by FLINN SCIENTIFIC

PROGRAM CONTENTS

VOLUME 1
TABLE OF CONTENTS

INSTRUCTIONAL SEGMENT 1

Combustion, Heat, and Energy 2

ANCHORING PHENOMENON How does this fire keep burning?

GO ONLINE to find hands-on and virtual labs, CERs and Modeling activities, and other resources — authentic readings, videos and animations — that complete the Experiences.

INSTRUCTIONAL SEGMENT 2

Atoms, Elements, and Molecules 96

ANCHORING PHENOMENON What distinguishes the minerals in this mountain?

INSTRUCTIONAL SEGMENT 3

Understanding Chemical Reactions 196

ANCHORING PHENOMENON How can we produce better foods?

GO ONLINE to find hands-on and virtual labs, CERs and Modeling activities, and other resources — authentic readings, videos and animations — that complete the Experiences.

ASSESSMENTS

- Pre/Post-Test
- End-of-Course Test
- Experience Notebook Problem Bank

INSTRUCTIONAL SEGMENT 1

- Quizzes
- 3-D Assessments
- Online Problem Bank

INSTRUCTIONAL SEGMENT 2

- Quizzes
- 3-D Assessments
- Online Problem Bank
- Benchmark 3-D Assessment

INSTRUCTIONAL SEGMENT 3

- Quizzes
- 3-D Assessments
- Online Problem Bank
- Benchmark 3-D Assessment

FLINN SCIENTIFIC

PERFORMANCE-BASED ASSESSMENTS

INSTRUCTIONAL SEGMENT 1

- Measure Energy in Combustion Reactions
- Electricity and Wind Energy
- Investigate the Rock Cycle

INSTRUCTIONAL SEGMENT 2

- Evaluate Atomic Structure with Flame Tests
- Gravimetric Analysis of Periodic Trends
- Qualitative Analysis and Chemical Bonding

INSTRUCTIONAL SEGMENT 3

- Road Deicers
- Analysis of Basic Copper Carbonate
- Identify Evidence of Chemical Reactions
- The Stoichiometry of Filling a Balloon
- Enthalpy of a Neutralization Reaction

FLINN SCIENTIFIC

INQUIRY LABS

INSTRUCTIONAL SEGMENT 1

- Energy Densities of Organic Fuels
- Measure Energy Flow in Chemical Reactions
- Matter Transformation in Combustion
- Introduction to Electromagnetism
- Thermal Energy and Heat Transfer
- Evaluate the Thermal Equilibrium of Metals
- Observe Convection Currents
- The Rise and Fall of Pangaea

INSTRUCTIONAL SEGMENT 2

- Bean Bag Isotopes
- Evaluate Atomic Spectra
- Evaluate the Bohr Model of the Atom
- Model Electron Configuration
- Develop a Periodic Table
- Elemental Metals, Nonmetals, and Metalloids
- Periodic Trends and Properties
- Characteristics of Ionic Bonds
- Investigate Metallic Bonds
- Investigate Covalent Bonds
- Intermolecular Forces
- Chemical Names and Formulas

INSTRUCTIONAL SEGMENT 3

- Material Properties and Bond Type
- Measure the Energy of a Phase Change
- Melt Ionic and Covalent Compounds
- Modeling Metals, Ceramics, and Polymers
- Investigate Surface Tension
- Aqueous Solutions
- Describe Small-scale Matter Using the Mole
- Mole Ratios
- Determine an Empirical Formula
- Preparation of Solutions
- Evaluate Chemical Reactions
- Types of Chemical Reactions
- Predict Chemical Reactions
- Identify Unknowns Through Stoichiometry
- Determination of Reaction Output
- Formation of Barium Iodate
- The Thermodynamics of Hand Warmers
- Hess's Law and the Combustion of a Metal
- The Heat of Melting Ice

FLINN SCIENTIFIC

ENGINEERING DESIGN CHALLENGES

INSTRUCTIONAL SEGMENT 1

- Energy Efficient Cookware
- Conservation of Mass in Chemical Reactions

INSTRUCTIONAL SEGMENT 2

- Build a Spectroscope from Household Materials
- Growing Crystals in Gel
- Evaluate Metals for a Commercial Application

INSTRUCTIONAL SEGMENT 3

- Abrasive Compounds
- Building a Better Bike
- An Empirical Formula Challenge
- Water Purification
- Build a Film Canister Rocket
- Flameless Heating Systems

ANIMATIONS

INSTRUCTIONAL SEGMENT 1

- Combustion Works
- How Temperature Affects the Color of Glowing Objects
- Particle Party 3D animation
- A Journey Through Earth's Mantle

INSTRUCTIONAL SEGMENT 2

- A Quick Look At the Parts of an Atom
- How to Write Electron Configurations
- The Design of the Periodic Table
- Ionization Energy
- Formation of Ionic Compounds
- Formation of Covalent Compounds
- Predicting Bond Type

INSTRUCTIONAL SEGMENT 3

- Phase Transitions and Partcle Motion
- Metallic Solids and Covalent Network Solids
- Intermolecular Forces and Surface Tension in Water
- Moles are Many
- Introduction to STP
- Bonds Breaking and Forming
- Attractions in Solutions
- Stoichiometry Calculations
- Bond Energy and Enthalpy
- Energy Changes in Changes of State

End-of-Book Resources

Combustion, Heat, and Energy

How does this fire keep burning?

Investigation 1
Combustion—Matter, Energy, and Change

Investigation 2
Energy Transfer and Conservation

Investigation 3
Earth's Interior

ANCHORING PHENOMENON

Inquiry Launch Look at the image of the crater. What additional information do you need in order to explain what is happening?

Write a series of questions about the phenomenon that would help you explain why and how this crater is on fire.

GO ONLINE to engage with real-world phenomena. Watch the anchoring phenomenon video and preview the optional **problem-based learning experience**.

INVESTIGATIVE PHENOMENON

GO ONLINE to Engage with real-world phenomena by watching a video and completing a CER interactive worksheet.

Why are wildfires so difficult to extinguish?

Combustion—Matter, Energy, and Change

The biomass of forests burns as a result of combustion, a chemical reaction. If there is a climate cycle of a wet period, which generates a lot of biomass, and a dry period, which causes that biomass to die and dry out, then there may be huge forest fires that burn out of control. Once you have viewed the Investigative Phenomenon video and used the claim-evidence-reasoning worksheet to draft an explanation, answer the following reflection questions about wildfires.

1. **CCC Energy and Matter** Where did the mass of the forest trees come from? What happens to that mass when the forest burns?

2. **SEP Develop a Model** Why don't trees spontaneously catch on fire and burn all the time? Why don't fires stop immediately as soon as they start? Develop a model for what has to happen for a large fire to occur.

EXPERIENCE 1

Introduction to Energy

GO ONLINE to Explore and Explain the energy content of foods, fuels, and other everyday materials in your life.

Matter and Energy in Systems

Chemistry is all about matter: things that have mass. The universe is made out of matter and energy. Ordinary matter is composed of atomic particles. In chemistry, you study the interactions of atoms and the particles that make them up, including the electrons that bind atoms together.

In chemistry, you will investigate chemical interactions. In every case, changes occur within a system that has interacting components. These changes are driven by transfers and/or transformations of energy. Defining a system and its components is a way to understand the changes that occur in any part of nature, whether it is a chemical system, a biological system, or the solar system. Changes within a system involve a movement of matter driven by a flow of energy. If anything is happening, then energy is flowing. If there is no flow of energy, then nothing happens.

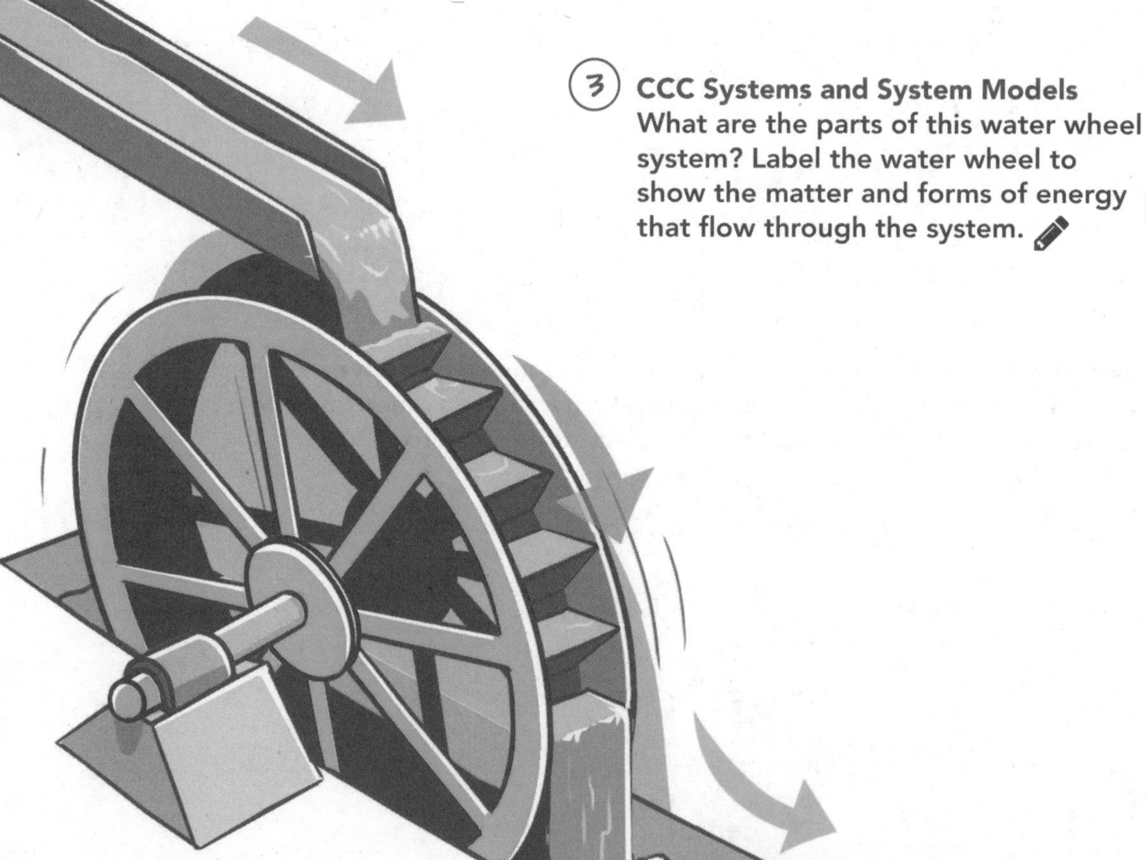

(3) **CCC Systems and System Models What are the parts of this water wheel system? Label the water wheel to show the matter and forms of energy that flow through the system.**

Definitions of Energy

Energy is the capacity for doing work or producing heat. Energy can be hard to define because it takes so many different forms and can do so many different things.

Potential Energy The energy stored within a system is called **potential energy.** Every substance has a certain amount of energy stored inside it.

Matter is made of atoms that are often bonded together. The energy stored in chemical bonds is known as **chemical potential energy.** The energy stored in the nuclei of atoms is nuclear energy. Gravitational and elastic are two other types of potential energy.

Kinetic Energy The energy of an object's motion is called **kinetic energy.** As with potential energy, there are several types of kinetic energy. Electrical energy can be a form of kinetic energy, through the motions of charged particles. Thermal energy is the total kinetic energy possessed by all of the individual vibrating particles that make up an object.

There are other forms of energy as well, such as electromagnetic radiation, which includes microwaves, x-rays, and visible light.

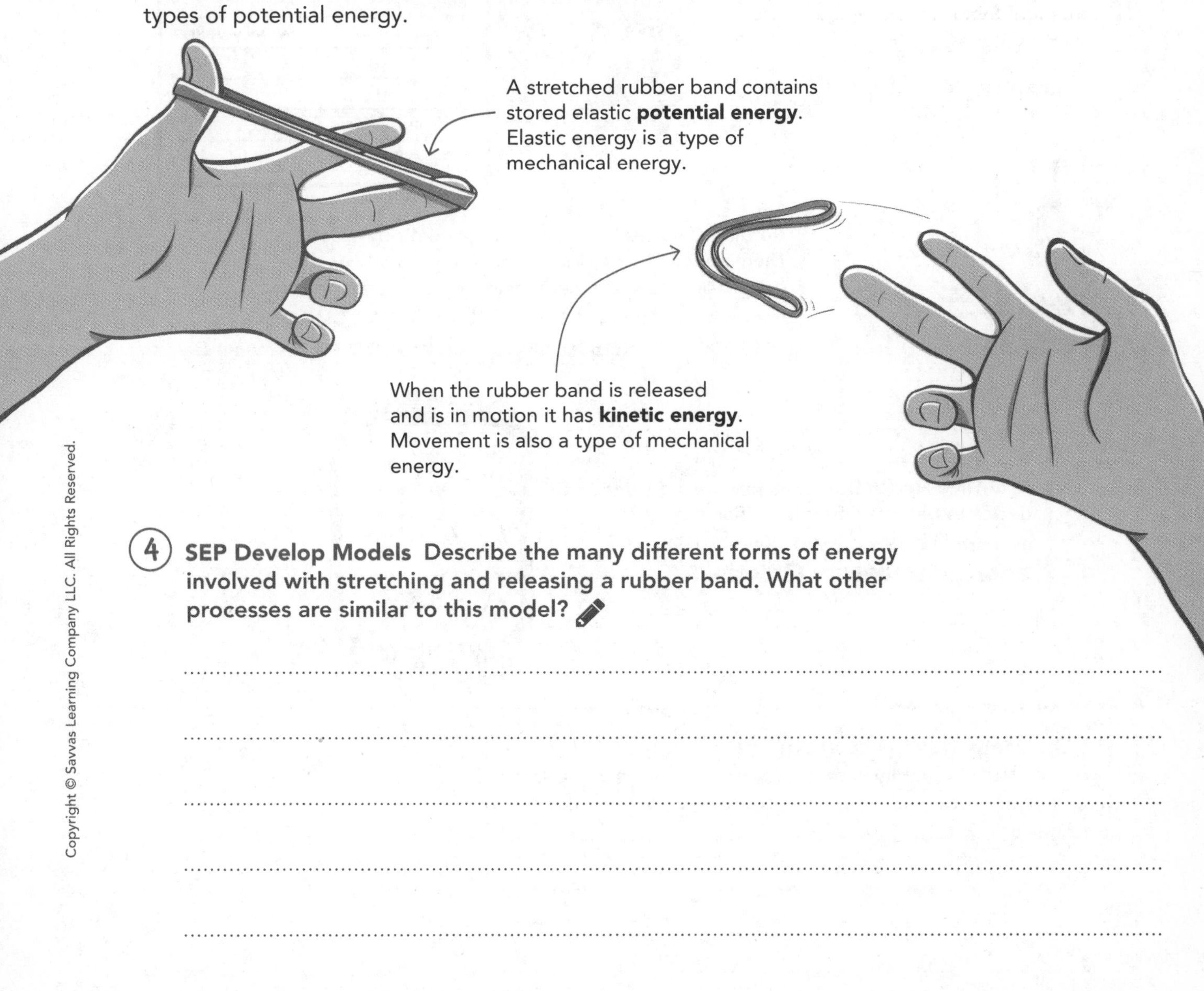

A stretched rubber band contains stored elastic **potential energy**. Elastic energy is a type of mechanical energy.

When the rubber band is released and is in motion it has **kinetic energy**. Movement is also a type of mechanical energy.

4 **SEP Develop Models** **Describe the many different forms of energy involved with stretching and releasing a rubber band. What other processes are similar to this model?**

Units of Energy

What units can you use to show **how much energy?**

The joule The SI unit of energy is the joule (J). One joule of heat raises the temperature of 1 g of pure water 0.2390°C.

$$1\ J = 0.2390\ cal$$

A joule can also be defined in terms of mechanical energy.

$$1\ J = 1\ kg{\cdot}m/s^2$$

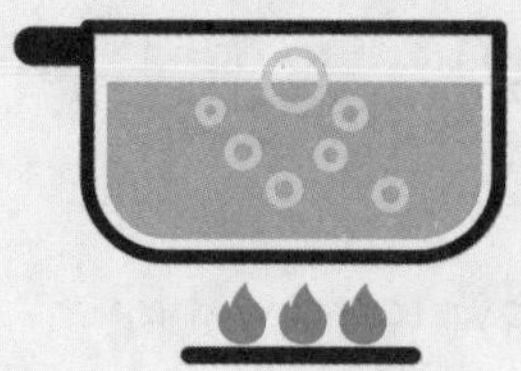

The calorie The calorie (cal) is a non-SI unit. One calorie of heat raises the temperature of 1 g of pure water 1°C.

$$1\ cal = 4.184\ J$$

Calorie (with a capital C) The energy content of foods and beverages is usually given in Calories.

$$1\ Calorie = 1{,}000\ calories$$

Nutrition Facts

Serving Size 1 Bottle

Amount Per Serving	
Calories 20	
	% Daily Value
Total Fat 0 g	**0%**
Sugars 12 g	**4%**
Sodium 260 mg	**11%**
Potassium 75 mg	**2%**

Burning Calories During exercise, your body uses chemical reactions to break down sugars and fats. Like a fire, these reactions release heat, but in a controlled way. For example, **breaking down a sugar cube releases as much heat as burning it.**

Real-Time Health Data You may wear a health device to get real-time information as you exercise. **These devices express energy in dietary Calories.**

(5) **SEP Use Math** **How much energy has your body used, in joules, if your health device indicates that 450 Calories were burned during your workout? How many Calories are in a dinner containing 3.5×10^6 joules?**

Energy Flow and Transformations

Unlike matter, energy does not have mass or volume. You can only detect energy because of what it does. If you apply a force to a stationary object by pushing it, then energy has been transferred from you to the object. You can't see the energy, but you can calculate it.

Kinetic Energy $= \frac{1}{2}mv^2$ (m = mass (kg); v = velocity (m/s))

Gravitational Potential Energy $= mgh$ (g = acceleration of gravity (9.8 m/s^2); h = height (m))

Thermochemistry is the study of energy changes that happen during chemical reactions and changes in state. In chemical reactions, substances change to other substances with a different amount of chemical potential energy. You can detect those energy changes by observing heat transfer, work, or a combination of both. **Heat** is energy that transfers from one object to another because of a temperature difference between the objects. Heat flows spontaneously from a warmer object to a cooler object.

Potential Energy When you buy gasoline, you are buying stored chemical potential energy.

Transforming Potential Energy
The controlled explosions of the gasoline in the combustion chamber of a car's engine transform the chemical potential energy into kinetic mechanical energy that propels the car. Some of the potential energy is also transformed into heat.

6 **SEP Reason Quantitatively** **Show that the units of kinetic energy (from $\frac{1}{2}mv^2$) and of gravitational potential energy (from *mgh*) are the same.**

Rate of Energy Flow

The rate of energy flow is called **power,** and it is measured in watts (W). A watt is equivalent to 1 joule/second, or 1 kg•m^2/s^2. You may be familiar with power from using electricity. Light bulbs are described by the number of watts of electrical power they use. But power is used to describe the flow rates for all energy transformations. **Heat flow** is the rate at which heat moves from one object to another. The rate that you cool off when you go outside on a cold day can be measured in watts.

Power from Water The amount of power available from a waterfall is dependent on the amount of water flowing and the height of the falls. Compare the sizes of these two waterfalls.

The height and volume of this waterfall are much larger, resulting in **greater gravitational potential energy** and a higher rate of energy flow.

7 **SEP Calculate Water flows over Niagara Falls at the average rate of 2,400,000 kg/s, and the average height of the falls is about 50 m. Knowing that the gravitational potential energy of falling water per second = mass (kg) × height (m) × gravity (9.8 m/s^2), what is the power of Niagara Falls? How many 15 W LED light bulbs could it power?**

The Law of Conservation of Energy

No matter what experiments you do in class, the **law of conservation of energy** requires that energy is neither created nor destroyed.

> When energy is transferred or transformed from one system to another in any physical or chemical process, all the energy can always be accounted for.

Sometimes the transfer of energy is hard to see, especially in the case of friction. Take a book and drop it on the floor. The gravitational potential energy that the book had before it was dropped is transformed to kinetic energy of motion as the book falls. But what happened to the energy when the book hit the floor? All of the kinetic energy of the book transformed into frictional heat of the floor, air, and book, and some amount of sound energy. If you could add up all the final frictional and sound energy, it would equal the gravitational potential energy the book started with. With a few exceptions, such as light energy passing through the vacuum of space, whenever work is done, some energy will be lost as heat.

(8) **SEP Develop Models Describe the energy inputs and outputs for the campfire. Use the law of conservation of energy to construct a valid qualitative equation that includes all the input and output energies involved.**

....

....

....

Transforming Stored Energy As the logs burn, chemical reactions occur. Energy stored in the logs is transferred to the products of the reactions and transformed to other types of energy.

The logs are **fuel** for the fire.

Temperature

Temperature is a measure of the average kinetic energy of the vibrating particles of a material. If you heat an object by transferring energy to it, the atoms will vibrate more vigorously, and its temperature will increase.

Temperature Scales In science, temperatures are measured using either the Celsius or Kelvin scale, though most of the United States still uses the Fahrenheit scale.

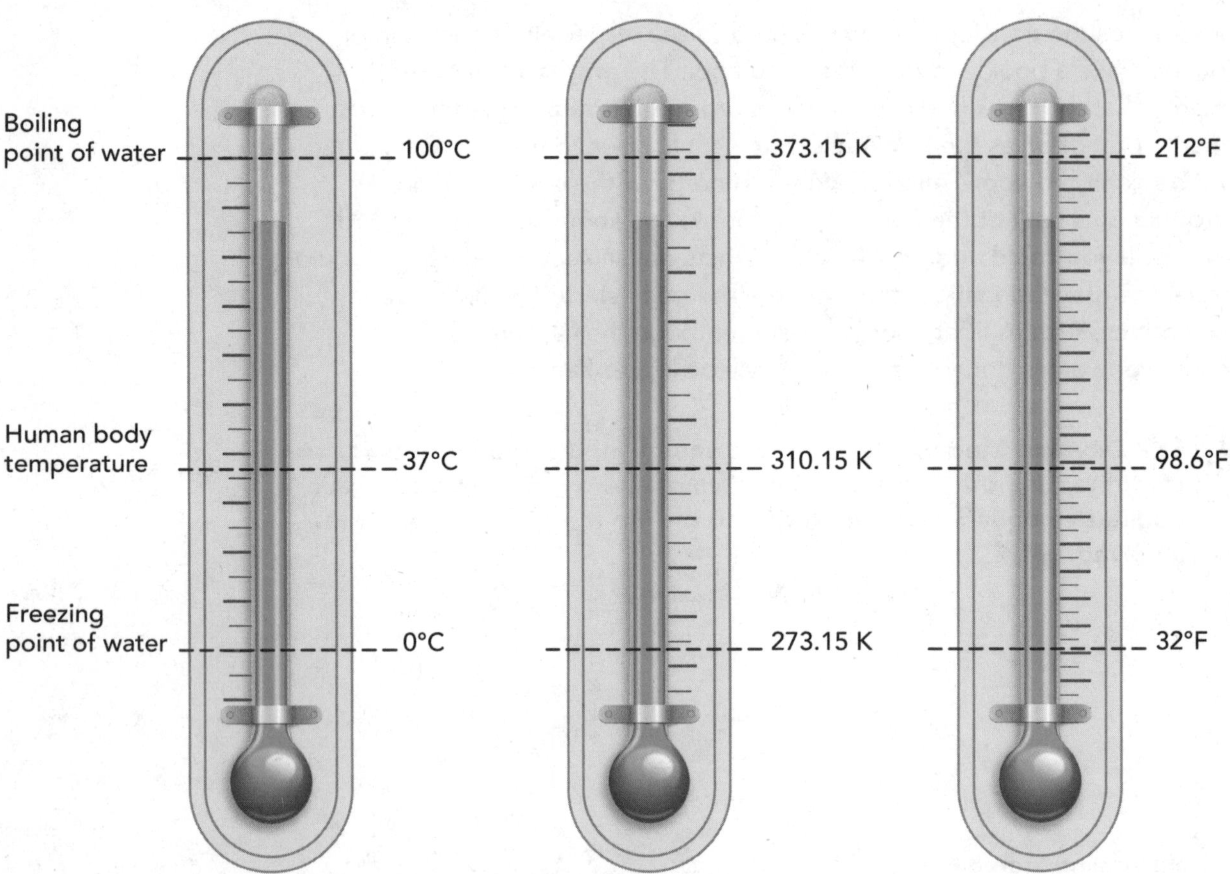

Celsius The Celsius scale is based on the freezing and boiling points of water. Those points are 0°C and 100°C, respectively, defined at standard atmospheric pressure.

Kelvin The Kelvin scale is based on the lowest temperature that is theoretically possible: 0 K, or absolute zero.

Fahrenheit On the Fahrenheit scale, the freezing point of water is 32°F. The boiling point is 212°F.

9 **CCC Scale, Proportion, and Quantity** **How are the Celsius, Kelvin, and Fahrenheit scales similar? How are they different? Considering their differences, think of one scenario in which each scale is more convenient to use.**

The Difference Between Temperature and Heat Temperature is measured in degrees. It is not the same as heat, which is measured in joules. Although an increase in heat causes an increase in temperature, the amount the temperature changes will vary, depending on the substance. The amount of energy needed to raise the temperature of 1 kg of material by 1 degree K is called the **specific heat** (*C*) and is expressed as J/kg•K. Specific heat varies for different materials. For example, the specific heat of granite is 790 J/kg•K while the specific heat of water is 4181 J/kg•K.

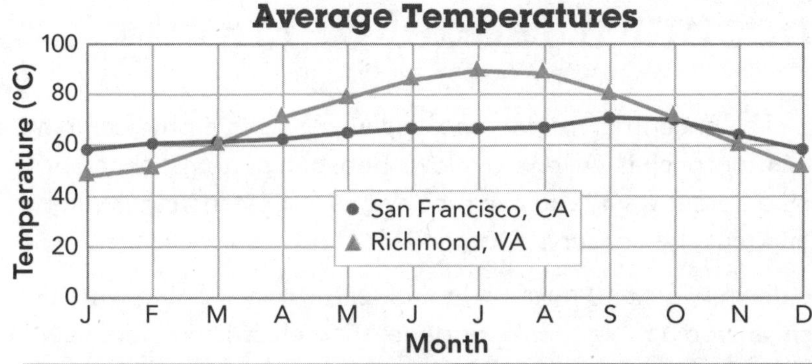

Specific Heat and Climate San Francisco and Richmond are at about the same latitude. San Francisco, on the Pacific Ocean, has less variation in temperature.

10 **SEP Interpret Data** Use the fact that water has a higher specific heat than rock (such as granite) to explain the differences in the temperature curves for the two cities in the graph.

Revisit

INVESTIGATIVE PHENOMENON

GO ONLINE to Elaborate and Evaluate your knowledge of energy by completing the class discussion and data analysis activities.

11 **CCC Matter and Energy** Wood needs to be given heat energy to reach the temperatures required for combustion to begin. What property of the wood would you need to know to predict how fast the wood would start to burn? Explain.

Modeling Energy

GO ONLINE to Explore and Explain the thermodynamics of a reaction in a bag and to find where California gets its energy.

A Conceptual Model of Energy

Energy is itself a conceptual model, because energy isn't a physical thing. You can't see it or touch it. As energy flows between systems, changing form in many different ways, you can model it as a substance that can be quantified and must be conserved, but in fact, it is only conceptual.

Water flows down rivers and through hydroelectric dams, doing work along the way such as eroding river banks or generating electricity. Electricity in the form of electrons flows through electric circuits, doing work such as turning on lights or televisions. But moving water and moving electrons are not themselves energy; they just carry the energy. Similarly, chemical equations describe the energy involved with changes in the composition, state, or phase of materials, but you can only see the reactants and products. You never see the energy itself.

Mechanical Potential Energy A hammer raised by a cam on a turning wheel gains gravitational potential energy. When it drops, potential energy is converted to kinetic energy.

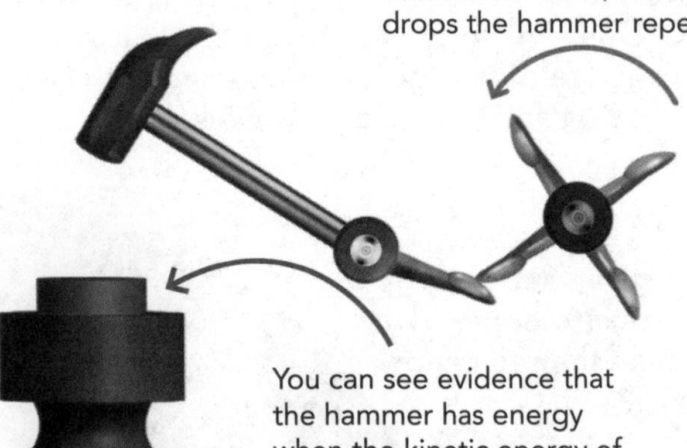

As the cam turns, it lifts and drops the hammer repeatedly.

You can see evidence that the hammer has energy when the kinetic energy of the hammer does work in shaping a piece of metal.

Chemical Potential Energy Molecules are held together by chemical bonds, which form through the electrical attraction between protons and electrons.

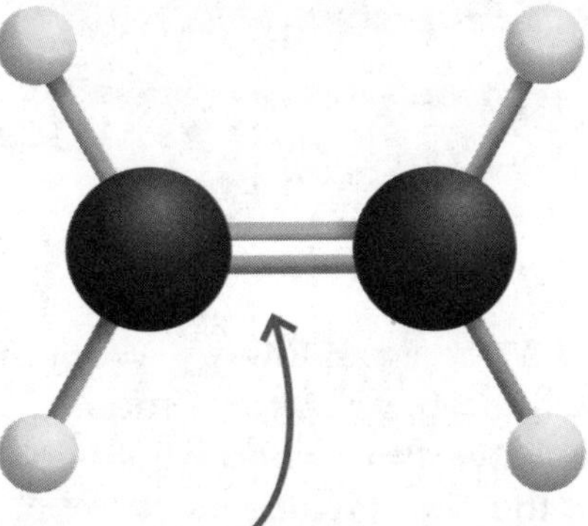

Potential energy is stored in the relative distances between atoms. When bonds break and distances change, chemical potential energy is converted into kinetic energy.

12 CCC Energy and Matter **Underline and identify the parts of the text on this page that use examples of how the flow of matter through a system is driven by energy and can do work.**

Forces and Energy

When change happens within or between systems, you can describe the changes using either forces or energy. Both will give you the correct answer because forces and energy are essentially the same thing. Energy can be described as the result of forces acting over a distance.

For example, imagine dropping a book to the floor. How could you calculate the velocity of the book when it hits the floor? You could do this using Newton's law that force equals mass times acceleration ($\mathbf{F} = m\mathbf{a}$). Acceleration is the change in velocity per change in time, so you could use the force of gravity to find the change in velocity.

You could also use energy to find the velocity. During free fall, gravitational potential energy is converted to kinetic energy. If you know how high the book was when it was dropped, you know its gravitational potential energy. Because this is the same as the kinetic energy, you can use the formula for kinetic energy to find the velocity. Both approaches will work because applying a force involves a transfer of energy.

Energy and Forces The motion of a book that is falling can be described and quantified either in terms of force (from gravity) or energy (from the potential energy lost). As the book falls to the ground, the force of gravity acts on the book increasing its velocity.

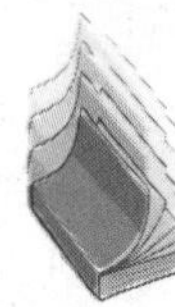

The amount of kinetic energy when the book hits the ground is the same as the amount of gravitational potential energy at the top.

Energy in Collisions When pool balls collide they apply forces on each other, transferring energy.

1. The first ball begins moving when it's struck with a stick.

2. It applies a force to a second ball when they collide. Some of first ball's kinetic energy is transferred to second ball.

3. The first ball changes direction when it collides with the second ball. Frictional forces between the balls and table cause the balls to slow down.

13 **CCC Energy and Matter Imagine a pool ball that bounces off of a bumper and slowly comes to a halt. Explain what happened at each point in terms of applied forces and energy transfers.**

Electrical Forces at Atomic Scales

The structure and interactions of matter at the bulk scale (on the macroscopic scale) are determined by electrical forces within and among atoms. Except for gravitational attraction, electrical forces govern almost all of our daily interactions, both at the atomic scale and the macroscopic scale. When you clap your hands, your hands don't actually touch—the atoms in your hands repel each other through electrical forces.

Opposites Attract The electrical force between particles with opposite charges is attraction. A positively charged particle and a negatively charged particle are attracted to each other.

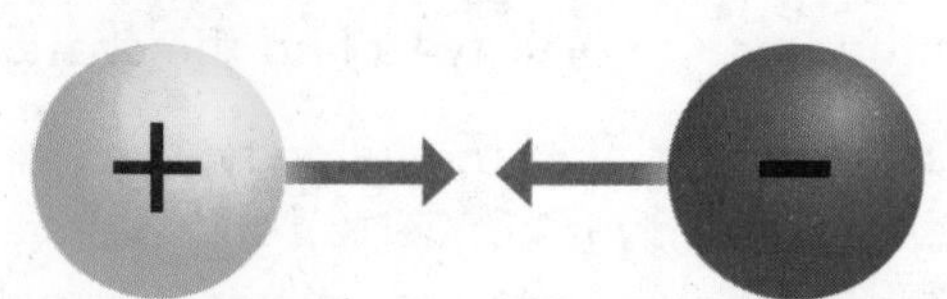

Like Charges Repel The electrical force between particles of the same charge is repulsion. Two positive charges repel each other. Similarly, two negative charges repel each other.

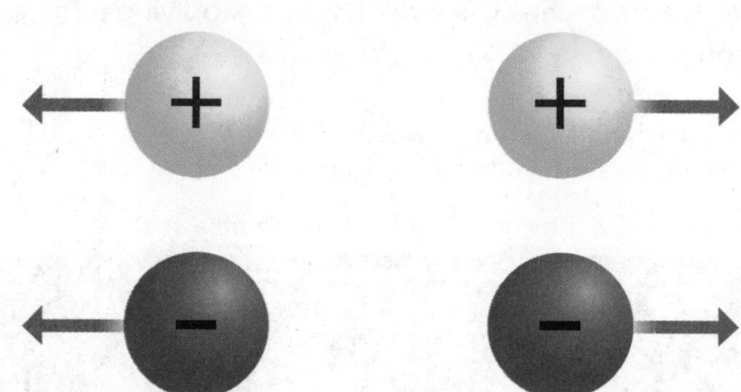

(14) **SEP Develop Models Draw arrows for all of the attractive and repulsive forces between the negatively charged electrons and positively charged protons in these atoms. Make sure your arrows clearly show the difference between attractive and repulsive forces. Note that the particles without a charge label are neutral.**

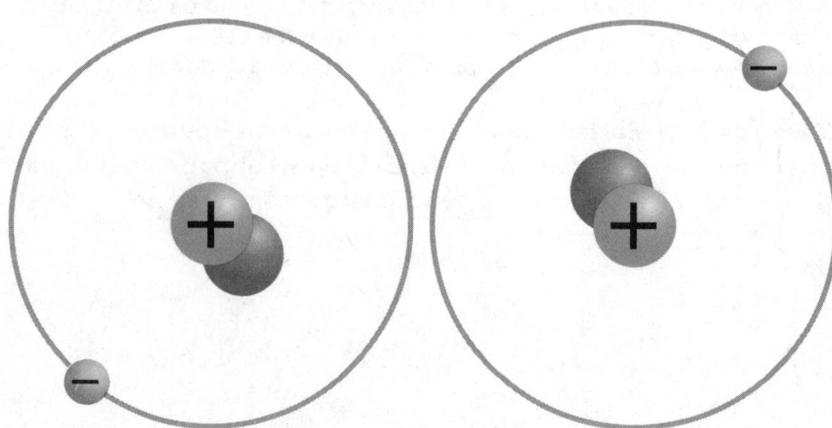

Atomic and Bulk Properties

The structure and behavior of substances at the bulk (or macroscopic) scale can be used to infer the strengths of electrical forces within and among atoms and molecules. For example, graphite and diamond are both made of carbon. Graphite is often used in pencils because it's very soft. Diamonds are very hard and strong. The reason for the differences between graphite and diamond is the different strengths of the electric forces bonding their atoms together.

Surface Tension Surface tension is another example of a property that differs depending on the electrical forces among atoms or molecules. The greater the force, the greater is the surface tension.

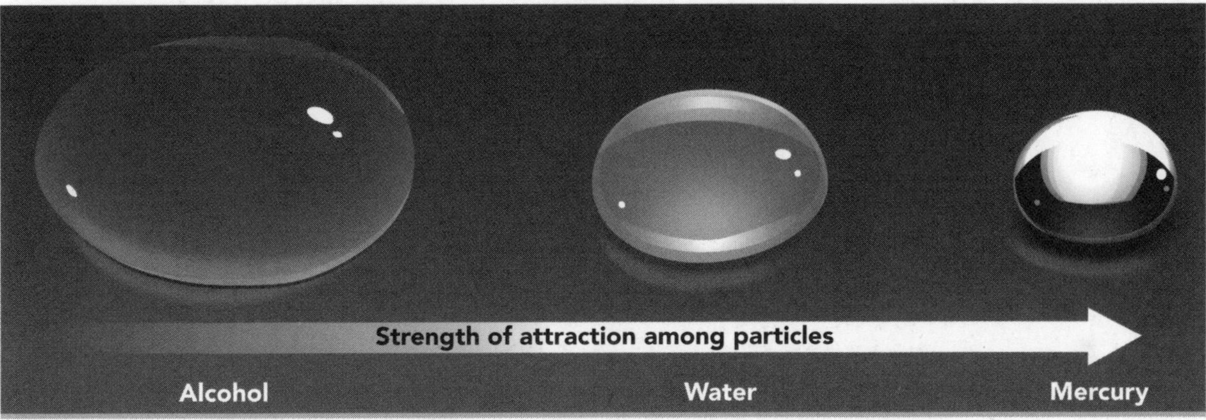

15 **CCC Patterns Changes in the state of matter (solid, liquid, gas) are the result of different energy levels at the molecular level. Look at the graph of the energy required to go from water ice to water vapor. Describe the energy of the water molecules for each state.**

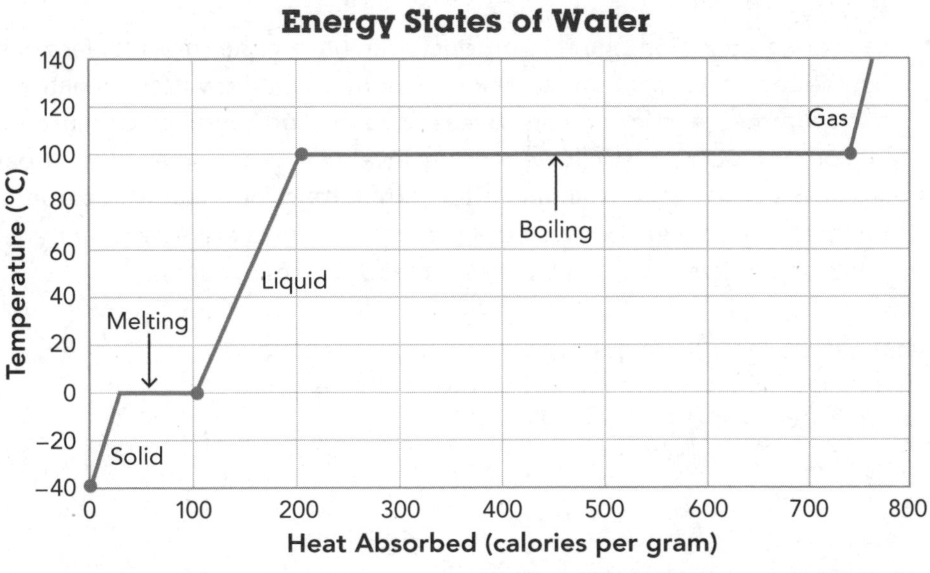

The Direction of Heat Flow

Heat flows from warmer to cooler objects. The greater the difference in temperature, the faster the heat flow. If your hands are cold, a hot heat pack will warm them up faster than a lukewarm heat pack.

Temperature Difference The flame has a higher temperature than the object, so heat flows from the flame to the object. The particles in the object closest to the flame begin to vibrate faster.

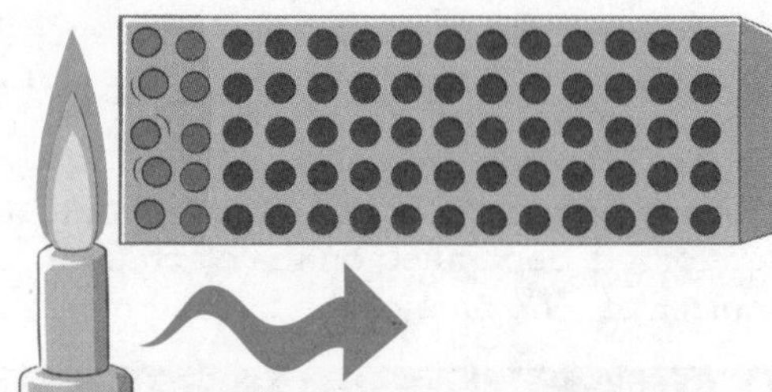

Heat flows from the flame to the object and from the warmer part of the object to the cooler part of the object.

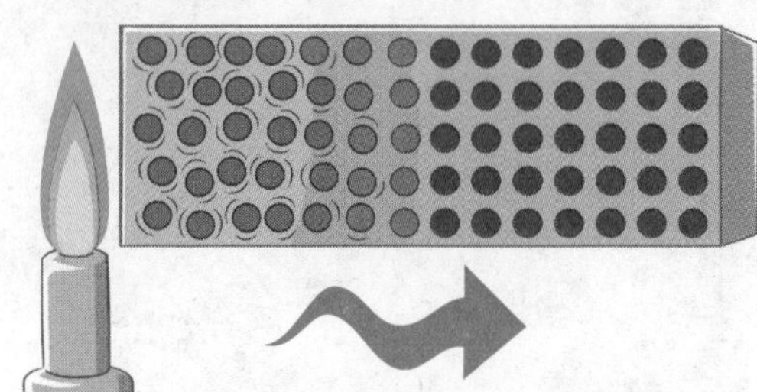

Heat continues to flow until all the particles are at the same temperature. All the particles in the object are vibrating faster.

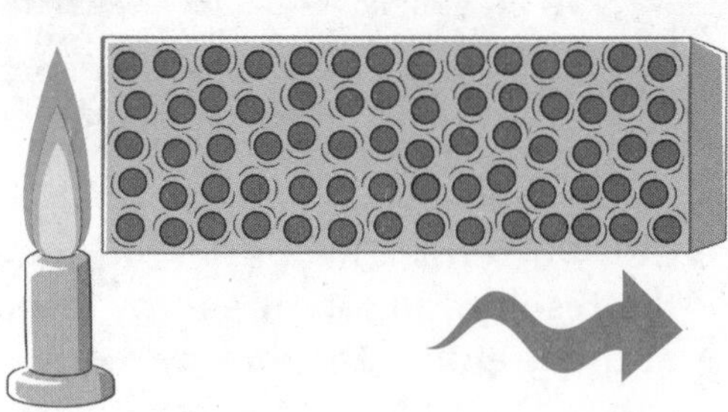

In a chemical reaction, the end products can have either more or less energy than the reactants. That affects the direction of heat flow in the reaction. In an **exothermic reaction,** heat is released to the surroundings because the reaction products are at a lower energy level than the reactants. Heat packs use exothermic reactions. In an **endothermic reaction,** heat is absorbed from the surroundings because the reaction products are at a higher energy level than the reactants. Cold packs use endothermic reactions.

16 **SEP Plan Your Investigation Design an experiment to show that the heat flow between adjacent objects of different temperatures is greater when the temperature difference is greater.**

Modeling Chemical Reactions

Chemical processes, their rates, and whether or not energy is stored or released are all a result of the collisions of molecules and the rearrangements of atoms into new molecules. All chemical reactions require a certain amount of energy to occur. This energy, the **activation energy,** is the minimum energy colliding particles must have in order to react. Reactions with low activation energies happen easily and quickly.

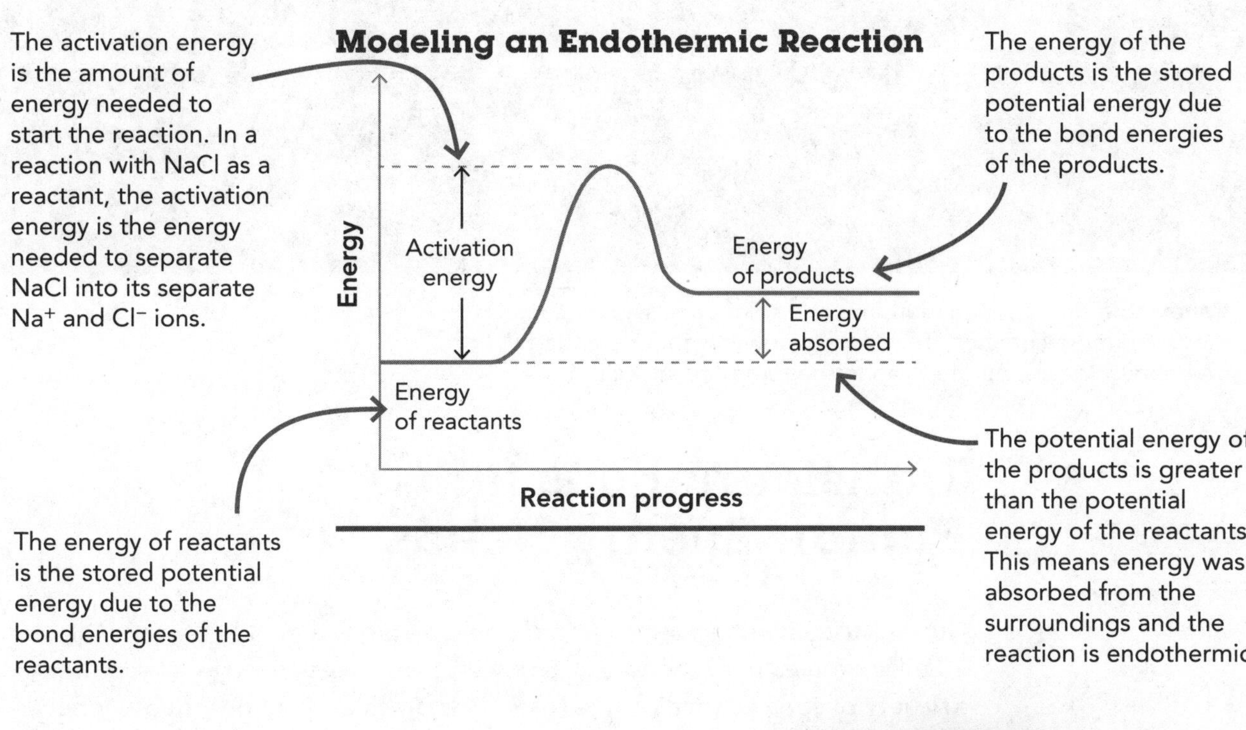

Modeling an Endothermic Reaction
The activation energy is the amount of energy needed to start the reaction. In a reaction with NaCl as a reactant, the activation energy is the energy needed to separate NaCl into its separate Na+ and Cl− ions.
The energy of the products is the stored potential energy due to the bond energies of the products.
Energy
Activation energy
Energy of products
Energy absorbed
Energy of reactants
Reaction progress
The energy of reactants is the stored potential energy due to the bond energies of the reactants.
The potential energy of the products is greater than the potential energy of the reactants. This means energy was absorbed from the surroundings and the reaction is endothermic.

17 **CCC Energy and Matter** There is no sodium found in nature in pure form due to its reactivity. What does this say about the activation energy of the reaction of sodium and water compared to the combustion of wax in a candle?

....

....

....

....

....

....

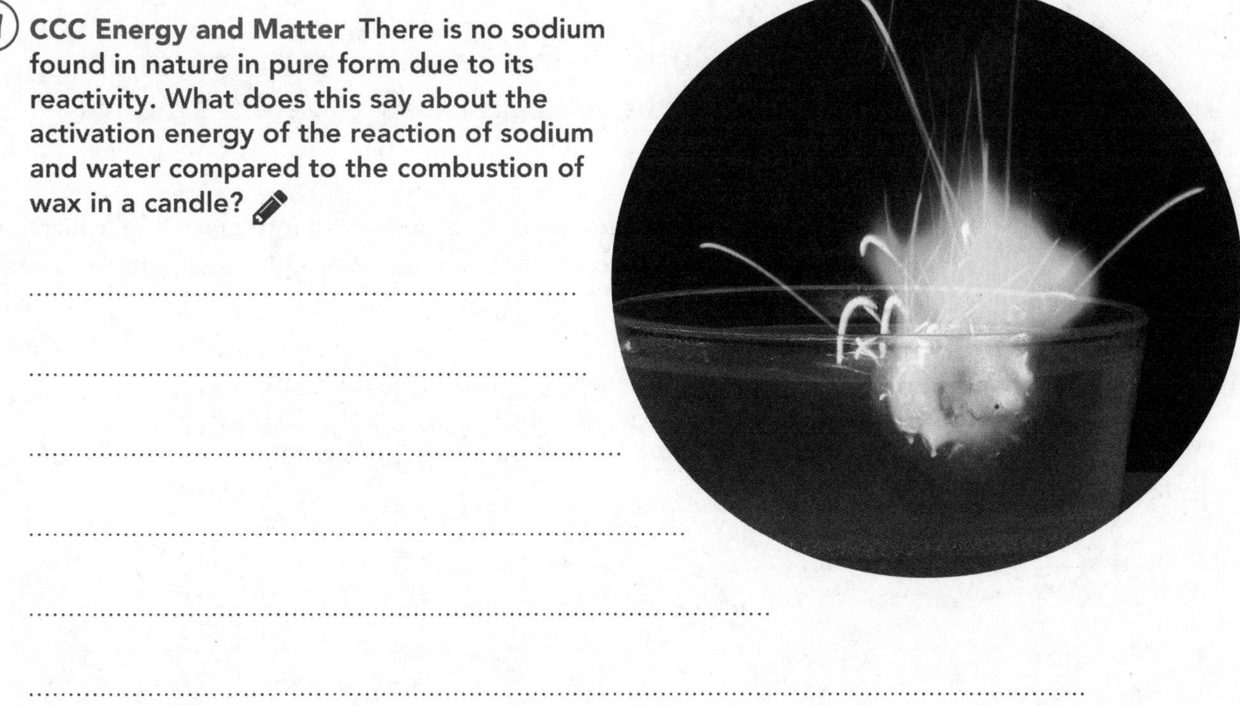

Renewable Energy Wind turbines and solar panels are becoming more and more common. They supply power without emitting greenhouse gases, but they cannot be turned on at will.

Transformations for Human Energy Needs

Humans use an immense amount of energy—more than 20 terawatts, or 20 trillion joules per second. To supply that vast need, energy is taken from a variety of sources that include fossil fuels, nuclear reactions, geothermal springs, sunlight, biomass, wind, rivers, waves, and tides.

Humans use energy for different purposes, so the energy goes through many different kinds of conversions.

A large fraction of the energy budget is converted into electricity, which can in turn be converted into forms that humans use—light, heat, motive power, and others.

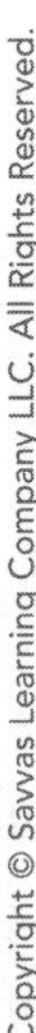

18 **CCC Energy and Matter Photovoltaic power from solar panels and biomass energy are obviously forms of solar energy, coming from sunlight. Explain why both wind power and hydroelectric power can also be considered to be forms of solar energy.**

Modeling the Energy Flow of Fuel Combustion

A common exothermic chemical reaction for human needs is the combustion of carbon-based fuels. Those fuels include wood, leaves, coal, oil, and natural gas. During combustion, oxygen reacts with the fuel to produce carbon dioxide and water, which are at a lower energy state than the reactants, so energy is released. Some of the energy is transformed into heat.

Some of the energy is transformed into light, which you see as a flame. The heat given off also provides the activation energy to ignite more of the fuel, so the reaction is self-sustaining.

For carbon-based fuels, the energy is originally in the form of sunlight, which is captured by the biochemical reactions of photosynthesis and stored as biomass.

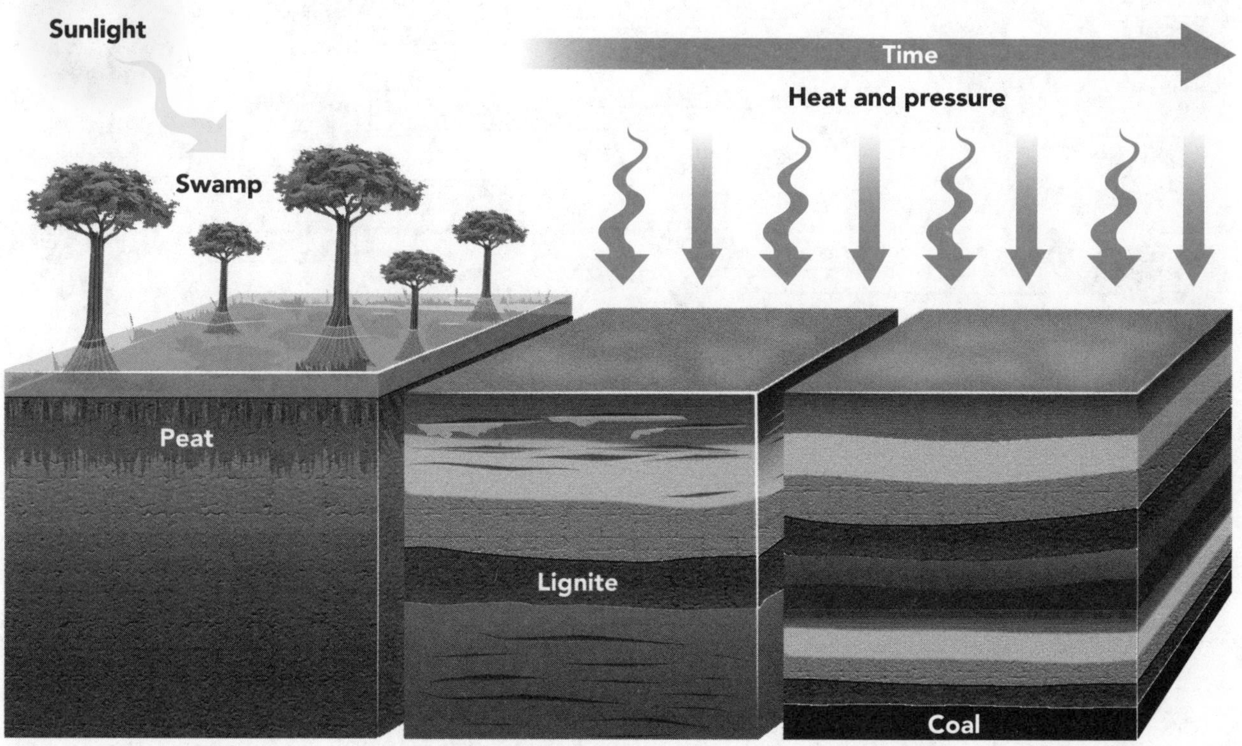

Energy from the Sun Plants transform light energy into biomass through photosynthesis. Peat forms in bogs from plant biomass that has not decomposed.

Burial and Compaction Over millions of years, heat and pressure produce chemical changes that release the hydrogen the biomass originally contained. Lignite, or brown coal, is formed.

Heat and Pressure With continued burial, the increasing heat and pressure convert lignite to bituminous and then anthracite coal. Shiny, black anthracite coal is composed almost entirely of carbon.

19 **SEP Use Math Calculate and compare the chemical energy of coal to its gravitational potential energy. Burning 1 kg of coal releases about 3 million joules of energy. If you could use all of the chemical energy to lift another kilogram of coal, how high could you lift it?**

Analyzing United States Energy Needs In the U.S. there are many different sources of energy. This energy is transformed for various uses. Almost forty percent of this energy is used for electricity generation. Overall, more energy is wasted, or lost as heat, than is used for energy services.

Estimated U.S. Energy Budget for 2017 (by percent)

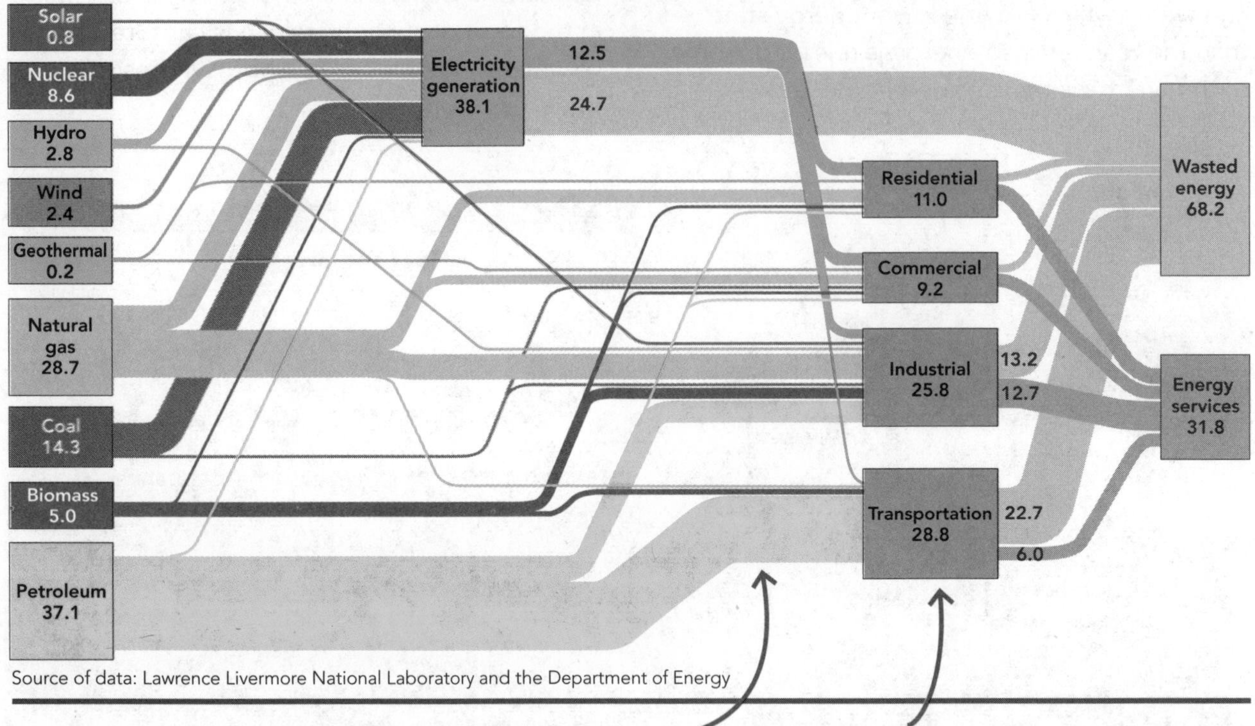

Source of data: Lawrence Livermore National Laboratory and the Department of Energy

The width of each ribbon is directly proportional to the amount of energy involved in that transformation.

Transportation uses 28.8% of the energy budget. The efficiency of the transportation budget is determined by calculating the ratio of energy that is used by energy services to the total transportation energy.

$\frac{6.0}{28.8} \times 100\% = 20.8\%$ efficiency

20 CCC Proportion What are the top three sources of U.S. electricity generation? Estimate the overall efficiency of U.S. electricity generation. How does this compare to the efficiency for transportation?

Revisit

INVESTIGATIVE PHENOMENON

GO ONLINE to Elaborate and Evaluate your design of an experiment to show conservation of mass in the reaction of baking soda and vinegar.

21 **Construct an Explanation** How does a forest fire model the energy flow of fuel combustion? Explain.

Conservation of Matter

GO ONLINE to Explore and Explain the conservation of matter in combustion reactions.

A Conceptual Model of Matter

Conceptual models of matter have some similarities to and some differences from models of energy. Like energy, matter can be tracked as it moves through and among systems. Matter, like energy, is also conserved—in chemical reactions, it can neither be created nor destroyed.

Unlike energy, however, matter consists of physical stuff, so you can touch it and hold it. You can also measure the quantity of matter. This is mass. In some situations it is sufficient to treat matter as a continuous substance, where bulk characteristics provide enough information. In chemistry, however, you must work with models of molecules, atoms, and their subatomic components—protons, neutrons, and electrons—to understand and predict chemical behavior.

Atom Atoms are composed of three particles: protons, neutrons, and electrons. Most of an atom is empty space.

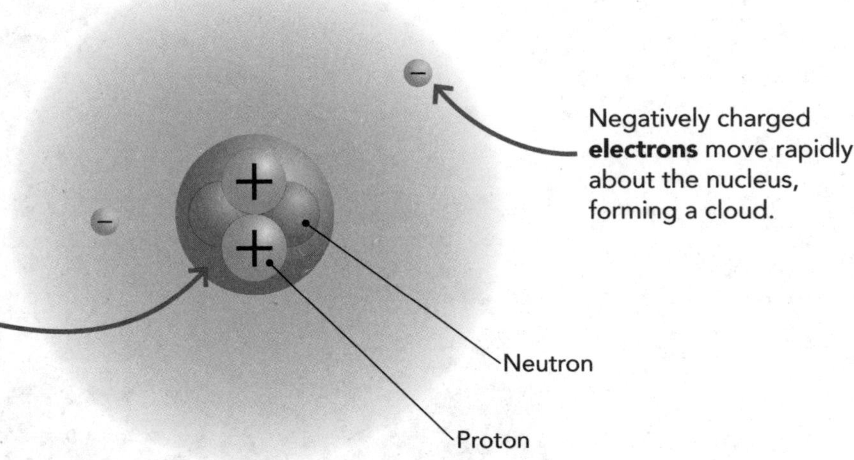

Negatively charged **electrons** move rapidly about the nucleus, forming a cloud.

Nearly all of the mass in the atom is in the **nucleus**, where positively charged protons and uncharged neutrons are bound together by the nuclear force.

22 SEP Use Models Explain why understanding the process of combustion requires using an atomic model of mass and not a continuous one.

Building Blocks of Chemistry

What determines the **mass and properties of atoms?**

Protons in Atoms An atom's **protons determine an atom's chemical properties.** An atom of a particular element will always have the same number of protons.

Proton

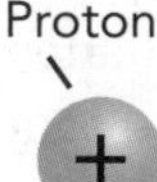

For example, lithium always has 3 protons.

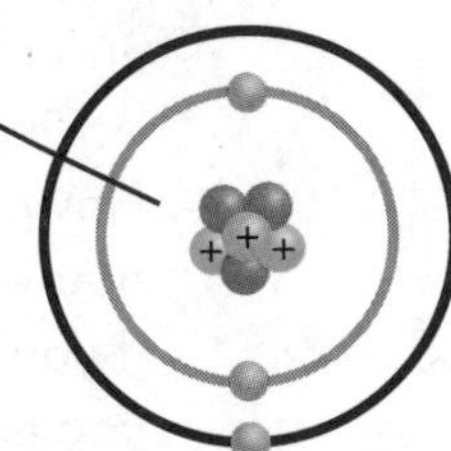

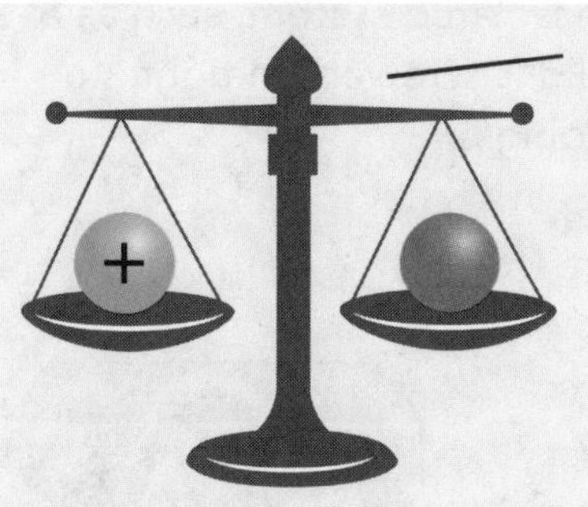

Protons and neutrons are nearly **equal in mass.**

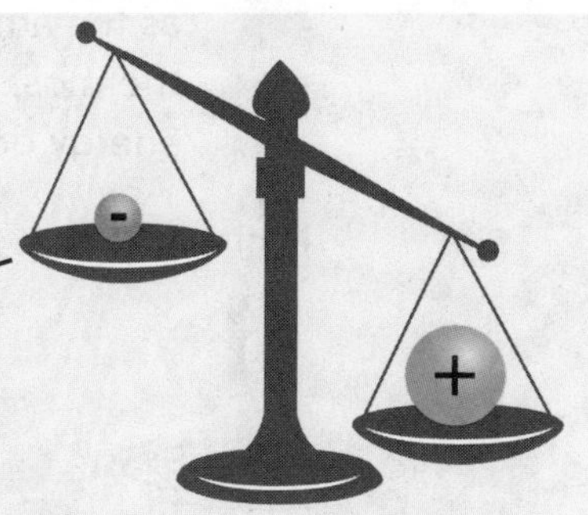

The mass of an electron is considered to be negligible because it is more than 1830 times smaller than the mass of a proton or a neutron.

Isotopes Atoms can have different numbers of neutrons. Atoms of the same element that have different numbers of neutrons are called isotopes. Since neutrons have no charge, they do not change the electrical forces among atoms. **Isotopes** not only **have different masses but also have different physical properties.**

3 protons
3 neutrons
3 electrons

3 protons
4 neutrons
3 electrons

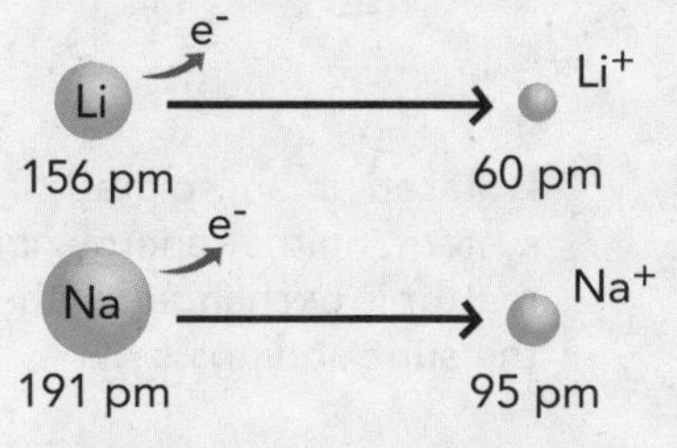

Positive ions that have lost an electron are smaller than their neutral atoms.

Ions Atoms can also have different numbers of electrons. Atoms of the same element that have different numbers of electrons are called ions. When **atoms gain or lose electrons, the sizes of the atoms and the electrical forces they exert change.** Sizes are in picometers (10^{-12} m).

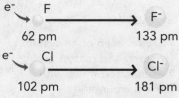

e⁻ F → F⁻
62 pm → 133 pm

e⁻ Cl → Cl⁻
102 pm → 181 pm

Negative ions that have gained an electron are larger than their neutral atoms.

23 CCC Patterns Explain the observed pattern of how the sizes and charges of atoms change with the addition and subtraction of electrons.

....

....

....

Open and Closed Systems

Thermochemistry is the study of the heat exchanged between systems and their surroundings. In an open system, such as an open saucepan with boiling water, both matter and energy are transferred to the surroundings. However, if you put a lid on the saucepan and create a closed system, matter cannot escape and is instead contained and conserved in the system. If you added the amount of water vapor in the pot to the liquid water that cooled and condensed on the lid, you would find that they are the same as the amount of water that evaporated. In an isolated system, such as a thermos, where the sides are insulated and a lid is screwed on tight, no energy or matter is transferred to the surroundings.

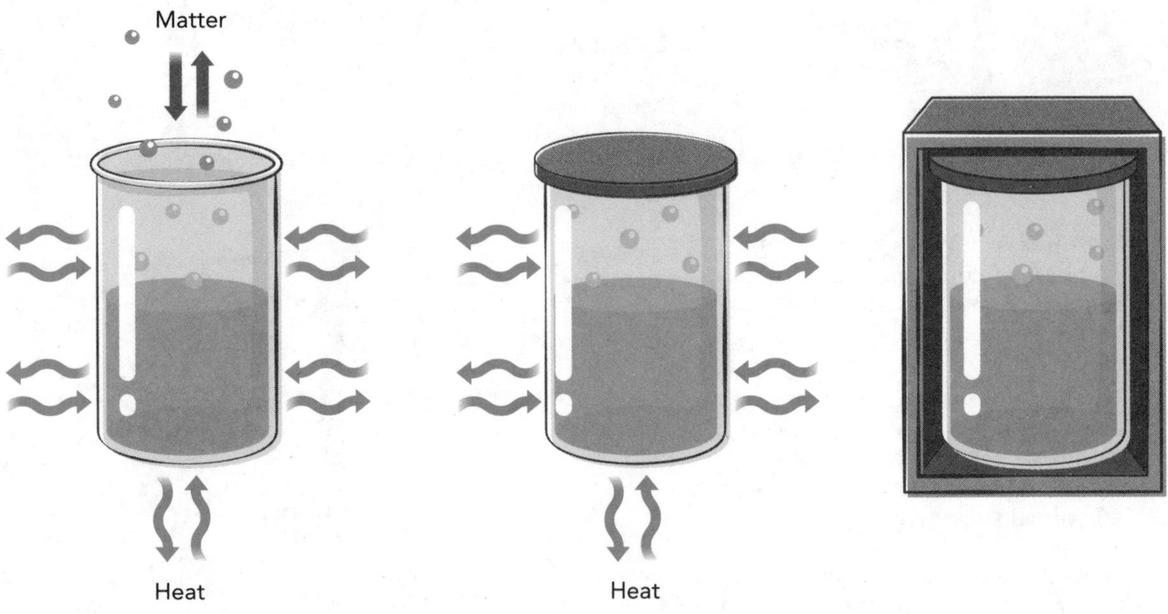

Open In an open system, energy and matter are exchanged freely with the surroundings.

Closed In a closed system, matter is conserved, but energy is exchanged with the surroundings.

Isolated In an isolated system, neither energy nor matter is exchanged with the surroundings.

24 SEP Design Your Solution Biosphere 2 was an attempt to have humans live within a perfectly closed system, as a model for living on other planets. The first attempt failed because the system began losing CO_2, which was chemically reacting with the exposed concrete walls. How would you go about designing a habitat that is a closed system? Explain how matter and energy would flow within the system.

Measuring the Flow of Matter

In chemistry, the flow of matter is modeled through equations that are similar to an equation you would use in algebra. In chemical equations the numbers and types of atoms are equal on both sides. It's important that both sides are equal because, according to the law of conservation of matter, matter is conserved and can neither be created nor destroyed in a physical change or chemical reaction. The masses on both sides of the equation must be equal. The numbers of atoms on both sides of the equations must also be equal.

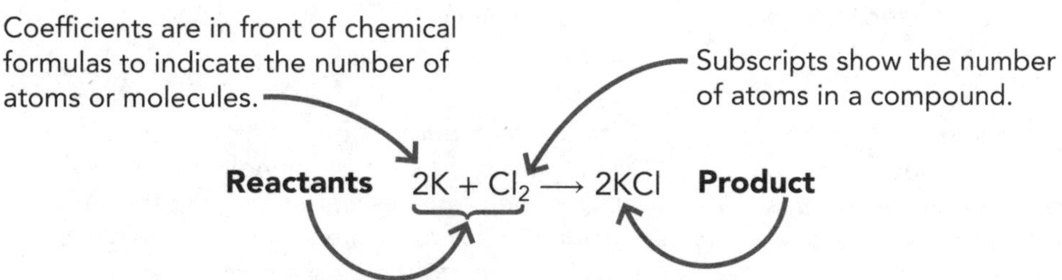
Coefficients are in front of chemical formulas to indicate the number of atoms or molecules.
Subscripts show the number of atoms in a compound.
Reactants
$2K + Cl_2 \longrightarrow 2KCl$
Product

There are two potassium (K) atoms and two chlorine (Cl) atoms on each side of the equation.

25 **SEP Using Mathematical and Computational Thinking** Iron (Fe) reacts with oxygen gas (O_2) to form rust (Fe_2O_3). **Balance the equation below by writing in the coefficients to ensure that the same number of each kind of atom appears on both sides of the equation.**

____ Fe + ____ $O_2 \longrightarrow$ ____ Fe_2O_3

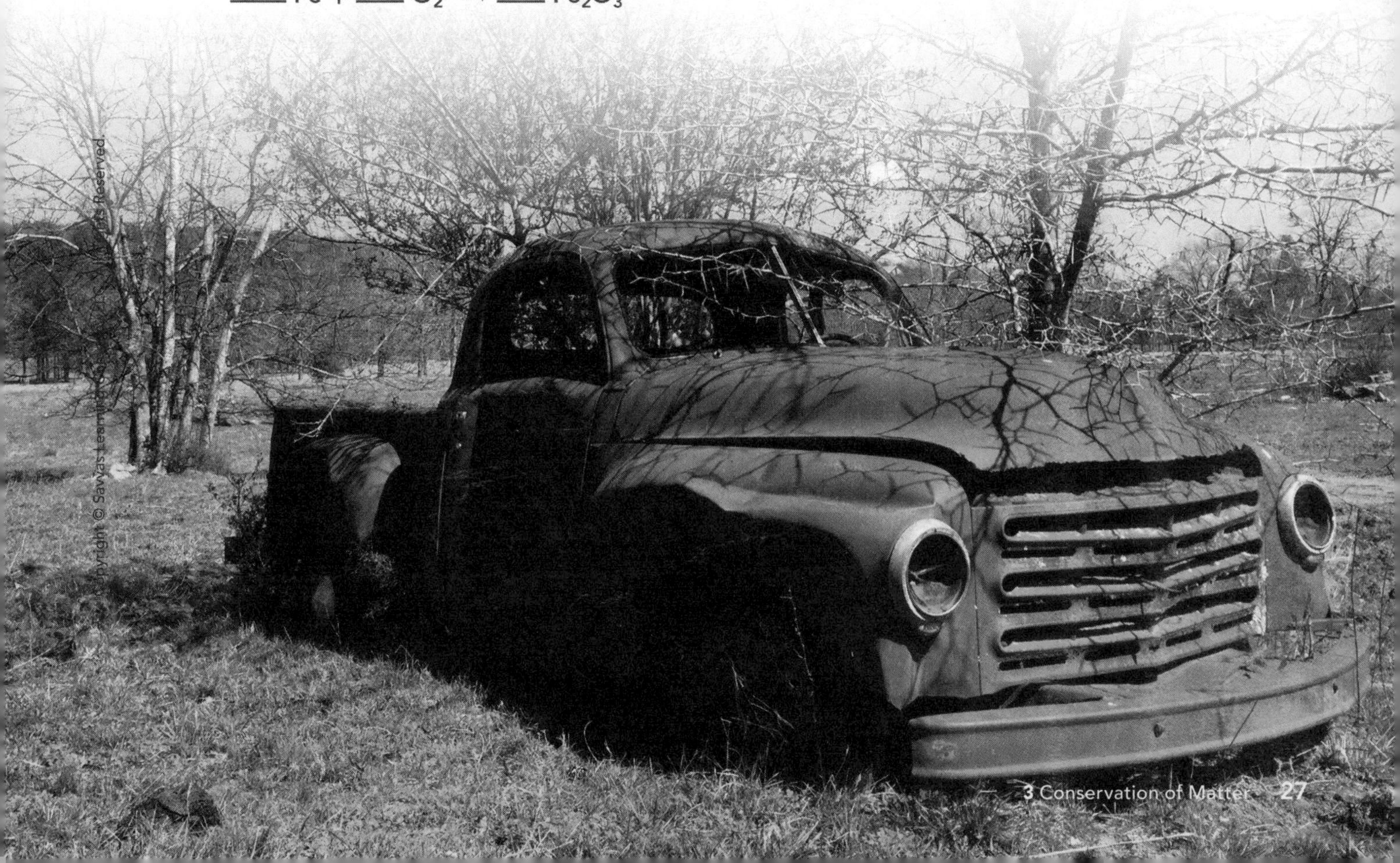

Conservation of Matter During Combustion

In combustion reactions, oxygen gas reacts with a molecule, often releasing energy in the form of both heat and light (a flame). The fuel that burns is often a hydrocarbon, containing atoms of both hydrogen and carbon. In all cases, matter is conserved during the reaction. The same numbers of atoms exist before and after the combustion reaction. In the combustion of propane, oxygen reacts with propane. The products of the reaction depend on the amount of oxygen present. But in all cases, the numbers of carbon, hydrogen, and oxygen atoms are conserved.

Complete Combustion In the presence of sufficient oxygen, complete combustion of propane produces water, carbon dioxide, and energy. Energy from the reaction is transferred to the pot of water on the burner.

$C_3H_8 + 5O_2 \longrightarrow 3CO_2 + 4H_2O + \text{Heat}$

A blue flame is an indicator of complete combustion.

Incomplete Combustion In the presence of insufficient oxygen, the incomplete combustion of propane produces water, carbon dioxide, carbon monoxide, and energy. Less energy is produced than with complete combustion.

$2C_3H_8 + 9O_2 \longrightarrow 4CO_2 + 2CO + 8H_2O + \text{Heat}$

A yellowish-orange flame is an indicator of incomplete combustion.

26 **SEP Reason Quantitatively** Use the chemical equations for the complete combustion and the incomplete combustion of propane to show that matter is conserved in both situations.

Combustion and Work

The energy of combustion is used to generate heat and light, but it can also do work. Work is the product of the net force on an object and the distance through which the object is moved. Work has units of energy, so it's measured in joules.

work (joules) = force (newtons) × distance (meters), or

$$W = Fd$$

Rockets You know that the expansion of hot gases during combustion can be used to push a piston, and that if several pistons are fired with the correct timing, they can power a car. Another, more direct, application of mechanical work using combustion is a rocket. In a rocket, solid or liquid fuels are burned to produce hot gases. Because the gases take up a much greater volume than the fuel, the rocket gets pushed in the direction opposite to the direction in which the gases expand. That is how NASA rockets reach the moon, Mars, and other planetary bodies.

Lift Off! The model rocket in the photo quickly gains speed and reaches its maximum height in a few seconds. The rockets used by NASA burn for several minutes and can gain enough speed to escape Earth's gravity.

Forces generated by the rapid expansion of the hot gases from a rocket's exhaust push the rocket upward.

Gas-Powered Turbines One of the largest uses of combustion is the burning of fossil fuels to generate electricity. In electric power plants driven by the burning of coal, natural gas, or oil, the heat given off by combustion produces expanding gas that pushes through a set of turbines, making them spin. A turbine is a rotary mechanical device that extracts energy from a flowing fluid and converts it into useful work.

Electricity-generating turbines run by combustion may be powered by burning gases, or they may be powered by steam that is produced in a boiler. The actual generation of electricity is done using wires and magnets, according to the laws of electromagnetism, but the energy originally comes from combustion.

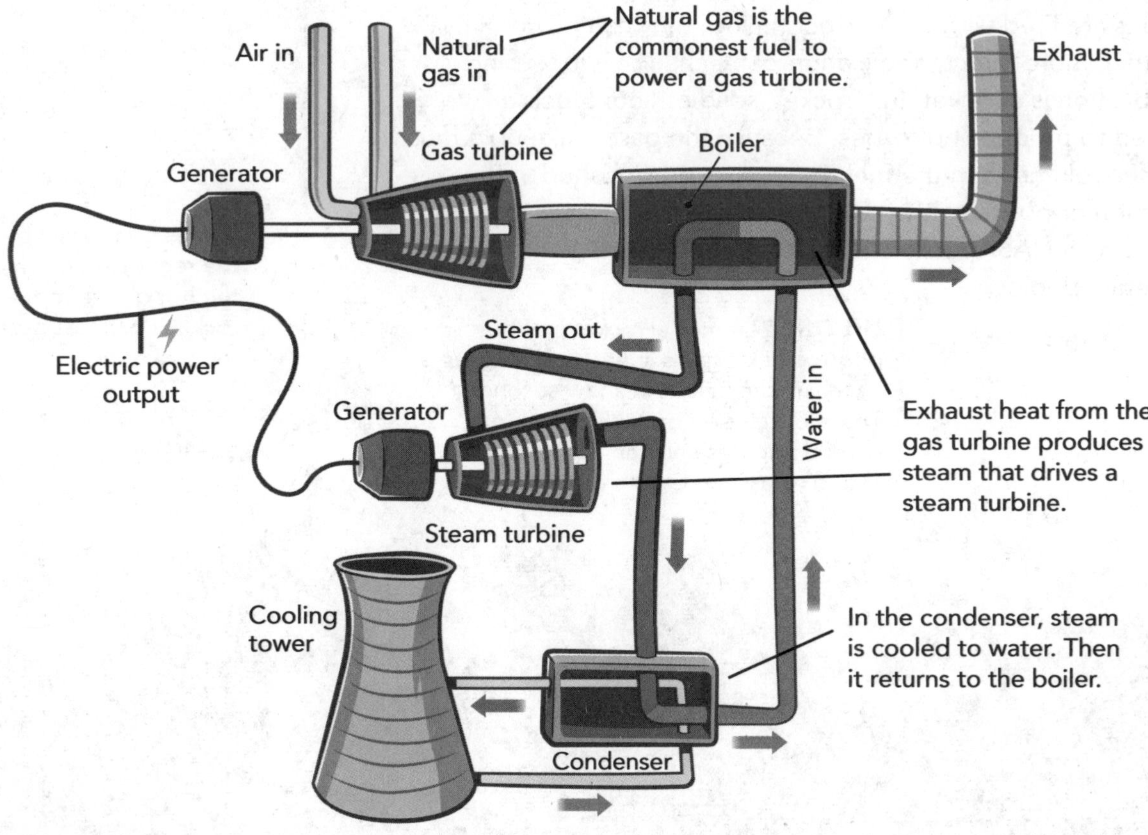

27 CCC Energy and Matter Recall that force = mass × acceleration. Explain why the acceleration of a model rocket increases over time, even if the force from the burning of the rocket fuel remains constant.

....

....

....

When Matter Isn't Conserved

During nuclear reactions, certain forms of matter can be created or destroyed, and matter, or mass, is converted into energy. Consider the equation $E = mc^2$, where m is the mass (kg) and c is the speed of light in a vacuum, which is 300 million m/s. Since c is squared in the formula, making a very big number, you can see that converting a small amount of mass releases an enormous amount of energy. Matter is destroyed during fission, fusion, and the decay of radioactive elements such as uranium. Energy can also be converted into matter, which is what occurred with the formation of the universe in the first seconds of the Big Bang. Matter is often thought of as a form of energy, so although matter is not always conserved, energy is always conserved.

Fission Fission is used in some power plants to make electricity.

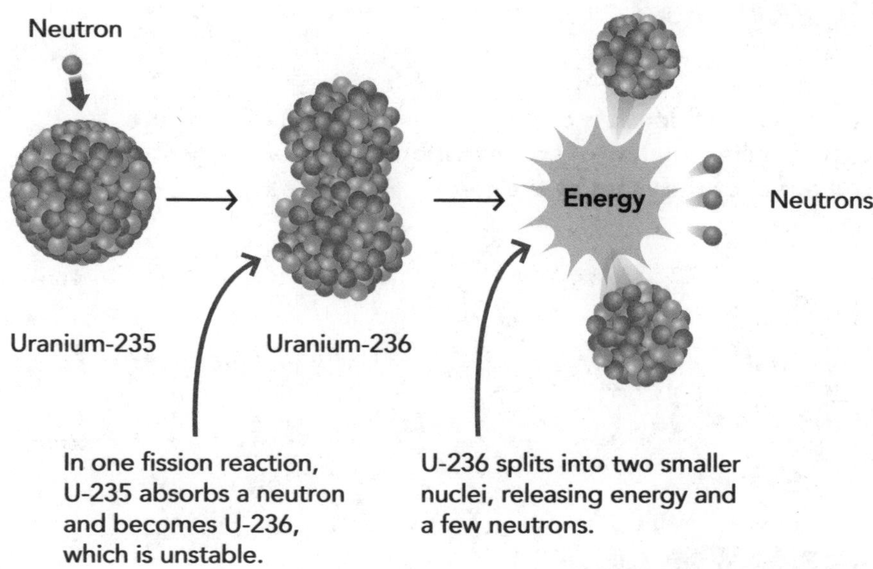

Neutron
Energy
Hydrogen nuclei
Helium nucleus
Positrons
In one set of fusion reactions, the net reaction is that four protons combine to form a helium nucleus and two positrons
Neutrons
Uranium-235
Uranium-236
In one fission reaction, U-235 absorbs a neutron and becomes U-236, which is unstable.
U-236 splits into two smaller nuclei, releasing energy and a few neutrons.

Fusion Fusion occurs in the center of stars, releasing the energy you eventually see as sunlight.

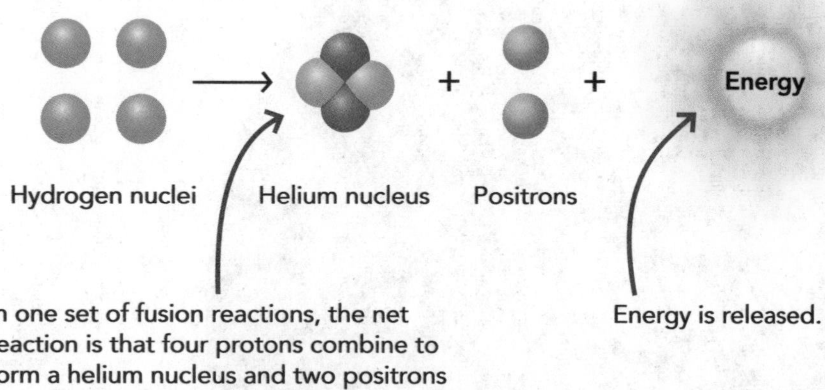

(28) **CCC Energy and Matter** Electric power plants that use nuclear fission reactions rely on a controlled self-sustaining chain reaction of splitting atoms. By examining the diagram for nuclear fission, explain how a chain reaction might occur. Explain why it is important to control the rate of the chain reaction.

Revisit

INVESTIGATIVE PHENOMENON

GO ONLINE to Elaborate and Evaluate your design of an experiment to show conservation of matter in the reaction of baking soda and vinegar.

(29) Before the fire, the forest consists of large trees. After the fire, there is only ash. Explain what the law of conservation of matter suggests happened to the rest of the mass of the trees.

GO ONLINE to Evaluate what you learned about foods, fuels, and energy by using the available assessment resources.

In the Performance-Based Assessment, you analyzed data to compare different types of fuel based on the property of energy density. Wrap up your analysis by answering the following questions.

30 **SEP Define Problems** Imagine you and a partner are engineers discussing which alternative fuel to use in your design for a new eco-friendly tractor. Together, agree on and list some criteria and constraints to help you evaluate possible fuels for your tractor design.

Criteria	Constraints

31 **Revisit the Anchoring Phenomenon** Recall the fiery crater that introduced Instructional Segment 1. How do you think matter and energy are conserved in that system?

INVESTIGATIVE PHENOMENON

GO ONLINE to Engage with real-world phenomena by watching a video and to complete a modeling interactive worksheet.

How does California get electricity from geothermal energy?

Energy Transfer and Conservation

Once you have viewed the Investigative Phenomenon video and completed the modeling exercise to understand how electricity may be obtained from geothermal energy, answer these questions.

1. **CCC Energy and Matter** What signs of energy transfer do you see in the photo? How do you think geothermal energy from inside Earth is being used to produce electricity?

2. **SEP Plan Investigations** Ground-source heat pumps can be used to efficiently heat or cool a house. Describe some of the factors that should be considered before installing such a system in a home.

EXPERIENCE 1

Manifestations of Energy

GO ONLINE to Explore and Explain the various manifestations of energy and energy flow.

Kinetic Energy of Particles

An object in motion has kinetic energy. Motion is described by its velocity, **v**, which is a vector; it has both magnitude and direction. The **momentum** of an object is equal to its mass times its velocity; it is another vector, **p** = *m***v**. The **kinetic energy** of a moving particle is also a function of velocity, but it is a scalar. It has magnitude but not direction: $KE = \frac{1}{2}mv^2$. Energy can take many different forms, but it is always a scalar.

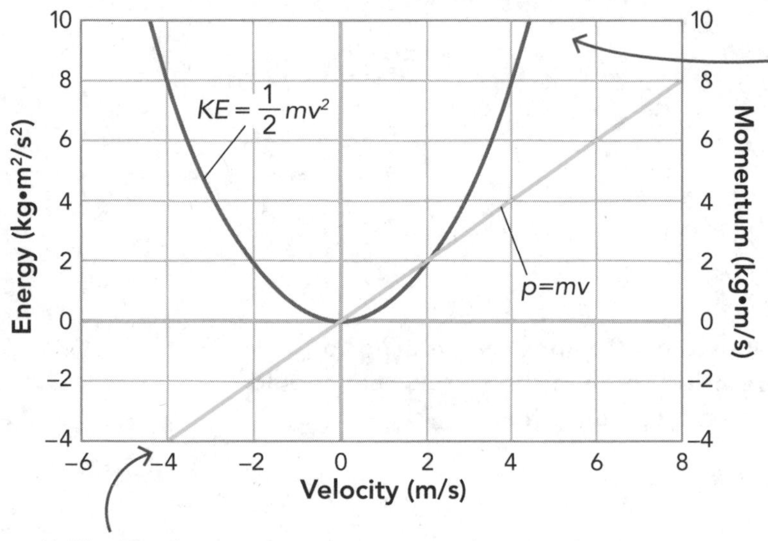

(3) **CCC Matter and Energy** **A 20-kg curling stone is sliding in a positive direction at 4 m/s. A second curling stone is sliding at the same speed but in the opposite direction. What is the net kinetic energy of the two stones? What is their net momentum?**

Thermal Energy of Substances

Thermal energy can be defined as the kinetic energy of the atoms of a substance. Atoms are always in motion, and that motion is a function of temperature. The same holds true for gases, liquids, and even solids—atoms vibrating in place in a solid still have thermal energy. The net momentum of all the particles adds up to zero if the material isn't in motion. Yet there is still thermal energy, because kinetic energy is proportional to the square of an individual particle's velocity and is always positive. Thermal energy is a function of the total number of particles in a substance: the greater the mass of a substance, the greater is its thermal energy.

Energy of Particles in a Gas Each individual particle has kinetic energy. The sum of the kinetic energies of all the particles in a gas is its thermal energy.

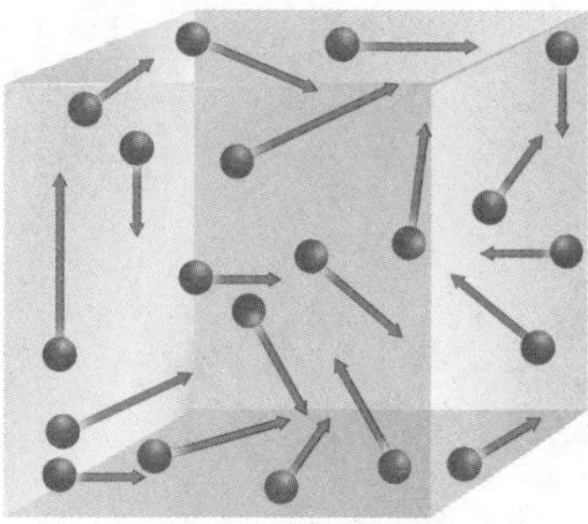

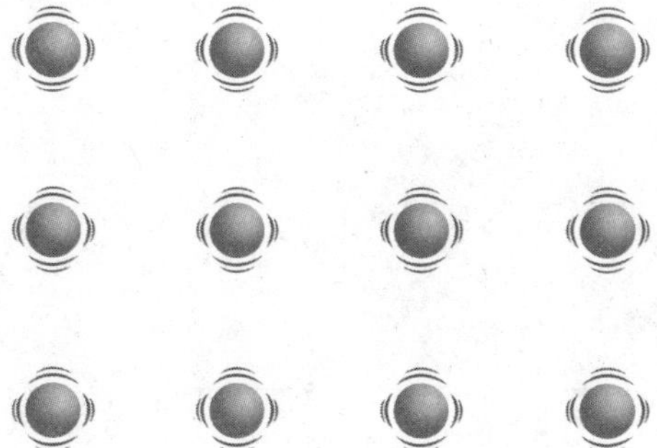

Energy of Particles in a Solid Atoms are locked in place, bonded to each other, but they are still oscillating. The sum of the vibrational energy for all of the atoms in a solid substance is its thermal energy.

4 SEP Plan and Carry Out an Investigation **Plan an investigation using water, a glass, and a bucket to demonstrate that thermal energy is not the same as temperature.**

....

....

....

....

Thermal Energy vs. Internal Energy

Temperature is not a direct measure of a system's total thermal energy. The total thermal energy (sometimes called the total internal energy) of a system depends jointly on the temperature, the total number of atoms in the system, and the state of the material. The total internal energy of a substance is very difficult to measure, as it includes the potential energy states of all of the individual particles (neutrons, protons, and electrons) that make up the atoms.

As a result, the thermal energy is usually only used to refer to the change in the kinetic energy of the particles of a substance, as seen by its change in temperature while in a single state.

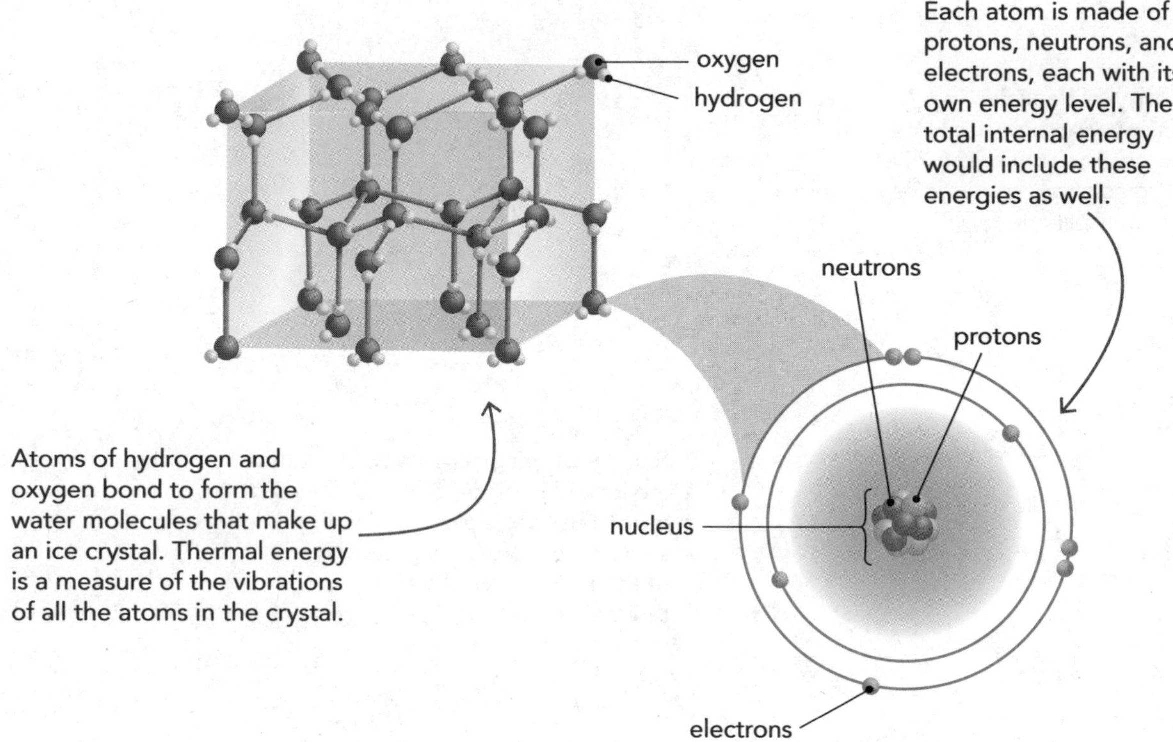

oxygen
hydrogen
Each atom is made of protons, neutrons, and electrons, each with its own energy level. The total internal energy would include these energies as well.
neutrons
protons
Atoms of hydrogen and oxygen bond to form the water molecules that make up an ice crystal. Thermal energy is a measure of the vibrations of all the atoms in the crystal.
nucleus
electrons

5 **SEP Plan and Carry Out an Investigation** **Plan an investigation using solid and liquid water to show that thermal energy is not the same as temperature.**

....

....

....

....

Electricity

Electricity is a form of energy associated with electrically charged particles. In the case of an electric current through a wire, the charged particles are electrons. The flow of electrons is called the **current,** *I* (in amperes, or amps). The **resistance** to the flow of current through the circuit is *R* (in ohms). The greater the resistance in a circuit, the less is the current. The rate of flow of energy, or the **power,** in a circuit (in watts) is given by $P = RI^2$. The relation is similar to the kinetic energy of an object, $KE = \frac{1}{2}mv^2$.

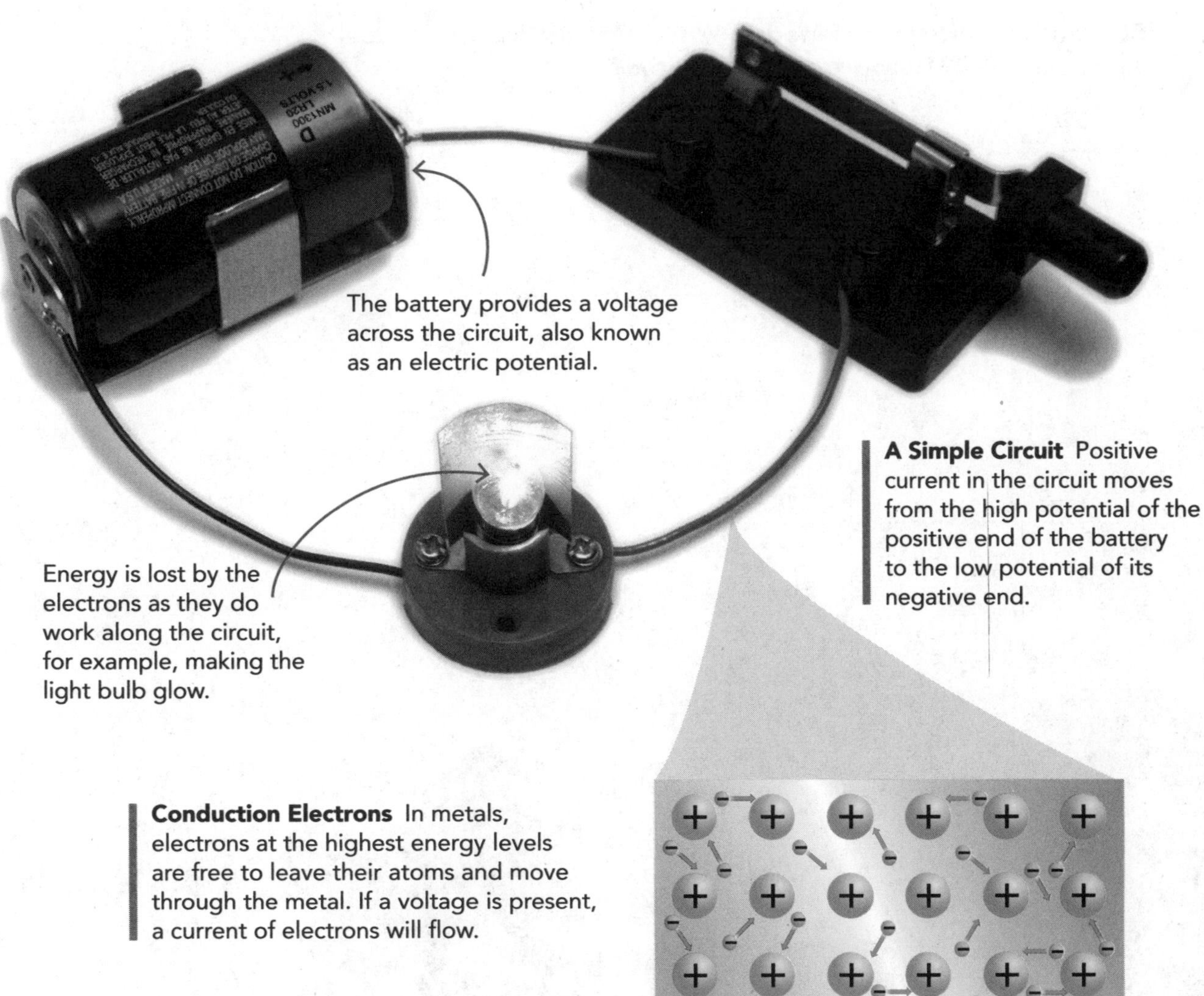

The battery provides a voltage across the circuit, also known as an electric potential.

Energy is lost by the electrons as they do work along the circuit, for example, making the light bulb glow.

A Simple Circuit Positive current in the circuit moves from the high potential of the positive end of the battery to the low potential of its negative end.

Conduction Electrons In metals, electrons at the highest energy levels are free to leave their atoms and move through the metal. If a voltage is present, a current of electrons will flow.

CCC Use Mathematics and Computational Thinking **Suppose that the power used by a light bulb in a circuit is 16 W, and the bulb has a resistance of 4 ohms. Calculate the current (in amps) flowing through it.**

Revisit

INVESTIGATIVE PHENOMENON

GO ONLINE to Elaborate and Evaluate your understanding of the various manifestations of energy and energy flow by completing the modeling activity and peer review.

In the modeling activity assigned at the beginning of this investigation, you drew the main features of a system for converting geothermal energy into electricity. With a partner, reevaluate that model.

7 **SEP Identify Limitations of Models What concepts did your model help explain well? How is the model limited? Explain.**

EXPERIENCE 2

Mechanisms of Heat Flow

GO ONLINE to Explore and Explain the ways heat can be transferred from one place to another.

Heat

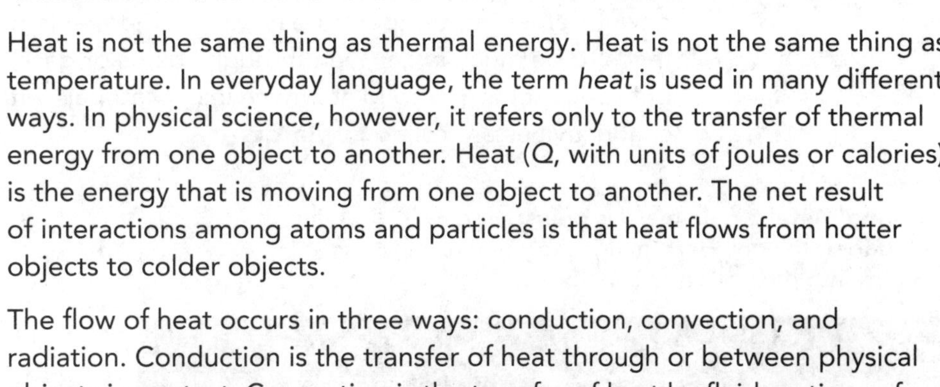

Heat is not the same thing as thermal energy. Heat is not the same thing as temperature. In everyday language, the term *heat* is used in many different ways. In physical science, however, it refers only to the transfer of thermal energy from one object to another. Heat (Q, with units of joules or calories) is the energy that is moving from one object to another. The net result of interactions among atoms and particles is that heat flows from hotter objects to colder objects.

The flow of heat occurs in three ways: conduction, convection, and radiation. Conduction is the transfer of heat through or between physical objects in contact. Convection is the transfer of heat by fluid motions of the materials. Radiation is the transfer of heat through electromagnetic radiation. In many natural circumstances, all three mechanisms occur simultaneously. However, energy generally moves primarily by only one of the methods, depending on the circumstances.

Lava Lamp A lava lamp is a good example of the transfer of heat through all three mechanisms. A light shines into the bottom of a glass bottle containing two different types of liquid, one water-based and one oil-based.

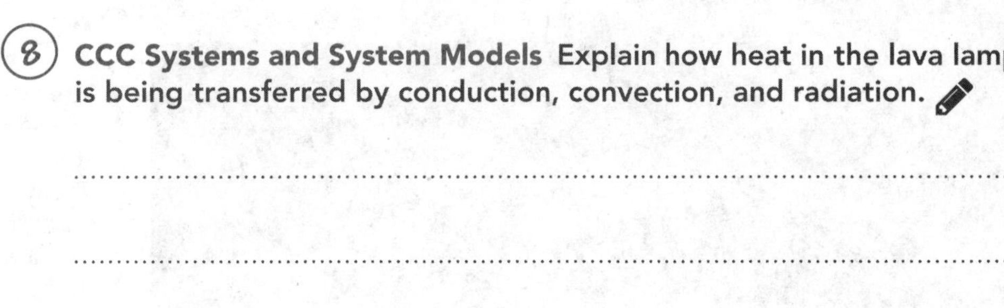

8 **CCC Systems and System Models Explain how heat in the lava lamp is being transferred by conduction, convection, and radiation.**

Thermal Conduction

For most materials other than metals, thermal **conduction** occurs through the oscillations of adjacent atoms. Atoms oscillate more actively when they are hotter. If hotter atoms are in contact with cooler atoms, there will be frequent collisions among them, and overall, energy will pass from the hotter to the cooler atoms.

Over time, with continued collisions, the energy will diffuse through a material or between adjacent materials. How efficiently heat is conducted through a material is measured as its **thermal conductivity**, *k*, in units of power per length-temperature (W/m·K). Thermal conduction through solids tends to be much faster than through liquids or gases because the distances between atoms in a solid are much less. Materials with very low thermal conductivities are called **insulators**.

Casting Metal Liquid metal is poured into a mold for it to cool. Heat immediately begins to flow into the walls of the mold.

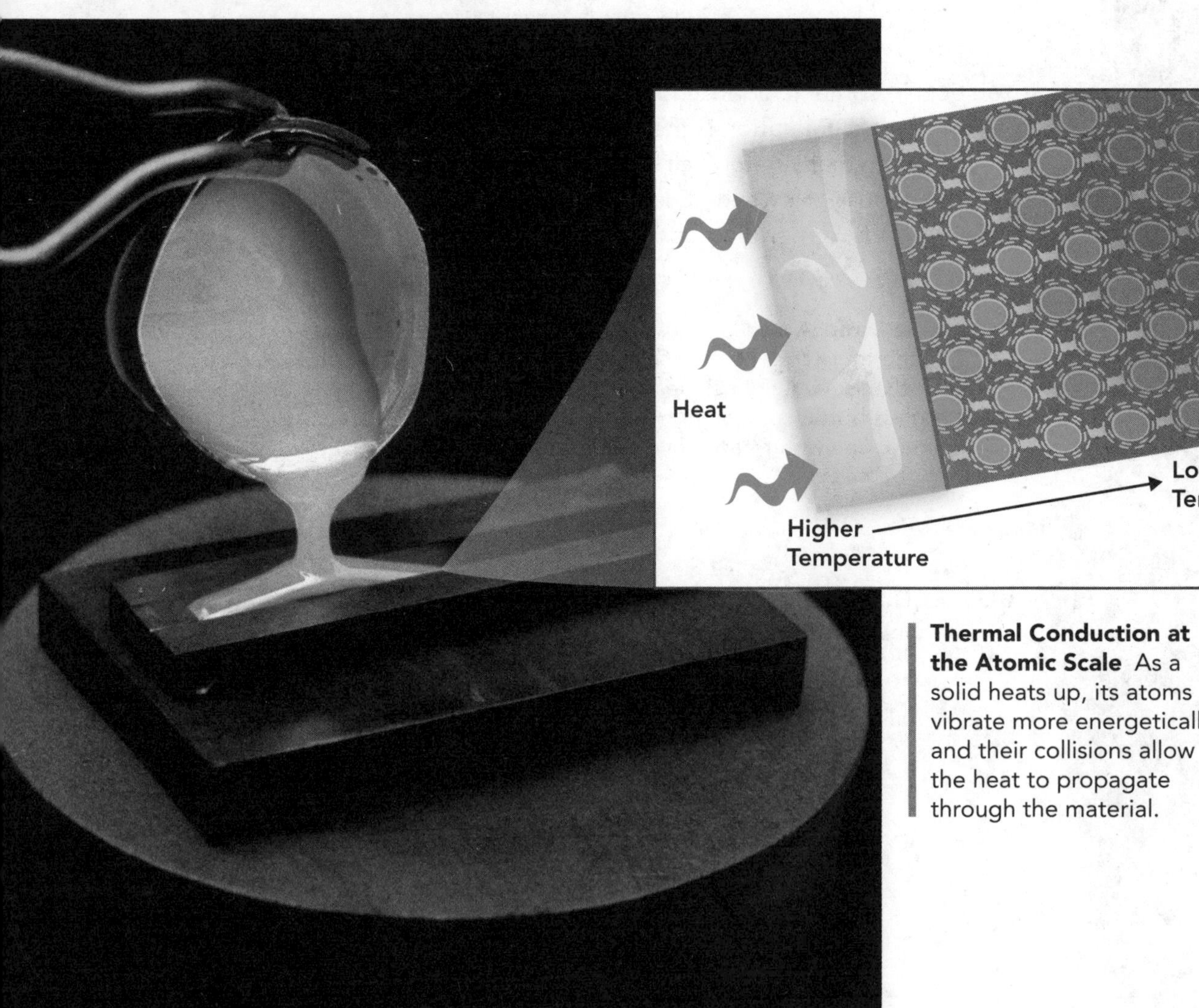

Thermal Conduction at the Atomic Scale As a solid heats up, its atoms vibrate more energetically, and their collisions allow the heat to propagate through the material.

Heat Flow If an amount of heat Q (in joules) flows through a material in a time t (in seconds), then $q = \frac{Q}{t}$ is the total rate of heat flow (in J/s, or watts). If the heat flow takes place within an area A, then q/A measures the amount of heat per unit time per unit area. That quantity is called the heat flux (ϕ). The total heat flowing through a surface of area A every second is the heat flux multiplied by the area ($q = \phi A$).

The rate of heat flow is faster for materials with high k or when there is a large temperature difference across the region of heat flow. The rate of heat flow is also faster when the heat doesn't have as far to go. The equation for heat conduction through a sheet of material is: $\phi = k\frac{(T_1 - T_2)}{L}$, where L is the thickness of the sheet, T_1 is the temperature of the hotter side, and T_2 is the temperature of the colder side.

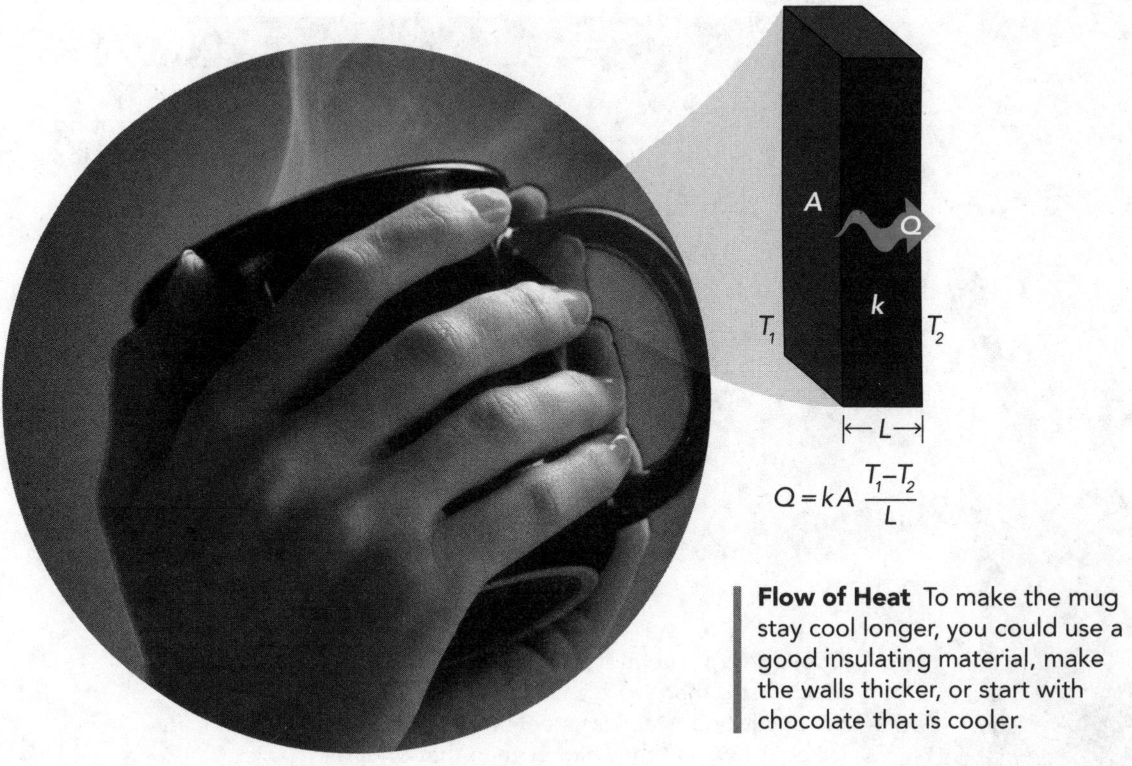

Flow of Heat To make the mug stay cool longer, you could use a good insulating material, make the walls thicker, or start with chocolate that is cooler.

Hot Cup As the wall of a ceramic mug slowly conducts heat from the hot chocolate it holds, the temperature of the outer surface of the mug will increase until it may be too hot to hold.

9 **SEP Mathematics and Computational Thinking** Use the units of k, T, and L and the equation $\phi = k\frac{(T_1 - T_2)}{L}$ to show that the units of ϕ are power, or energy per time, per area (W/m^2).

Conduction in Metals

Thermal conduction in metals is a special case of conduction, because the heat is carried by movements of the electrons as well as by movements of the atoms. The electrons at the highest energy levels dissociate from the atoms and drift through the metal. Electrons that are heated collide with and transfer heat to the vibrating atoms. Because of the high mobility of the electrons, the result is a rate of conduction that is much higher than from the atomic vibrations alone.

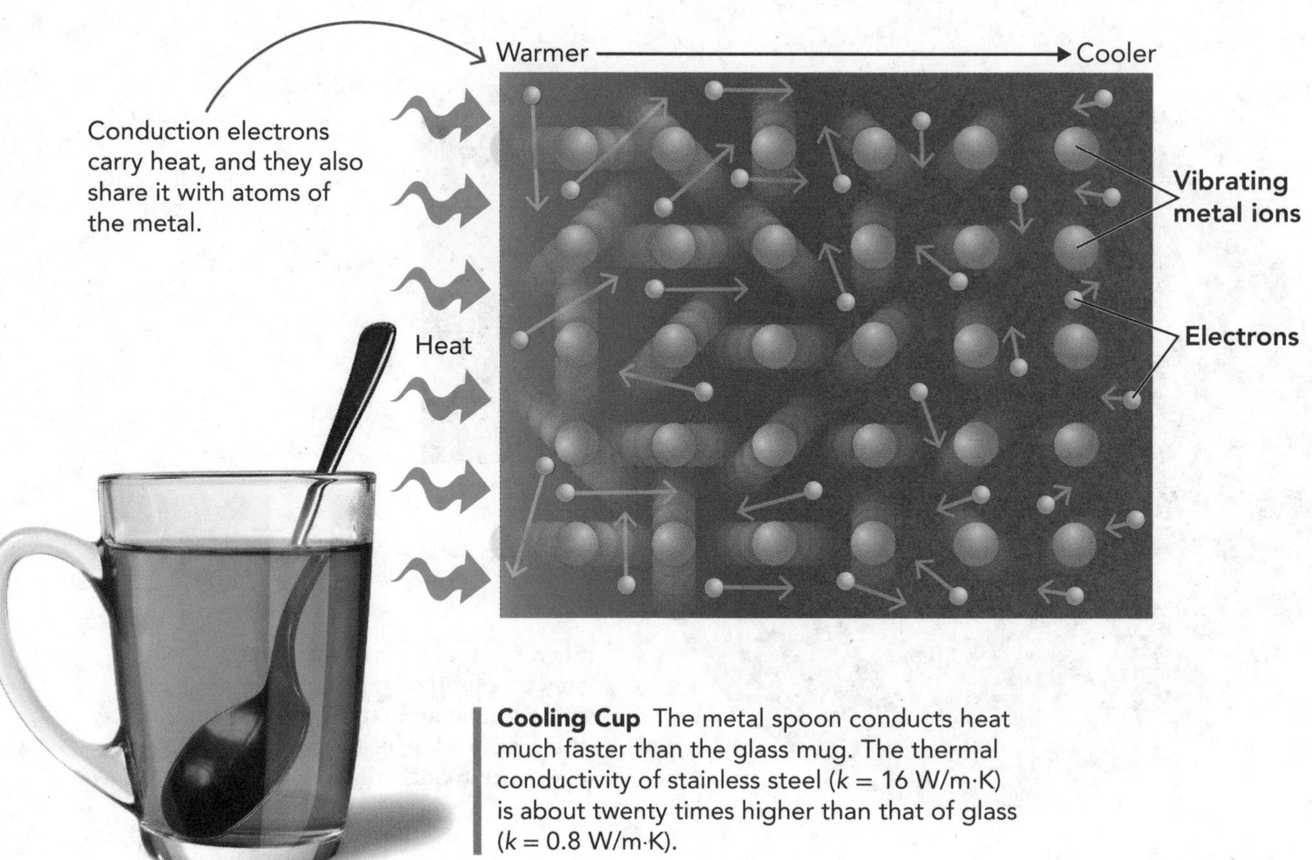
Warmer
Cooler
Conduction electrons carry heat, and they also share it with atoms of the metal.
Heat
Vibrating metal ions
Electrons

Cooling Cup The metal spoon conducts heat much faster than the glass mug. The thermal conductivity of stainless steel ($k = 16$ W/m·K) is about twenty times higher than that of glass ($k = 0.8$ W/m·K).

(10) SEP Computational Thinking **Suppose that a piece of polystyrene insulation board has a thermal conductivity of $k = 0.04$ W/m·K. In comparison, copper has a thermal conductivity of about 400 W/m·K. If you want to make a wall of copper that provides the same insulation as a 4-cm polystyrene board, how thick does the copper wall have to be (in meters)?**

Convection: Density and Viscosity

Convection is the cycling of fluid materials, driven by differences in density. When a portion of a fluid is denser than the surrounding fluid, it will sink and displace less dense portions of the fluid, which will rise. Convection is commonly driven by thermal energy, because materials expand and become less dense when their temperature increases. Other differences in density also produce convection, for instance when salty water sinks below fresh water. Both sorts of convection can operate at the same time.

On Earth, convection can occur within gases (in the atmosphere), liquids (in the ocean), or solids (in Earth's mantle). All three can behave as fluids. Whether a liquid or solid behaves as a fluid depends on the time scale involved. Liquid water can behave like a solid if you skip a rock across it, and solid rock can flow like a liquid, given enough time.

Atlantic Ocean Currents Warm (and buoyant) water flows northward, while cold and salty (and dense) North Atlantic water sinks and flows southward.

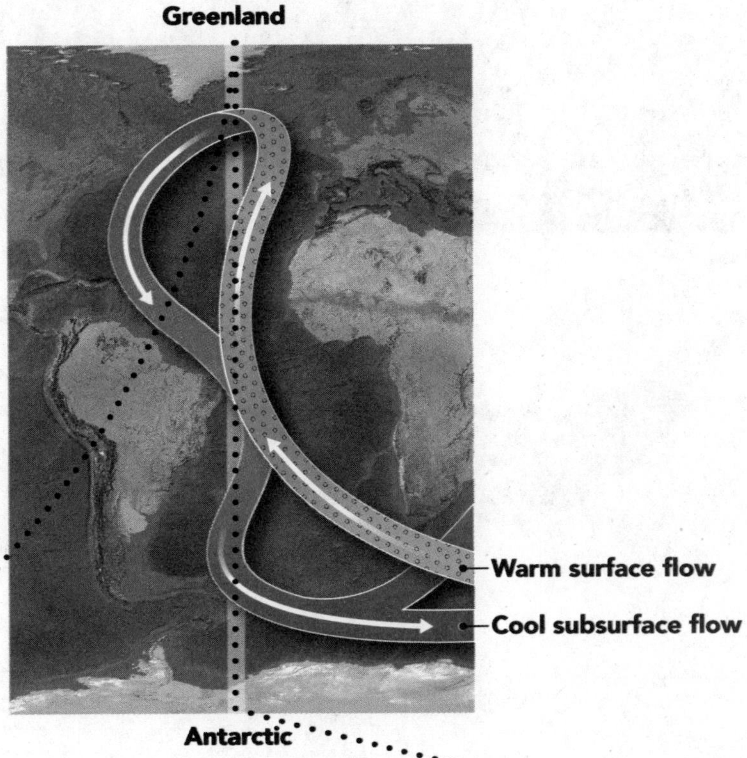

The global cycle of ocean convection begins with dense seawater sinking near Greenland. The water has high density because it is both cold and salty.

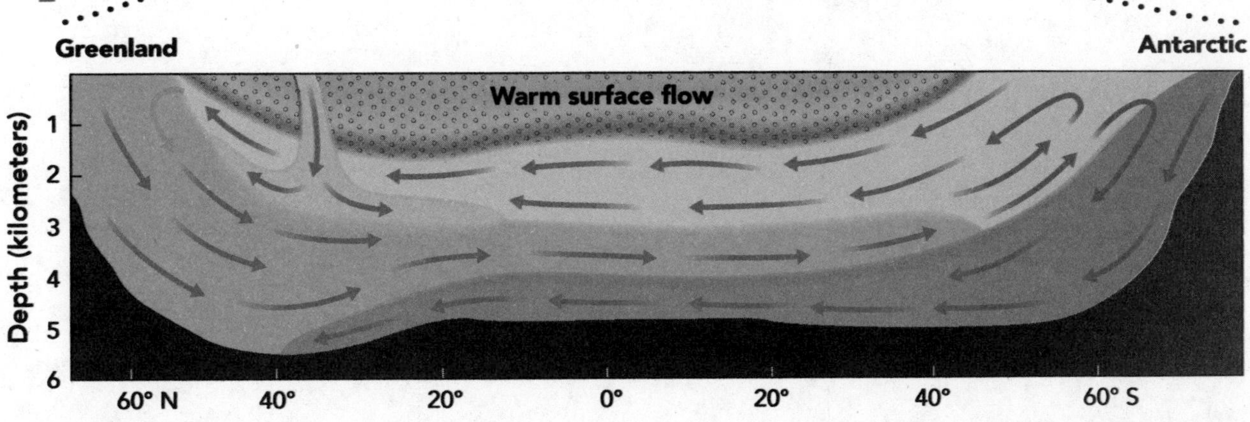

Viscosity The **viscosity** of a material is its resistance to flowing. It is measured in pascal-seconds (Pa·s, or kg/m·s). Solids have high viscosities, so they flow more slowly than liquids or gases. Whether a liquid or solid behaves as a fluid depends on the time scale involved. Liquid water can behave like a solid if you skip a rock across it, and solid rock can flow like a liquid given enough time.

Skipping Stone Water is a liquid that flows easily and has a low viscosity. Yet, if you skip a rock across the surface of a lake, the water behaves like a solid for the brief fraction of a second that the stone is in contact with it.

Viscosities of Common Materials
Materials with high viscosities, such as rocks in Earth's mantle, undergo convection only very slowly, but convection does take place.

Material	Typical Viscosity (Pa·s)
Air	0.000018
Water	0.001
Honey	2–10
Mantle rocks	10^{20}–10^{22}

11 **SEP Communicate Information** Write a definition for *fluid* that incorporates time into a model of solids and liquids.

....

....

....

Hot Air Balloons The oldest mode of air transportation, the hot air balloon, operates through thermal convection driven by the heat from a flame source in the basket.

When the flame is burning, air above it is heated, expands, and rises to the top of the balloon.

Hot air cools as it moves away from the flame, contracts, and sinks down along the sides of the balloon.

Thermal Convection

Thermal convection is an efficient way to move heat when conduction rates are low. Unlike conduction, convection involves the transport of heat through the motion of atoms from bottom to top in a material. For thermal convection, density differences are a result of heating. Materials expand when they are heated, a familiar phenomenon known as **thermal expansion**. Expanding materials become less dense and therefore more buoyant.

A common example of thermal convection is a pot of water heating on a stove. Heat from a flame causes the water at the bottom of the pot to expand, become less dense, and rise to the top of the pot, where it loses its heat to the room and contracts. It then becomes more dense and sinks back to the bottom to begin the cycle again.

12 **CCC Systems and System Models Pilots of hot air balloons are able to steer them somewhat by moving them up or down to enter different air currents that move in different directions. Explain how the flame can be used to do that.**

The Onset and Style of Convection

Many factors control how convection within a material occurs. An index of the behavior is the Rayleigh number, *Ra*, defined for a box-shaped volume of material having length *L*, width *W*, and height *H* as follows:

$$Ra = \frac{\rho^2 c_p g \alpha (T_1 - T_2)\ LWH}{\mu k}$$

In the formula, the Rayleigh number is proportional to the specific heat c_p, the acceleration of gravity g, the coefficient of thermal expansion α, the temperature difference between the bottom and top of the box $(T_1 - T_2)$, and the volume of the material *LWH*. The Rayleigh number is also proportional to the square of the density ρ and inversely proportional to the viscosity μ and the thermal conductivity k.

If the Rayleigh number is above a critical value, usually about 500, convection will occur. Below that, it will not. The higher the Rayleigh number is, the more vigorous and chaotic the convection will be. Increasing the volume is a particularly effective way to increase the speed and efficiency of convection.

Slow Convection This simulation has a low Rayleigh number. It is sluggish, with wide plumes of hot material rising and cold material sinking.

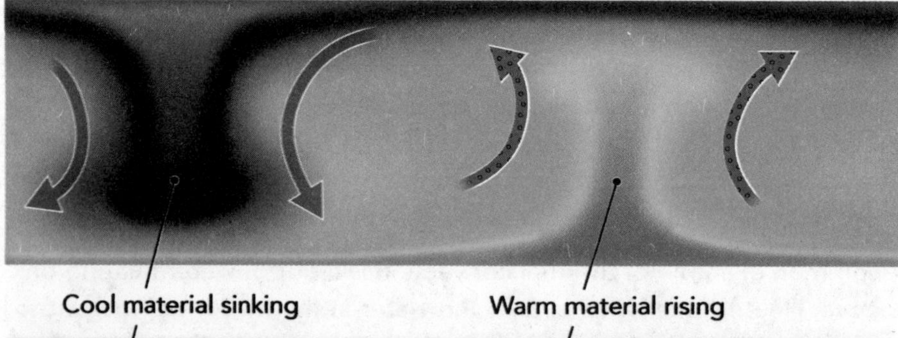

Fast Convection This simulation has a high Rayleigh number, with narrow plumes that are constantly changing and shifting.

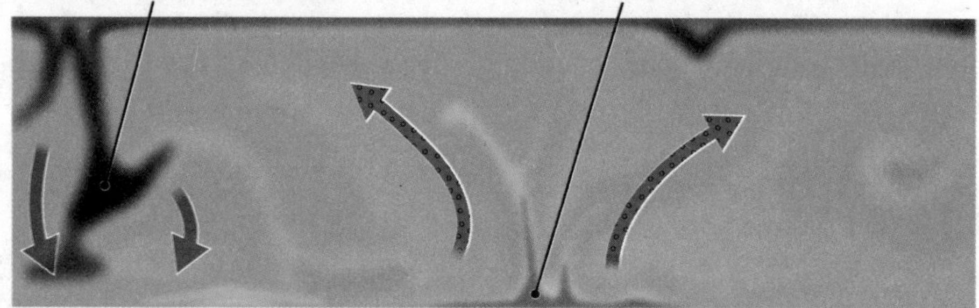

13 **CCC Energy and Matter** **Construct an explanation for why convection in orbit around Earth—for example, aboard the International Space Station—would be impossible.**

SAMPLE PROBLEM

Does Earth's Mantle Undergo Convection?

Convection within Earth's mantle drives the motion of tectonic plates. You can confirm that convection is occurring by calculating the value of *Ra*.

Approximate Earth's mantle as a box that is 3000 km on a side (*L*, *W*, and *H* are all 3,000,000 m). Assume that the temperature difference ($T_1 - T_2$) between the top and the bottom of the mantle is 3500 K, rock density ρ is 4000 kg/m^3, and specific heat c_p is 800 J/kg·K. Also assume that the thermal expansion coefficient α is 0.00003/K, gravity *g* is 10 m/s^2, viscosity μ is 10^{21} kg/m·s, and thermal conductivity k is 2 J/m·K·s.

ANALYZE List the knowns and unknown.

Knowns	Unknown
$p = 4000$ kg/m^3	Rayleigh number $Ra = ?$
$c_p = 800$ J/kg·K	
$g = 10$ m/s^2	
$\alpha = 0.00003$/K	
$T_1 - T_2 = 3500$ K	
$LWH = (3{,}000{,}000\text{ m})^3$	
$\mu = 10^{21}$ kg/m·s	
$k = 2$ J/m·K·s	

CALCULATE Solve for the unknown.

Write the equation for *Ra*.

$$Ra = \frac{p^2 c_p g \alpha (T_1 - T_2)\, LWH}{\mu k}$$

Substitute the knowns into the equation and solve.

$Ra = [(4000\text{ kg/m}^3)^2(800\text{ J/kg·K})(10\text{ m/s}^2)(0.00003 \times 1/\text{K})(3500\text{ K})(3{,}000{,}000\text{ m})^3] \div [(10^{21}\text{ kg/m·s})(2\text{ J/m·K·s})] =$ about 181,000,000

Evaluate Does the result indicate that the mantle is undergoing convection?

Yes it does, because *Ra* is much greater than 500.

(14) **Would convection occur if Earth's mantle were a box 30 km on a side?**

GO ONLINE for more practice problems.

Thermal Boundary Layers

In many physical systems involving convection, critical parts of the system are the layers of fluid at the boundaries where heat enters or leaves the convection cell, usually at the top or at the bottom. Those regions, called **thermal boundary layers**, conduct heat but do not undergo convection (or convection only happens within themselves).

Thermal boundary layers often have steep thermal gradients within them, and they play a controlling role in how fast a volume of material heats up or cools down.

Thermal boundary layers are relatively stable.

Within a material undergoing convection, the thermal gradient tends to be less steep, because of mixing. For example, at the top of the ocean is a thermal boundary layer where thermal energy flows into the ocean if the water is cooler, or out of the ocean if the air is cooler. Likewise, there is a thermal boundary layer at the bottom of the atmosphere where it is in direct contact with the surface.

Boundary Layers The temperature is about the same throughout most of the pot. Nearly all of the temperature change occurs in the narrow thermal boundary layers at the top and bottom of the liquid.

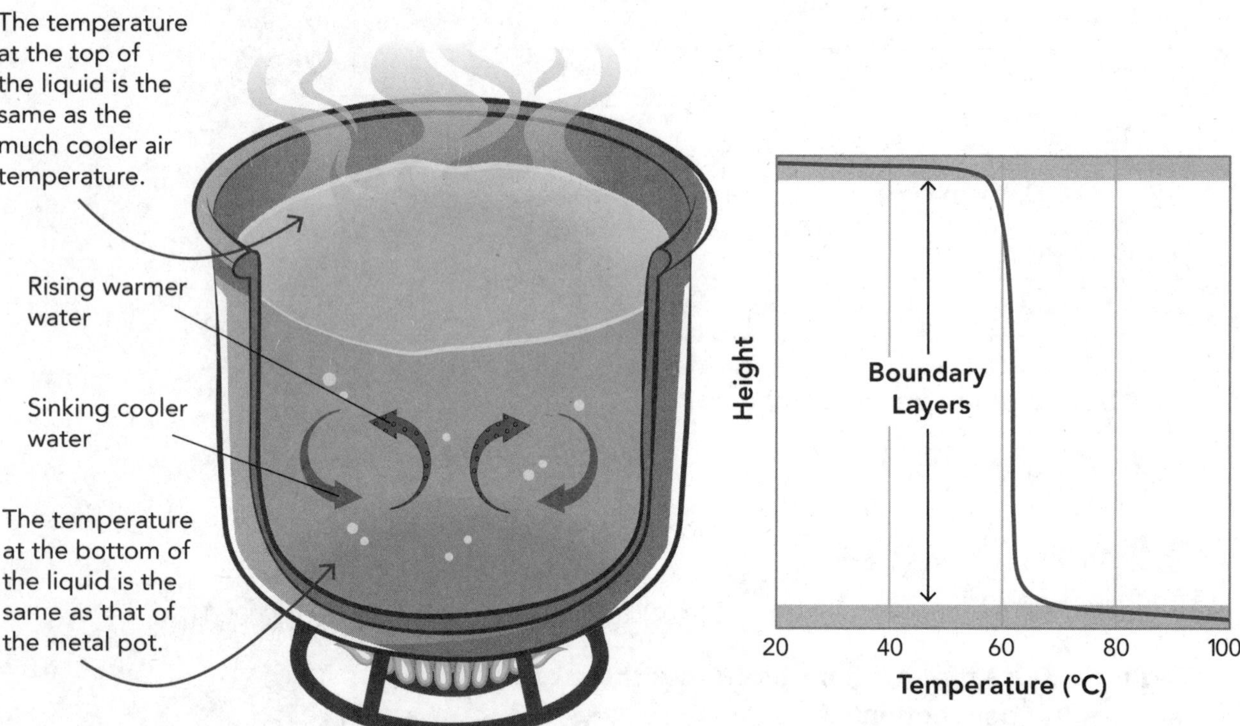

The temperature at the top of the liquid is the same as the much cooler air temperature.
Rising warmer water
Sinking cooler water
The temperature at the bottom of the liquid is the same as that of the metal pot.
Height
Boundary Layers
20
40
60
80
100
Temperature (°C)

15 **CCC Energy and Matter How do you think the vertical temperature profile across the pot will change after the pot has been on the burner for several minutes?**

Temperature and Radiation

Atoms not only absorb radiation but also reemit it, losing heat in the process. The frequency and the total amount of energy of the emitted radiation are functions of the temperature of the object. For example, objects with a temperature of about 5500°C, such as the photosphere of the sun or the filament of an incandescent light bulb, emit much of their energy in the visible spectrum. You see them as giving off light. In fact, all objects around you emit radiation, but not much in the visible spectrum. Objects that are 37°C, such as you, emit the greatest amount of radiation in the infrared spectrum. You can see this light using infrared goggles.

Infrared Image Infrared cameras assign false colors to different wavelengths of infrared radiation. Such cameras can be used to find where heat is leaking out of a house or to tell instantly if a person has a fever. This image shows a woman holding a cup with a hot drink.

Planck's Radiation Distribution The thermal radiation spontaneously emitted by the atoms of objects can often be approximated as **black-body radiation**, which describes radiation by an object over a continuous range of frequencies. The shape of the curve is determined by the temperature of the object and is called the Planck distribution. The wavelength of the peak of the curve decreases as temperature increases. When an object such as a piece of metal is heated up, it first starts to glow red as the peak of the Planck distribution moves from the infrared into the red portion of the visible spectrum. As the object reaches higher temperatures, the peak moves further into the visible spectrum. The object glows orange, yellow, and finally white, as all colors are emitted. The total energy emitted by an object increases rapidly with temperature, as it is proportional to T^4.

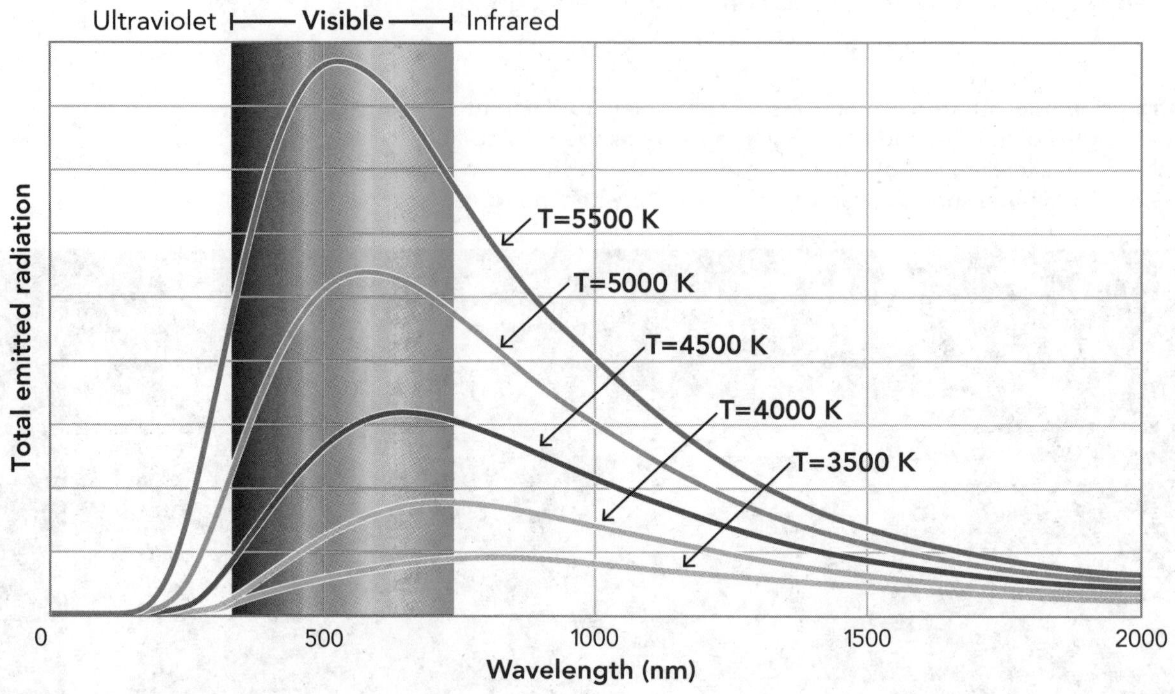

Black-body Radiation The radiation emitted by an object forms a curve that is peaked at a single frequency. As the temperature of the object increases, two things happen. The peak shifts to shorter wavelengths (or higher frequencies), and the overall amount of energy released, which is represented by the area under the curve, increases rapidly.

16 **CCC Energy and Matter The surface of the sun is at a temperature of about 5800 K. Suppose that the sun were the same size, but it had a temperature of 7000 K instead of 5800 K. Use the graph of Planck's law to predict the ways that the sun's light would be different.**

Conduction, Convection, and Radiation

In many physical systems, all three of the mechanisms of heat flow operate simultaneously. However, the relative importance of the three mechanisms can vary widely. For example, all materials continuously emit radiation, but radiation is most efficient through gases or a vacuum. Radiation is very inefficient within opaque solids, because it only travels a short distance before it is absorbed again. For example, light does not pass through most rocks. Convection is usually the fastest way for heat to flow within liquids, which are very mobile but are dense enough to limit radiation. Conduction is usually the most efficient way for heat to flow through solids, although even solids can transfer heat through convection efficiently if the conditions are right.

All Three Modes of Heat Flow A radiator in a home is misnamed. It should be called a conductor-convector-radiator, because all three processes are happening.

Convection Air warmed by the radiator becomes less dense and rises toward the ceiling. At the window, the air cools, becomes denser, and falls toward the floor.

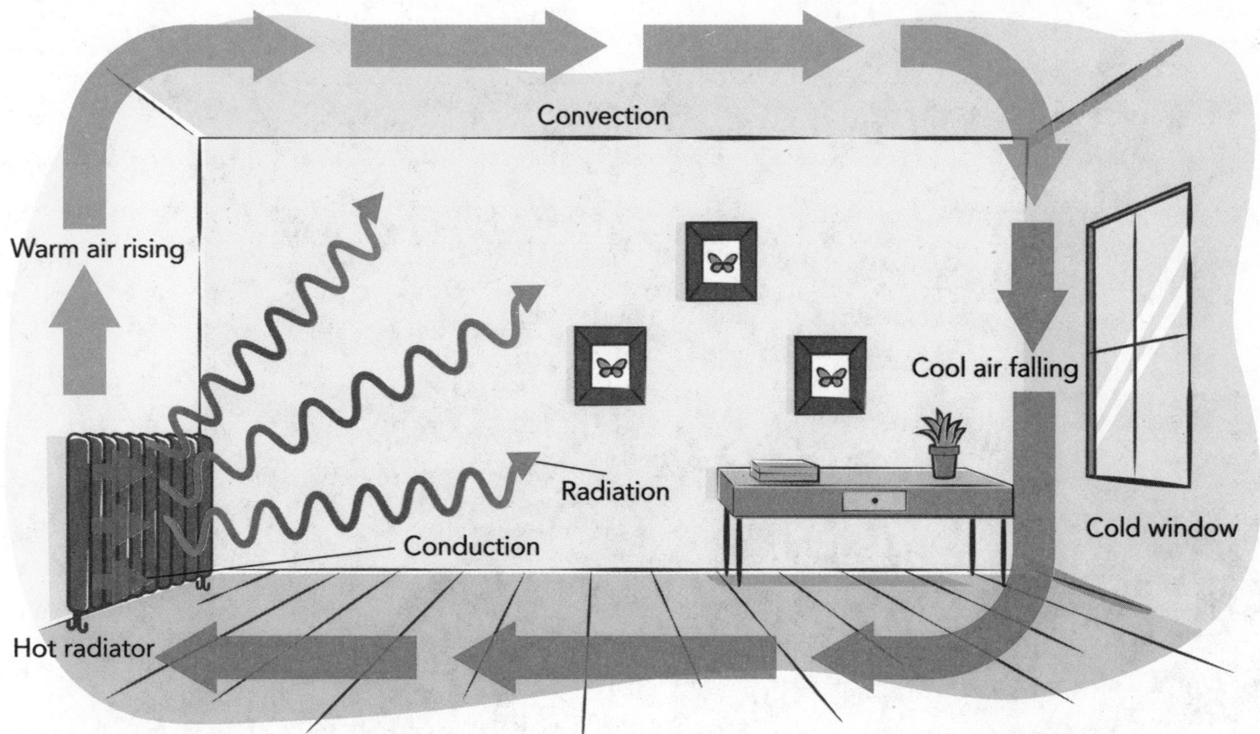

Conduction Heat is transferred from the metal radiator to the air by direct contact.

Radiation Heat is transferred by warm surfaces through the emission of electromagnetic waves. No direct contact is needed to transfer heat by radiation.

(17) **SEP Develop and Use Models Describe how a desk lamp heats up a room through all three modes of heat transport.**

....

....

....

Revisit

INVESTIGATIVE PHENOMENON

GO ONLINE to Elaborate and Evaluate your knowledge of heat and the mechanisms of heat flow by completing the CER worksheet and the data analysis activity.

In the modeling activity assigned at the beginning of this investigation, you outlined a system in which heat must constantly be transferred. With a partner, reevaluate your model.

18 **SEP Develop Models How could you use concepts from this learning experience to make your model more detailed? Explain.**

Thermal Equilibrium

 **GO ONLINE** to Explore and Explain entropy and thermal equilibrium.

Entropy

Entropy is a measure of the disorder of a system—the opposite of the order of the system. It is an important concept that describes the behavior of matter and energy within physical systems. In general, it is more likely for a physical system to be disordered than to be highly ordered.

The second law of thermodynamics states that the entropy of an isolated system never decreases. Therefore a system always spontaneously evolves toward the state with the maximum entropy, which is a state of thermodynamic equilibrium.

If a volume of gas is released into the corner of an empty room, it quickly becomes evenly distributed throughout the room. The system goes from a high-order, low-entropy state to a low-order, high-entropy state. The properties of pressure, density, and temperature within a system all tend to become uniform over time. If you watched a video of a cloud of smoke coming together to converge at a point, you would know that the video was being shown backward.

Entropy and Thermodynamic Equilibrium

How does entropy change as a **system approaches equilibrium?**

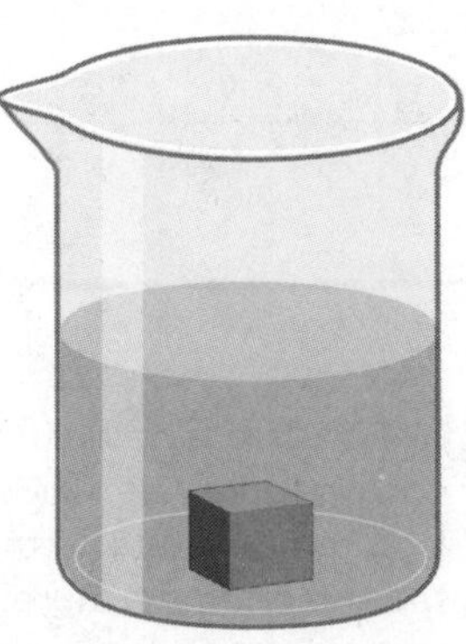

The molecules of the solid sugar cube are in a small volume of the beaker, and the system has **low entropy.**

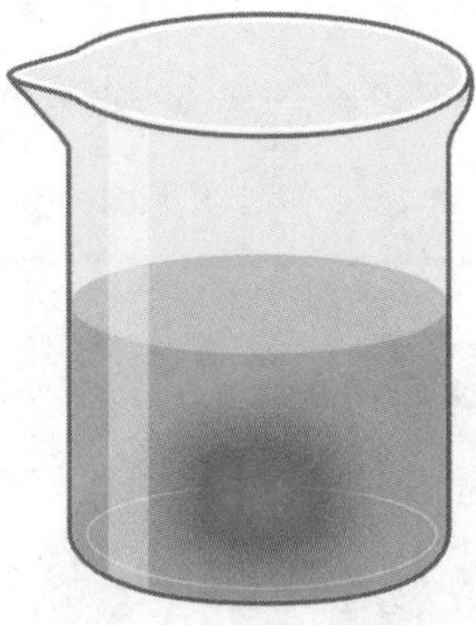

As the sugar dissolves, the sugar molecules spread out, and **entropy increases.**

When the sugar is completely dissolved, the molecules are randomly distributed, and **entropy is a maximum.**

Entropy and Thermal Equilibrium

The principle of increasing entropy also applies to the flow of heat. The second law of thermodynamics requires that the net result of interactions among particles is that heat flows from hotter objects to colder objects, and not the other way around.

Over time, a system will tend toward a state of **thermal equilibrium**, where heat is no longer flowing. If you leave a glass of cold water in a room, the water will absorb heat from the room until it is at the same temperature as the rest of the room. At that point, it will have reached thermal equilibrium. Heat would never flow out of the glass of ice water, making the glass colder and the rest of the room hotter. For a single body, thermal equilibrium occurs when the temperature of the entire body is the same. Entropy is at a maximum.

Changing Temperature In a typical oven, food warms up quickly at first. As thermal equilibrium is reached, there is a decrease in heat flow, and the temperature changes more slowly.

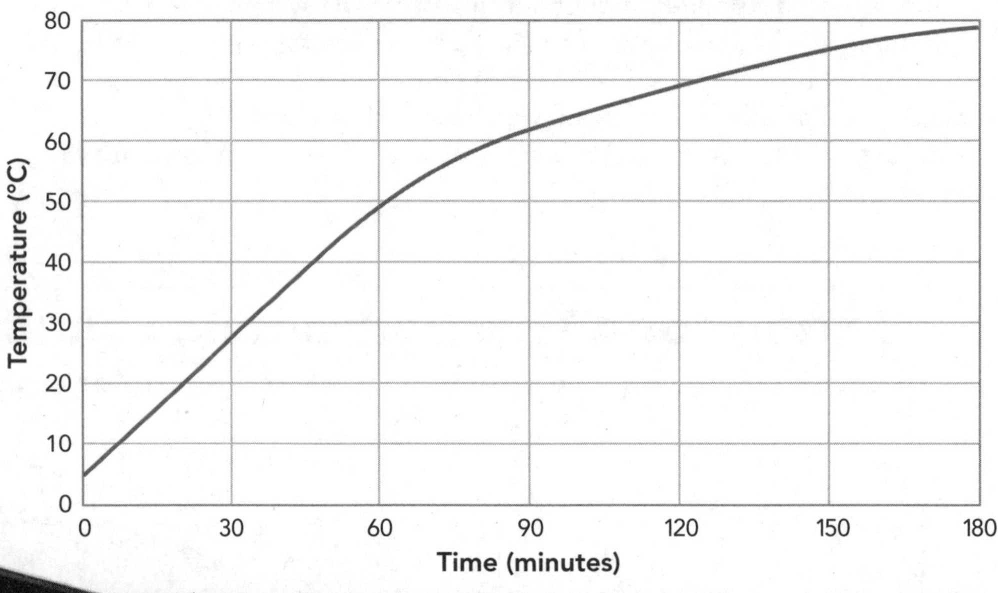

Ready to Eat The time needed to fully cook a turkey depends on the starting temperature of the turkey, the oven temperature, and the size of the turkey.

Thermal Equilibrium Between Two Connected Bodies If two objects of different temperatures are connected by a conducting channel, the two objects will eventually reach thermal equilibrium, even if they are not in direct contact. The rate at which thermal equilibrium is reached depends on the thermal energy of the objects (which depends on their temperature and mass) and on the thermal conductivity of the bridge.

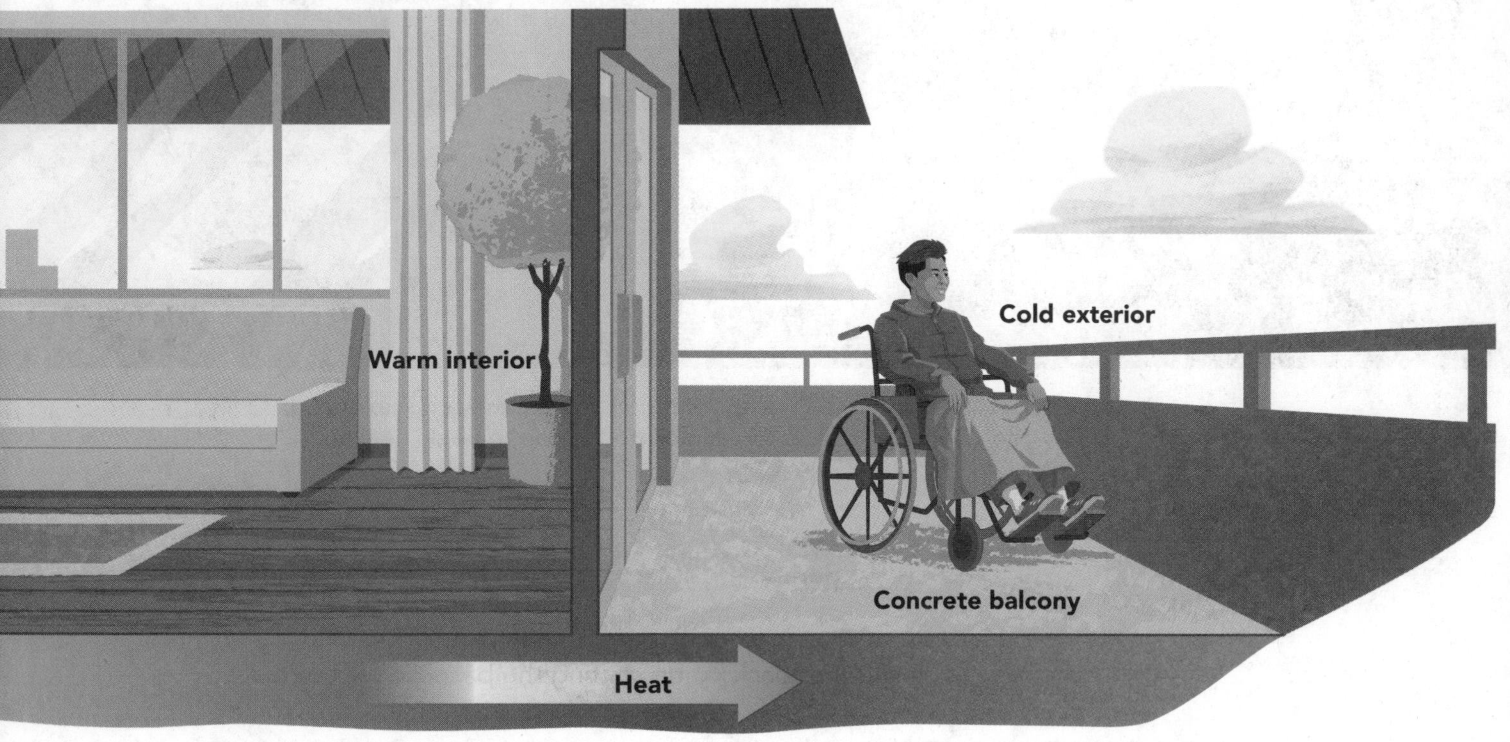

Flowing Heat If the weather suddenly turns cold, the indoor room will be warmer than the outdoor balcony. Heat will begin to flow through the conducting channel (the floor) from the left to the right.

19 **CCC Systems and System Models Using the axes below, plot the curve of temperature of the indoor room from the time the temperature drops to the time that thermal equilibrium is reached. Assume that the heating has not been turned on.**

Shifting Equilibrium As soon as all the butter in the pan warms up enough to melt, cool chopped vegetables will go into the pan to begin heating.

System Feedbacks and Equilibrium

In most natural systems, thermal equilibrium is never actually reached. System interactions and feedbacks keep shifting the baseline for thermal equilibrium. As soon as the temperature approaches an equilibrium, some factor changes and the temperature tends toward a new equilibrium. In nature, systems always tend toward thermal equilibrium, but they never get there, because energy inputs and outputs keep changing.

The water in a pond, for example, warms up during the daytime, approaching thermal equilibrium with the energy input from the sun. When the sun sets, that input changes, and the water approaches a new equilibrium, at a lower temperature.

20 CCC Systems and System Models A pan at 20°C is put on a stove burner until it reaches equilibrium at 80°C. Soon after the pan is put on the stove, a cube of butter at 0°C is dropped into it. On the axes, plot temperature versus time for the bottom of the pan and also for the center of the cube of butter.

SAMPLE PROBLEM

Equilibrium Delay

The graph below compares daily mean annual temperatures and the seasonal length of daylight for the city of Chicago over a period of one year. What does the graph tell you about the time it takes for the system to reach thermal equilibrium?

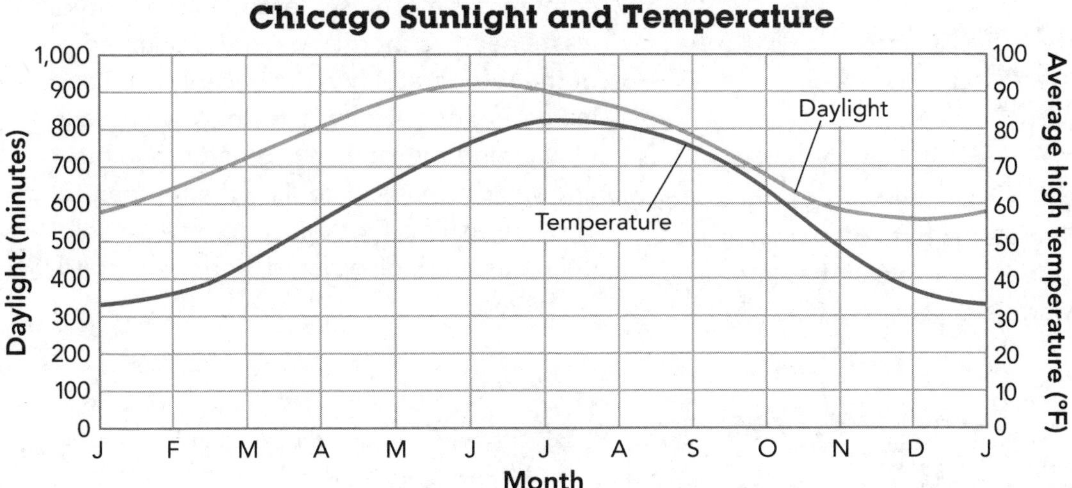

IDENTIFY Interpret the graph.

Determine the months and values for the peak and trough of average temperature and length of daylight during the year.

Longest day is in June: 910 minutes.
Warmest day is in July: 82°F.
Shortest day is in December: 560 minutes.
Coldest day is in January: 32°F.

COMPARE Describe the differences in the curves.

Determine the offset between the two curves.

The peaks of the two curves, in June and July, are offset by about a month. The same is true of the troughs.

ANALYZE Construct an explanation.

Construct an explanation for why the two curves are offset.

The curves are offset by about a month, because it takes the land that long to reach equilibrium with the energy input from the sun.

21 CCC Patterns If Chicago had experienced its average highest temperature in August, which month would have had the longest day? Explain your reasoning.

....

....

....

GO ONLINE for more practice problems.

Self-Organization Within Open Systems

It is important to know the boundaries of the second law of thermodynamics. The law does not mean that everything everywhere always becomes disordered.

Within a closed system, there can be regions of increasing order and complexity.

A good example is a kitchen with a refrigerator. When the refrigerator is turned on, the air inside it gets colder, and cold air has less entropy than warm air.

That seems to defy the second law, because the entropy of the air in the refrigerator has decreased, but a closer look at all the changes in this system shows what actually happens.

Some of the electrical energy that powers the compressor motor is released in the form of waste heat, as thermal energy is pumped out of the refrigerator, warming the kitchen and increasing its entropy. The entropy increase of warming the kitchen is greater than the entropy decrease of cooling the refrigerator. The net result is that the system as a whole becomes more disordered, and the second law is obeyed.

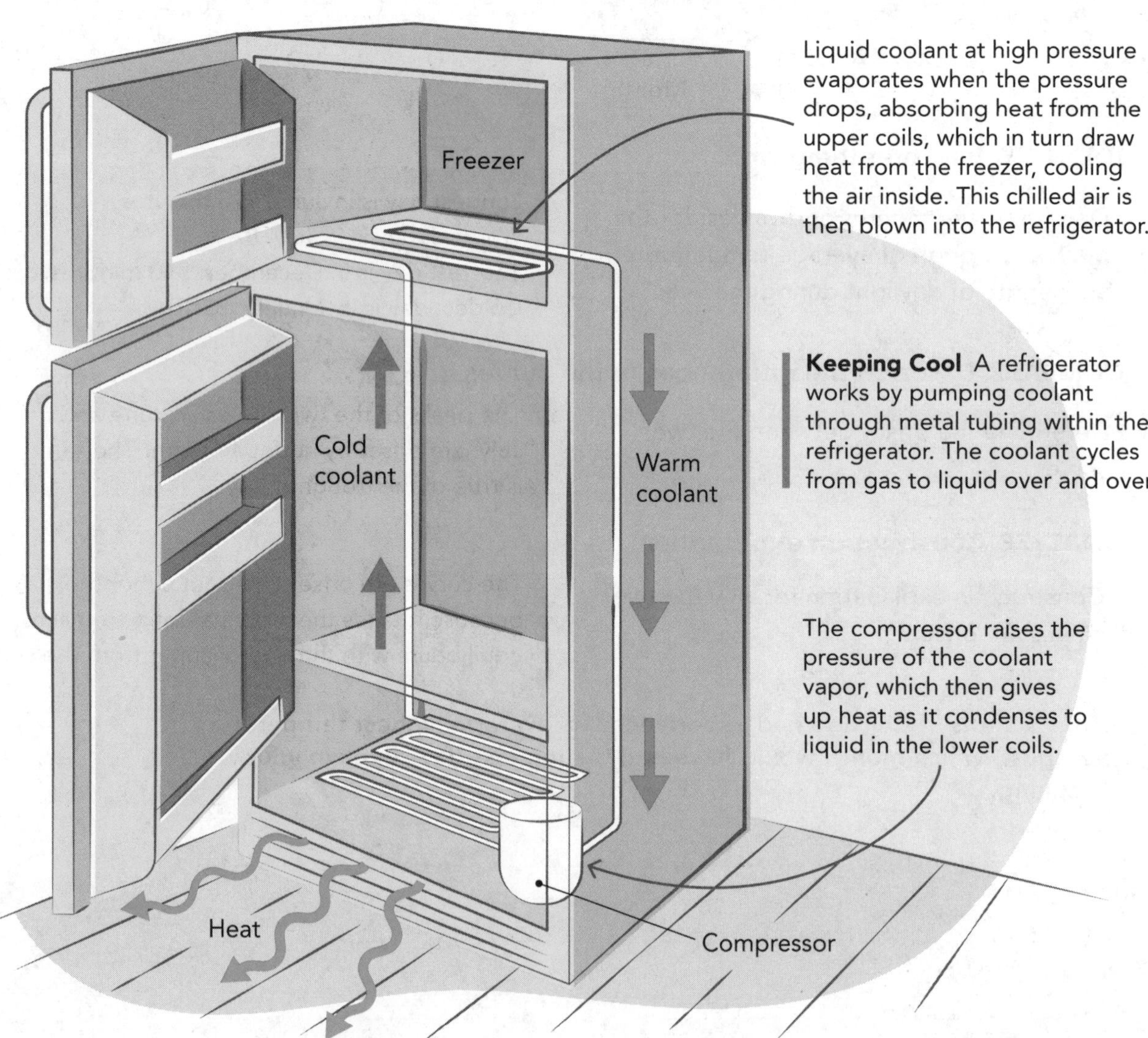

Freezer
Cold coolant
Warm coolant
Heat
Compressor
Liquid coolant at high pressure evaporates when the pressure drops, absorbing heat from the upper coils, which in turn draw heat from the freezer, cooling the air inside. This chilled air is then blown into the refrigerator.
The compressor raises the pressure of the coolant vapor, which then gives up heat as it condenses to liquid in the lower coils.

Keeping Cool A refrigerator works by pumping coolant through metal tubing within the refrigerator. The coolant cycles from gas to liquid over and over.

Self-organization Matter organizes itself into complex structures. This is the natural outcome of its properties and the forces of nature. This self-organization reduces entropy, but only locally. The total entropy of a whole closed system always increases. Even as atoms bond to form Earth's complex crystals, molecules, and organisms, the total entropy of the universe increases.

Snowflake Water molecules bond in particular patterns that depend on the conditions within clouds. The result is the hexagonal structure of ice crystals.

Pyrite Crystal Iron and sulfur atoms self-organize into cubic structures at the atomic level, forming the mineral pyrite. Large-scale crystals of pyrite reflect this pattern.

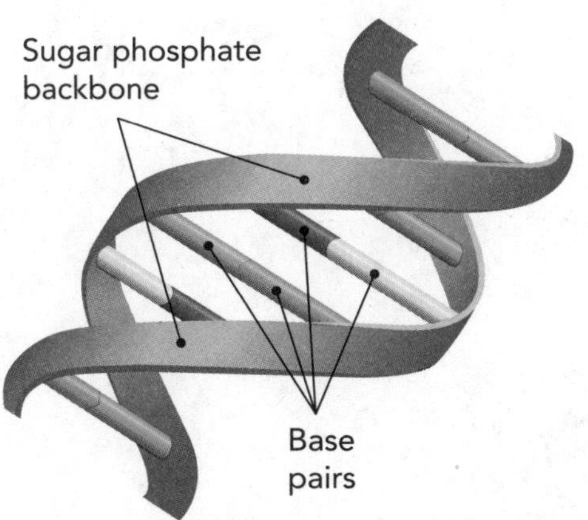

Double Helix Atoms of hydrogen, oxygen, nitrogen, carbon, and phosphorus self-organize into the complex pattern of DNA, a macromolecule that is essential for life.

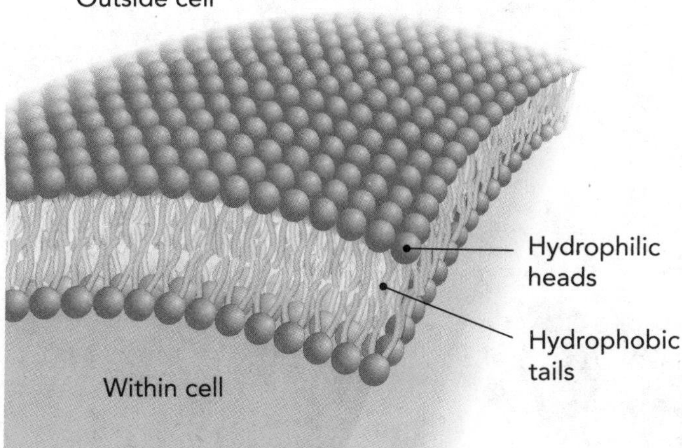

Phospholipid These molecules have a hydrophilic (water-loving) head and a hydrophobic (water-repelling) tail. They form organic membranes by self-organizing into double sheets in which adjacent molecules have the same alignment.

22 SEP Construct Explanations Explain why you cannot cool your kitchen by leaving your refrigerator door open.

....

....

Revisit

INVESTIGATIVE PHENOMENON

GO ONLINE to Elaborate and Evaluate your knowledge of entropy and thermal equilibrium by completing a CER worksheet and a data analysis activity.

In the modeling activity assigned at the beginning of this investigation, you sketched parts of a geothermal plant. With a partner, reevaluate your model.

(23) **SEP Engage in Argument What parts of your model suggest that the plant is not in thermal equilibrium?**

GO ONLINE to Evaluate what you learned about energy transfer and conservation by using the available assessment resources.

In the Performance-Based Assessment, you tried different approaches to produce electricity from an alternative source (a source that is not a fossil fuel). Wrap up your analysis by answering the following questions.

24 **SEP Define Problems** **Imagine you and a partner are engineers discussing which alternative materials to use in a design for a solar-energy cooker. Together, agree on and list some criteria and constraints to help you evaluate possible materials for your design.**

Criteria	Constraints

25 **Revisit the Anchoring Phenomenon** **Think about the burning crater introduced at the beginning of this Instructional Segment. Use what you learned in this Investigation to explain why the crater doesn't get even hotter over time.**

INVESTIGATIVE PHENOMENON

GO ONLINE to Engage with real-world phenomena by watching a video and to complete a CER interactive worksheet.

Why are there so many volcanoes in California?

INVESTIGATION 3

Earth's Interior

Once you have viewed the Investigative Phenomenon video and used the Claim-Evidence-Reasoning worksheet to craft an explanation, answer the following questions about things that might cause a volcanic eruption.

1 **CCC Energy and Matter** Look at the photo of Mount Shasta in northern California. List two natural events that might cause the volcano to erupt and two effects that an eruption might have.

Causes of an Eruption	Effects of an Eruption

2 **SEP Plan Investigations** Of the possible causes of an eruption mentioned on your list, choose one that is not easily observable. How could you provide evidence that it is taking place?

EXPERIENCE 1

Heat Flow Within Earth

GO ONLINE to Explore and Explain how heat is transferred in Earth's interior.

Probing Earth's Interior

Investigating Earth's interior poses some unique challenges. Scientists can't see it or visit it. As a result, they have to use remote sensing methods. For example, they can use waves generated during earthquakes to get a picture of Earth's interior. They can also use variations in Earth's gravitational field to understand underground variations in temperature and composition, and changes in Earth's magnetic field to understand the convection of liquid iron in the core.

Seismic Waves Earthquakes emit different types of waves that behave differently as they travel through rock and other materials. P waves, or compression waves, go through solids and liquids. S waves, or shear waves, travel only through solids.

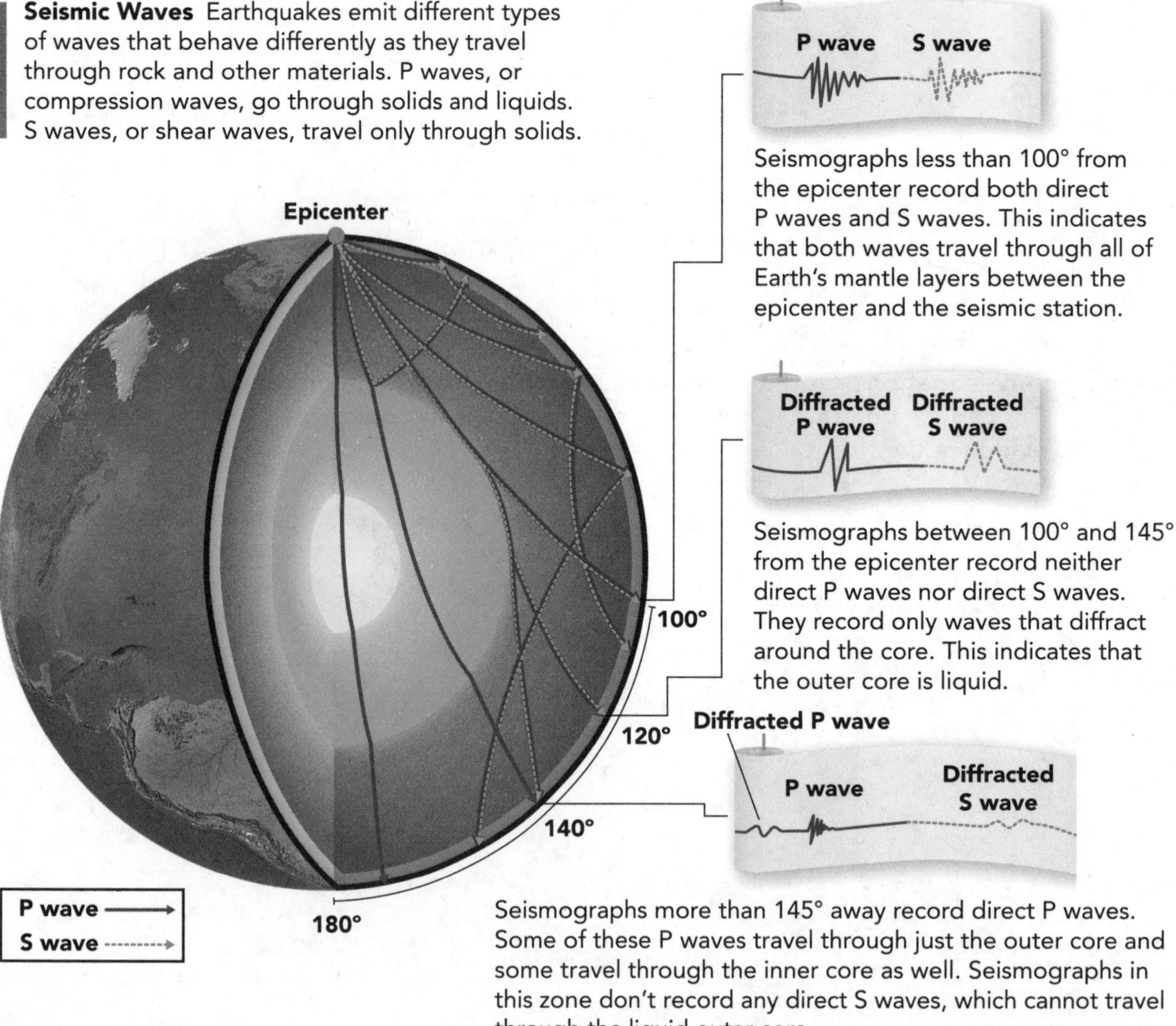

Seismographs less than 100° from the epicenter record both direct P waves and S waves. This indicates that both waves travel through all of Earth's mantle layers between the epicenter and the seismic station.

Seismographs between 100° and 145° from the epicenter record neither direct P waves nor direct S waves. They record only waves that diffract around the core. This indicates that the outer core is liquid.

Seismographs more than 145° away record direct P waves. Some of these P waves travel through just the outer core and some travel through the inner core as well. Seismographs in this zone don't record any direct S waves, which cannot travel through the liquid outer core.

Density of Earth Materials

Earth is composed of many different kinds of materials, each with a different density. **Density** is the mass per unit volume of a given substance. The density of an object is equal to the object's mass divided by its volume: $d = m/V$.

Density is largely a function of chemical composition, or the kinds of atoms that make up a substance.

The chemical composition of Earth materials is a direct result of the elements that were available in the solar system when the planet formed.

Density also depends on the temperature and pressure of a material, which determine its physical state. How the elements that make up Earth bond with each other at different temperatures and pressures determines their densities and where you find them inside Earth.

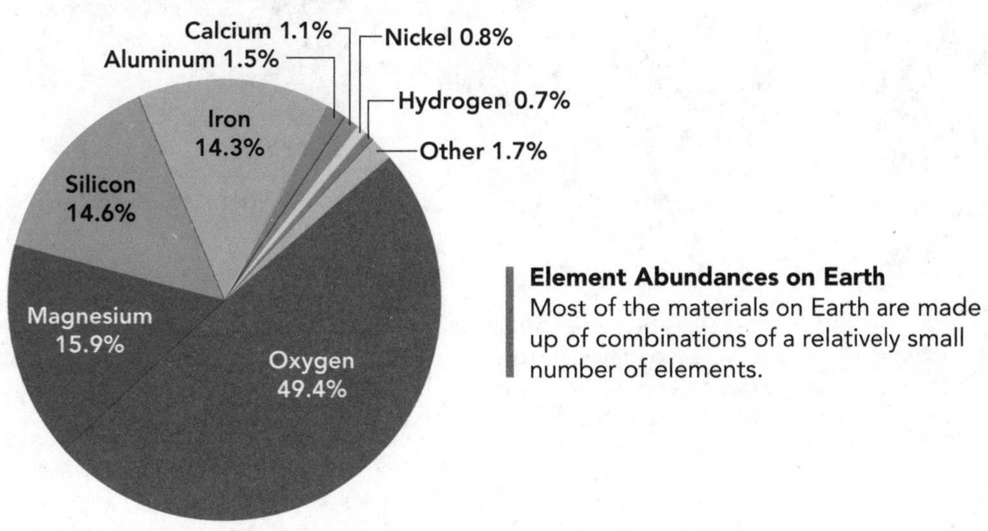

Element Abundances on Earth Most of the materials on Earth are made up of combinations of a relatively small number of elements.

3 **SEP Develop and Use Models** Most of the rocks in Earth's crust are silicates. Silicates contain combinations of silicon dioxide (SiO_2) and various other minerals. Why does that make sense given the percentages of elements available within the Earth system?

Earth's Layers

Composition Earth is made up mostly of rock and metal. Gravity pulls denser materials, like metal, more strongly toward Earth's center. Less dense materials, like rock, remain closer to Earth's surface. Thus, Earth has three main compositional layers based on density: an iron core at its center; a dense, rocky mantle; and a lower-density rocky crust.

Differences in composition and density exist within each layer. For example, oceanic crust is denser than continental crust, because it has a different composition. The inner core and outer core have slightly different compositions, although both are mostly made of iron and nickel. The upper and lower mantle also have different compositions.

Formation of Earth Earth formed as a result of accretion of smaller particles. Differentiation sorted materials into layers according to their density.

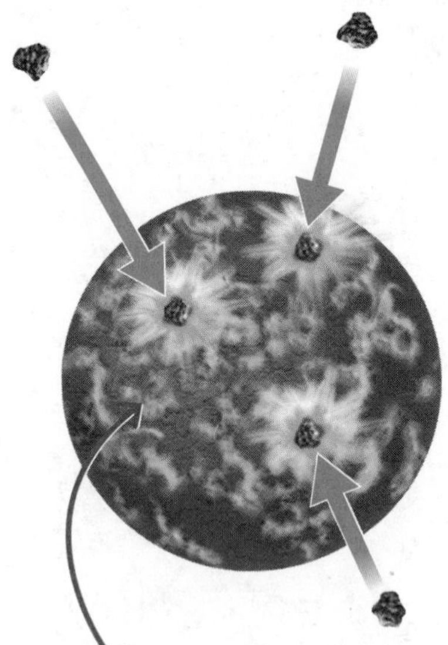

As Earth grew from the collision of particles, kinetic energy from the collisions converted to thermal energy. The forming planet was at some point mostly or completely molten.

Materials became sorted as less dense materials rose to the surface and denser materials sank to the center, converting gravitational potential energy into more heat.

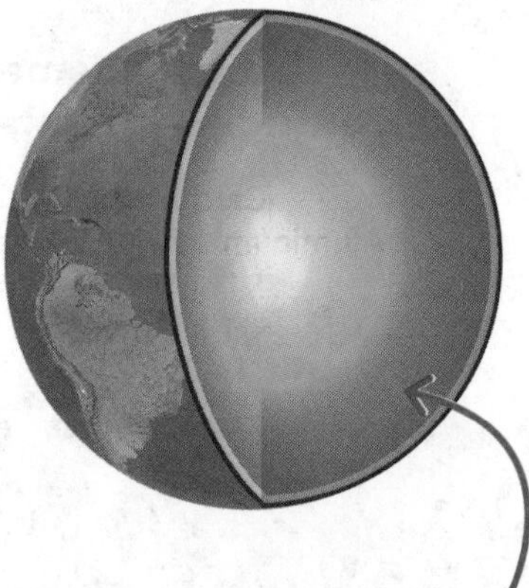

The planet has been cooling for billions of years, but heat from radioactive decay in the mantle causes ongoing separation of materials into layers.

Physical Properties Temperature and pressure vary throughout Earth's layers from surface to core. Temperature increases quickly with depth through Earth's top 200 km to over 1400°C, but then the rate of increase remains gradual most of the way to the bottom of the mantle. Pressure increases gradually with depth, due to both the increasing density of the layers and the mass of overlying layers being pulled toward Earth's center.

Increasing temperature tends to cause substances to melt, while increasing pressure tends to stiffen substances, making them harder to melt. These two competing factors determine the state and physical properties of Earth's layers. Therefore, Earth scientists divide Earth's interior into five layers based on physical properties: lithosphere, asthenosphere, mesosphere, outer core, and inner core.

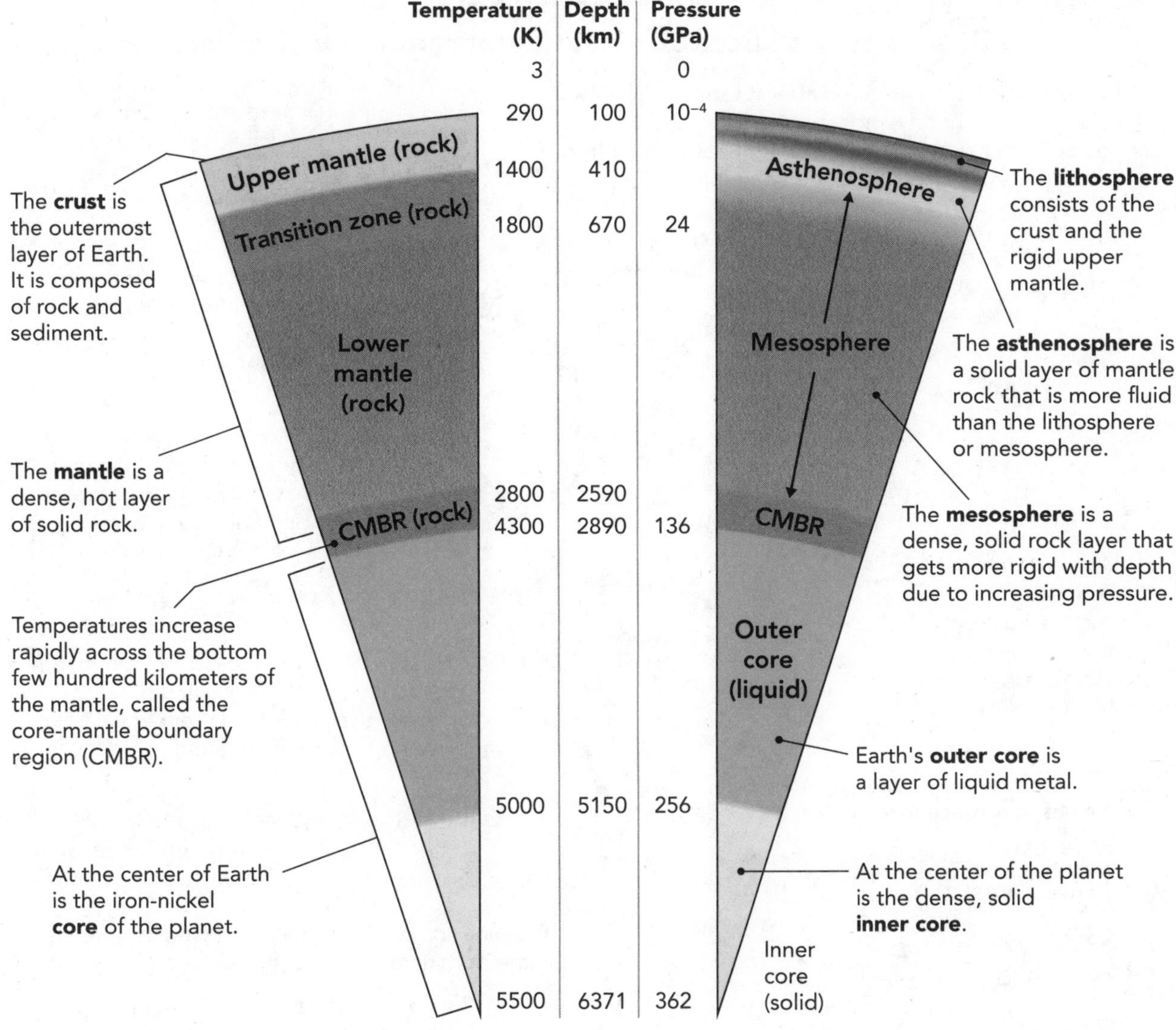

Earth Layers by Chemical Composition
Boundaries between compositional layers are mostly sharp.
Earth Layers by Physical Properties
Boundaries resulting from temperature and pressure changes tend to be gradual.
Temperature (K)
Depth (km)
Pressure (GPa)
3
0
290
100
10⁻⁴
1400
410
1800
670
24
2800
2590
4300
2890
136
5000
5150
256
5500
6371
362
Upper mantle (rock)
Transition zone (rock)
Lower mantle (rock)
CMBR (rock)
The crust is the outermost layer of Earth. It is composed of rock and sediment.
The mantle is a dense, hot layer of solid rock.
Temperatures increase rapidly across the bottom few hundred kilometers of the mantle, called the core-mantle boundary region (CMBR).
At the center of Earth is the iron-nickel core of the planet.
Asthenosphere
Mesosphere
CMBR
Outer core (liquid)
Inner core (solid)
The lithosphere consists of the crust and the rigid upper mantle.
The asthenosphere is a solid layer of mantle rock that is more fluid than the lithosphere or mesosphere.
The mesosphere is a dense, solid rock layer that gets more rigid with depth due to increasing pressure.
Earth's outer core is a layer of liquid metal.
At the center of the planet is the dense, solid inner core.

4 **CCC Structure and Function** **Why might it be useful for scientists to have multiple models for describing Earth's interior structure? Describe how one model might be more useful than the other depending on the context.**

....

....

....

....

....

....

Conduction, Convection, and Radiation within Earth

How does **heat** from Earth's interior **reach the surface?**

Earth's Internal Heat Soon after it formed, Earth was mostly, if not entirely, molten. Over the past 4.6 billion years, Earth has slowly cooled, with heat flowing from the hot interior toward the cooler surface.

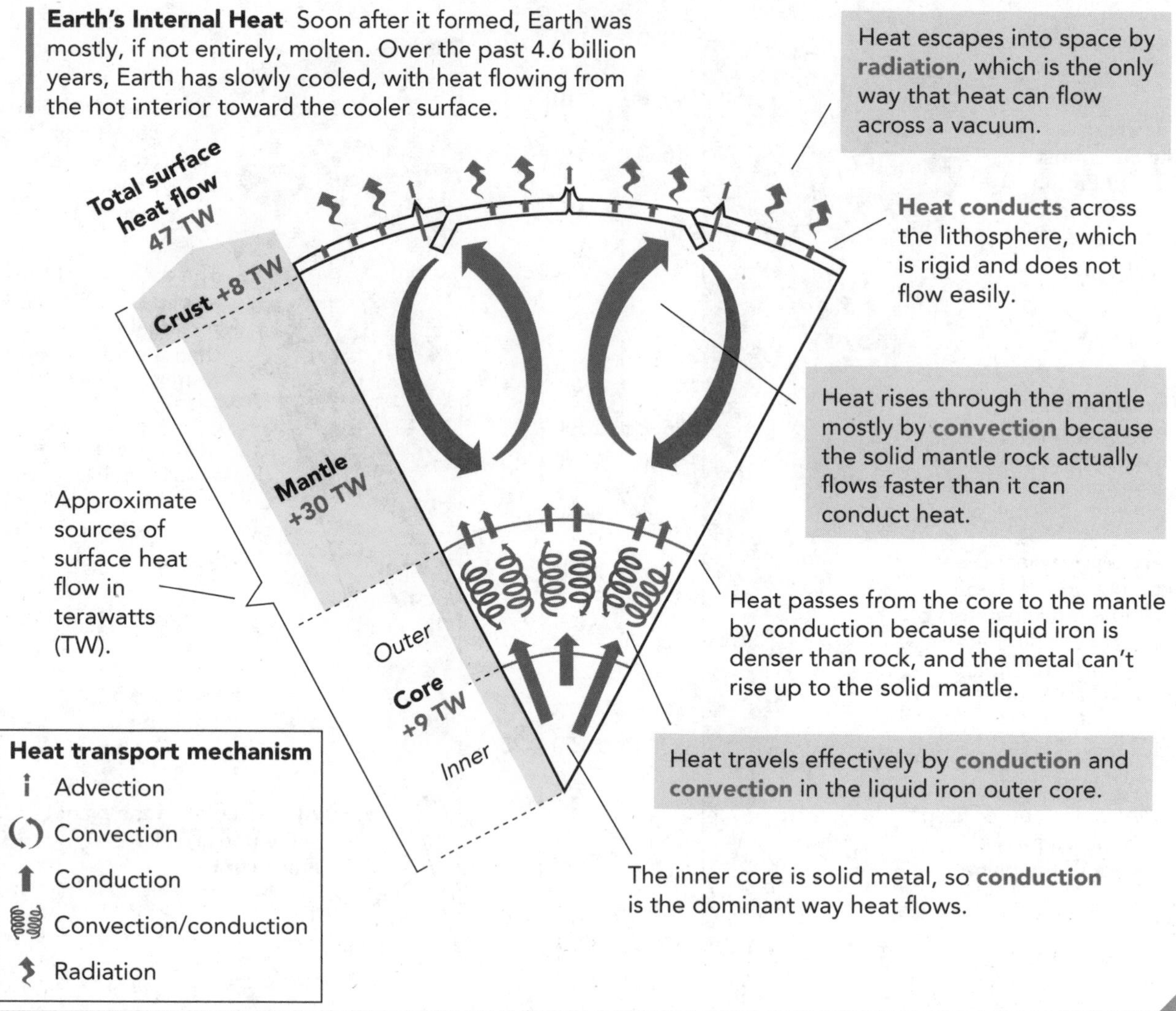

Heat escapes into space by radiation, which is the only way that heat can flow across a vacuum.
Total surface heat flow 47 TW
Heat conducts across the lithosphere, which is rigid and does not flow easily.
Crust +8 TW
Heat rises through the mantle mostly by convection because the solid mantle rock actually flows faster than it can conduct heat.
Mantle +30 TW
Approximate sources of surface heat flow in terawatts (TW).
Outer
Core +9 TW
Inner
Heat passes from the core to the mantle by conduction because liquid iron is denser than rock, and the metal can't rise up to the solid mantle.
Heat travels effectively by conduction and convection in the liquid iron outer core.
The inner core is solid metal, so conduction is the dominant way heat flows.
Heat transport mechanism
Advection
Convection
Conduction
Convection/conduction
Radiation

5 **SEP Develop and Use Models** Use the information from the infographic to complete the table.

Earth's layer	Methods of Heat Transfer	Physical State of the Material
Lithosphere		
Mantle		
Outer core		
Inner core		

Core Convection and Magnetism

Convection within the liquid outer core causes Earth's magnetic field. The outer core is very fluid and likely flows as easily as pancake syrup. Convection patterns shift over years to decades, which causes Earth's magnetic field to continually shift. Occasionally, Earth's magnetic field flips so that the north and south poles reverse. Although these magnetic reversals happen randomly and infrequently, they provide important evidence for understanding Earth's history.

Earth's magnetic field Spiraling gyres of convecting liquid iron generate a magnetic field that is mostly dipolar, similar to the magnetic field of a bar magnet.

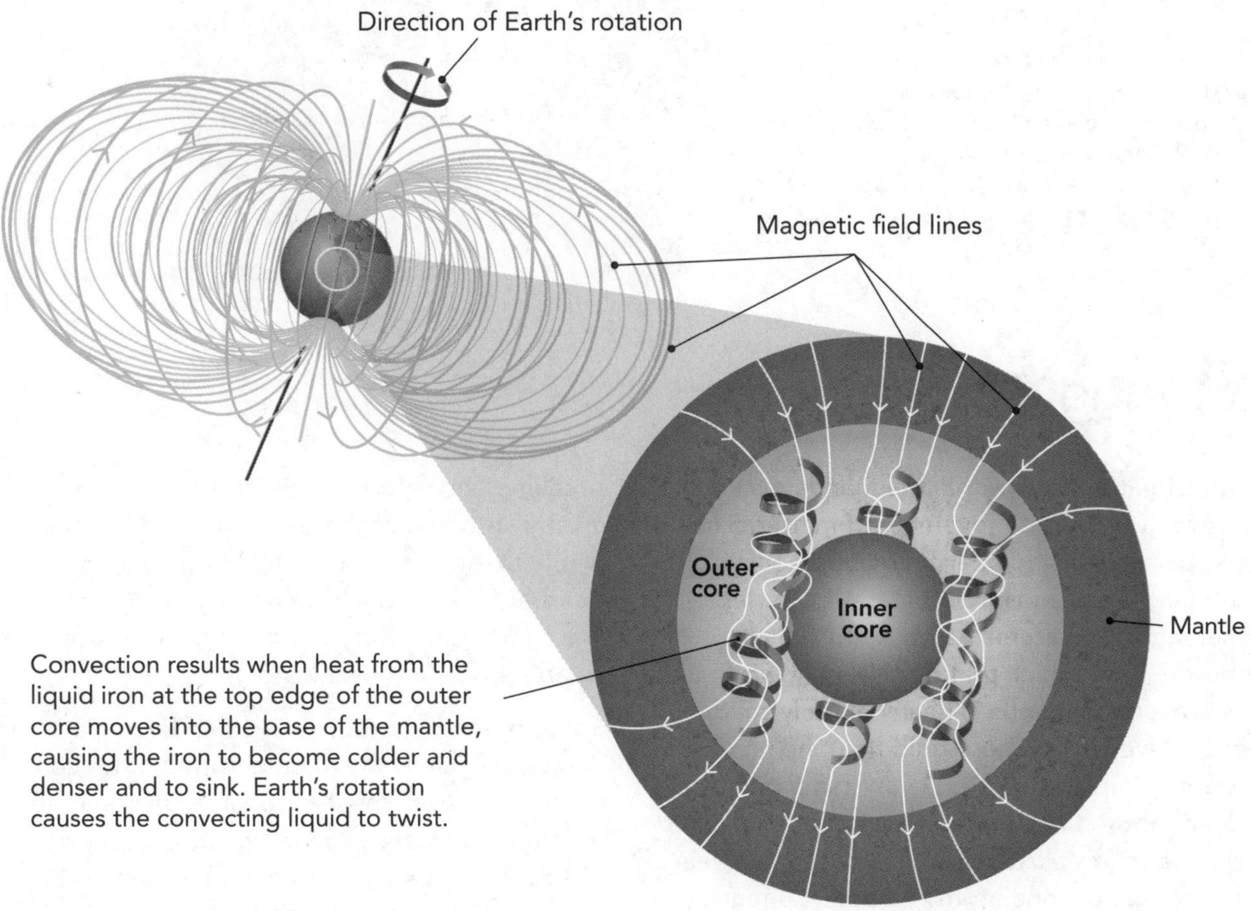

Direction of Earth's rotation
Magnetic field lines
Outer core
Inner core
Mantle
Convection results when heat from the liquid iron at the top edge of the outer core moves into the base of the mantle, causing the iron to become colder and denser and to sink. Earth's rotation causes the convecting liquid to twist.

6 **SEP Construct Explanations Construct an explanation for why the physical properties of the inner core, outer core, and lower mantle are essential for the development of Earth's magnetic field.**

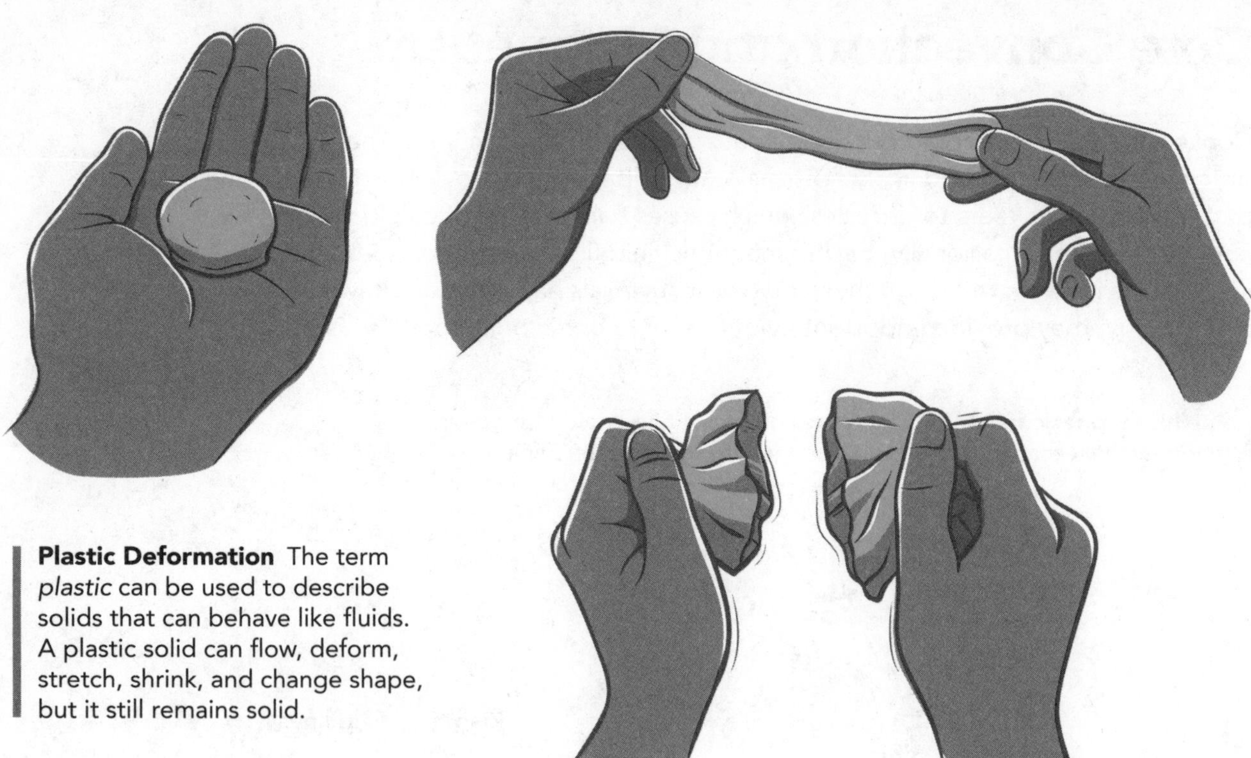

Plastic Deformation The term *plastic* can be used to describe solids that can behave like fluids. A plastic solid can flow, deform, stretch, shrink, and change shape, but it still remains solid.

Mantle Convection

Most heat transfer within the mantle occurs by convection, or the movement of matter. Since temperatures within Earth's mantle go as high as 4000°C and most rocks at Earth's surface melt at temperatures below 1100°C, it is reasonable to think that Earth's mantle is liquid. However, the mantle is nearly entirely solid and is even much more rigid than the hardest rocks at Earth's surface. The extreme pressure deep inside the planet keeps the rock solid and stiff, so it flows just a few centimeters per year. The rocks flow one atom at a time, continually breaking and reforming the bonds within the crystal structure of the rocks. At this rate, the whole mantle can completely turn over in hundreds of millions of years. That may sound like a long time, but it is just a small fraction of Earth's 4.6-billion-year history.

Some of the heat that drives mantle convection conducts up into the mantle from the hot core below. However, most is generated within the mantle and crust by the radioactive decay of just four isotopes: potassium-40, thorium-232, uranium-235, and uranium-238.

7 **SEP Construct Explanations** Write definitions for *solid* and *fluid* that include the ability of some solids to flow.

....

....

....

....

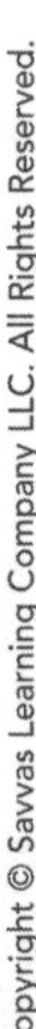

Seismic Images of the Mantle

Temperatures within the mantle are not homogeneous; they vary from one location to another and over time, as the rocks flow. Scientists can use seismic data to develop models that show these temperature variations within a certain region. Seismometers around the world collect data about the speed of seismic waves generated by earthquakes. The data are then combined to create 3D images called *seismic tomograms*, which can be sliced horizontally like maps of Earth's surface. These models show temperature variations within the mantle.

About 95% of the variation in seismic wave speed is due to vertical changes in the density and compressibility of layers within the mantle. The remaining 5% are horizontal variations, however, and they provide important clues about dynamic motions within Earth's mantle.

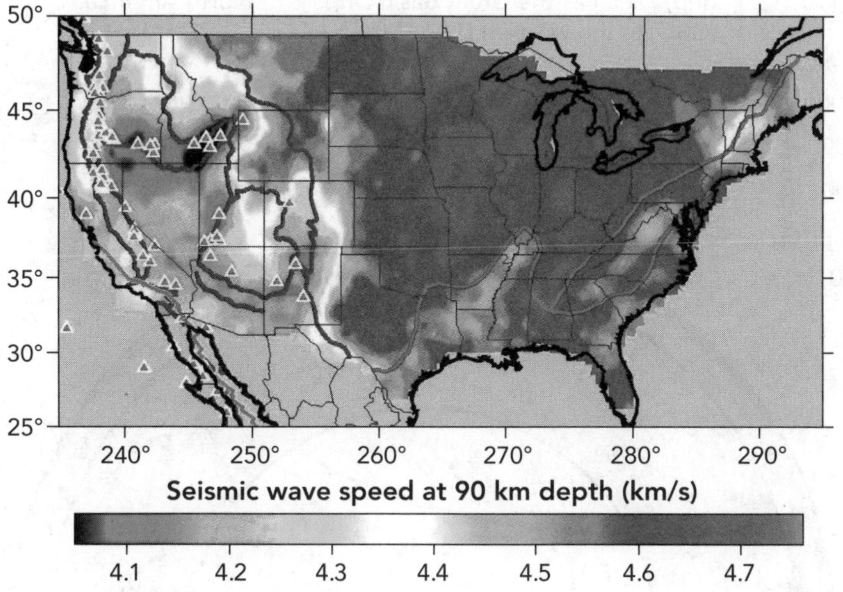

Data from Shen, W. and M. H. Ritzwoller (2016)

Mantle Rock Temperatures
Temperature is inversely related to wave speed, so where speed is slower, the mantle is hotter. Note that mantle rock is hotter beneath the western U.S than beneath the eastern U.S.

— Active plate boundary
═ Boundaries between geologic regions
▲ Volcano

8 **SEP Develop and Use Models** **What do you notice about the average seismic wave speeds at a depth of 90 km in the locations where volcanoes have occurred? Does this support or refute the idea that the heat for volcanic magma is a deep feature?**

Mantle Downwelling

The convection pattern in a region depends on the relative temperatures of rock at the region's boundaries. For mantle convection, the boundaries are the top and bottom of the mantle. Heat conducts from the core into the mantle and from the mantle into the crust; heat is also generated within the mantle by radioactive decay. The temperature differential between top and bottom causes movement of rock between colder and warmer zones. Downward movement within the mantle is known as downwelling. Most mantle convection is driven by the downwelling of oceanic lithosphere.

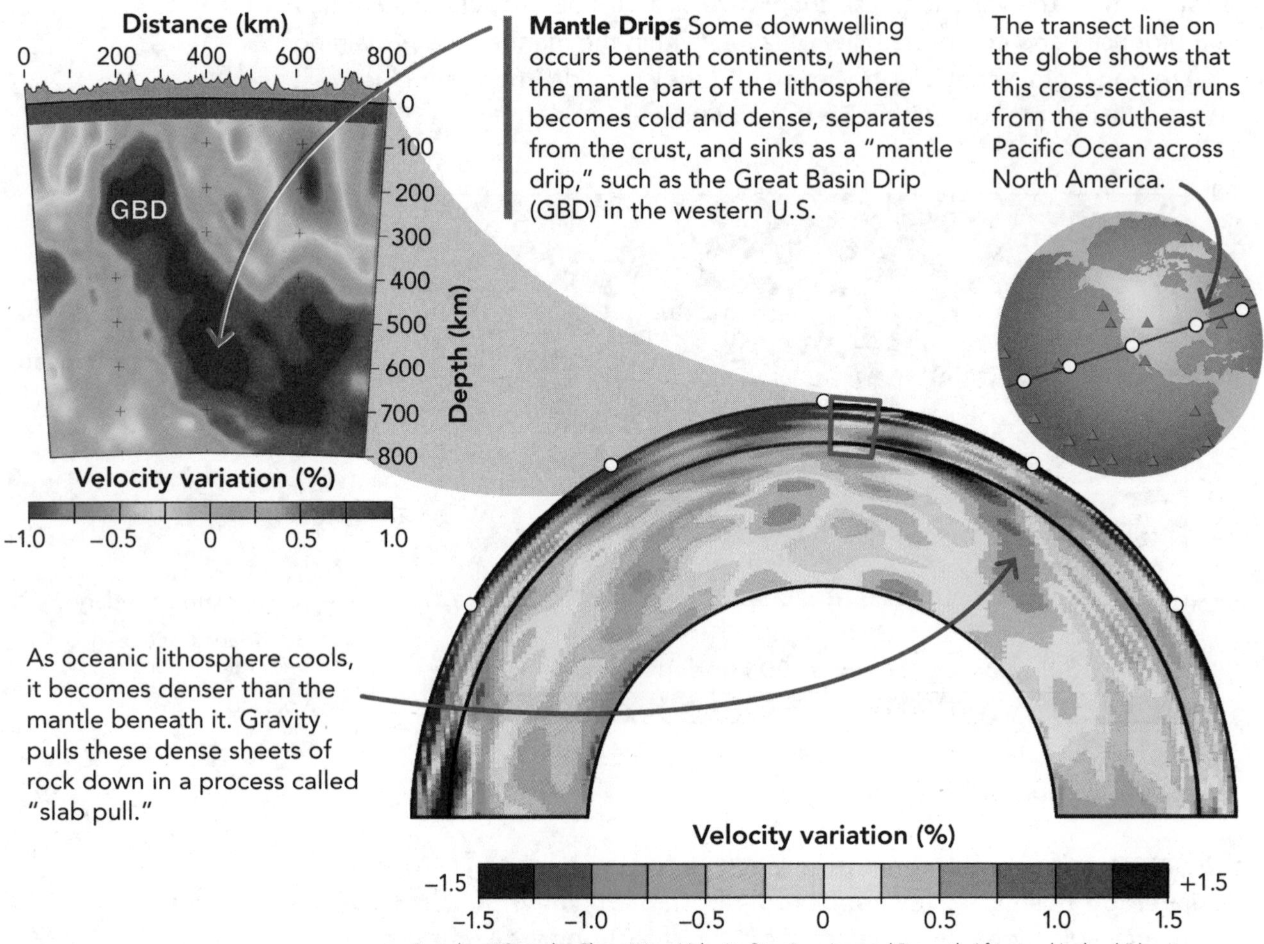

Distance (km)
0
200
400
600
800
0
100
200
300
400
500
600
700
800
Depth (km)
GBD
Velocity variation (%)
–1.0
–0.5
0
0.5
1.0
Mantle Drips Some downwelling occurs beneath continents, when the mantle part of the lithosphere becomes cold and dense, separates from the crust, and sinks as a "mantle drip," such as the Great Basin Drip (GBD) in the western U.S.
The transect line on the globe shows that this cross-section runs from the southeast Pacific Ocean across North America.
As oceanic lithosphere cools, it becomes denser than the mantle beneath it. Gravity pulls these dense sheets of rock down in a process called "slab pull."
Velocity variation (%)
–1.5
+1.5
–1.5
–1.0
–0.5
0
0.5
1.0
1.5

Based on "Complex Shear Wave Velocity Structure Imaged Beneath Africa and Iceland," by Jeroen Ritsema et. al., Science Magazine, December 1999.

9 **SEP Develop and Use Models A pot of soup heated from below (on a stove) or internally throughout (in a microwave oven) are two possible models for convection in Earth's mantle. Explain their limitations and suggest a better model.**

Mantle Upwelling

Upward movement of rock within the mantle is known as upwelling. Most upwelling within the mantle is just a broad return flow to replace the sinking oceanic lithosphere.

However, a small but significant portion of upward flow occurs in the form of hot, solid mantle plumes that originate near the core-mantle boundary. The rock in these plumes is hotter than the surrounding mantle rock. Because rock expands when it gets hotter, the rock in plumes is less dense than the surrounding cooler rock. This difference in density causes the hotter, less-dense mantle plume rock to rise toward the surface.

Near the surface, the pressure release allows some of this hot rock to melt and erupt as volcanoes, such as those found in Hawaii, Yellowstone, Iceland, and Tahiti.

Mantle Plumes The red region shows seismically slow mantle rock beneath Africa that is likely hot and rising. Arrows show the proposed direction of flow. This is the largest anomalous structure within Earth. Mantle plumes such as this are often associated with hot-spot volcanoes at Earth's surface.

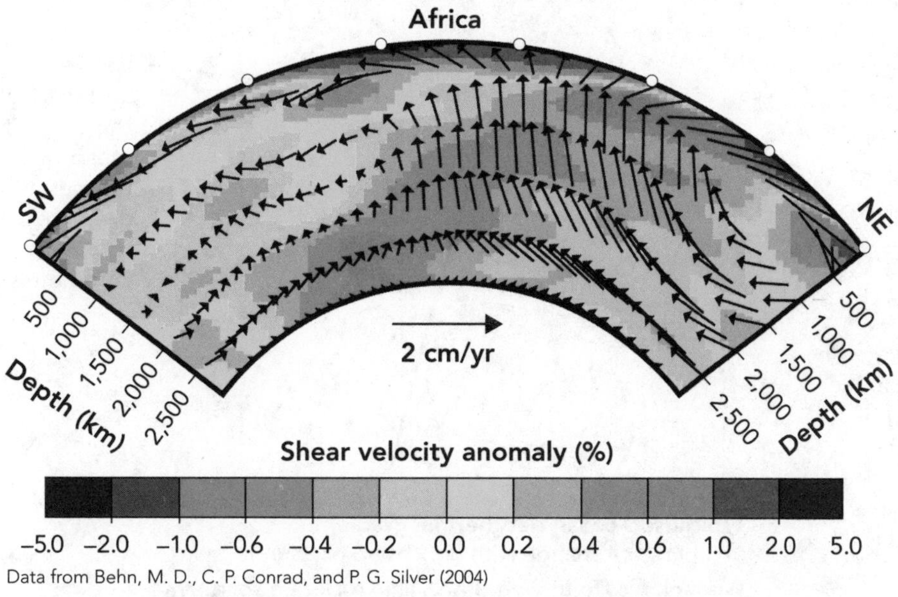

Data from Behn, M. D., C. P. Conrad, and P. G. Silver (2004)

10 **CCC Scale, Proportion, and Quantity How are the rates of mantle upwelling and mantle downwelling related to the conservation of mass in the Earth system?**

Lithosphere Conduction

Earth loses heat from its interior quite slowly. The rate of heat loss is calculated to be about 47 TW (terawatts) per year, or 0.092 W/m^2. For comparison, this is just 0.04% of the heat flow into the surface Earth system from solar radiation, which is about 123,000 TW, or 240 W/m^2. This slow rate of internal heat loss is due to the very poor conduction of heat through the solid surface rocks of Earth's lithosphere.

Because of this poor conduction, Earth's temperature increases rapidly with depth, at a rate of about 25 °C (45 °F) with each kilometer. In the deepest mines, temperatures reach over 140 °F. This temperature gradient prevents deep drilling into Earth, but it also allows for the potential harnessing of geothermal energy. Water can be pumped down into hot rock to produce steam, which is used to generate electricity.

Partial and Complete Melting The graph shows how Earth's temperature and pressure at different depths determine the physical state of rocks.

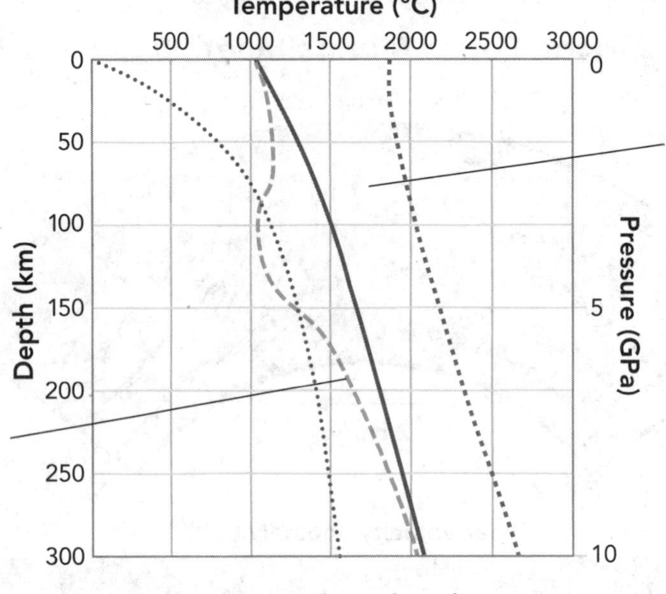

Earth's Geotherm
Temperature (°C)
500
1000
1500
2000
2500
3000
Depth (km)
0
50
100
150
200
250
300
Pressure (GPa)
0
5
10
Between the Solidus and the Liquidus is the zone of partial melting. At these temperatures and pressures, rock begins to melt but is not completely molten.
The presence of water in the mantle significantly lowers the melting temperature of rock, particularly in the zone of the asthenosphere.
···· **Typical sub-ocean geothermal gradient** (temperature change with depth and pressure)
--- **Wet solidus** (To the left of this line, rocks are solid.)
— **Dry solidus** (To the left of this line, rocks are solid.)
··· **Liquidus** (To the right of this line, rocks are molten.)

11 **SEP Analyze Data Use the curves in the graph to explain why magma forms in subduction zones, where water-rich ocean seafloor sinks into the mantle, and to predict the depth where the magma of subduction zone volcanoes originally comes from.**

Heat Loss from Earth's Lithosphere Many measurements were made across land and the ocean floor to map the flow of heat out of Earth's surface.

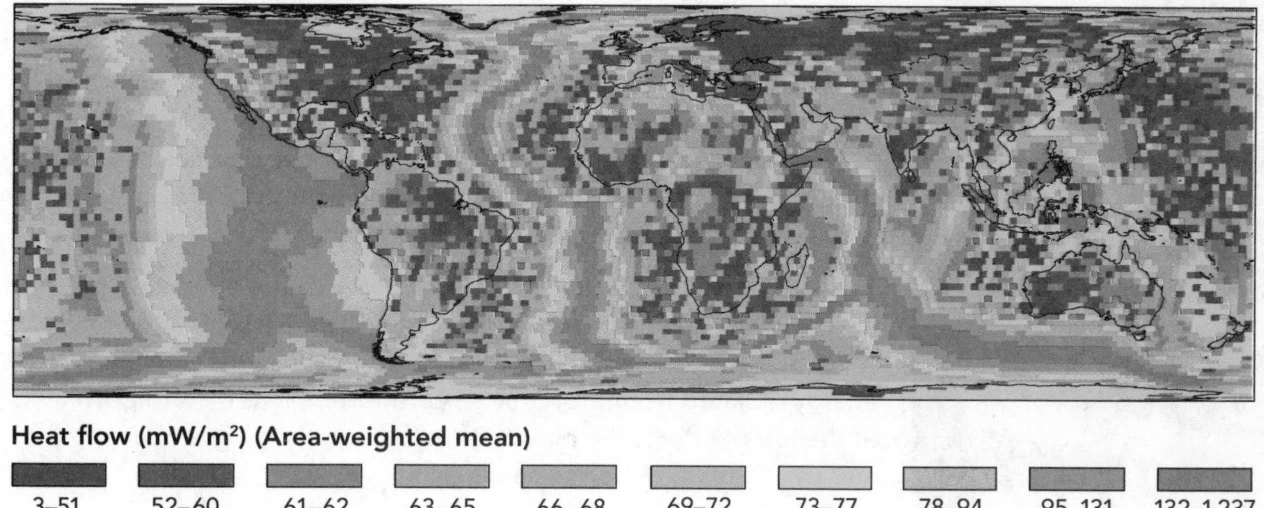

Heat flow (mW/m²) (Area-weighted mean)

3–51	52–60	61–62	63–65	66–68	69–72	73–77	78–94	95–131	132–1,237

Source: Davies, J. H. (2013)

Heat Flow from Earth's Surface Heat flow conducting out of Earth's surface is not evenly distributed. Rates of heat loss are higher near volcanoes and where Earth's crust is younger. They are lowest in older continental and oceanic crust.

Earth's slow rate of heat loss is essential to life. Although most of the energy in Earth's atmosphere and oceans comes from the sun, heat conducted across the lithosphere to Earth's surface helps warm these systems. Even after 4.6 billion years of cooling from the inside out, the planet is still very geologically active and is able to maintain surface temperatures that support life. Mantle convection not only brings heat to the surface but also replenishes the gases of our atmosphere and the water of our ocean.

12 CCC Energy and Matter Examine the map of heat flow from Earth's lithosphere. What patterns do you observe in the distribution of heat flow? Do any of the areas with high heat flow surprise you?

....

....

....

....

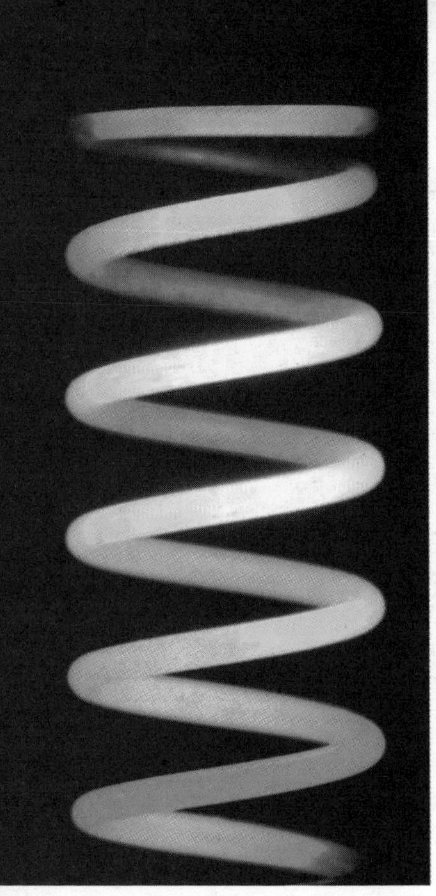

Radiation Out Into Space

The only way that heat can leave Earth and enter the vacuum of space is through radiation, because radiation is the only form of heat transfer that does not require matter. Heat radiates from Earth's surface and moves through space as electromagnetic waves. Radiation does occur inside of Earth, but it is very inefficient within rock. Radiation is much more efficient in the atmosphere, however, and nearly perfectly efficient in outer space.

The rate of energy radiation from Earth's surface is a function of the temperature, which ranges from −90°C in the coldest parts of Antarctica to 57°C in the hottest deserts. Because the amount of energy radiated from the surface is proportional to the 4th power of the temperature, the hotter Earth's surface becomes, the more energy is radiated out into space.

Radiation from Hot Metal Energy radiates from this glowing metal coil as visible light and as heat. This energy moves through space as electromagnetic waves.

SAMPLE PROBLEM

Energy Conversion Calculations

Suppose that the energy conducting out of Earth's crust through a soccer field that is 100 m × 65 m can be captured and converted into electricity. Assume that energy conducts out of the ground at the planetary average rate of 0.092 W/m^2. How many 60-watt lightbulbs could you power?

ANALYZE **The knowns and unknown.**

Knowns	Unknown
Average energy loss per unit area = 0.092 W/m^2	Number of lightbulbs = ?
Soccer field dimensions: 100 m × 65 m	
Area of a rectangle $A = l \times w$	
Rate of energy use per lightbulb: 60 W	

CALCULATE **Solve for the unknown.**

Use the equation for the area of a rectangle to determine the area of the soccer field.

$A = l \times w$

$A = 100\text{ m} \times 65\text{ m} = 6500\text{ m}^2$

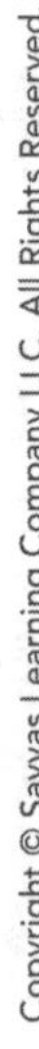

Multiply by Earth's rate of energy loss per unit area to find the field's rate of energy loss	$6500\ m^2 \times \left(\frac{0.092\ W}{1\ m^2}\right) = 598\ W$
Use the known rate of energy use per lightbulb to find the number of lightbulbs that can be powered by the field.	$598\ W \times \left(\frac{1\ \text{lightbulb}}{60\ W}\right) = 9.47$ lightbulbs
Round down to the nearest number of lightbulbs.	9 lightbulbs

EVALUATE Does the result make sense?

Each square meter of Earth's surface releases a very small amount of heat, but this adds up over Earth's large surface area. A small area such as a soccer field would not release much energy.

13 CCC Scale, Proportion, and Quantity **Modern, energy-efficient clothes dryers require about 1800 watts. Could you run a dryer off of the energy from your soccer field? Explain.**

....

....

GO ONLINE for more practice problems.

Revisit

INVESTIGATIVE PHENOMENON

GO ONLINE to Elaborate and Evaluate your knowledge of heat flow within Earth by completing the class discussion and data analysis activities.

In the CER worksheet assigned at the beginning of this investigation, you drafted a scientific argument about volcanoes in California. With a partner, reevaluate the evidence cited in your arguments.

14 SEP Engage in Argument **Do you think mantle upwelling or downwelling is occurring under California? Use evidence to support your claim.**

....

....

....

....

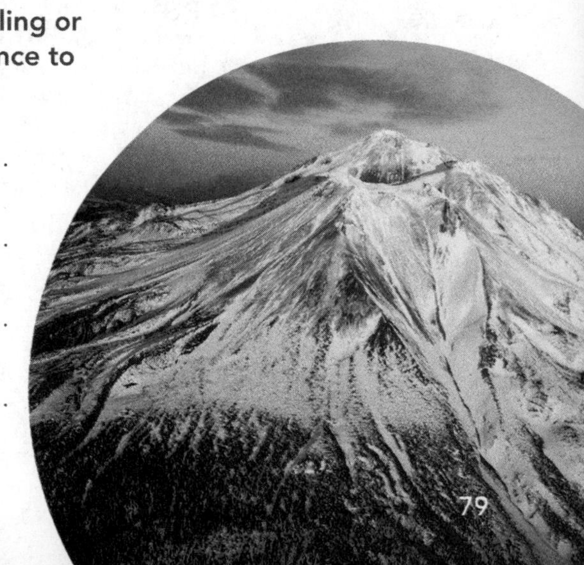

EXPERIENCE 2

Plate Tectonics

GO ONLINE to Explore the dynamic nature of Earth's uppermost layers.

Earth's Fractured Surface

The theory of **plate tectonics** provides the unifying framework through which all of Earth's geologic history can be understood. According to the theory, Earth's lithosphere is broken into more than a dozen mostly rigid pieces called "plates." These pieces move very slowly across Earth's surface, powered by convection currents in the mantle. Most geologic activity occurs where the plates separate, collide, or grind past one another.

Tectonic Plates There are two main types of plates: oceanic and continental. Oceanic plates are denser than continental plates.

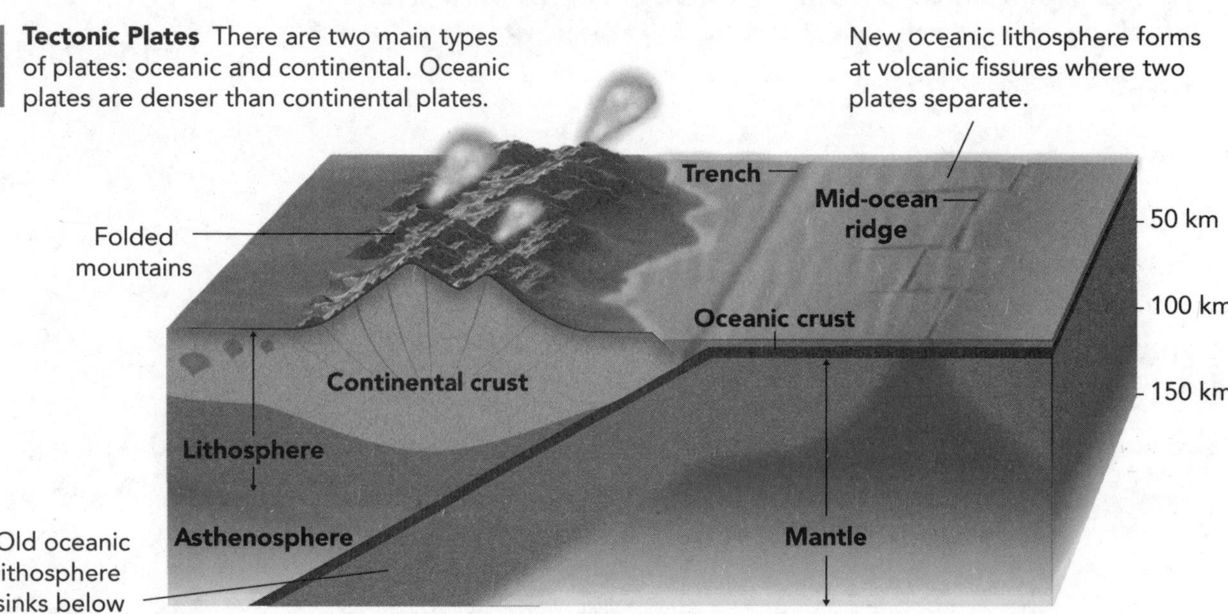

New oceanic lithosphere forms at volcanic fissures where two plates separate.
Trench
Mid-ocean ridge
Folded mountains
50 km
100 km
150 km
Oceanic crust
Continental crust
Lithosphere
Asthenosphere
Mantle
Old oceanic lithosphere sinks below another plate where two plates collide and one plate is denser than the other.

15 **SEP Engage in Argument from Evidence** Identify three reasons why plate tectonics can be described as the surface expression of the cycling of matter due to the flow of energy via mantle convection.

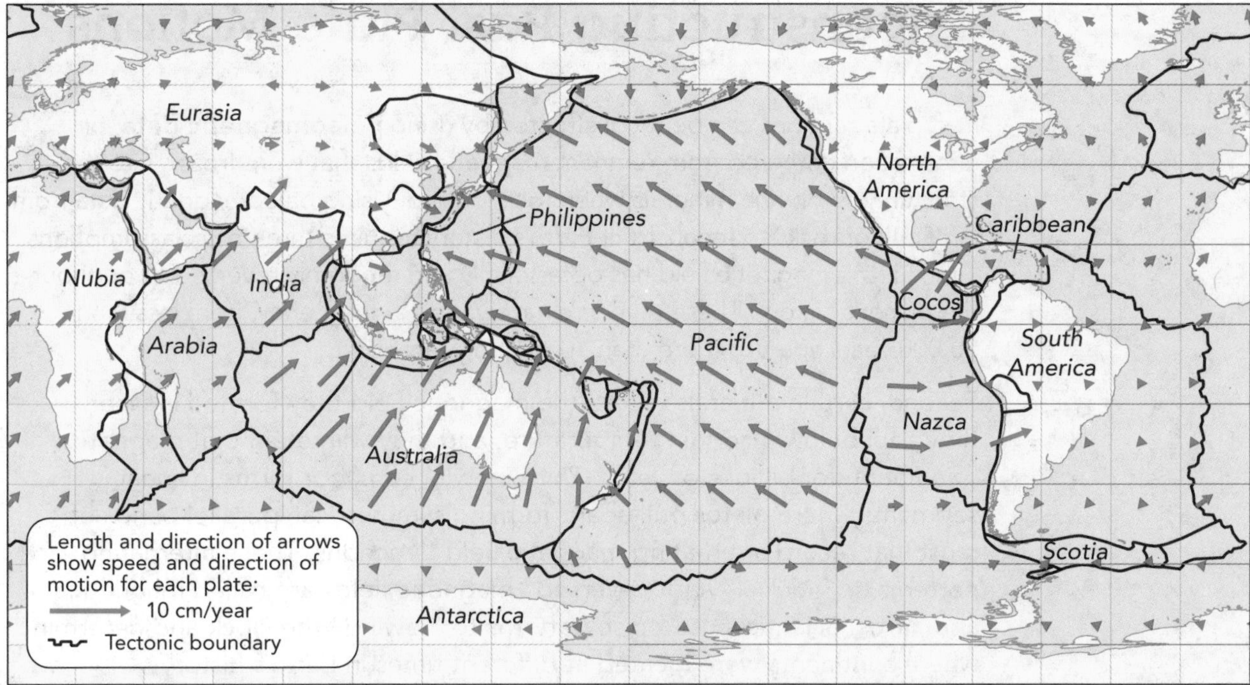

Plate Motion as Recorded by GPS On average, plates containing continents move slowly, usually 0–3 cm/yr, whereas plates without continents move faster, up to 10 cm/yr.

Measuring Current Plate Motions

The overall movement of plates is very slow and steady. Before the invention of modern communication technologies, determining the relative velocities of plates was difficult. Now, geoscientists use Global Positioning System, or GPS, technology. This is the same technology that is used by cell phones and other devices to show a person's location on a map. Data from GPS satellites can be used to determine exactly what direction tectonic plates are moving and how fast.

As with any motion, plate motions must be described relative to a frame of reference. For plate motions, the locations of hot spot volcanoes are commonly used for reference. Hot spot volcanoes are considered stationary relative to Earth's deep mantle because they are often the surface expression of mantle plumes that originate near the core-mantle boundary.

Because Earth's surface isn't growing or shrinking, the area of new plates that form each year equals the area of old plates that are sinking into the mantle or deforming during collisions.

16 **SEP Analyze and Interpret Data Which two plates that share a plate boundary are moving away from each other fastest? Make a claim about the features of the plates and how those features affect the rate of motion of the plates.**

Reconstructing Past Plate Motions

Past plate motions can be reconstructed by using **paleomagnetic data**, or information gathered from remnant magnetic fields that were frozen into the structure of iron-rich minerals when rock formed. Using paleomagnetic data from ocean-floor rocks to reconstruct Earth's history requires three basic assumptions. First, Earth's magnetic field has occasionally and randomly reversed throughout the planet's history. These reversals have varied in frequency, from less than 50,000 years apart to more than 10 million years apart.

Second, certain minerals record the magnetic field they formed in when they cool below a certain temperature, and they will retain that magnetic orientation for billions of years. Third, new ocean floor forms in linear segments where plates pull apart, forming symmetrical, parallel bands of crust that record alternating magnetic field directions. These alternating patterns of "normal" and "reversed" magnetic fields are called magnetic anomalies. Scientists use these patterns to "rewind" the clock and determine where continents were located at different times in Earth's history.

Magnetic Seafloor Anomalies This graph compares the calculated magnetic profile based on Earth's known reversals (top/orange line) against the observed magnetic reversals recorded in rocks on either side of a mid-ocean ridge (bottom/green line). The predicted and observed patterns of reversals match strongly.

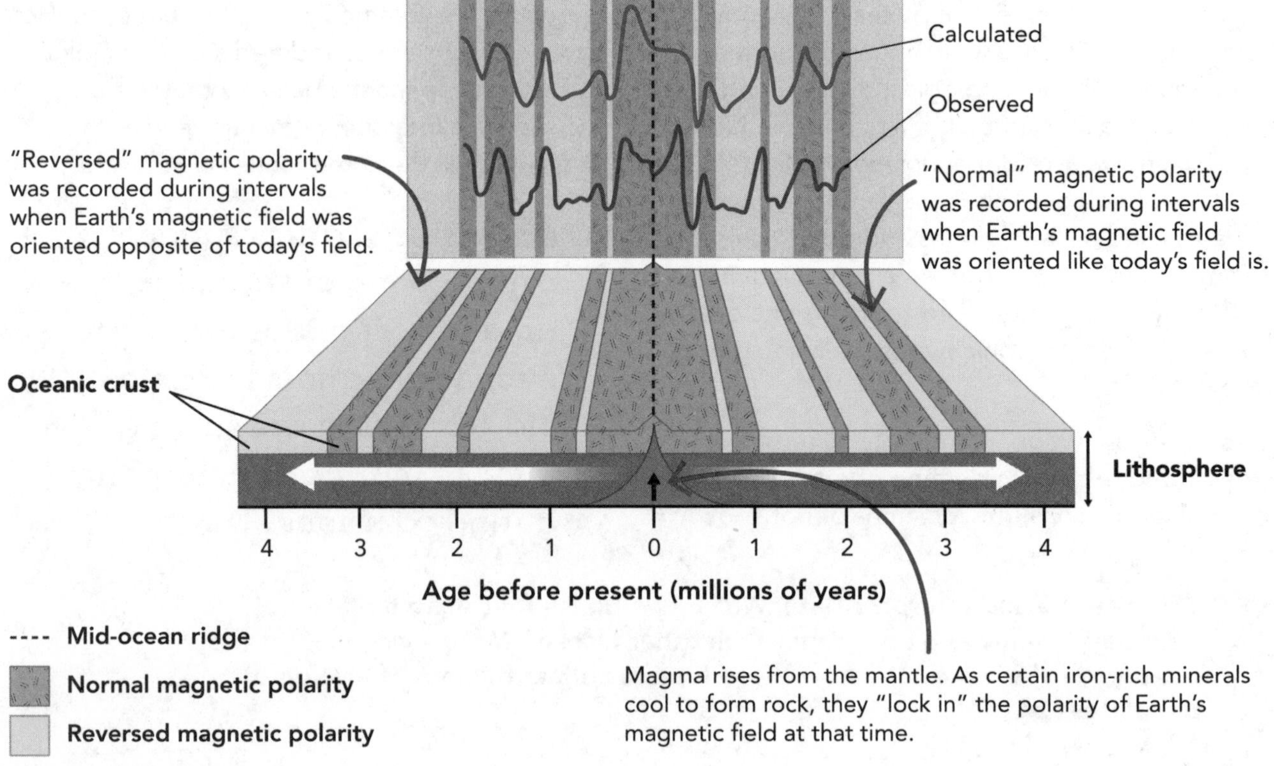

Calculated
Observed
"Reversed" magnetic polarity was recorded during intervals when Earth's magnetic field was oriented opposite of today's field.
"Normal" magnetic polarity was recorded during intervals when Earth's magnetic field was oriented like today's field is.
Oceanic crust
Lithosphere
4
3
2
1
0
1
2
3
4
Age before present (millions of years)
Mid-ocean ridge
Normal magnetic polarity
Reversed magnetic polarity
Magma rises from the mantle. As certain iron-rich minerals cool to form rock, they "lock in" the polarity of Earth's magnetic field at that time.

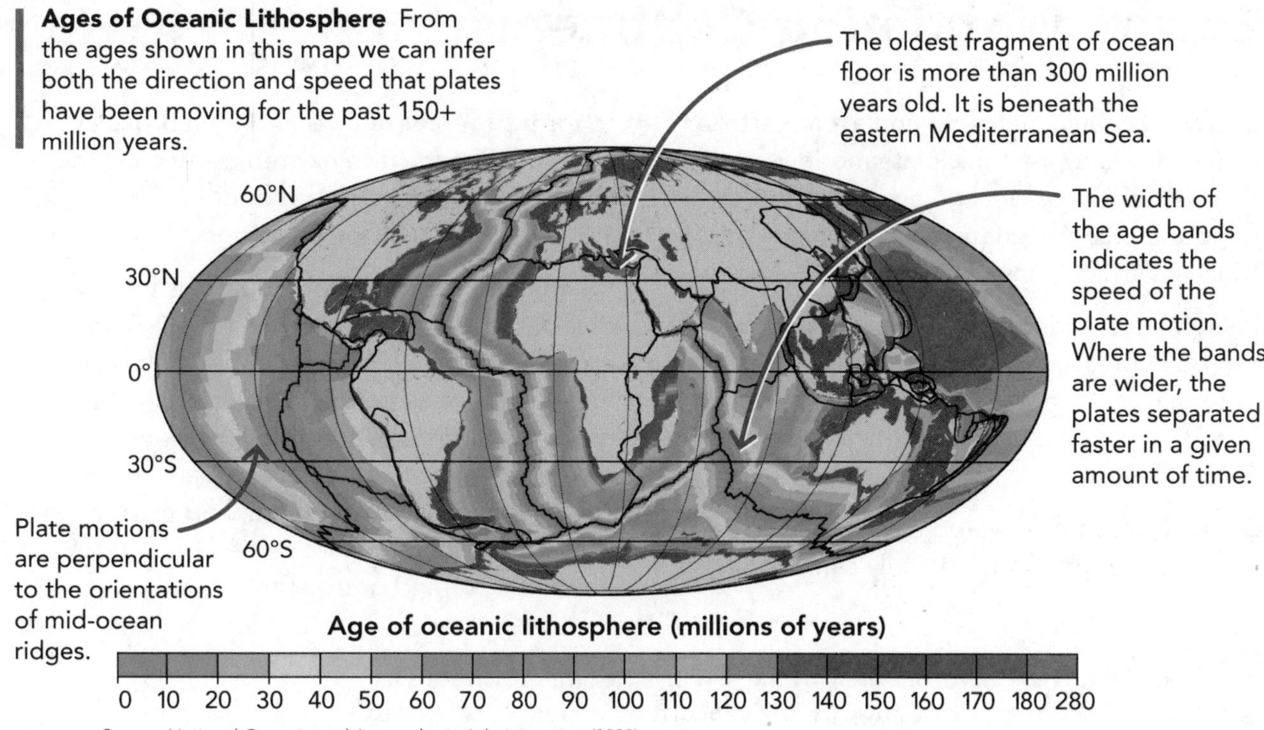

The oldest fragment of ocean floor is more than 300 million years old. It is beneath the eastern Mediterranean Sea.
The width of the age bands indicates the speed of the plate motion. Where the bands are wider, the plates separated faster in a given amount of time.
Plate motions are perpendicular to the orientations of mid-ocean ridges.
60°N
30°N
0°
30°S
60°S
Age of oceanic lithosphere (millions of years)
0 10 20 30 40 50 60 70 80 90 100 110 120 130 140 150 160 170 180 280

Ages of Oceanic Lithosphere From the ages shown in this map we can infer both the direction and speed that plates have been moving for the past 150+ million years.

Source: National Oceanic and Atmospheric Administration (2008)

Seafloor Age Maps Scientists use magnetic anomaly data and radiometric dating methods to construct ocean floor age maps. Most seafloor rock is less than 180 million years old. But Earth is twenty-five times older than that. This means that ocean lithosphere sinks back into the mantle before it gets very old.

Tectonic plate motions averaged out over the past 5 million years are almost identical to the current motions of the plates. This means that the interiors of plates move steadily, even though their boundaries can alternately lock up and slip suddenly during earthquakes.

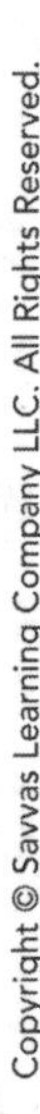

17 **CCC Patterns Look at the map of the ages of oceanic lithosphere. Which two plates that share a boundary are moving the fastest away from each other? Explain your answer. Do these data match the GPS data?**

....

....

....

....

....

Earth's Wandering Continents

Because oceanic plates do not last at Earth's surface for long, tectonic plate motions more than 180 million years ago are calculated by using the paleomagnetism of continental rocks, which can be billions of years old.

Paleomagnetic data from continental rocks can be compared with their absolute ages as determined by radiometric dating, to provide a history of where plates were at various times in Earth's past.

Scientists have discovered a pattern in plate motions: Continents repeatedly came together to form **supercontinents** and then broke apart. Supercontinents have existed at several times in Earth's past, including at about 0.3, 0.6, 1.2, 1.8, 2.6, and 3.6 billion years ago.

When continents collide, mountains form, and associated volcanic activity chemically alters rocks. This concentrates valuable metals and minerals, such as gold and silver. Past plate motions are also responsible for oil and gas reserves. As continents pulled apart, ocean basins formed between them, and the remains of marine organisms that settled on the ocean floor later formed petroleum reserves.

18 **CCC Patterns California did not exist when Rodinia formed. On the Rodinia map, draw an X on the place that is closest to where California would eventually be. For orientation, use Canada's Hudson Bay (it did not exist either, but its eventual location is shown). Draw an O on the place on the continent that was next to Laurentia closest to where you drew the X. On the Pangaea map, draw an X and an O to mark the corresponding locations.**

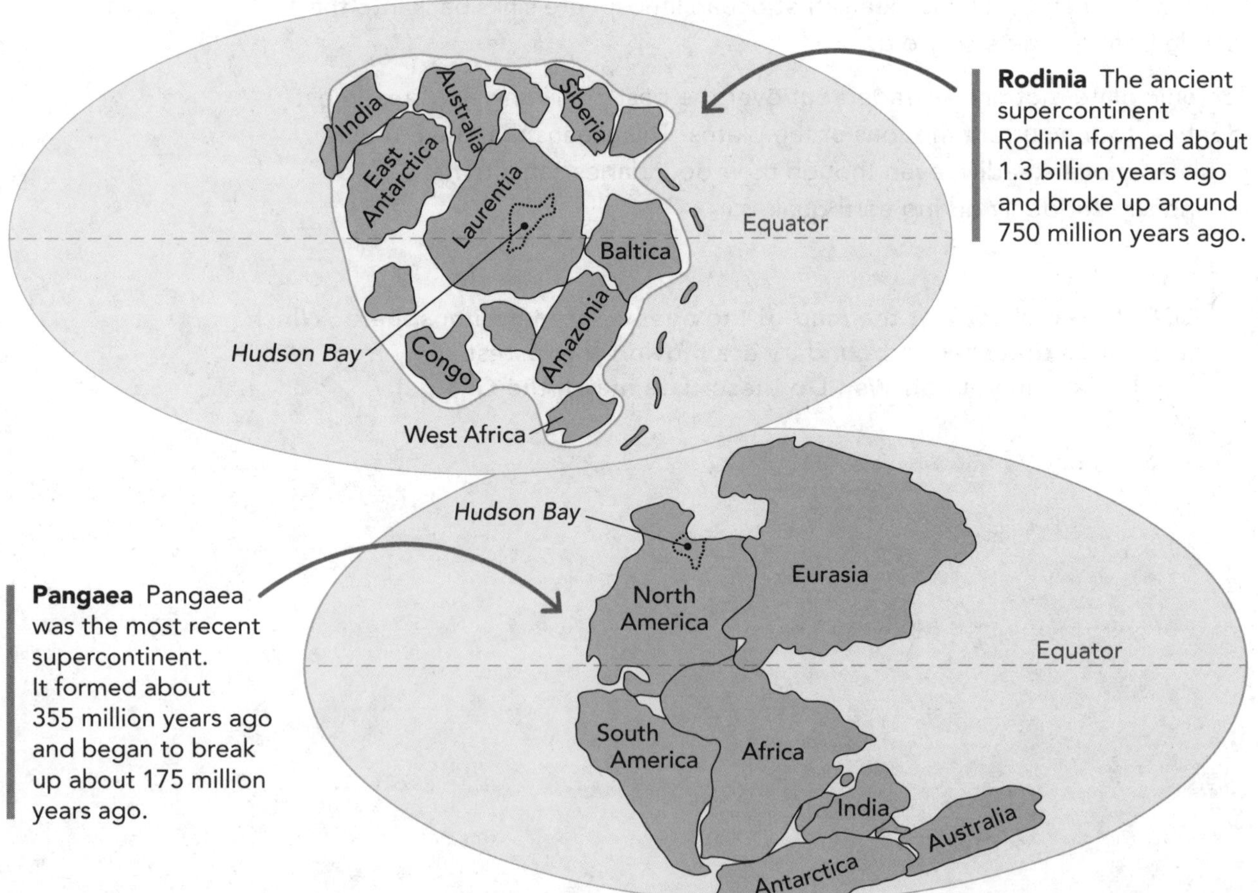

Rodinia The ancient supercontinent Rodinia formed about 1.3 billion years ago and broke up around 750 million years ago.

Pangaea Pangaea was the most recent supercontinent. It formed about 355 million years ago and began to break up about 175 million years ago.

Plate Boundaries

Today and at any given moment in Earth's past, most of the geologic action—such as earthquakes, volcanic eruptions, mountain formation, and new ocean development—has occurred at the borders between tectonic plates. These areas are known as **plate boundaries.**

Plate boundaries are not sharp lines. They are typically hundreds of kilometers wide. For example, the Pacific–North American plate boundary in California is about 300 km across.

Most areas of continents were once at or near plate boundaries, so the crust almost everywhere shows the scars of being fractured and folded from past plate collisions.

Diffuse Plate Boundaries
One-sixth of Earth's surface is actually part of plate boundaries, where the crust is being actively deformed. This means that high hazards from earthquakes exist in many places, not just the centers of plate boundaries.

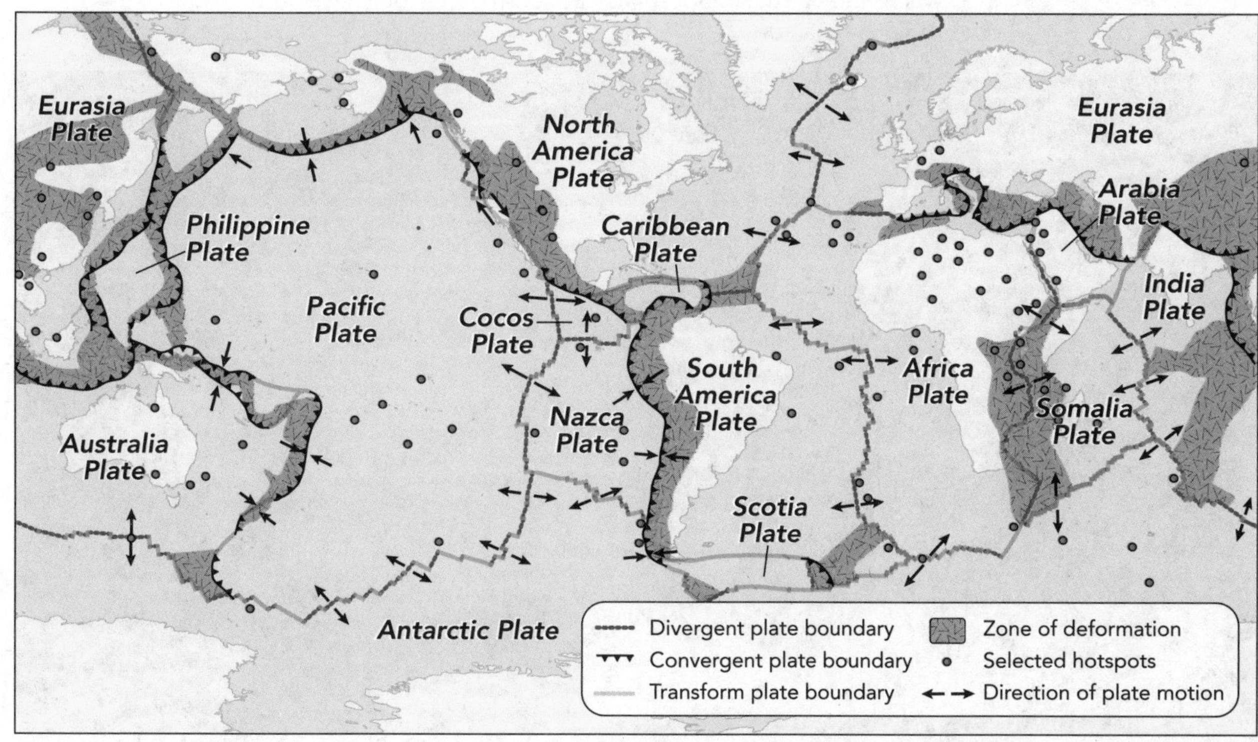

19 **CCC Cause and Effect** **Based on the map, what patterns can you identify related to the type of plate boundary and the size of a diffuse boundary? Why do you think these patterns exist?**

....

....

....

....

Spreading Boundaries

Continental Rifting Where tectonic plates pull apart, long, linear rift valleys form. As the rifting continues, a line of volcanic fissures forms in the center of the valley, erupting magma that hardens to become new rock, widening the valley. If rifting continues, eventually an ocean basin may form.

This process can be seen today in eastern Africa. There, rift valleys are slowly tearing the continent into two separate plates called the Nubian and Somalian Plates. In about 15 million years, a narrow and shallow ocean could form between them. If spreading continues, that ocean might grow into a large, mature ocean like the Atlantic Ocean.

Thingvellir National Park A dramatic rift valley has formed on land where the North American and Eurasian plates pull away from each other in Iceland.

Seafloor Spreading As oceanic plates pull apart at a mid-ocean ridge, hot mantle rock rises to fill the void in the central rift valley, forming new ocean floor. The continuous process of formation of new seafloor and the expansion of an ocean basin is called **seafloor spreading.**

As new ocean floor moves away from the ridge, it is gradually covered up by a thickening layer of marine sediments consisting mainly of rock particles and dead ocean plankton that sink to the ocean floor. Over millions of years, heat and pressure can turn these sediments into petroleum reserves.

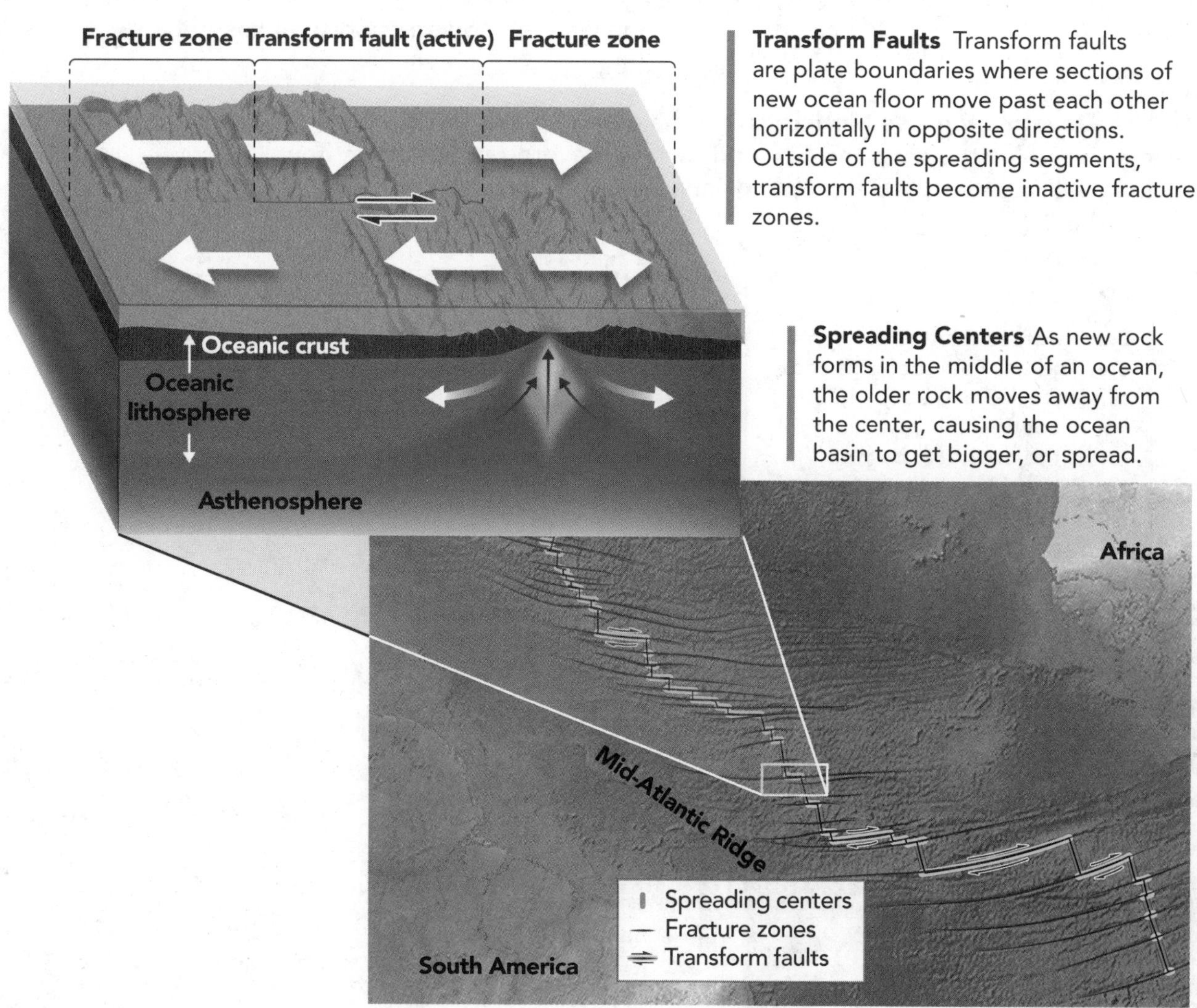

Transform Faults Transform faults are plate boundaries where sections of new ocean floor move past each other horizontally in opposite directions. Outside of the spreading segments, transform faults become inactive fracture zones.

Spreading Centers As new rock forms in the middle of an ocean, the older rock moves away from the center, causing the ocean basin to get bigger, or spread.

20 SEP Use Math and Computational Thinking The total length of mid-ocean ridge spreading centers is about 80,000 km. The average spreading rate of ridges is 1.25 cm/yr. Calculate the area of new ocean crust that forms each year.

Transform Boundaries

Transform boundaries occur where tectonic plates slide past each other, so that lithosphere is neither formed nor destroyed. They are also known as strike-slip boundaries. Transform boundaries are not common on land, but they are common in the ocean, where they connect together segments of spreading ridges.

Transform faults are not always perfectly straight. If they bend, a hole may develop along the fault, as in California's sinking Salton Sea, or binding may push rock up, as in the San Gabriel Mountains north of Los Angeles.

21 SEP Develop and Use Models Using the map and the fact that the relative velocity across the San Andreas fault averages 4.0 cm/yr, how long will it be before Palm Springs and San Francisco border one another?

San Andreas Fault California's San Andreas Fault deforms and offsets rock along about 1,200 km of continental crust and forms the boundary between the Pacific Plate and the North American Plate.

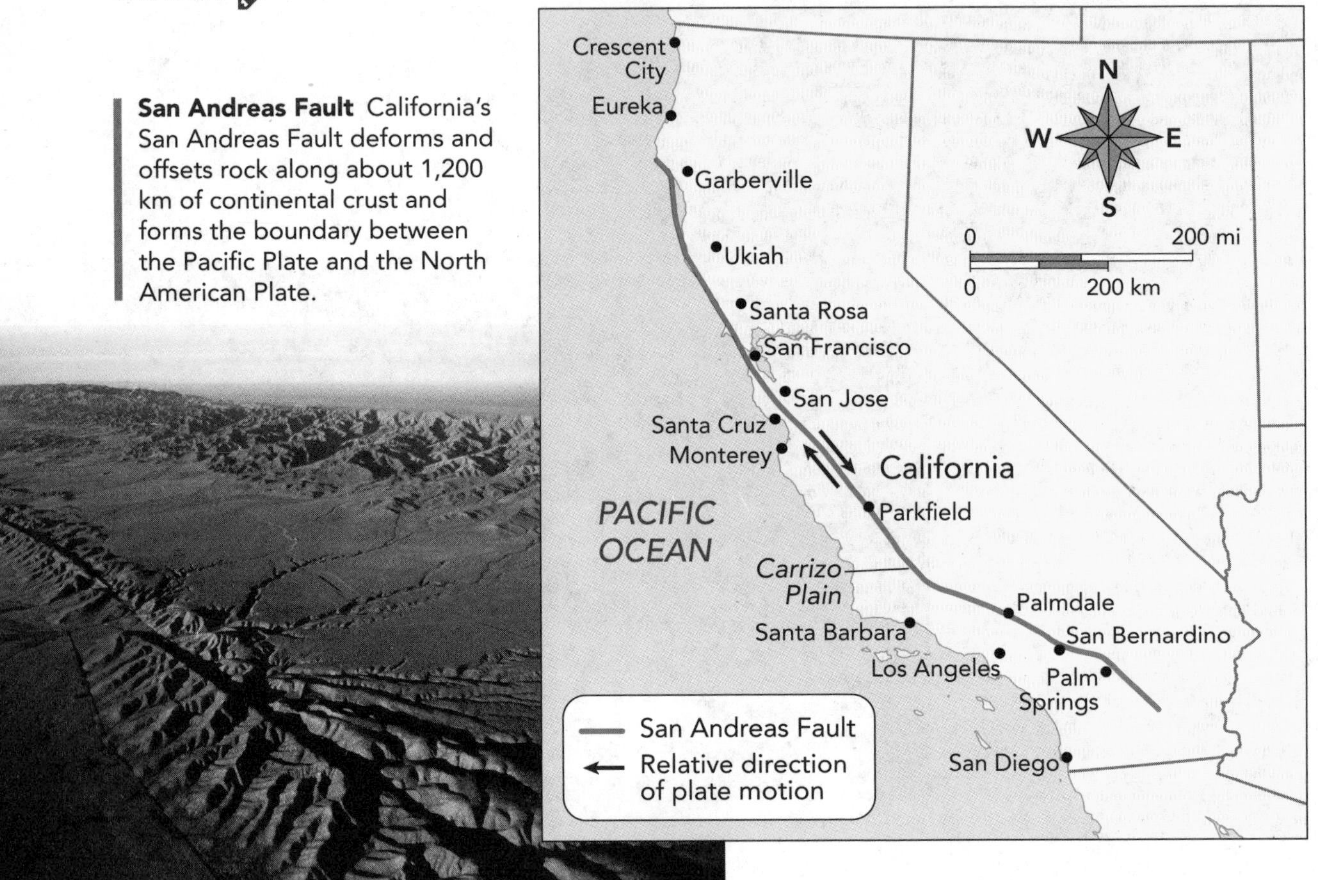

Continental Collisions

Continental crust is less dense than oceanic crust or mantle rock. Continental crust also tends to be rather thick. Therefore, when tectonic plate movements bring two continental plates together, neither crust sinks into the mantle. Instead, the rocks at the edges of the continents smash into each other and suture together.

As the continental collision zone gets squeezed and shortened horizontally, the rock is pushed both up and down. This means that the taller a mountain is at the surface, the deeper its crustal "roots" are. Ice cubes floating in water show similar behavior, with bigger ice cubes floating both higher above the water surface and deeper below it than smaller cubes. This equilibrium of the buoyancy of the lithosphere is called **isostasy.**

Colliding Continents The rock layers of continental crust get significantly deformed through folding and faulting during a collision. Sediments and rocks from the ocean floor are compressed and deformed in the suture between two colliding continents.

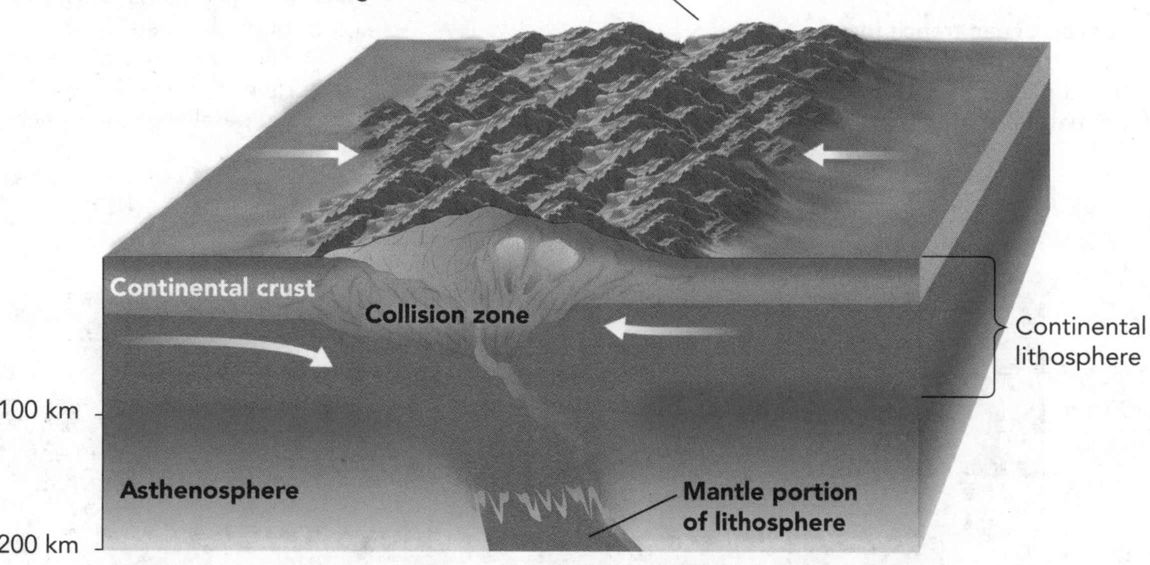

(22) **SEP Develop and Use Models** **As two continents collide and a mountain is pushed upward, the mountain root is also pushed downward. Explain why this happens using the model of placing an increasing stack of books onto a mattress.**

....

....

....

....

Subduction Zones

As oceanic plates move away from mid-ocean ridges and age, they become denser. If a plate becomes denser than the surrounding rock, it may sink into the mantle and move beneath another plate, or *subduct*. Areas where this process occurs are called **subduction zones.**

Subduction zones have characteristic landforms that usually include a deep ocean trench, a wedge of ocean sediments on the overlying plate, and a row of volcanoes.

Subduction zones also experience lots of earthquakes. Earthquakes occur because of the compression of rock in the colliding plates and the bending of the subducting plate. Most of the world's earthquakes (and all of the largest ones) occur at subduction zones.

Ocean-Continent Subduction Where an oceanic plate collides with a continental plate, the denser oceanic plate will sink into the mantle and move beneath the less dense continental plate.

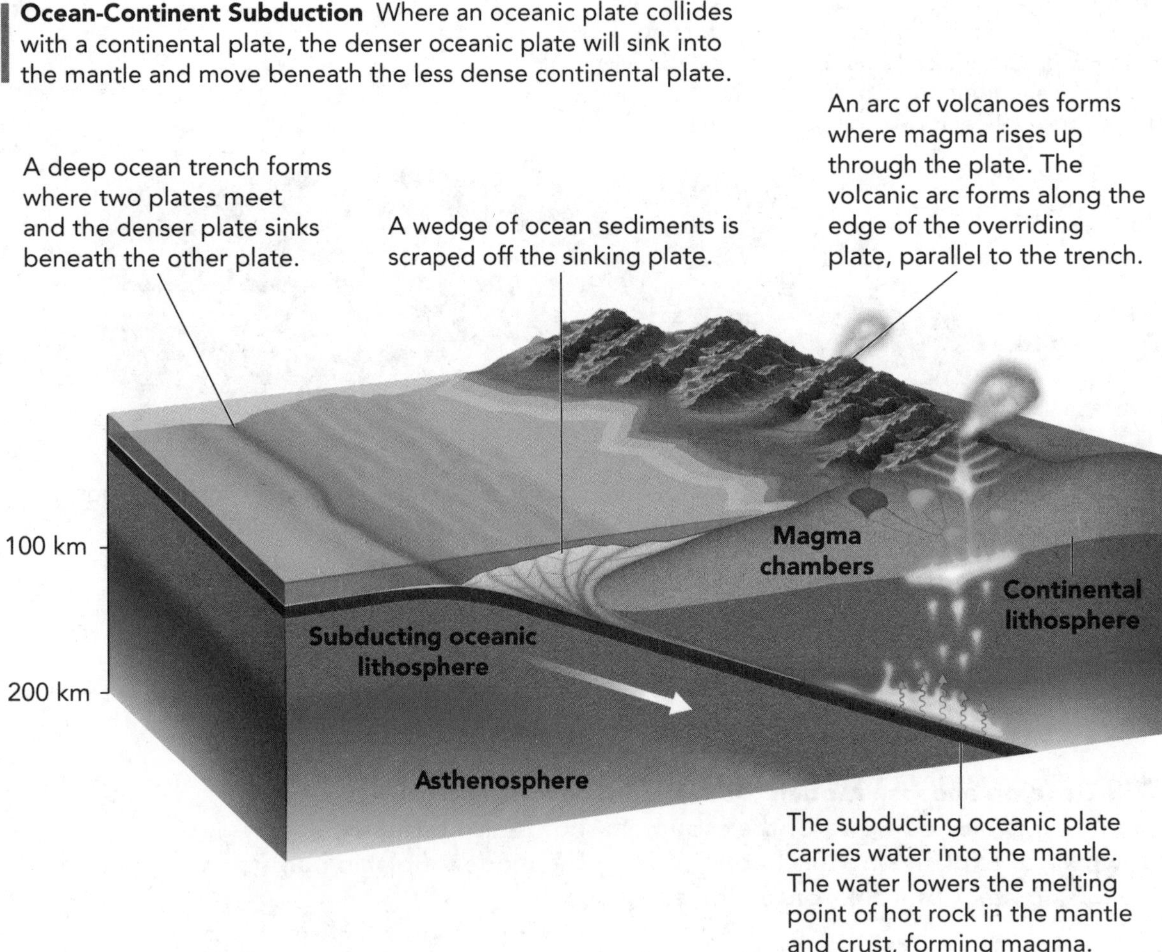

A deep ocean trench forms where two plates meet and the denser plate sinks beneath the other plate.
A wedge of ocean sediments is scraped off the sinking plate.
An arc of volcanoes forms where magma rises up through the plate. The volcanic arc forms along the edge of the overriding plate, parallel to the trench.
100 km
200 km
Magma chambers
Continental lithosphere
Subducting oceanic lithosphere
Asthenosphere
The subducting oceanic plate carries water into the mantle. The water lowers the melting point of hot rock in the mantle and crust, forming magma.

Subduction zones also occur where two oceanic plates collide. The same geologic processes and set of landforms that occur at an ocean-continent subduction zone occur at an ocean-ocean subduction zone. One unique feature of an ocean-ocean subduction zone is the formation of volcanic island arcs. Examples include the Aleutian Islands in Alaska and many of the islands of Indonesia.

Plates may contain both oceanic and continental crust. When the leading edge of a subducting plate runs out of oceanic crust, the configuration of the plate boundary may change to an ocean-continent collision, or to a continent-continent collision.

Ocean-Ocean Subduction Where an oceanic plate collides with another oceanic plate, the older—and therefore denser and deeper—plate is usually the one that subducts.

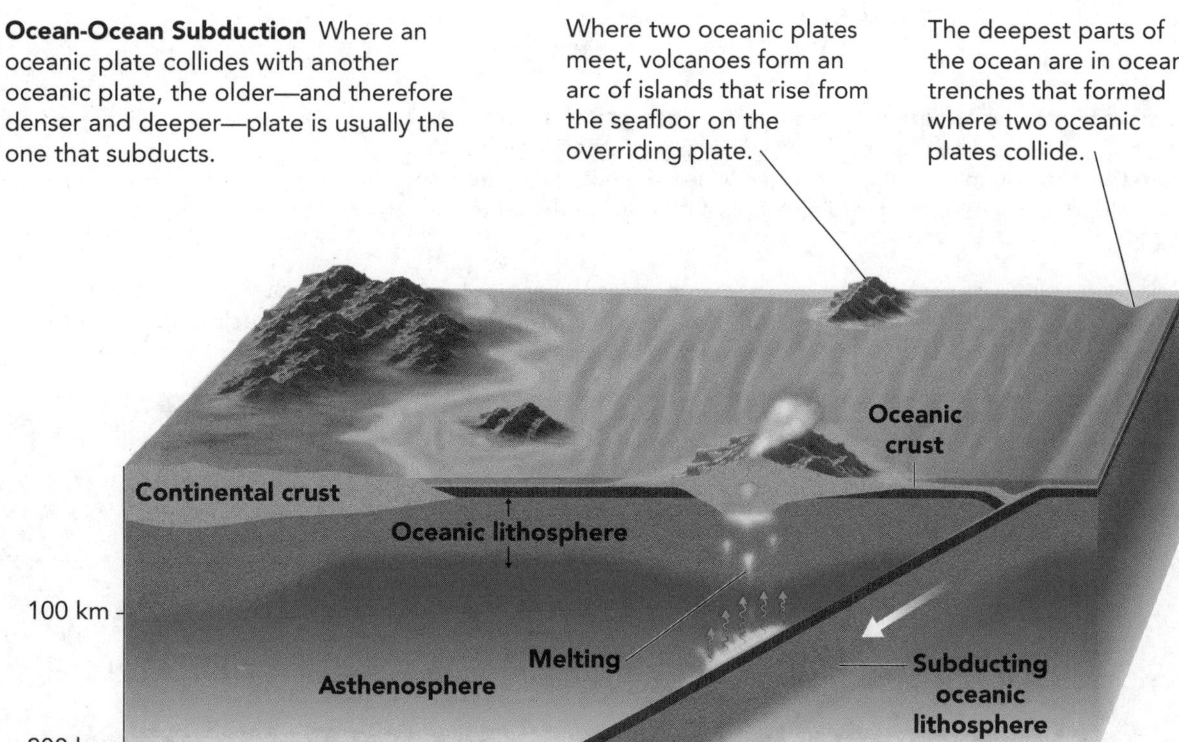
Where two oceanic plates meet, volcanoes form an arc of islands that rise from the seafloor on the overriding plate.
The deepest parts of the ocean are in ocean trenches that formed where two oceanic plates collide.
Oceanic crust
Continental crust
Oceanic lithosphere
100 km
Melting
Asthenosphere
Subducting oceanic lithosphere
200 km

(23) **SEP Plan and Carry Out Investigations** **Suppose that you were a geologist trying to figure out how a long and narrow sea, such as the Red Sea, formed. What geologic features would you look for to determine whether the current shape of the sea is a result of seafloor spreading or ocean subduction?**

Plate Boundaries and Mineral Resources

Most valuable minerals and metals, such as platinum, gold, and silver, exist in extremely low concentrations within Earth's crust. Fortunately, plate tectonic processes naturally concentrate these valuable mineral resources.

When seafloor rocks enter subduction zones, the elements are subjected to hydrothermal circulation associated with volcanic activity. Concentrations of valuable elements are carried upward in hot fluids and are injected into cold crustal rocks. As the fluid cools, the elements precipitate out to form rich ore veins.

Concentration of Minerals At mid-ocean ridges, water enters the crust and is heated by magma at the spreading center. Elements from the crust dissolve in the hot water. When the hot water reenters the cold, deep ocean, dissolved elements settle out of the water.

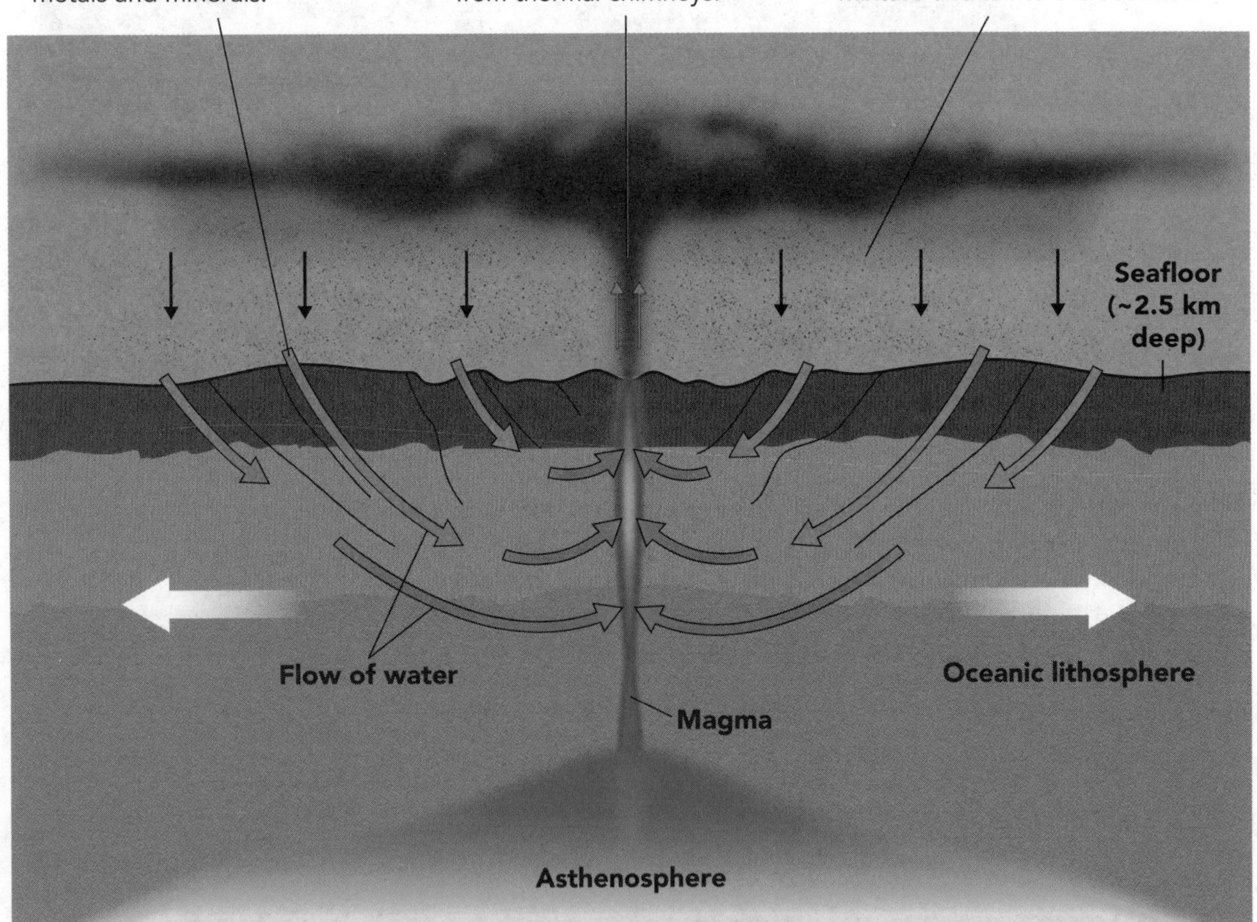

Cold water sinks into the crust. The water heats up, dissolving metals and minerals.
Hot water rises toward the surface and is erupted from thermal chimneys.
As the hot water cools, metal and minerals precipitate out of the mixture and fall to the seafloor.
Seafloor (~2.5 km deep)
Flow of water
Oceanic lithosphere
Magma
Asthenosphere

SAMPLE PROBLEM

Calculations of Mass and Volume

Gold (Au) exists in Earth's crust at a volume concentration of only about 3 parts per billion (ppb), or 3×10^{-9}. The mass of gold is about 7.5 times greater than the mass of an equal volume of typical continental crustal rock. If gold were distributed evenly throughout the continents, how many metric tons of crustal rock would you have to grind up to make one 8.00 g gold ring? (For this estimate, assume that the mass of gold is in fact 7.50 times greater than that of an equal volume of crustal rock.)

ANALYZE **The knowns and unknown.**

Knowns	Unknowns
concentration of Au in rock: 3×10^{-9} x total volume of rock	mass of rock required = ? metric tons
mass of ring band = 8.00 g	
mass of gold = 7.5 × mass of an equal volume of continental crust	
1 Mg (metric ton) = 10^6 g	

CALCULATE **Solve for the unknown.**

Find the mass of a volume of rock equal to the volume of the ring.

$$8.00 \text{ g Au} \times \left(\frac{1.00 \text{ g rock}}{7.50 \text{ g Au}}\right) = 1.07 \text{ g of rock}$$

Because this takes up the same volume as the Au ring, the Au concentration in rock can be used to find the mass of rock needed.

$$1.07 \text{ g} = 3 \times 10^{-9} \times \text{total mass of rock}$$

Rewrite the equation in terms of the total amount of rock, and solve.

$$\text{total mass of rock} = \frac{1.07 \text{ g}}{(3 \times 10^{-9})}$$
$$= \text{about } 4 \times 10^8 \text{ g}$$

Convert g to Mg.

$$= 4 \times 10^8 \text{ g} \times \left(\frac{1 \text{ Mg}}{10^6 \text{ g}}\right)$$
$$= 400 \text{ Mg}$$

EVALUATE **Does the result make sense?**

At a concentration of 3 parts per billion, you would need to process approximately 400 metric tons of continental crust to get 8 g of gold. This is why geochemical processes that concentrate minerals are important for human resource use.

24 **CCC Scale, Proportion, and Quantity** **A standard gold bar weighs approximately 12.4 kg. Assuming that the gold exists only at the volume concentration identified above, how many metric tons of continental rock would have to be processed to make a standard gold bar?**

GO ONLINE for more practice problems.

Revisit

INVESTIGATIVE PHENOMENON

GO ONLINE to Elaborate and Evaluate your knowledge of plate tectonics by completing the class discussion and data analysis activities.

In the CER worksheet, you drafted a scientific argument about volcanoes in California. With a partner, reevaluate the evidence cited in your arguments.

25 **SEP Engage in Argument** **What aspects of the theory of plate tectonics could help you improve your argument? Explain.**

☑ASSESSMENT

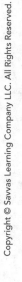

GO ONLINE to Evaluate what you learned about the constant transfer of energy and matter in Earth's interior by using the available assessment resources.

In the Performance-Based Assessment, you analyzed the rock cycle to learn new details about Earth's history and its natural events. Wrap up your analysis by answering the following questions.

26 **SEP Use Models How does the model of plate tectonics help to explain the different transformations observed in the rock cycle?**

....

....

....

....

....

....

Revisit
ANCHORING PHENOMENON

27 **Revisit the Anchoring Phenomenon** **Think about the blaze presented at the beginning of Instructional Segment 1. Use what you have learned to answer the question "How could all this flammable material accumulate in such a remote place?"**

....

....

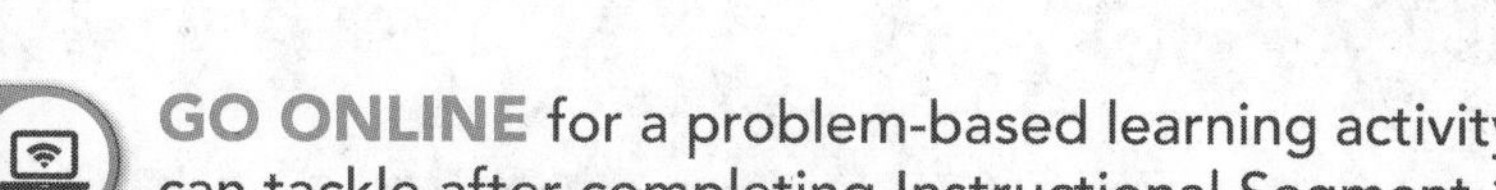

GO ONLINE for a problem-based learning activity that you can tackle after completing Instructional Segment 1.

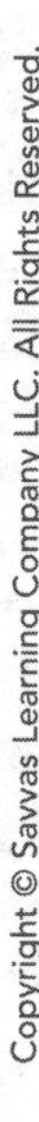

Atoms, Elements, and Molecules

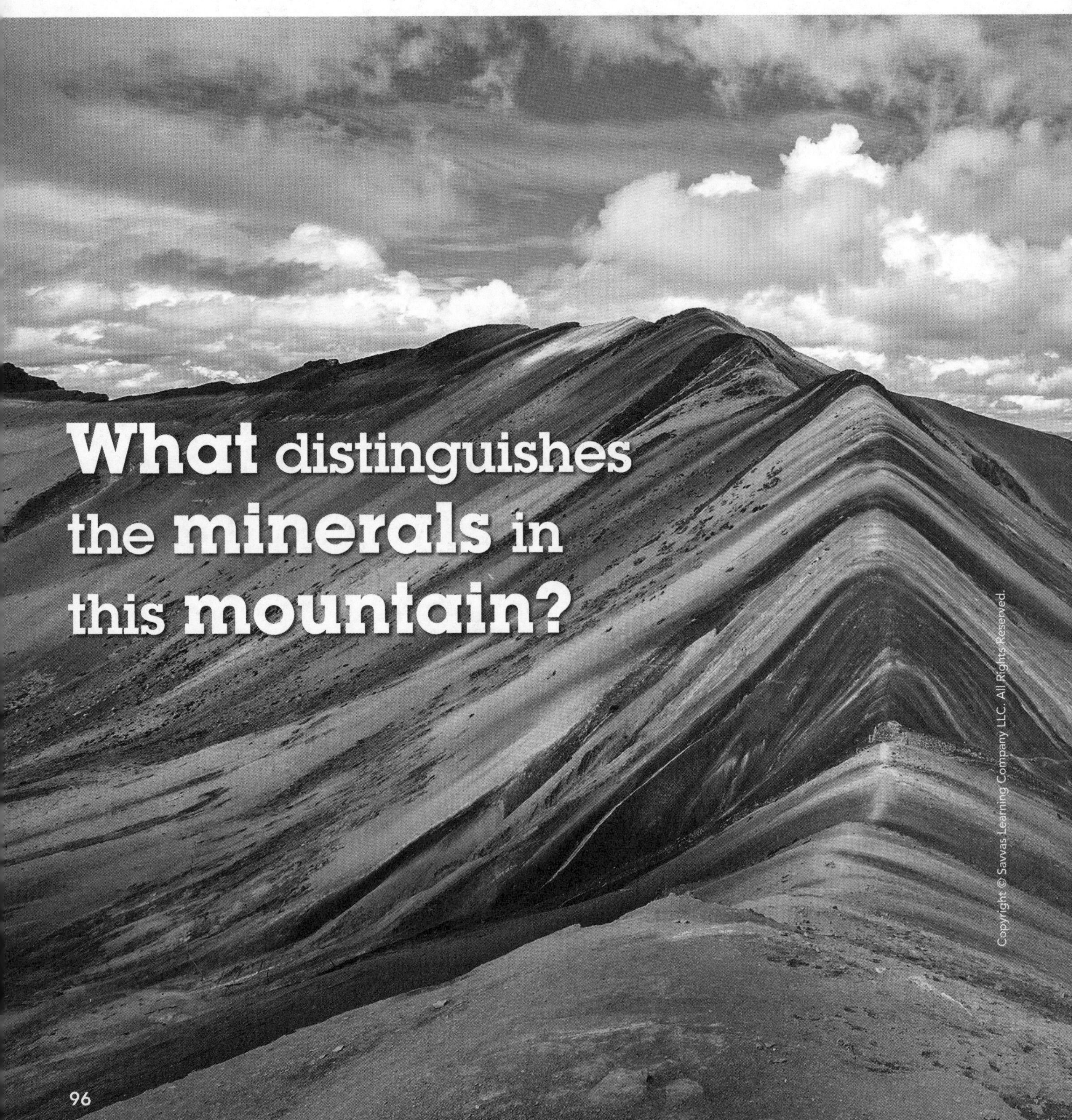

Investigation 4
Atomic Structure

Investigation 5
The Periodic Table

Investigation 6
Chemical Bonding

ANCHORING PHENOMENON

Inquiry Launch Look at the image of the mountain. What evidence might you need in order to explain the bands of different colors?

Brainstorm ideas for an experiment (or test) that would yield evidence that helps explain the phenomenon.

GO ONLINE to Engage with real-world phenomena. Watch the anchoring phenomenon video and preview the optional **problem-based learning experience**.

INVESTIGATIVE PHENOMENON

GO ONLINE to Engage with real-world phenomena by watching a video and to complete a modeling interactive worksheet.

What causes the colors in a fireworks display?

Atomic Structure

Once you have viewed the Investigative Phenomenon video and completed the modeling exercise to help explain the phenomenon you observed, answer these reflection questions about fireworks and a related phenomenon.

1. **CCC Matter and Energy** What colors are the fireworks in the photo? How do you think the matter and energy of fireworks of different colors are similar and different?

2. **SEP Construct an Explanation** Neon signs, such as "Open" signs, use electricity and give off light continuously when they are turned on. What similarities and differences can you identify between neon signs and fireworks? What might be happening at the atomic level to explain these differences?

EXPERIENCE 1

Modeling Atoms

GO ONLINE to Explore and Explain the makeup and properties of atoms and isotopes.

Visualizing the Atom

Matter is made of particles, called atoms, that are too tiny to see without powerful microscopes. An **atom** is the smallest particle of an element that retains its identity in a chemical reaction. Atoms are extremely small. A single row of 100,000,000 copper atoms would produce a line only 1 cm long. Because of the creative experiments of many scientists, we know that atoms are made of even smaller particles called subatomic particles. **Protons** are positively charged subatomic particles. **Neutrons** are subatomic particles with no charge. **Electrons** are negatively charged subatomic particles. An electron cloud surrounds the **nucleus,** which is the dense central core made of protons and neutrons.

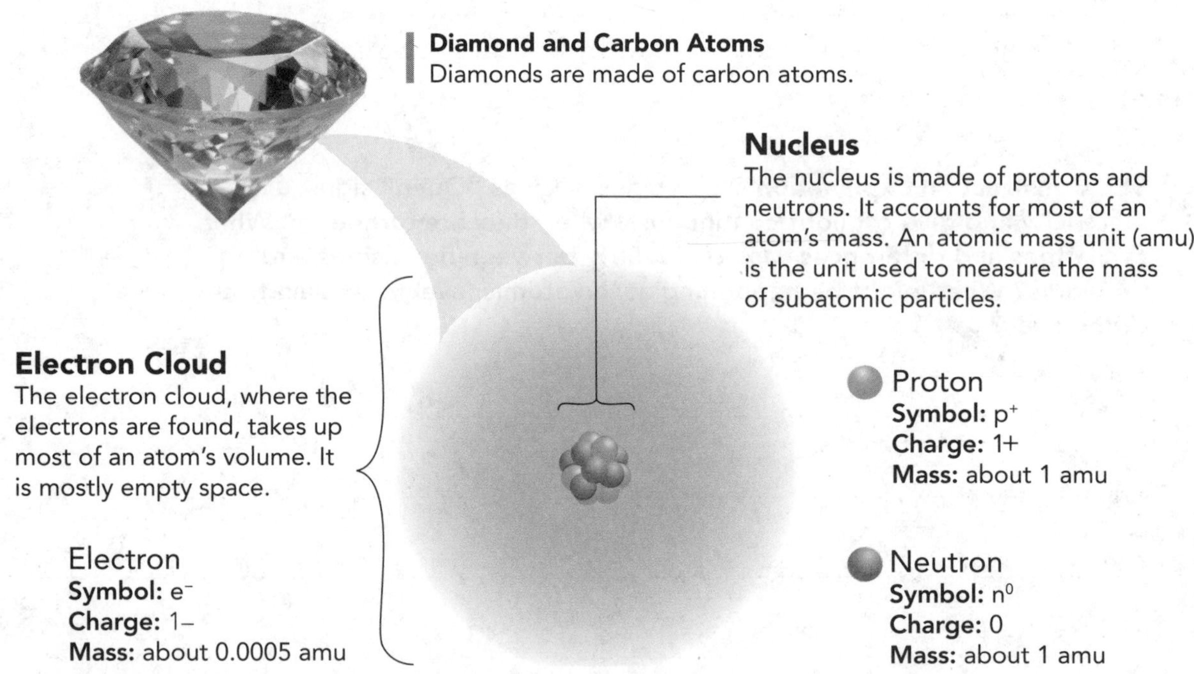

Nucleus
The nucleus is made of protons and neutrons. It accounts for most of an atom's mass. An atomic mass unit (amu) is the unit used to measure the mass of subatomic particles.
Electron Cloud
The electron cloud, where the electrons are found, takes up most of an atom's volume. It is mostly empty space.
Electron
Symbol: e^-
Charge: 1–
Mass: about 0.0005 amu
Proton
Symbol: p^+
Charge: 1+
Mass: about 1 amu
Neutron
Symbol: n^0
Charge: 0
Mass: about 1 amu

Diamond and Carbon Atoms
Diamonds are made of carbon atoms.

(3) **CCC Scale, Proportion, and Quantity** **Which subatomic particles account for most of an atom's mass and volume?**

....

....

Types of Atoms

Atomic Number An **element** is the simplest form of matter that has a unique set of properties. The number of protons in an atom is what makes one element different from another. The number of protons in the nucleus of an atom is called an element's **atomic number.** For example, carbon has 6 protons and has an atomic number of 6.

Atoms are electrically neutral particles because they have no net charge.

Therefore, for an atom to be neutral, the number of protons (positively charged particles) must equal the number of electrons (negatively charged particles).

Helium The element helium is less dense than air, so it is used in balloons.
Atomic number: 2
Number of protons: 2
Number of electrons: 2

Silver The element silver is reflective and resists corrosion, so it is often used in jewelry.
Atomic number: 47
Number of protons: 47
Number of electrons: 47

4. **CCC Scale, Proportion, and Quantity Identify the numbers of protons and electrons in fluorine and iodine.**

The element **fluorine** helps prevent tooth decay and is found in many toothpastes.
Atomic number: 9
Number of protons: ....
Number of electrons: ....

The element **iodine** is often used to clean skin before surgery.
Atomic number: 53
Number of protons: ....
Number of electrons: ....

The Periodic Table There are 118 elements, all with different atomic numbers. They are organized into a table called a periodic table. A **periodic table** is an arrangement of elements in which the elements are separated into groups based on a set of repeating properties. The elements are listed in order from left to right and top to bottom by atomic number. The organization of the periodic table allows you to easily compare the properties of one element (or a group of elements) to another element (or group of elements). Elements above and below each other tend to have similar properties.

Chemical Symbols All elements have a name, but an element's name is often not convenient to use. Each element can be represented by a one- or two-letter **chemical symbol.** It is these chemical symbols that are used to represent the elements in the periodic table, as well as in chemical formulas for compounds. When writing the formula for a compound, you combine the symbols of the elements that make up the compound. For example, the chemical formula for water is H_2O.

Symbols With One Letter The symbol for hydrogen is H. Its atomic number is 1, so it is the first element in the periodic table.

Symbols With Two Letters The symbol for helium is He. The second letter in a symbol is always lowercase. Helium's atomic number is 2, so it is the second element in the periodic table.

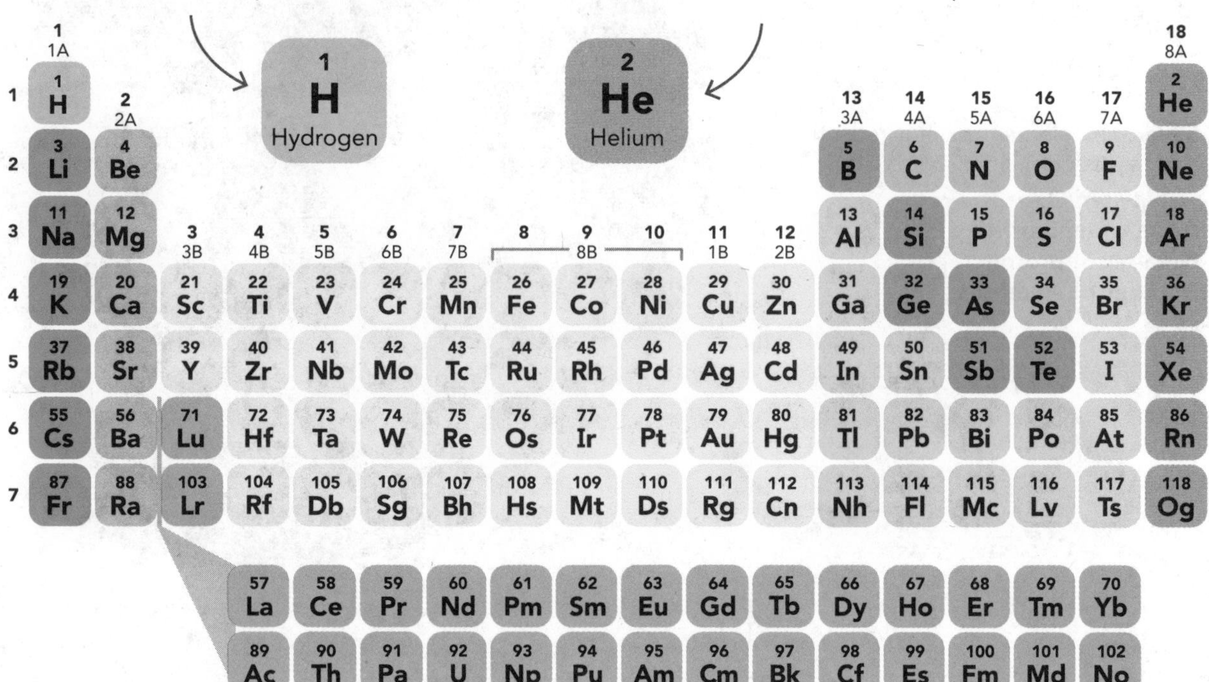

5 **Infer** Based on the organization and colors in the periodic table, which two elements do you think are most similar in terms of their properties: magnesium (Mg), barium (Ba), and gold (Au)? Explain.

....

....

Mass Number

Most of the mass of an atom comes from protons and neutrons. The total number of protons plus neutrons in an atom is called the **mass number.** If you know the atomic number and mass number of an atom, then you can determine the number of neutrons in the atom.

Representing Atoms The composition of any atom can be represented in shorthand notation using the element's chemical symbol, **atomic number**, and **mass number.**

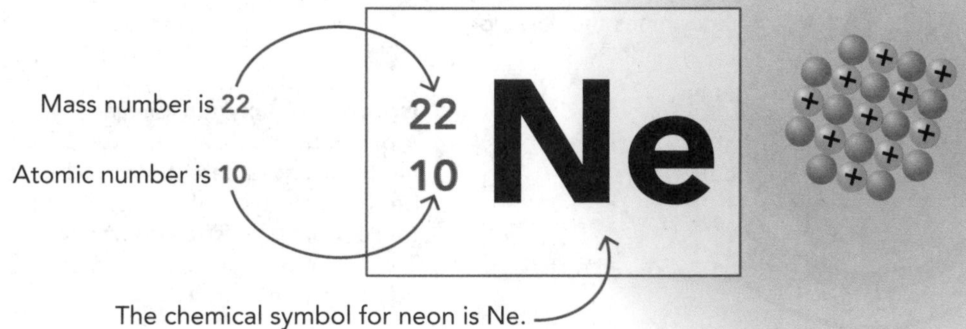

Mass number is 22
Atomic number is 10
22
10
Ne
The chemical symbol for neon is Ne.

Neon-22 You can also represent atoms by using the name of the element and the mass number.

Mass Number and Neutrons You can calculate the number of neutrons from the atomic number and the mass number of an atom. For example, let's calculate the number of neutrons in neon.
Number of neutrons = mass number − atomic number
Number of neutrons = 22 − 10 = 12

OPEN

Neon is one element in this sign. Such signs are often called neon signs, even if they contain other elements.

6 **SEP Use Mathematics Complete the table by identifying the atomic number and mass number for each atom and then using those data to determine the numbers of protons, neutrons, and electrons.**

Composition of Atoms

Atom	Atomic number	Mass number	Protons	Electrons	Neutrons
$^{23}_{11}Na$					
$^{32}_{16}S$					
silver-108	47				
gold-197	79				

Isotopes

All atoms of an element have the same number of protons. However, atoms of the same element may have different numbers of neutrons. **Isotopes** are atoms that have the same number of protons but different numbers of neutrons. Since isotopes of an element have different numbers of neutrons, they also have different mass numbers.

Sizes of Dogs Dogs come in a variety of sizes. The mass of each can be large or small, but they are all still dogs. Their DNA determines they are dogs.

Isotopes of Oxygen Similarly, atoms may have different numbers of neutrons and different masses but still be the same type of atom. All three of these atoms are isotopes of oxygen. They have 8 protons, but different numbers of neutrons.

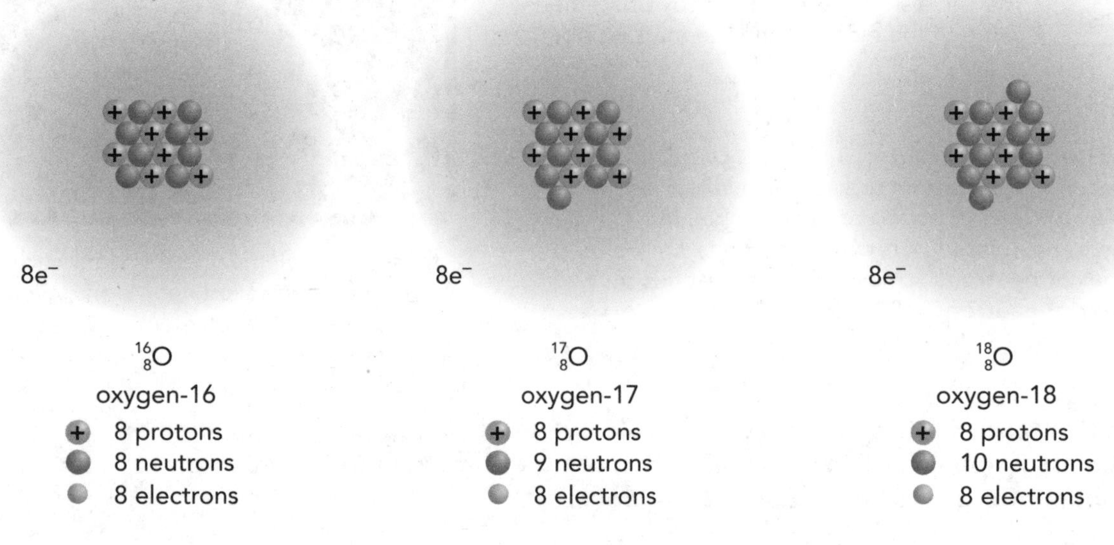

$^{16}_{8}O$	$^{17}_{8}O$	$^{18}_{8}O$
oxygen-16	oxygen-17	oxygen-18
8 protons	8 protons	8 protons
8 neutrons	9 neutrons	10 neutrons
8 electrons	8 electrons	8 electrons

7 **SEP Communicate Information How does the overall charge of oxygen-16 compare to the overall charge of oxygen-17 and oxygen-18? Use the models of isotopes to help explain your answer.**

....

....

....

Atomic Mass

Comparing the Masses of Atoms It's not convenient to measure the mass of a single atom because the mass is so small. Instead, it's more useful to compare the relative masses of atoms using a reference isotope. A reference isotope is an isotope whose mass can be measured accurately and is used as the basis for a scale to compare the masses of other atoms.

Understanding Atomic Mass

How is the **mass of an atom determined?**

Carbon-12 The isotope carbon-12 is used as a standard to compare the relative masses of atoms. Carbon-12 has 6 protons, 6 neutrons, and 6 electrons. **Scientists have assigned carbon-12 a mass of exactly 12 atomic mass units.**

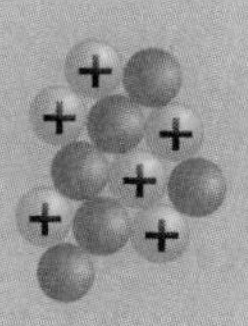

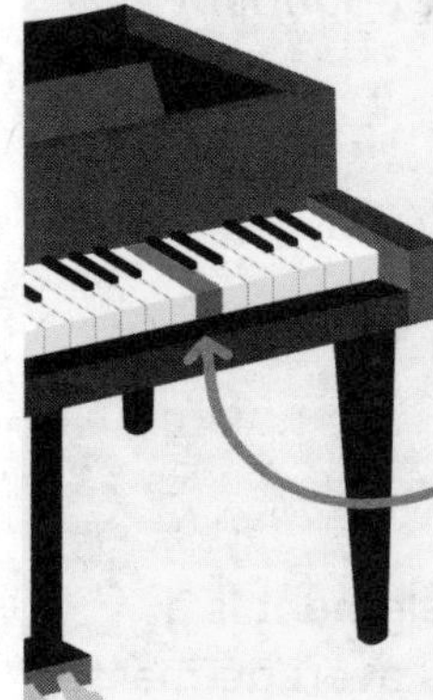

Piano Key to Piano If you measure the mass of a piano with and without a piano key, you likely wouldn't see a difference between the two masses. The mass of a piano key is negligible compared to the mass of the whole piano.

Even though the mass is insignificant, each key is essential to the function of the piano.

Electron to Atom Similarly, the mass of an electron is negligible compared to the mass of a proton or neutron.

Each electron is essential to the properties of an atom.

Mass of proton 1.67×10^{-24} g

Mass of neutron 1.67×10^{-24} g

Mass of electron 9.11×10^{-28} g

Atomic Mass Unit An atomic mass unit (amu) is one twelfth of the mass of a carbon-12 atom.

$1 \text{ amu} = \frac{1}{12} \times 12 \text{ amu}$ **1 amu = about the mass of a proton or neutron**

8. **SEP Develop Models** Each helium atom has two protons. Sketch models of helium-3 and helium-4, which have approximate masses of 3 amu and 4 amu, respectively. Label and differentiate protons, neutrons, and electrons in your models.

Isotope Abundance and Atomic Mass In nature, most elements occur as a mixture of two or more isotopes. Each isotope of an element has a fixed mass and a natural percent abundance.

Comparing Abundances of Bromine, Chlorine, and Silicon Isotopes

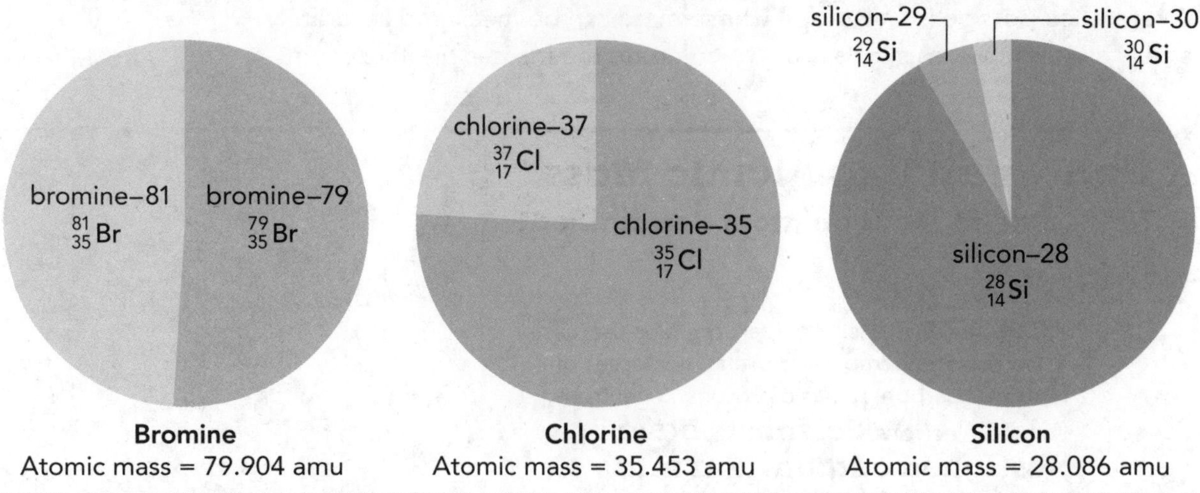

Bromine
Atomic mass = 79.904 amu

Chlorine
Atomic mass = 35.453 amu

Silicon
Atomic mass = 28.086 amu

9 SEP Analyze Data Look at the graphs. How does an element's atomic mass compare to the mass number of its most abundant isotope?

....

....

The **average atomic mass,** or atomic mass for short, of an element is a weighted average of the masses of its isotopes. A weighted average mass reflects the masses and the relative abundances of the isotopes as they occur in nature.

10 SEP Use Computational Thinking Copper has two isotopes, copper-63 and copper-65. It has an atomic mass of 63.546 amu. Sketch a pie graph that shows the approximate abundance of each copper isotope based on the atomic mass.

Calculating Atomic Mass Isotopes that are more common in nature have greater importance in atomic mass calculations—just like tests may be assigned greater importance in calculating your final grade. To calculate the atomic mass of an element, multiply the mass of each isotope by its natural abundance, expressed as a decimal, and then add the products. The resulting sum is the weighted average mass of the atoms of the element as they occur in nature.

Class Grade Teachers sometimes assign different weights to different types of assignments when calculating your class grade.

First, the teacher determines the types of assignments and assigns each type a weight based on its relative importance.

Assignment Type	Weight		Score		Weighted Score
Homework	20%	×	85	=	17.0
Tests	50%	×	75	=	37.5
Labs	30%	×	90	=	27.0
Total:	**100%**			**Total:**	**81.5**

As assignments are completed, the weights are used to calculate a student's class grade.

Atomic Mass Atomic mass is calculated similarly. You can even set it up in the same table format, if you wish. Here's how to calculate the atomic mass of magnesium.

The percent abundance is like the weight in the class grade table. It's the multiplier factor. The sum of the percent abundances should always be 100%.

Isotope	Percent Abundance		Mass (amu)		Mass Contribution
magnesium-24	79%	×	24	=	19.0
magnesium-25	10%	×	25	=	2.5
magnesium-26	11%	×	26	=	2.9
Total:	**100%**			**Total:**	**24.4**

The mass contribution of each isotope is like the weighted score. Add all the contributions to find the atomic mass. It should always be closer to the mass of the most abundant isotope—in this case, 24 amu.

(11) **Compare In what ways are final grade calculations and atomic mass calculations similar?**

....

....

SAMPLE PROBLEM

Atomic Mass Estimations

Element X has two naturally occurring isotopes. The isotope with a mass of 10 amu (^{10}X) has a relative abundance of 20 percent. The isotope with a mass of 11 amu (^{11}X) has a relative abundance of 80 percent. What is the atomic mass of element X?

ANALYZE List the knowns and the unknown.

Knowns	Unknown
mass of ^{10}X = 10 amu	atomic mass of X = ? amu
relative abundance of ^{10}X = 20%	
mass of ^{11}X = 11 amu	
relative abundance of ^{11}X = 80%	

CALCULATE Solve for the unknown.

Use the mass and the decimal form of the percent abundance to find the mass contributed by each isotope.

for ^{10}X: 10 amu × 0.20 = 2.0 amu
for ^{11}X: 11 amu × 0.80 = 8.8 amu

Add the atomic mass contributions for the two isotopes.

atomic mass of X = 2.0 amu + 8.8 amu = 10.8 amu

EVALUATE Does the result make sense?

The calculated value is closer to the mass of the more abundant isotope, as would be expected.

(12) **Use the information in the table to estimate the atomic masses for carbon and bromine, and record your answers in the table.**

Natural Percent Abundance of Stable Isotopes of Some Elements

Name	Symbol	Natural percent abundance	Mass (amu)	Atomic mass
Hydrogen	$^{1}_{1}H$ $^{2}_{1}H$ $^{3}_{1}H$	99.985 0.015 negligible	1.0078 2.0141 3.0160	~1
Helium	$^{3}_{2}He$ $^{4}_{2}He$	0.0001 99.9999	3.0160 4.0026	~4
Carbon	$^{12}_{6}C$ $^{13}_{6}C$	98.89 1.11	12.000 13.003	
Nitrogen	$^{14}_{7}N$ $^{15}_{7}N$	99.63 0.37	14.003 15.000	~14
Bromine	$^{79}_{35}Br$ $^{81}_{35}Br$	50.69 49.31	78.92 80.92	

GO ONLINE for more practice problems.

Using Atomic Mass The periodic table shown earlier in this experience is a simplified version. Reference periodic tables usually include additional information such as an element's atomic mass. However, the mass number is not included. The atomic mass, not mass number, is used in most scientific calculations.

13 **Compare and Contrast** **How does an element's atomic mass differ from its mass number?**

....

....

....

Revisit

INVESTIGATIVE PHENOMENON

GO ONLINE to Elaborate on and Evaluate your knowledge of the makeup of atoms and atomic mass calculations by completing the class discussion and data analysis activities.

In the modeling worksheet you completed at the beginning of the investigation, you sketched a model to help explain the color generation of different fireworks. With a partner, evaluate your models.

14 **SEP Evaluate Models** **How can you revise your models to be more accurate, given what you learned in this experience?**

....

....

....

....

EXPERIENCE 2

Atomic Emission Spectra and the Bohr Model

GO ONLINE to Explore and Explain the Bohr model of the atom and the atomic emission spectra of elements.

Atomic Emission Spectra

Emission Spectra When an element absorbs energy in a gaseous state, electrons become excited and the atom becomes unstable. When the electrons release energy, the atom can emit light. The light an element emits is composed of specific wavelengths of light. The **atomic emission spectrum** is the pattern formed when light emitted by an element is separated into the different wavelengths it contains. Differing wavelengths, or distances between crests of waves, of light result in different colors of light.

Separating Colors A spectroscope is a tool that uses a prism to separate light into its individual colors. Each color of light has a characteristic wavelength. A spectroscope shows different outputs for different inputs.

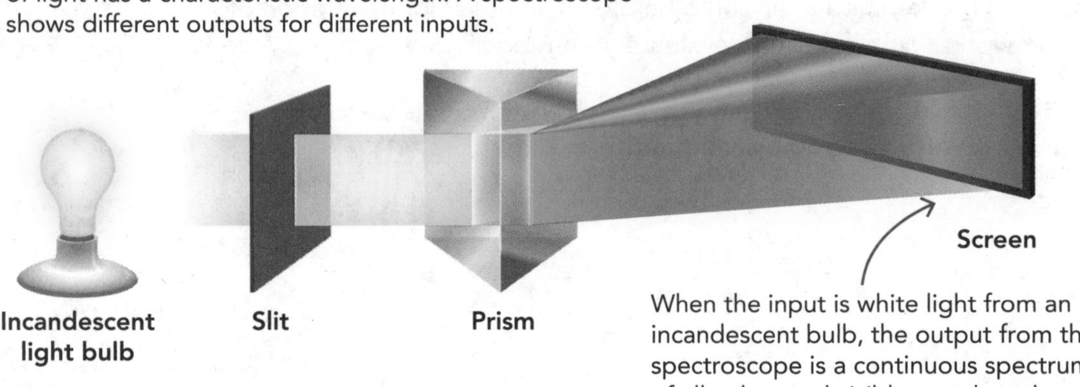

When the input is white light from an incandescent bulb, the output from the spectroscope is a continuous spectrum of all colors and visible wavelengths.

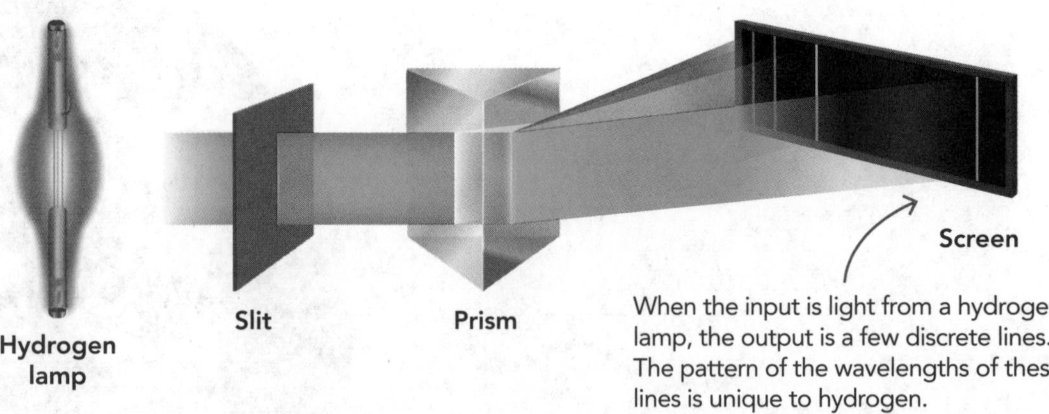

When the input is light from a hydrogen lamp, the output is a few discrete lines. The pattern of the wavelengths of these lines is unique to hydrogen.

Elemental Fingerprints Each element emits specific colors of light that correspond to specific wavelengths. The atomic emission spectrum of each element is like a person's fingerprint. No two elements have the same atomic emission spectrum. Furthermore, no matter where a sample of a given element is collected, the spectrum will be the same.

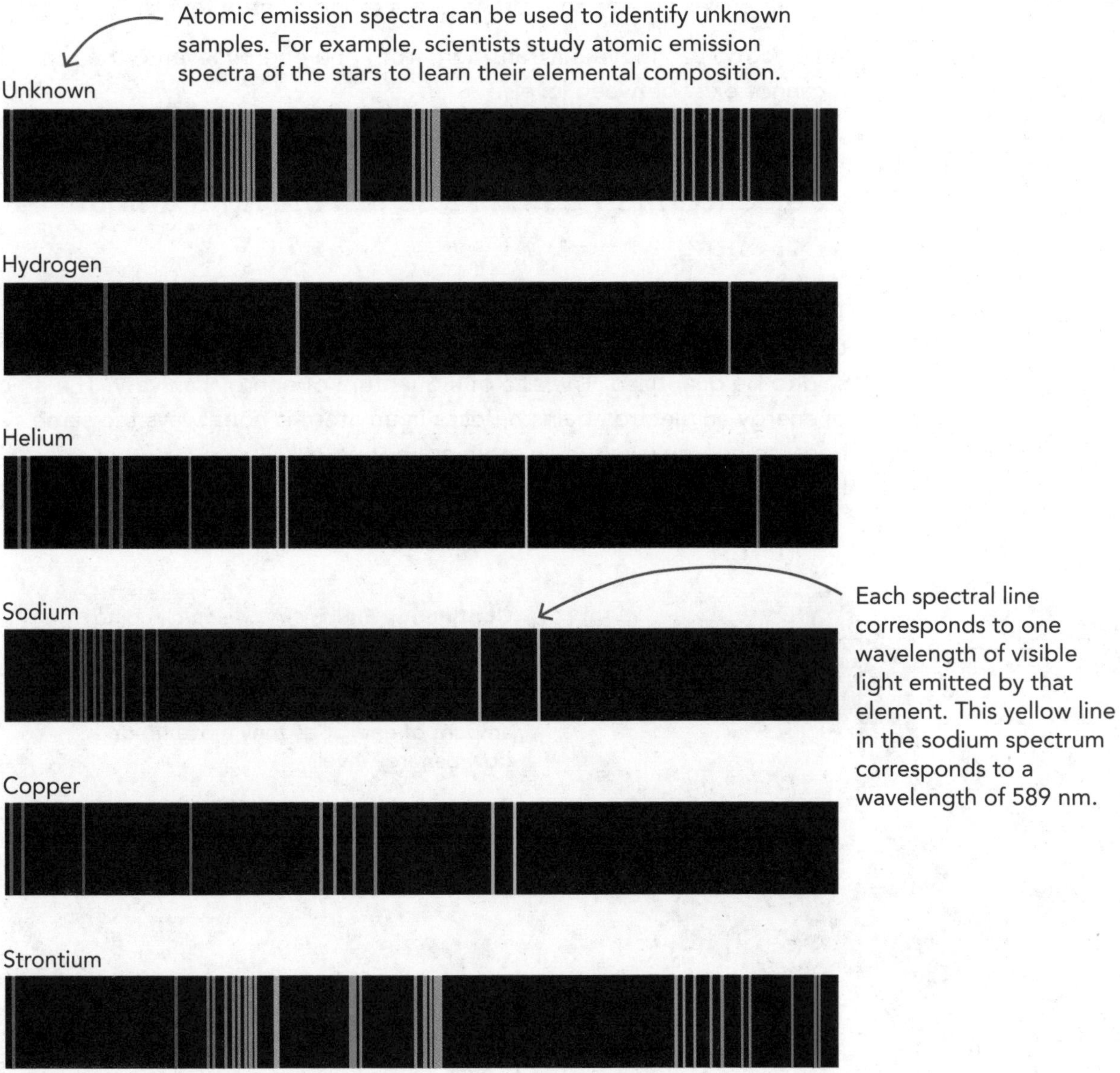

Atomic emission spectra can be used to identify unknown samples. For example, scientists study atomic emission spectra of the stars to learn their elemental composition.

Unknown

Hydrogen

Helium

Sodium

Each spectral line corresponds to one wavelength of visible light emitted by that element. This yellow line in the sodium spectrum corresponds to a wavelength of 589 nm.

Copper

Strontium

15 **SEP Analyze Data What is the identity of the element that produced the unknown emission spectrum and what information does the spectrum give about the source of the element? Explain your answer.**

The Bohr Model

Energy Levels in Atoms In 1913, Niels Bohr, a young Danish physicist, proposed an atomic model that described electrons as moving in circular orbits around the nucleus. Each orbit in his model has a fixed energy. The fixed energies an electron can have are called **energy levels.**

An electron can move, or transition, from one energy level to the other, but it cannot exist between levels.

To move from one energy level to another, an electron must gain or lose just the right amount of energy.

The amount of energy required to move an electron from one energy level to another is a **quantum** of energy. This is why the energy of an electron is said to be quantized. The size of a quantum of energy can vary. The amount of energy an electron gains or loses in an atom is not always the same because energy levels in an atom are not equally spaced. Higher energy levels are closer together than lower energy levels.

Continuous Energy A person climbing a ramp can take big or small steps. If energy levels in atoms were continuous, electrons could absorb or give off any amount of energy as they move up or down energy levels.

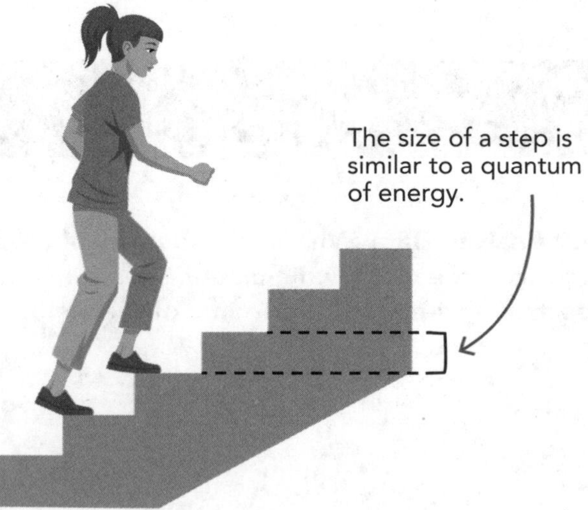

The size of a step is similar to a quantum of energy.

Quantized Energy A person climbing stairs can only take a certain sized step to move up or down the stairs. The size of the step is quantized. Similarly, electrons must absorb or give off a certain amount of energy to move between energy levels.

Explaining Emission Spectra Bohr's model predicted the specific frequencies of light of the atomic emission spectrum of hydrogen. Each line of a specific frequency in the spectrum corresponds to a specific electron transition.

Understanding Bohr's Atomic Model

Why do hydrogen **atoms emit specific wavelengths of light** according to Bohr's model?

The Bohr Model Bohr developed his atomic model to explain the hydrogen emission spectrum. His model could not explain the emission spectra of other elements because electrons do not move in circular paths, as he thought.

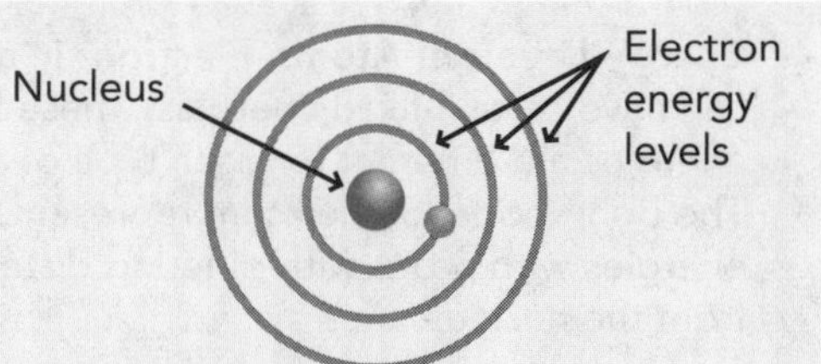

Ground State The electron is in the **lowest possible energy level.**

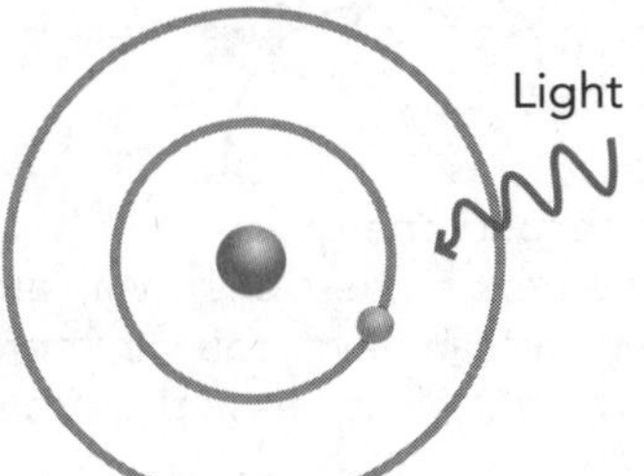

An atom absorbs a specific amount of energy, causing the electron to jump to a higher energy level.

Excited State The electron has gained energy and is in a **higher energy level.**

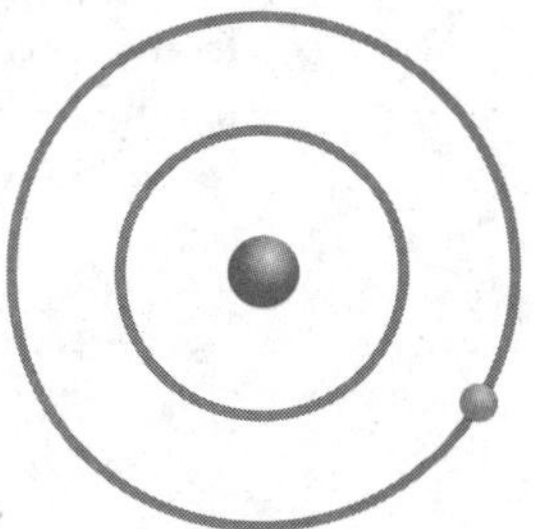

The atom emits a specific amount of energy as the electron returns to a lower energy level.

Emission Spectrum Lines Hydrogen atoms absorb or emit light with an energy exactly equal to the energy difference between energy levels in the atom. **Each spectral line has a specific wavelength and is for one electron transition to a lower energy level.**

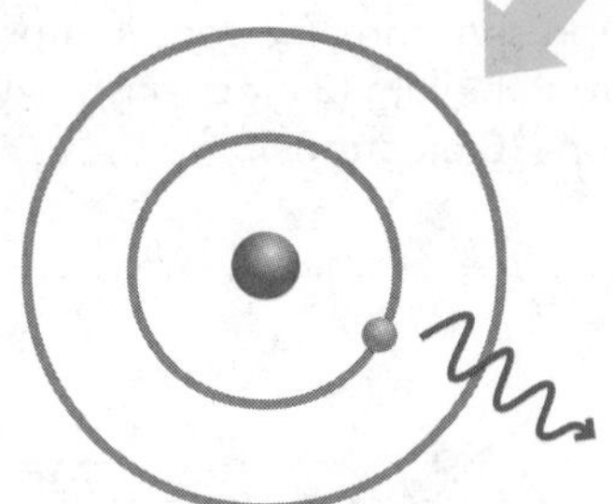

16 **CCC Matter and Energy** Each color of light has a specific amount of energy. A hydrogen atom will absorb and emit red, blue-green, blue, and violet light but not yellow or orange light. Explain this phenomenon.

....

....

....

....

Bohr Model Representations of Atoms

The Bohr model, proposed in 1913, is not completely correct. Scientists have since learned more about the atom's structure through experiments and calculations. However, many people continue to use the Bohr model today for a few reasons. The Bohr model is a simplified picture of an atom with many features that are nearly correct. Additionally, many important properties of atoms can be exemplified using this model.

Energy Levels in Atoms Electrons in atoms can have certain fixed energies. These fixed energies are different for each type of atom. The Bohr model of the atom represents these energies with orbits with differing distances from the nucleus.

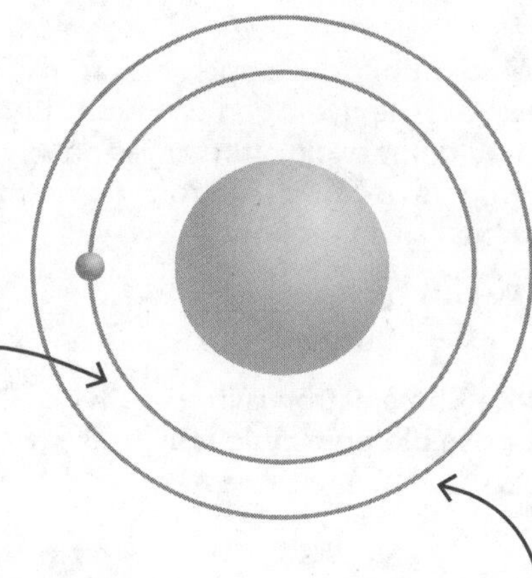

The innermost orbit corresponds to the lowest energy an electron can have. You can represent up to two electrons in this orbit.

The second energy level corresponds to the next highest energy an atom's electrons can have. You can represent up to eight electrons in this orbit.

Bohr Models for Some Atoms These Bohr models show how you can represent the electrons in atoms of hydrogen (1 electron), helium (2 electrons), oxygen (8 electrons), and neon (10 electrons).

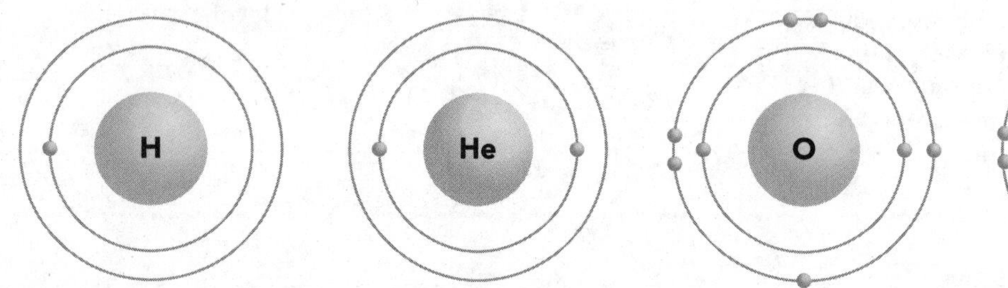

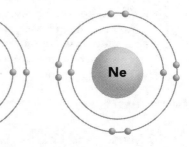

(17) **CCC Patterns A fluorine atom has 9 electrons. Draw the Bohr model for fluorine using the pattern you observe for the Bohr models for hydrogen, helium, oxygen, and neon.**

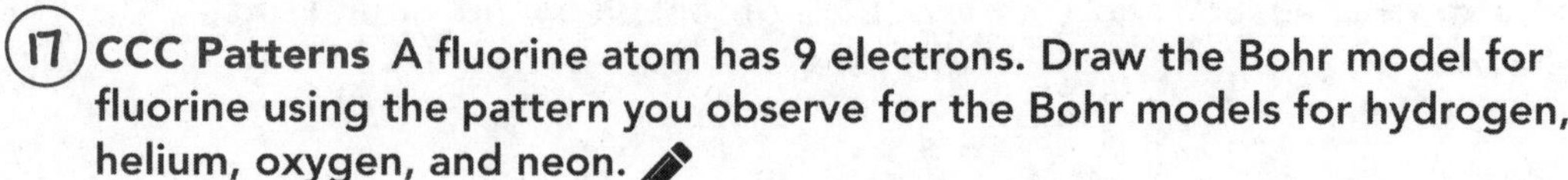

Revisit

INVESTIGATIVE PHENOMENON

GO ONLINE to Elaborate on and Evaluate your knowledge of atomic emission spectra by completing the class discussion and engineering design activities.

In the modeling worksheet you completed at the beginning of the investigation, you sketched a model to help explain the color generation of different fireworks. With a partner, evaluate your models.

18 **SEP Construct an Explanation** **Compare and contrast the colors and wavelengths of the light emitted from two different colors of fireworks, based on the elements they contain. Explain why these elements have different atomic emission spectra.**

EXPERIENCE 3

Modern Atomic Theory

GO ONLINE to Explore and Explain the modern model of the atom.

Revising the Atomic Model

The Quantum Mechanical Model In 1926, Erwin Schrödinger proposed and solved a mathematical equation that describes the behavior of the electron in a hydrogen atom. This modern description of electrons in atoms, called the **quantum mechanical model,** came from the solutions to the Schrödinger equation.

The quantum mechanical model is similar to the Bohr model in that the energies of electrons are restricted to certain values. The quantum mechanical model, however, does not specify an exact path for electrons moving around the nucleus. For each energy level, the Schrödinger equation defines a region of space, called an **atomic orbital,** where there is a high probability of finding an electron.

Electron Locations The modern model of the atom uses three-dimensional atomic orbitals to describe the probable locations of electrons around the nucleus.

When you watch a flying hummingbird, you can't pinpoint the exact location of a wing at any instant. The wing has some probability of being anywhere in the blurry region. Similarly, scientists represent the likely locations of electrons in an atom with a fuzzy cloudlike region.

This representation of the atom is called an electron cloud model. The dots in the cloud are more dense where the probability of finding an electron is high and less dense where the probability is low.

The Shell Model The shell model of the atom is a simplified version of the quantum mechanical model. It describes the main electron energy levels, called principal energy levels, as shells. Each principal energy level has a different number of sublevels, or subshells.

Shell Model Explained

What is included in **the shell model** of the atom?

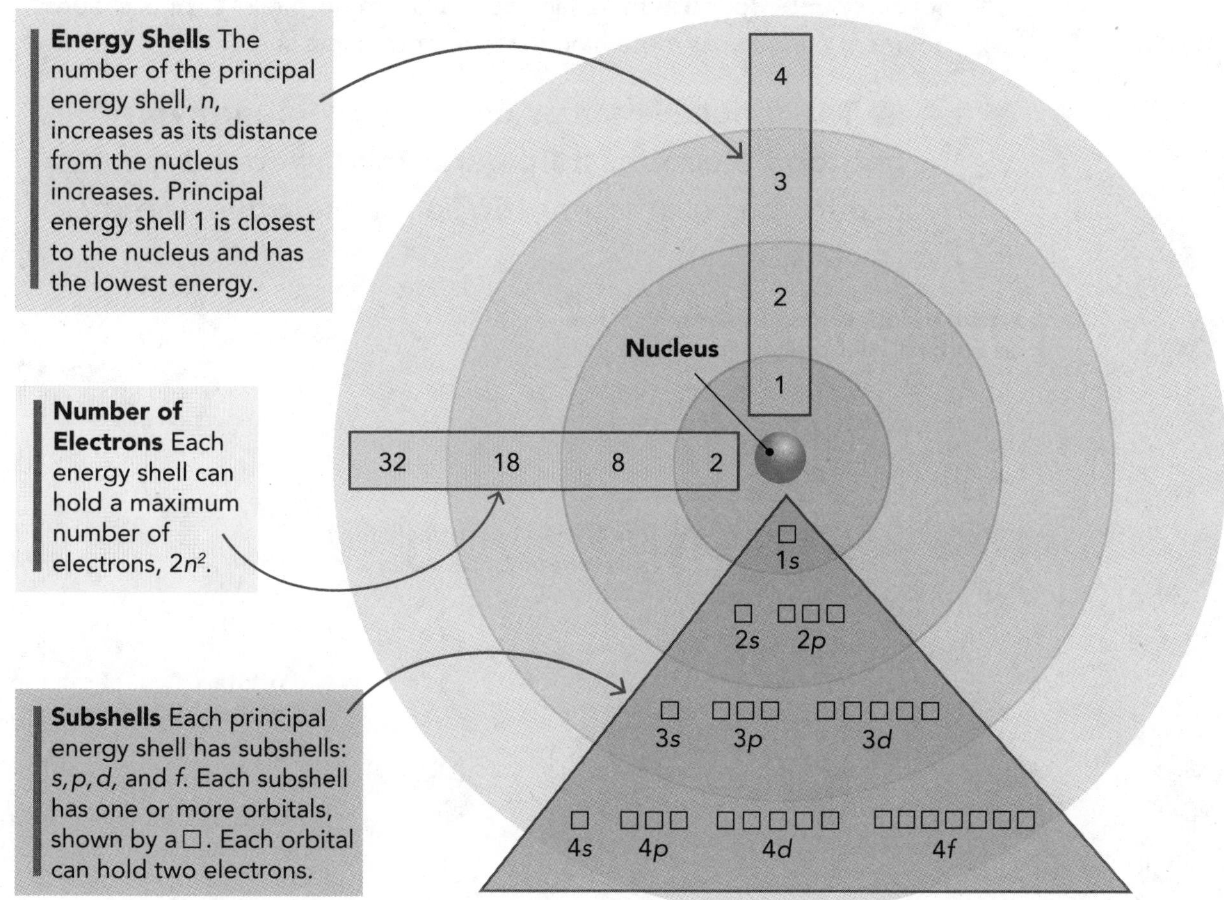

Energy Shells The number of the principal energy shell, *n*, increases as its distance from the nucleus increases. Principal energy shell 1 is closest to the nucleus and has the lowest energy.
4
3
2
1
Nucleus
Number of Electrons Each energy shell can hold a maximum number of electrons, $2n^2$.
32
18
8
2
Subshells Each principal energy shell has subshells: *s, p, d,* and *f*. Each subshell has one or more orbitals, shown by a □. Each orbital can hold two electrons.
1s
2s 2p
3s 3p 3d
4s 4p 4d 4f

Each shell has a certain number of subshells.

Principal Shell	1	2	3	4
Subshells	1*s*	2*s*, 2*p*	3*s*, 3*p* 3*d*	4*s*, 4*p* 4*d*, 4*f*

Each subshell has a specific number of orbitals.

Subshell	*s*	*p*	*d*	*f*
Number of Orbitals	1	3	5	7

19 **SEP Use Models Why does the number of electrons in each principal energy shell increase as the number of the shell increases?**

Atomic Orbitals

Shapes of Orbitals Atomic orbitals in an atom are denoted by the letters *s*, *p*, *d*, and *f*. Each shell has one *s* orbital. It is spherical because the probability of finding an electron at a given distance from the nucleus does not depend on direction. All shells, except the first one, have three *p* orbitals, which are dumbbell-shaped. There is a probability of finding an electron anywhere inside the dumbbell-shaped orbitals, but electrons are not likely to be found in the space outside of the orbitals. Orbital shapes get more complex as more electrons are added in a shell.

The repulsive forces between the negatively charged electrons help explain why each type of orbital has a different shape and relative energy.

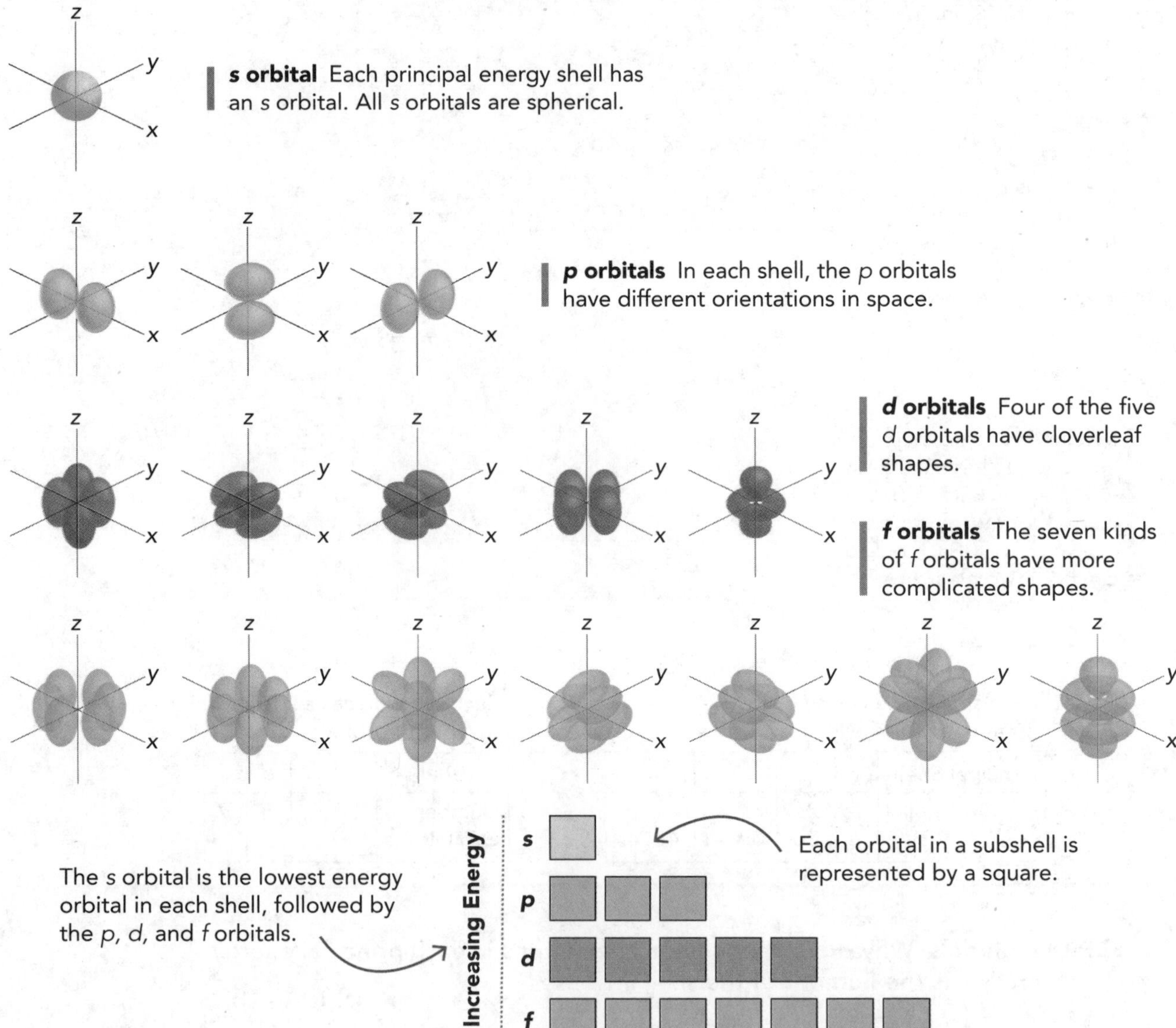

s orbital Each principal energy shell has an *s* orbital. All *s* orbitals are spherical.

***p* orbitals** In each shell, the *p* orbitals have different orientations in space.

***d* orbitals** Four of the five *d* orbitals have cloverleaf shapes.

***f* orbitals** The seven kinds of *f* orbitals have more complicated shapes.

Each orbital in a subshell is represented by a square.

The *s* orbital is the lowest energy orbital in each shell, followed by the *p*, *d*, and *f* orbitals.

Overlapping Orbitals The individual atomic orbitals in an atom overlap in three-dimensional space.

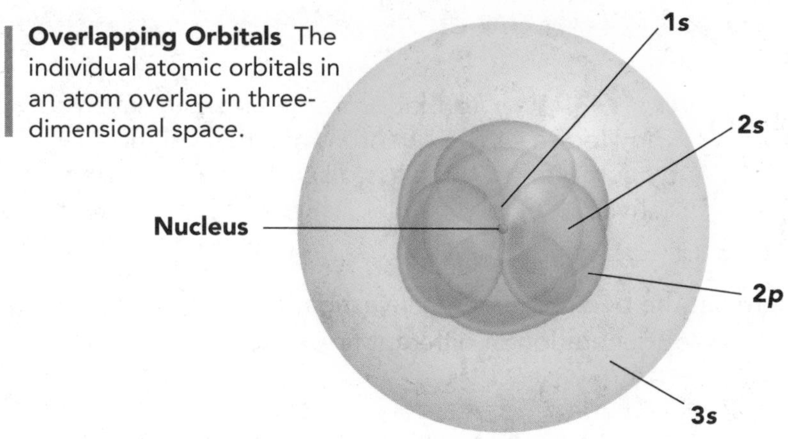

Orbitals in a Magnesium Atom A magnesium atom has 12 electrons that are found in the 1*s*, 2*s*, 2*p*, and 3*s* subshells. The 1*s* orbital is the closest to the nucleus, while the 3*s* orbital is the farthest away.

Relative Energies of Subshells In a given shell, the orbitals in each subshell have the same energy. For example, the three *p* orbitals all have the same energy. Within a given shell, the order of subshells from lowest to highest energy is $s < p < d < f$. However, the subshells within a shell can overlap with the subshells of another shell.

Subshell Energies Subshells have different energies because the electrons in an atom repel each other. Electrons populate the lowest possible energy subshells first. The zigzag line shows how energy increases from one subshell to the next.

Within a subshell, the orbitals have the same energy. All three 2*p* orbitals have the same energy. They have more energy than the 2*s* orbital, but they have less energy than the 3*s* orbital.

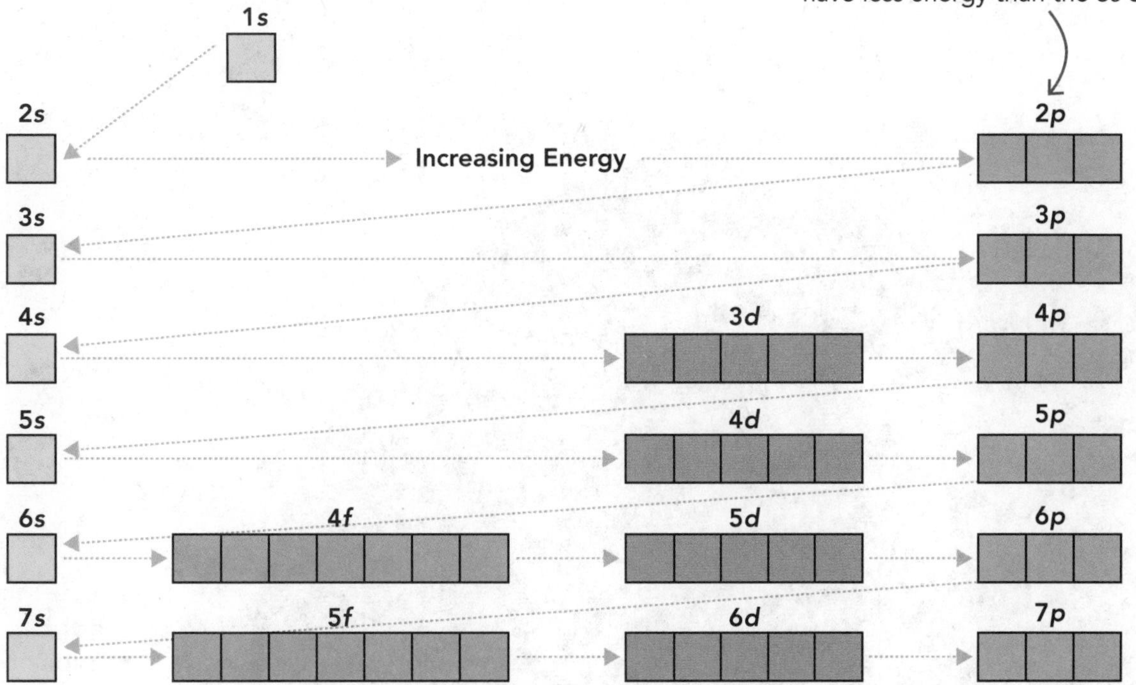

20 SEP Use Models List the subshells that hold the 25 electrons in a manganese atom in order of increasing energy.

....

Revisit

INVESTIGATIVE PHENOMENON

GO ONLINE to Elaborate on and Evaluate your knowledge of the quantum mechanical model by completing the class discussion and writing activities.

In the modeling worksheet you completed at the beginning of the investigation, you sketched a model to help explain the color generation of different fireworks. With a partner, evaluate your models.

(21) **SEP Revise an Explanation** **Rather than saying the electrons transition between energy levels to produce the colors in fireworks, how might you refine this description using your new knowledge of the quantum mechanical model? What does this tell you about the energies of the orbitals?**

EXPERIENCE 4

Electrons in Atoms

GO ONLINE to Explore and Explain electron configurations of atoms.

Electron Configurations

The ways in which electrons are arranged in various orbitals around the nuclei of atoms are called **electron configurations.** The table shows the electron configurations of the first eleven elements on the periodic table. Notice the order in which the 1*s*, 2*s*, and 2*p* orbitals are filled.

Filling Orbitals Both the orbital diagrams and written electron configurations show how electrons are arranged in the subshells with the lowest possible energy.

The number of electrons equals the atomic number of the element.

Each arrow represents an electron.

An electron configuration lists the orbitals that have electrons.

Electron Configuration Examples

Element	Number of electrons	Orbital diagram 1*s*	2*s*	2*p*			3*s*	Electron configuration
H	1	↑						$1s^1$
He	2	↑↓						$1s^2$
Li	3	↑↓	↑					$1s^22s^1$
Be	4	↑↓	↑↓					$1s^22s^2$
B	5	↑↓	↑↓	↑				$1s^22s^22p^1$
C	6	↑↓	↑↓	↑	↑			$1s^22s^22p^2$
N	7	↑↓	↑↓	↑	↑	↑		$1s^22s^22p^3$
O	8	↑↓	↑↓	↑↓	↑	↑		$1s^22s^22p^4$
F	9	↑↓	↑↓	↑↓	↑↓	↑		$1s^22s^22p^5$
Ne	10	↑↓	↑↓	↑↓	↑↓	↑↓		$1s^22s^22p^6$
Na	11	↑↓	↑↓	↑↓	↑↓	↑↓	↑	$1s^22s^22p^63s^1$

Each subshell is represented by a coefficient and letter, for example, 1*s*.

A superscript represents the number of electrons in each subshell. For example, the 1*s* orbital has 2 electrons in it.

Electrons pair only after each subshell is half full.

Energy and Stability in Electron Configurations

Role of Energy in Orbital Filling Energy plays an important role in determining how electrons are arranged, or configured, in an atom. Electrons occupy the lowest energy subshells first. That is why the 1*s* orbital is always filled before the 2*s* orbital. Once the 2*s* subshell is filled, electrons are added to the three 2*p* orbitals. These three orbitals are of equal energy. In subshells with more than one orbital, one electron occupies each orbital before two electrons pair up in an orbital. To occupy the same orbital, two electrons must have opposite spins; that is, the electron spins must be paired. **Spin** is a property of electrons that may be thought of as clockwise (spin-up) or counterclockwise (spin-down) orientation. A vertical arrow indicates an electron and its spin orientation.

Writing Electron Configurations

How do you **write an electron configuration?**

Step 1 Use the atomic number to determine the number of electrons, which is equal to the number of protons.

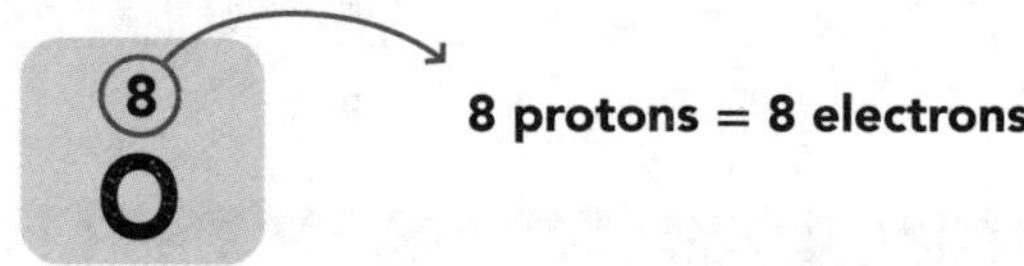

Step 2 Fill in the subshells with arrows to represent the 8 electrons.

List the subshells in order of **lowest to highest energy.** Use the diagram of how subshell energy increases as a guide. → 1s [ ] 2s [ ] 2p [ ][ ][ ]

Each orbital can hold a **maximum of two electrons.** → 1s [||] 2s [||] 2p [ ][ ][ ]

Pairs of electrons have **opposite spins,** written as arrows pointing in opposite directions. → 1s [↑↓] 2s [↑↓] 2p [ ][ ][ ]

Each orbital in a subshell **needs one electron before electrons are paired.** → 1s [↑↓] 2s [↑↓] 2p [↑↓][↑][↑]

Step 3 Write the electron configuration.

List subshells in order of lowest to highest energy. → **1s 2s 2p**

Write the number of electrons in each subshell as a superscript. → $1s^2 2s^2 2p^4$

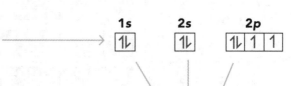

Energy and Stability If the yogi were to fall to the ground, he would have less energy, but his new position would be more stable. Similarly, atoms are more stable when the electrons are in the lowest energy orbitals.

Role of Stability in Orbital Filling Stability is also important in determining how electrons are configured in an atom. Unstable arrangements tend to become more stable by losing energy. This is why the lowest energy orbitals are filled first. The concept of stability also helps explain why one electron occupies each orbital of equal energy, for example the three *p* orbitals, before two electrons pair up in an orbital. Electrons repel one another; thus it is more stable to have only one electron in each orbital. An electron behaves similar to a tiny magnet with a north and south pole. When two electrons must exist in the same orbital, an opposite-spin arrangement allows them to gain stability because the magnetic attraction of the opposite poles cancels out some of the electric repulsion.

In an atom, electrons and the nucleus interact to make the most stable arrangement. An electron configuration shows this arrangement.

(22) **Apply Concepts** Use the concepts of energy and stability as they relate to orbital filling to write the electron configuration for iron.

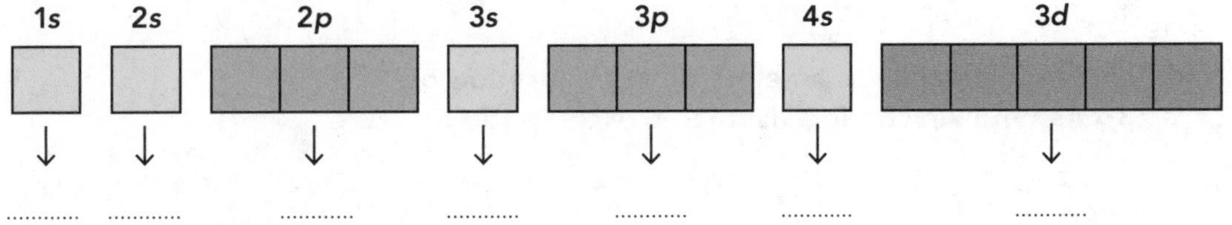

Patterns in Electron Configurations

Blocks of Elements in the Periodic Table The periodic table shows a pattern in electron configurations and is divided into blocks based on the highest occupied sublevels. The two groups on the left are in the *s* block because the highest energy electrons are in an *s* orbital in atoms of these elements. The groups on the far right are in the *p* block, while the middle groups are the *d* and *f* blocks. Because of the regular pattern in the way sublevels are filled, you can use the periodic table to help you write electron configurations.

The *s*, *p*, *d*, and *f* Blocks Elements in each block of the periodic table have their highest energy electrons in that subshell.

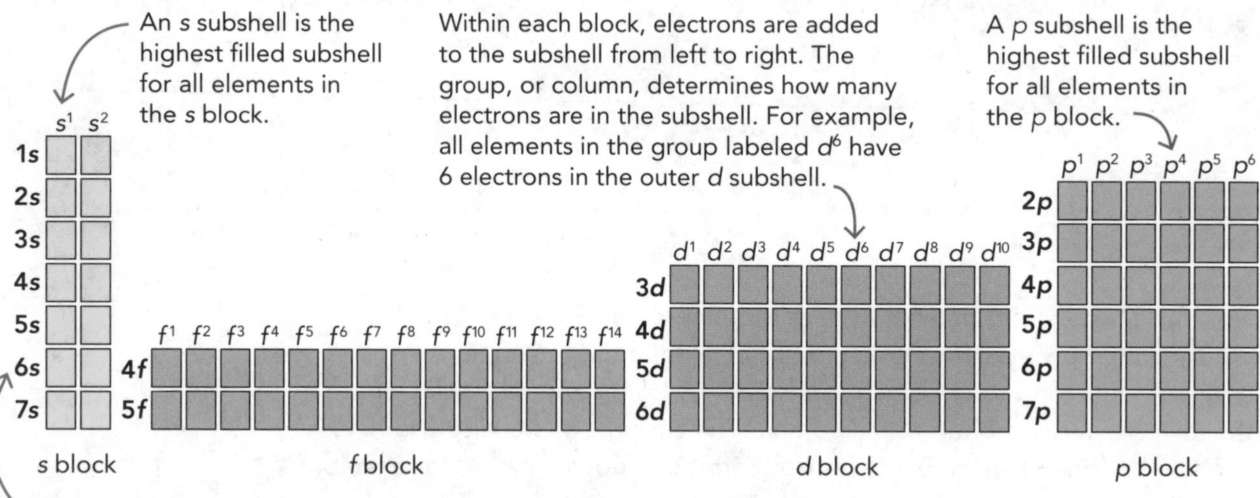
An s subshell is the highest filled subshell for all elements in the s block.
Within each block, electrons are added to the subshell from left to right. The group, or column, determines how many electrons are in the subshell. For example, all elements in the group labeled d6 have 6 electrons in the outer d subshell.
A p subshell is the highest filled subshell for all elements in the p block.
s1 s2
1s 2s 3s 4s 5s 6s 7s
f1 f2 f3 f4 f5 f6 f7 f8 f9 f10 f11 f12 f13 f14
4f 5f
d1 d2 d3 d4 d5 d6 d7 d8 d9 d10
3d 4d 5d 6d
p1 p2 p3 p4 p5 p6
2p 3p 4p 5p 6p 7p
s block
f block
d block
p block
The period, or row, number is the value of the principal energy shell, n. In Period 6, the principal energy shell for the s and p orbitals is 6.

Exceptions to Electron Configuration Rules Some actual electron configurations, such as those of chromium (Cr) and copper (Cu), differ from those that would be expected because they are more stable.

	Expected configuration	Actual configuration
Cr	$1s^22s^22p^63s^23p^63d^44s^2$	$1s^22s^22p^63s^23p^63d^54s^1$
Cu	$1s^22s^22p^63s^23p^63d^94s^2$	$1s^22s^22p^63s^23p^63d^{10}4s^1$

The actual configurations give chromium a half-filled *d* sublevel and copper a filled *d* sublevel. Filled energy sublevels are more stable than partially filled sublevels. Half-filled sublevels are less stable than filled sublevels but are more stable than other configurations.

23 CCC Patterns What element has an electron configuration of $1s^22s^22p^63s^23p^64s^2$ and which block is it in? Use the periodic table.

....

SAMPLE PROBLEM

Electron Configurations

The atomic number of the element osmium (Os) is 76. It is in the 6th period and has 6 electrons in its *d* subshell, its highest subshell. Write the full electron configuration of osmium so that all the subshells in each principal energy shell are grouped together.

ANALYZE Identify the relevant concepts.

The total number of electrons equals the atomic number. Electrons occupy the lowest energy sublevel first. Each sublevel can hold a specific number of electrons. All of the sublevels in the period above the element in the periodic table are full. The number of the principal energy level for the *s* and *p* subshells is equal to the period number. Period 6 also has the 4*f* and 5*d* subshells, and Periods 4 and 5 have the 3*d* and 4*d* subshells, respectively.

SOLVE Apply the concepts to this problem.

Determine the period and highest subshell.

Osmium is in the 6th period and the highest subshell is 5*d*.

Write the configurations for the full subshells in the first five periods in order of increasing energy.

Period 1: $1s^2$
Period 2: $2s^22p^6$
Period 3: $3s^23p^6$
Period 4: $4s^23d^{10}4p^6$
Period 5: $5s^24d^{10}5p^6$

Write the configuration for the 6th period, stopping when you have added 6 electrons to the highest sublevel.

Period 6: $6s^24f^{14}5d^6$

Finally, write the complete configuration so that all the subshells in each principal energy shell are grouped together.

$1s^22s^22p^63s^23p^63d^{10}4s^24p^64d^{10}4f^{14}5s^25p^65d^66s^2$

24 **Using a periodic table, write the full electron configuration of bromine (Br) so that all the subshells in each principal energy shell are grouped together.**

GO ONLINE for more practice problems.

Noble Gas Configurations Electron configurations can get quite long. It is convenient to write them using a noble gas to represent the core electrons. Core electrons are electrons in all the inner, or lower energy, shells. **Valence electrons** are electrons in the outermost energy shell. In all elements, the subshells for the core electrons are full. In noble gases, the subshells in the valence shell are also full. Their electron configurations are the same as the electron configuration of the core electrons in the elements in the row below them in the periodic table.

Writing Noble Gas Configurations

How do you **simplify electron configurations** using the periodic table?

Noble Gases The last group of elements in the periodic table have full subshells. These elements are called the noble gases.

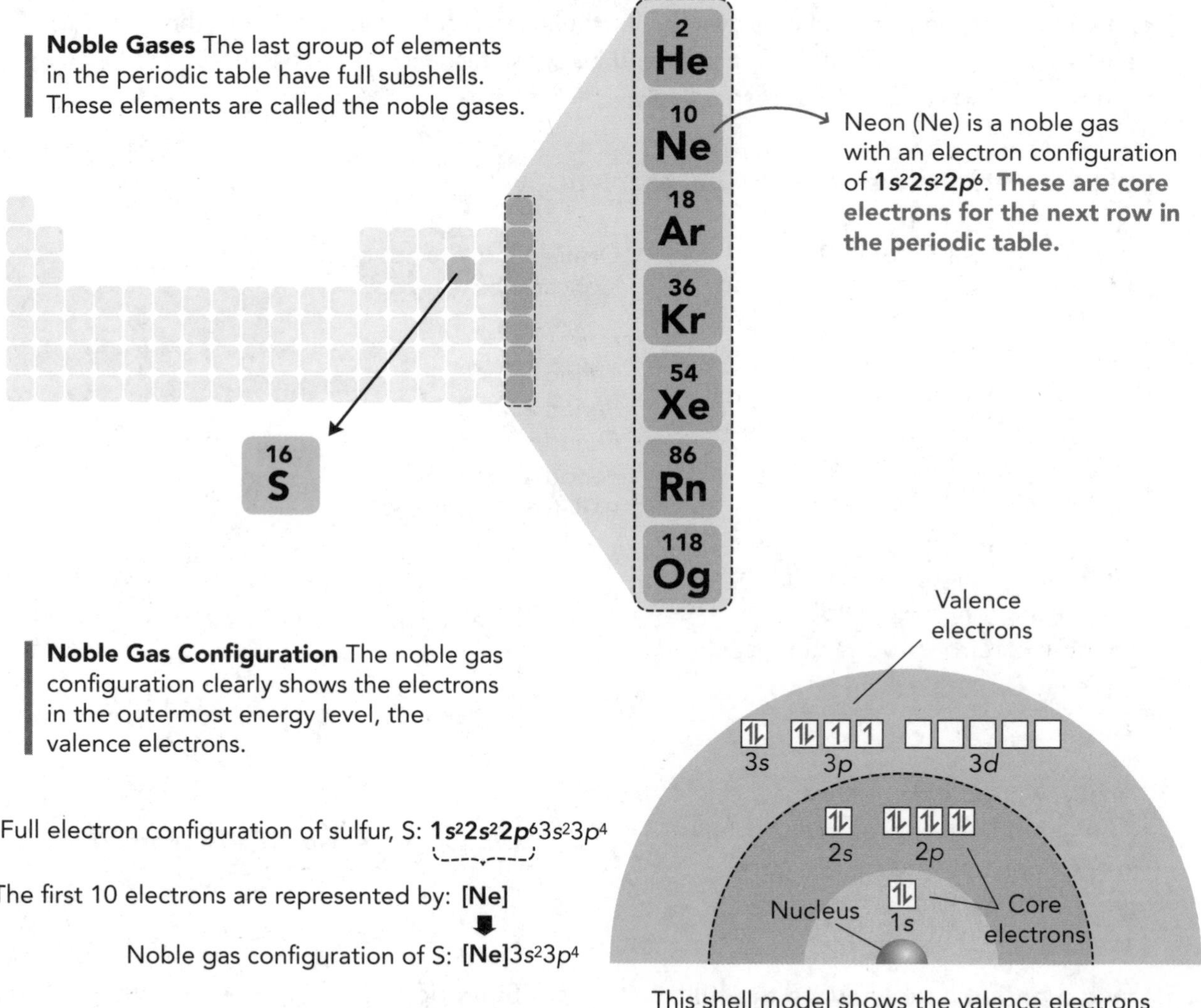

Noble Gas Configuration The noble gas configuration clearly shows the electrons in the outermost energy level, the valence electrons.

Full electron configuration of sulfur, S: $1s^2 2s^2 2p^6 3s^2 3p^4$

The first 10 electrons are represented by: **[Ne]**

Noble gas configuration of S: **[Ne]**$3s^2 3p^4$

This shell model shows the valence electrons and core electrons in a sulfur atom.

(25) **Apply Concepts** Use the periodic table to write the noble gas configuration for strontium (Sr).

....

Valence Electrons

Noble gas configurations are useful because they help differentiate the valence electrons in an atom. Valence electrons determine many of an atom's physical and chemical properties.

Electron dot structures are simple diagrams that show the number of valence electrons, represented as dots around the element symbol. Elements in the same group have the same number of electron dots because they have the same number of valence electrons. For example, carbon and silicon both have four dots in their electron dot structures.

Noble Gas Configurations and Electron Dot Structures for Period 3 Elements

Group	1	2	13	14	15	16	17	18
Element	11 **Na** Sodium	12 **Mg** Magnesium	13 **Al** Aluminum	14 **Si** Silicon	15 **P** Phosphorus	16 **S** Sulfur	17 **Cl** Chlorine	18 **Ar** Argon
Noble gas configuration	$[Ne]3s^1$	$[Ne]3s^2$	$[Ne]3s^23p^1$	$[Ne]3s^23p^2$	$[Ne]3s^23p^3$	$[Ne]3s^23p^4$	$[Ne]3s^23p^5$	$[Ne]3s^23p^6$
Number of valence electrons	1	2	3	4	5	6	7	8
Electron dot structure	Na •	• Mg •	• Al • (1 dot above)	• Si • (1 dot above, 1 below)	• P • (2 dots above, 1 below)	: S • (2 dots above, 1 below)	: Cl • (2 dots above, 2 below)	: Ar : (2 dots above, 2 below)

The number of dots around an element's symbol indicates the number of valence electrons. For example, silicon has 4 electrons.

Adding the superscripts in the noble gas configuration gives the number of valence electrons. For example, argon has 8 valence electrons (2 + 6 = 8).

26 **CCC Patterns Recall that elements above and below each other in the periodic table have similar physical and chemical properties. What do you think might account for these similar properties? Explain.**

....

....

....

....

Revisit

INVESTIGATIVE PHENOMENON

GO ONLINE to Elaborate on and Evaluate your knowledge of electron configurations by completing the peer review and writing activities.

In the modeling worksheet you completed at the beginning of the investigation, you sketched a model to help explain the color generation of different fireworks. With a partner, evaluate your models.

(27) **SEP Construct an Explanation Write the electron configuration for the element responsible for one color of firework. This configuration is the ground state electron configuration. When a valence electron is exicted, this electron configuration changes. Use this information to explain how the valence electrons are involved in emitting this color of light.**

GO ONLINE to Evaluate what you learned about atomic structure by using the available assessment resources.

In the Performance-Based Assessment, you used your observations of the colored light emitted in flame tests to help explain the structure of an atom. Wrap up your explanation by answering these questions.

28 **SEP Construct an Explanation** **The flame test solutions all contain ionic compounds with the same anion—the chloride anion—and they all produce flames with different colors. Why does the chloride anion not contribute to the flame test colors?**

29 **SEP Analyze Data** **Most commercially available emergency flares burn with a red flame. Based on your conclusions in the assessment exercise, what element(s) could be responsible for the red flame? Explain your reasoning.**

30 **Revisit the Anchoring Phenomenon** **How does what you learned in this investigation help explain the chemistry of minerals?**

INVESTIGATIVE PHENOMENON

GO ONLINE to Engage with real-world phenomena by watching a video and to complete a CER interactive worksheet.

Why are elements in pure form so rare?

но въ ней, мнѣ кажется, уже ясно выражается примѣнимость выставляемаго мною начала ко всей совокупности элементовъ, пай которыхъ извѣстенъ съ достовѣрностію. На этотъ разъ я и желалъ преимущественно найдти общую систему элементовъ. Вотъ этотъ опытъ:

			Ti=50	Zr=90	?=180.
			V=51	Nb=94	Ta=182.
			Cr=52	Mo=96	W=186.
			Mn=55	Rh=104,4	Pt=197,4
			Fe=56	Ru=104,4	Ir=198.
			Ni=Co=59	Pl=106,6,	Os=199.
			Cu=63,4	Ag=108	Hg=200.
H=1	Be=9,4	Mg=24	Zn=65,2	Cd=112	
	B=11	Al=27,4	?=68	Ur=116	Au=197?
	C=12	Si=28	?=70	Sn=118	
	N=14	P=31	As=75	Sb=122	Bi=210
	O=16	S=32	Se=79,4	Te=128?	
	F=19	Cl=35,5	Br=80	I=127	
Li=7	Na=23	K=39	Rb=85,4	Cs=133	Tl=204
		Ca=40	Sr=87,6	Ba=137	Pb=207.
		?=45	Ce=92		
		?Er=56	La=94		
		?Yt=60	Di=95		
		?In=75,6	Th=118?		

а потому приходится въ разныхъ рядахъ имѣть различно... числахъ предлагаемой та... системы очень ... ется прит...

The Periodic Table

The image shows a reproduction of Dmitri Mendeleev's 1869 periodic table. The element that is circled is gold, which was commonly used to make coins. Once you have viewed the Investigative Phenomenon video and used the claim-evidence-reasoning worksheet to draft an explanation, answer the following reflection questions about elements and their properties.

1. **CCC Patterns** **Do you see any patterns in how the elements are arranged on Mendeleev's 1869 periodic table? Describe a pattern and provide an example.**

2. **SEP Construct Explanations** **The periodic table has changed considerably since Mendeleev's early versions to today's modern version. What patterns displayed in these earlier versions of the periodic table drove the discovery of new elements? Explain.**

EXPERIENCE 1

The Periodic Table: An Overview

GO ONLINE to Explore and Explain the periodic table and how it was developed according to the periodic law.

Development of the Periodic Table

A few elements, including copper, silver, and gold, have been known for thousands of years. But there were only 13 elements identified by the year 1700. Chemists suspected that other elements existed and they had even assigned names to some of these elements, but they were unable to isolate the elements from their compounds.

In the late 1700s and 1800s scientists began to organize the known elements based on the properties of the elements. Many different scientists across the globe are credited with making contributions to the development of the periodic table. Three of these scientists are German chemist J. W. Dobereiner, English scientist John Newlands, and Russian chemist Dimitri Mendeleev.

Each scientist arranged the elements in different ways but they all used patterns in the properties of elements as a basis for their method of organization.

Using Patterns in Science The phases of the moon form a pattern over time based on the relationship between the moon's position and the positions of the Sun and Earth.

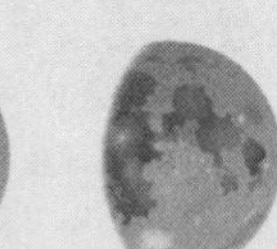

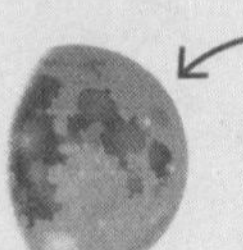

The pattern repeats about every 30 days. You can use the pattern to predict the phase of the moon well into the future.

The Periodic Table of the Elements

How was the periodic table developed?

1820 · 1830 · 1840 · 1850 · 1860 · 1870 · 1880

1829 Dobereiner's Triads Dobereiner arranged elements into groups of three, or triads. He noticed a pattern where the **middle element of a triad tended to have properties that were midway between those of the other two elements.**

Lithium, Li 6.941	Chlorine, Cl 35.453
Sodium, Na 22.990	**Bromine, Br 79.904**
Potassium, K 39.098	Iodine, I 126.90

For example, the average of the atomic masses of chlorine and iodine is 81.18. This is very close to the atomic mass of bromine.

1865 Newlands' Octaves Newlands organized the 56 known elements by atomic weight. He published the law of octaves, proposing that **every eighth element had similar properties to the first.** Newland did not account for elements that had not yet been discovered.

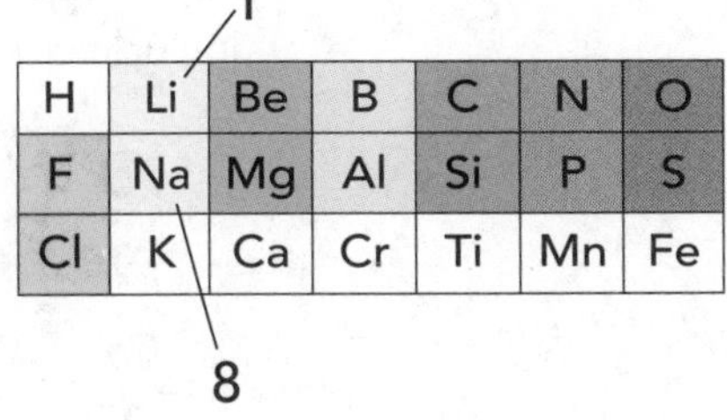

H	Li	Be	B	C	N	O
F	Na	Mg	Al	Si	P	S
Cl	K	Ca	Cr	Ti	Mn	Fe

1869–1871 Mendeleev's Periodic Tables Mendeleev published his first periodic table in 1869 by observing patterns and combining known information, such as Dobereiner's triads and Newlands octaves.

	I	II	III	IV	V	VI	VII	VIII
1	H 1							
2	Li 7	Be 9.4	B 11	C 12	N 14	O 16	F 19	
3	Na 23	Mg 24	Al 27.3	Si 28	P 31	S 32	Cl 35.5	
4	K 39	Ca 40	? 44	Ti 48	V 51	Cr 52	Mn 55	Fe, Co, Ni, Cu 56, 59, 59, 63
5	Cu 63	Zn 65	? 68	? 72	As 75	Se 78	Br 80	

In 1871, Mendeleev rearranged the 1869 table to a format that is similar to what is used today. He **predicted the existence of undiscovered elements** based on gaps in **patterns of properties.** He left spaces for these undiscovered elements in his periodic table.

③ **CCC Patterns How is the process of using patterns to predict phases of the moon similar to the process Mendeleev used to predict undiscovered elements?**

The Modern Periodic Table

Atomic Numbers Mendeleev arranged his periodic table in order of atomic mass. However, in some cases he broke this rule so that elements with similar properties would be in the same group. For example, he placed tellurium (atomic mass of 127.60) before iodine (atomic mass of 126.90) so that iodine could be in the same group as bromine.

Mendeleev developed his table before scientists knew about the structure of the atoms. He didn't know that the atoms of each element have a unique number of protons. Tellurium's atomic number is 52 and iodine's is 53, so it makes sense for tellerium to come before iodine in the periodic table. Atomic numbers clarified the arrangement of elements on the periodic table including Mendeleev's decision to place heavier tellurium ahead of iodine.

In all forms of today's modern periodic table, elements are arranged in order of increasing atomic number.

Each horizontal row of elements in the periodic table is a **period.** The properties of elements change as you move across a period. But the pattern of properties within a period repeat from one period to the next. This pattern gives rise to the **periodic law** which states that when elements are arranged in order of increasing atomic number, there is a periodic repetition of their physical and chemical properties. Each vertical column of elements is a **group.** Elements in the same group have similar physical and chemical properties.

32-Column Periodic Table In the periodic table, elements are arranged by increasing atomic number. In this 32-column version, each row represents a principal energy level.

	1 1A	2 2A															3 3B	4 4B	5 5B	6 6B	7 7B	8	9 8B	10	11 1B	12 2B	13 3A	14 4A	15 5A	16 6A	17 7A	18 8A
1	1																															2
2	3	4																									5	6	7	8	9	10
3	11	12																									13	14	15	16	17	18
4	19	20															21	22	23	24	25	26	27	28	29	30	31	32	33	34	35	36
5	37	38															39	40	41	42	43	44	45	46	47	48	49	50	51	52	53	54
6	55	56	57	58	59	60	61	62	63	64	65	66	67	68	69	70	71	72	73	74	75	76	77	78	79	80	81	82	83	84	85	86
7	87	88	89	90	91	92	93	94	95	96	97	98	99	100	101	102	103	104	105	106	107	108	109	110	111	112	113	114	115	116	117	118

In this version, elements 57 to 70 and 89 to 102 are placed within the other groups in order of atomic number. This results in a table with 32 columns.

(4) **SEP Use Models When and if element 119 is discovered, predict where it would be placed on the modern periodic table. Explain your reasoning.**

....

....

Metals, Nonmetals, and Metalloids Elements are broadly classified as metals, nonmetals, and metalloids. Across a period, the properties of elements become less metallic and more nonmetallic.

About 80 percent of the elements are **metals**. With the exception of mercury, all metals are solids at room temperature.

Most **nonmetals** are gases at room temperature. Five nonmetals (carbon, phosphorous, sulfur, iodine, and selenium) are solids and bromine is a liquid.

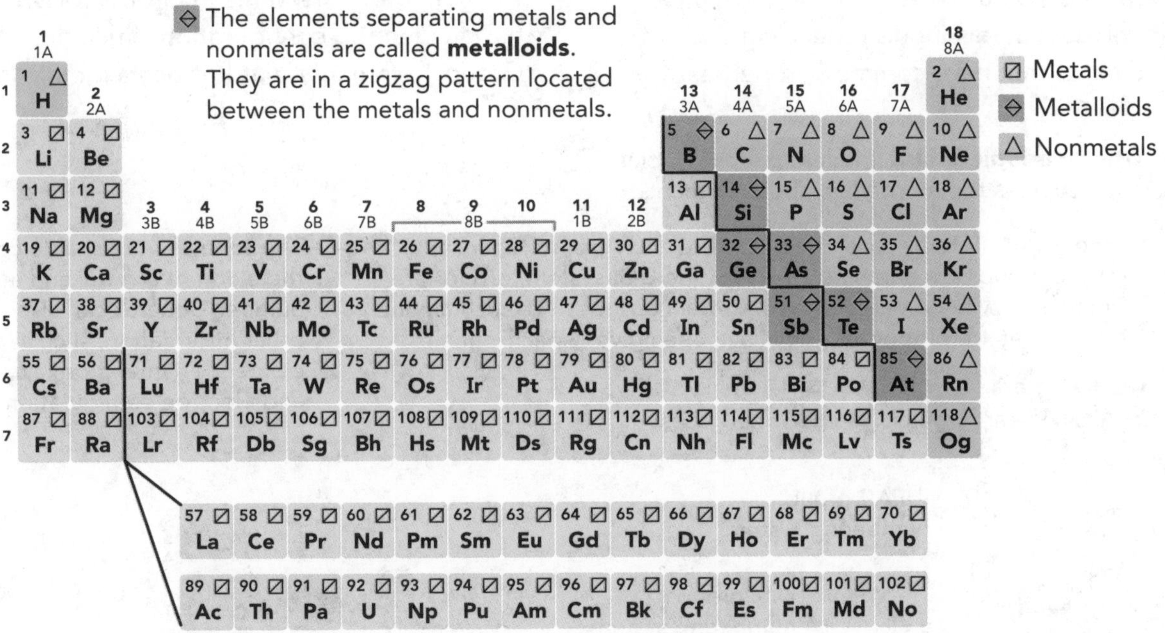

A **metal** is a type of element that is a good conductor of heat and electric current. Freshly cut metals reflect light causing them to be shiny. Most metals are malleable, meaning they can be shaped into different physical forms, like thin sheets. Many metals are ductile, meaning they can be pulled and stretched into wires.

A **nonmetal** is an element that tends to be a poor conductor of heat and electric current. Nonmetals tend to have properties opposite of those of metals. One exception, carbon as graphite, is a good conductor of electric current. Solid nonmetals tend to be brittle. That is, they shatter when hit with a hammer.

A **metalloid** is an element that tends to have properties that are similar to those of metals and nonmetals. Metalloids are all solids, do not exhibit luster and are poor conductors of heat and electricity. Metalloid behavior can be changed by using mixtures. For example, pure silicon is a poor conductor of electricity, however, mixing silicon and boron together produces a good electrical conductor. Such mixtures make excellent computer chips and are the basis for semiconductors and the consumer electronics industry. The ability to manipulate conductivity is one reason semi-conductors are used in many different devices.

5 **SEP Construct an Explanation From which area of the periodic table are you likely to find semiconductors? Explain.**

....

....

....

Modern Periodic Tables All modern periodic tables contain the 118 known elements arranged by atomic number. But, the information in each periodic square, the colors, and even the layout of the table can differ depending on the source of the table. The table in the previous section used colors to distinguish metals from nonmetals. The colors in the periodic table in this section distinguish specific groups of elements that have common properties.

The **main group elements,** also called representative elements, are the elements in Groups 1, 2, and 13 to 18. They display a wide range of physical and chemical properties. In their atoms, the *s* and *p* sublevels in the highest occupied energy level are partially filled. The square for hydrogen (H) is a different color than the other elements in Group 1. Hydrogen has an electron configuration similar to other Group 1 elements, but it is not a metal.

Using Periodic Tables Modern periodic tables are resources for information about elements.

In the IUPAC (International Union of Pure and Applied Chemistry) system, groups are numbered 1–18. In the U.S. system, groups are numbered 1A to 8A and 1B to 8B. Certain groups have such unique sets of common properties, they have been given specific names.

The squares in this table contain the element symbol and atomic number. Squares can also contain other information, such as the element's name, atomic mass, and electron configuration.

□ Alkali metals
⊟ Alkaline earth metals
○ Halogens
⊖ Nobel gases

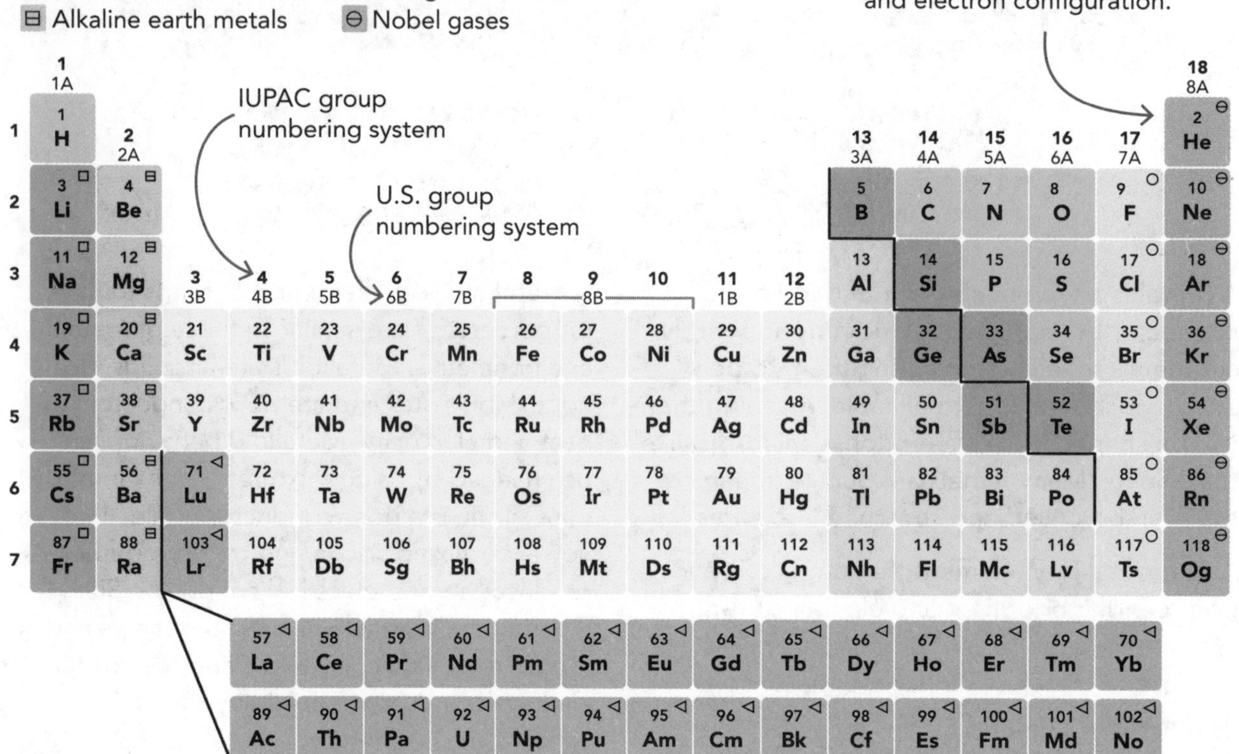

◁ For convenience, elements 57–71 and 89–103, the inner transition metals, are usually placed beneath Groups 1–18.

6 SEP Use Models Choose an element from the periodic table. Describe all the information you can learn about the element from using this periodic table.

....

....

Revisit

INVESTIGATIVE PHENOMENON

GO ONLINE to Elaborate and Evaluate your understanding of the design of the periodic table by completing the class discussion and writing activities.

7 **CCC Patterns** What patterns did you observe in the development of the periodic table? How were the patterns related to the timeline?

EXPERIENCE 2

The Periodic Table and Atomic Structure

GO ONLINE to Explore and Explain how the periodic table is used to identify the atomic structure of elements.

The Periodic Table as a Predictive Model

The electron configuration of an atom is the way electrons are arranged around the nucleus of an atom. An element's chemical and physical properties are due to the element's electron configuration. You can use the structure of the periodic table to determine an element's electron configuration and its chemical properties.

***s, p, d,* and *f* Blocks** Visualizing the periodic table as four distinct *s*, *p*, *d*, and *f* blocks helps determine an element's reactivity and chemical properties, without the need to write full electron configurations.

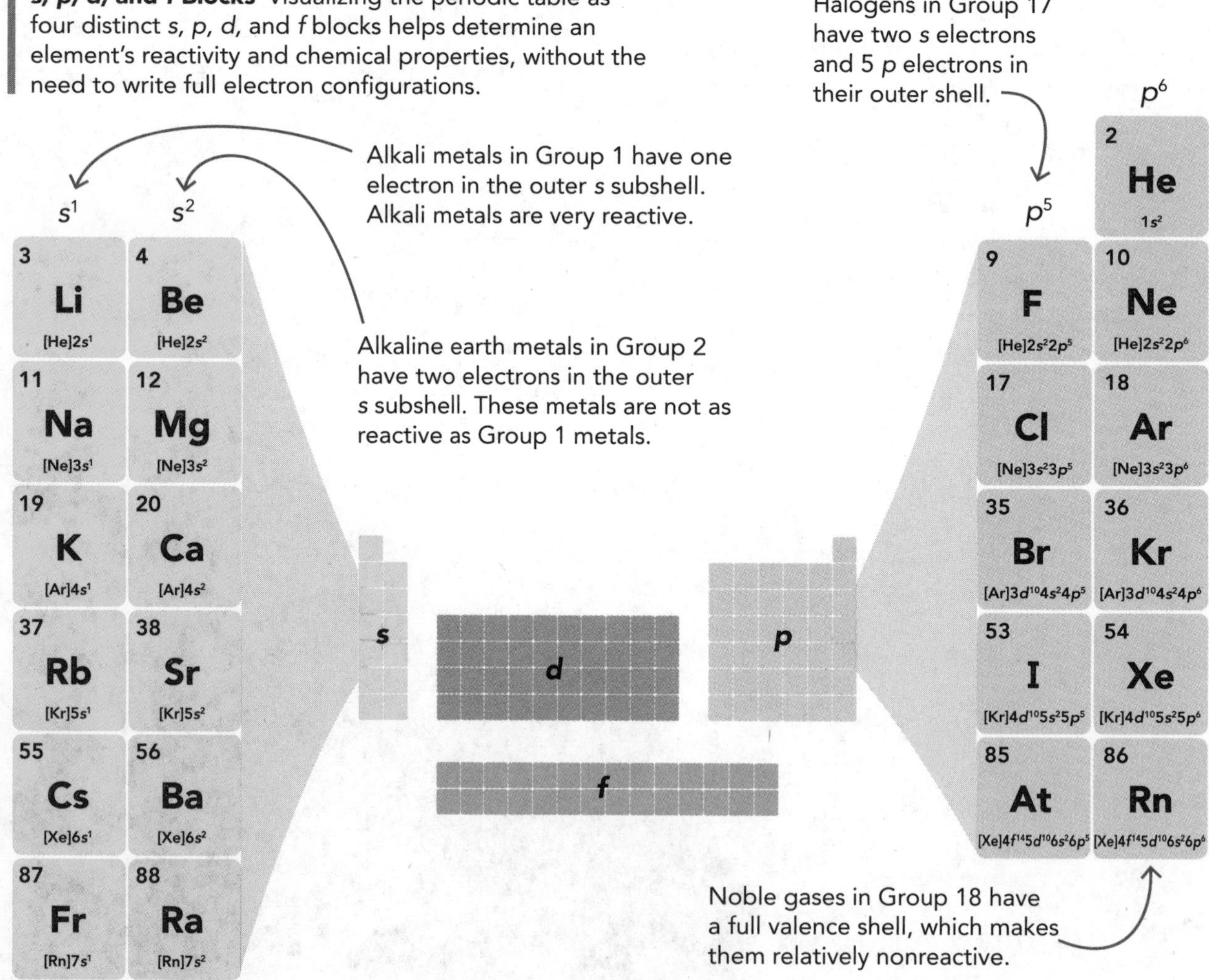

The periodic table is a predictive model based on the arrangements of electrons in the elements. The elements in the same group of the table have related outer shell electron configurations. Just as the electron configurations are similar within any group, so are the properties of the elements.

The periodic table can also be used to determine which electrons are core electrons and which electrons are valence electrons.

The periodic table can be used as a model to predict the electron configuration of any element based on its location. This is possible because of the systematic way electron configurations change across the periodic table.

Core and Valence Electrons There are 11 protons and 11 electrons in a sodium atom. Sodium's position in the periodic table indicates that ten of the electrons are core electrons in the same configuration as a neon atom, [Ne]. The other electron is a valence electron in the $3s^1$ energy level.

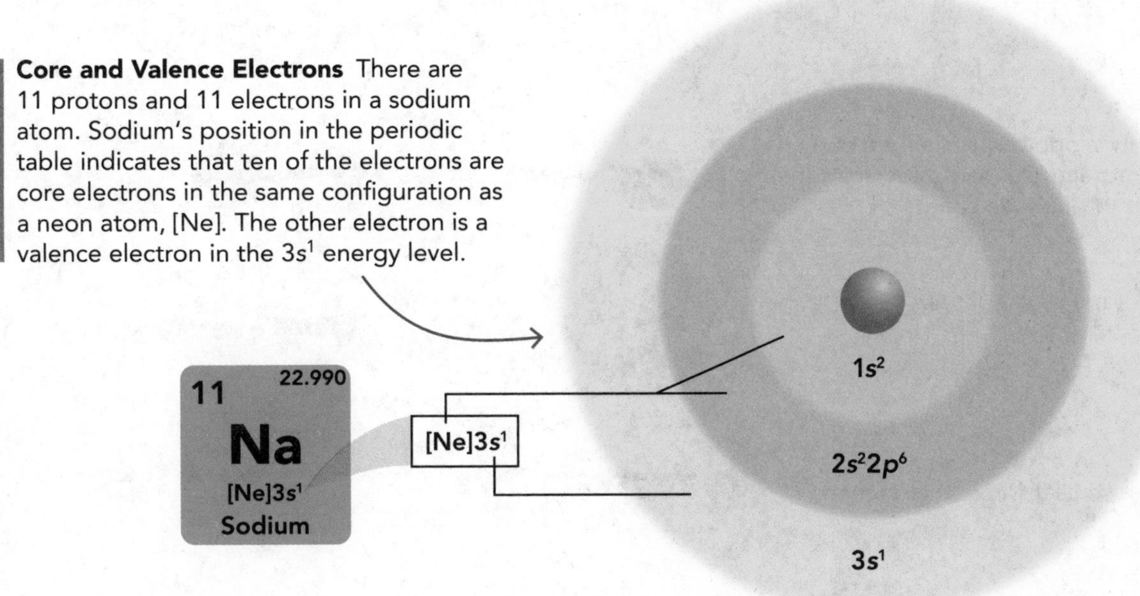

(8) **SEP Use models Use chlorine's position in the periodic table to draw a model of chlorine (Cl) that includes the nucleus, core electrons, and valence electrons.**

Coulomb's Law

Many properties of elements are a direct result of the element's electron configuration. Since atoms contain charged particles, it is useful to look at the interactions of charged particles before looking at the properties of atoms. We can use a mathematical model to help us interpret how strongly the nucleus attracts different electrons in an atom.

Coulomb's Law tells us that the strength of the force between two charged particles (the Coulombic force) depends on the charge of each particle and the distance between them.

The force (F) is directly proportional to charge, q. The larger the absolute value of the charge carried by each particle, the greater is the force between them.

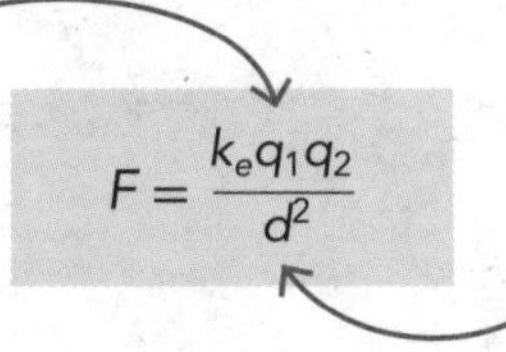

$$F = \frac{k_e q_1 q_2}{d^2}$$

The force is inversely proportional to the square of the distance (d) between the two particles. The farther apart the particles are, the weaker is the force. The equation also contains a proportionality constant, k_e.

Two oppositely charged particles attract. The particles have equal but opposite charges.

A larger charge produces a larger force of attraction.

A larger distance produces a smaller force of attraction.

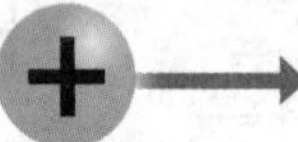
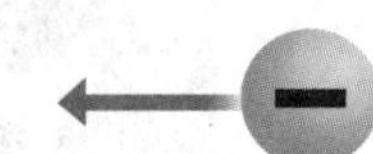

9 **SEP Develop and Use Models** Draw a model of the force between two negatively charged particles. Include in your model how the force changes if the charge of the particles change or if the distance between the particles change.

The Shielding Effect and Effective Nuclear Charge

Atoms of every element other than hydrogen contain multiple positively-charged protons and multiple negatively-charged electrons. There are a significant number of interactions between these charges to account for as the number of protons and electrons in the atom increases.

Shielding Effect Have you ever been drawn to a crowd but couldn't see the commotion because of all the other onlookers? Valence electrons are in a similar situation—they do not receive the full attractive force of the nuclear charge (from the positively charged protons) because the core electrons shield some of it from the valence electrons.

Negatively-charged electrons are attracted to the positively-charged nucleus.

Core electrons experience a greater force of attraction to the nucleus than valence electrons.

Valence electrons are repelled by core electrons. This repulsion offsets some of the attraction of the valence electrons to the nucleus.

Nucleus

Electrons

The repulsive forces between electrons work to reduce how much of the attractive force each electron "feels." This is called the shielding effect (screening effect). The amount of shielding an electron experiences depends on which orbital the electron is in. Inner core electrons always shield valence electrons, but valence electrons do not shield one another.

The **effective nuclear charge, Z_{eff},** is the net positive nuclear charge experienced by an electron in an atom. The charge is usually not the full nuclear charge because of the shielding effect. The effective nuclear charge can be estimated using the following equation:

Z_{eff} is the net positive nuclear charge experienced by an electron.

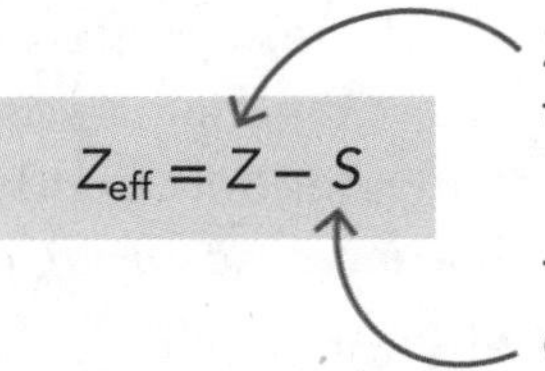

$$Z_{eff} = Z - S$$

Z is the number of protons and is equal to the charge of the nucleus.

The shielding constant, *S*, represents the amount of shielding. There are a special set of rules for calculating *S*, but we can estimate its value by adding up the number of inner shielding electrons.

Effective Nuclear Charge as a Periodic Trend

How does the number of **core and valence electrons** relate to the **effective nuclear charge, Z_{eff}?**

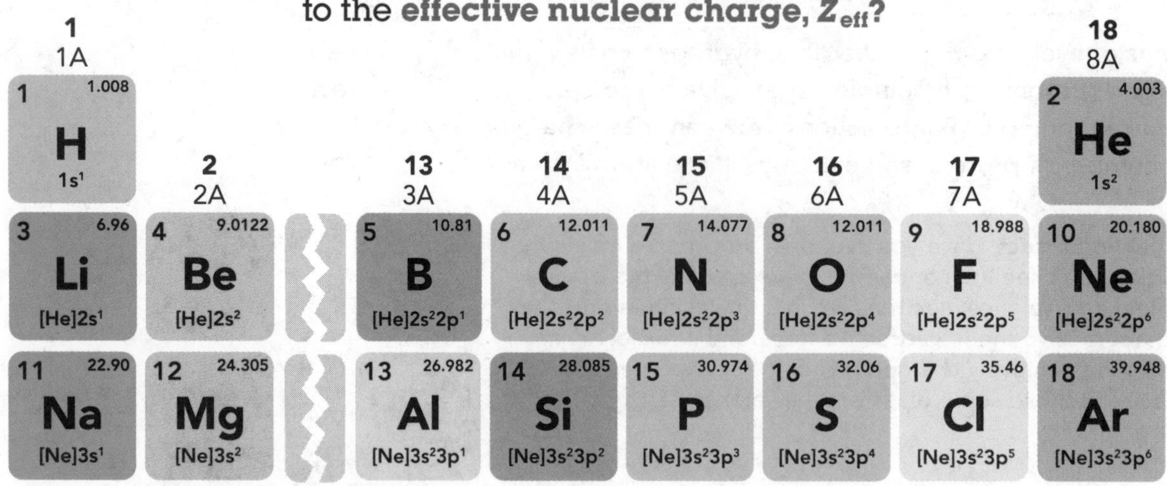

Effective Nuclear Charge From left to right across a period, the nuclear charge (*Z*) increases. But, the number of core electrons (*S*) stays constant. The result is that the **effective nuclear charge increases left to right** across any period for the main group elements (Groups 1, 2, and 13–18).

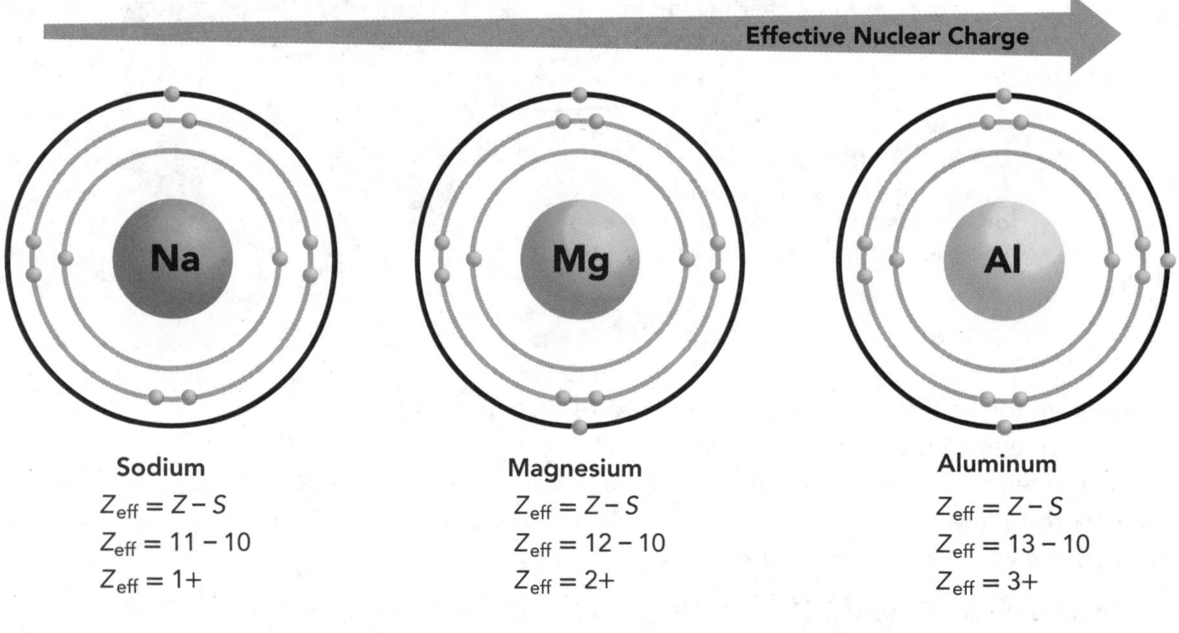

Sodium
$Z_{eff} = Z - S$
$Z_{eff} = 11 - 10$
$Z_{eff} = 1+$

Magnesium
$Z_{eff} = Z - S$
$Z_{eff} = 12 - 10$
$Z_{eff} = 2+$

Aluminum
$Z_{eff} = Z - S$
$Z_{eff} = 13 - 10$
$Z_{eff} = 3+$

The periodic table is organized according to the properties of specific elements and the repetition of these properties at regular intervals. Now that all of the elements in the main parts of the periodic table are well known, we can define the periodic trends that exist. For example, effective nuclear charge, Z_{eff}, increases from left to right across a period and decreases down a group.

(10) **SEP Develop Models** **Silicon and germanium are in the same group. How does the effective nuclear charge of silicon compare to that of germanium? Why is this the case? Draw models to justify your answer.**

Revisit

INVESTIGATIVE PHENOMENON

GO ONLINE to Elaborate and Evaluate your knowledge of the periodic table and atomic structure by completing the peer review and data analysis activities.

In the CER worksheet, you drafted a scientific argument for how electrons and the nucleus determine atomic structure and how this is reflected in the periodic table. You also defended your argument with evidence. With a partner, reevaluate the evidence cited in your arguments.

(11) **SEP Support Your Explanation with Evidence** **Explain why the periodic table is organized by atomic number. Provide evidence about atomic nuclei to support your explanation.**

EXPERIENCE 3

Periodic Trends

GO ONLINE to Explore and Explain various trends that appear in the periodic table and how they are related.

Atomic Radius

The periodic properties of elements are directly related to the effective nuclear charge experienced by their valence electrons. The principle of effective nuclear charge explains the trends in many periodic properties of the elements. Atomic size, ionic size, first ionization energy, and electron affinity all illustrate how the effective nuclear charge affects atomic properties.

Atoms do not have definite boundaries. Because of this uncertainty, chemists estimate the size of atoms in various ways. The **atomic radius** is one-half the distance between the nuclei of two atoms of the same element. It is used to estimate the size of an atom.

Atomic Radius Atomic radius is usually measured in picometers, pm. (1 pm = 1×10^{-12} m.) The smallest atoms are hydrogen and helium, each having an atomic radius of about 30 pm. Francium, the largest atom, has an atomic radius of about 260 pm.

Atomic radius increases from right to left within a period.

Atomic Radius

H 31																	He 28
Li 128	Be 96											B 84	C 75	N 71	O 66	F 57	Ne 58
Na 166	Mg 141											Al 121	Si 111	P 107	S 105	Cl 102	Ar 106
K 203	Ca 176	Sc 170	Ti 160	V 153	Cr 139	Mn 139	Fe 132	Co 126	Ni 124	Cu 132	Zn 122	Ga 122	Ge 120	As 119	Se 120	Br 120	Kr 116
Rb 220	Sr 195	Y 190	Zr 175	Nb 164	Mo 154	Tc 147	Ru 146	Rh 142	Pd 139	Ag 145	Cd 144	In 142	Sn 139	Sb 139	Te 138	I 139	Xe 140
Cs 244	Ba 215	Lu 187	Hf 175	Ta 170	W 162	Re 151	Os 144	Ir 141	Pt 136	Au 136	Hg 132	Tl 145	Pb 146	Bi 148	Po 148	At 150	Rn 150
Fr 260	Ra 221																

Atomic Radius

Atomic radius increases from top to bottom within a group.

Explaining Atomic Radius

How does **atomic radius change** within the periodic table?

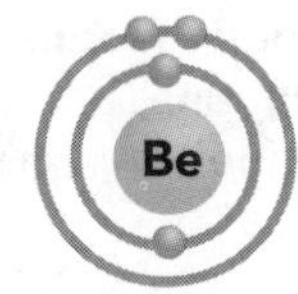

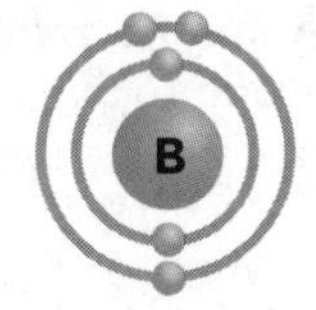

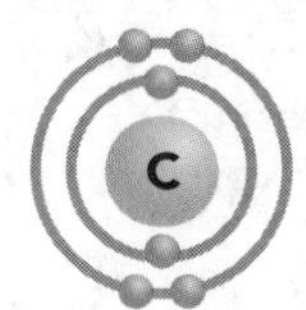

Periods The **decrease in atomic radius across a period** can be explained by changes in numbers of electrons and protons. As more protons are added across a period, Z_{eff} increases.

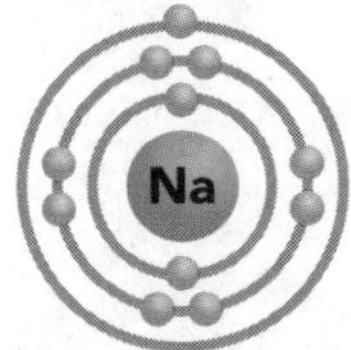

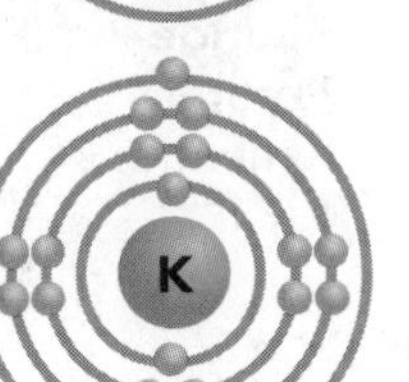

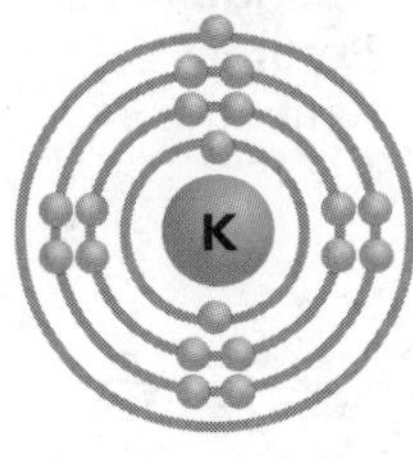

1	2	13	14	15	16	17
3 **Li** Lithium	4 **Be** Berylium	5 **B** Boron	6 **C** Carbon	7 **N** Nitrogen	8 **O** Oxygen	9 **F** Fluorine
11 **Na** Sodium						
19 **K** Potassium						
37 **Rb** Rubidium						
55 **Cs** Cesium						
87 **Fr** Francium						

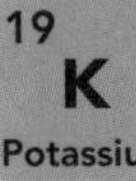

Groups Atomic radius becomes larger down a group because valence electrons occupy higher energy shells, which extend further away from the nucleus.

The **atomic radius decreases** across the period for the Period 2 elements Li, Be, B, C, and N.

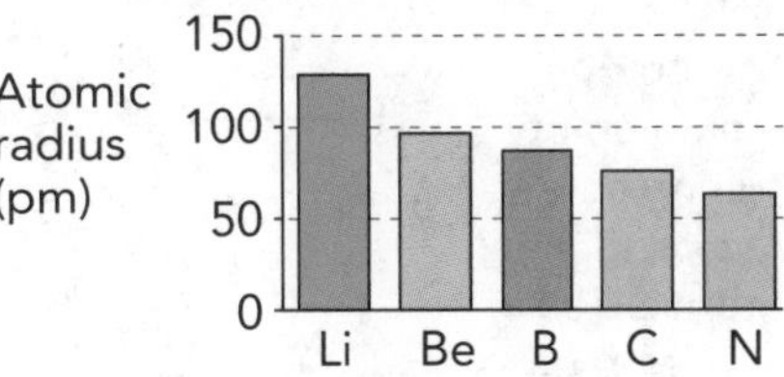

The **atomic radius increases** down the group for the Group 1 elements Li, Na, K, Rb, and Cs.

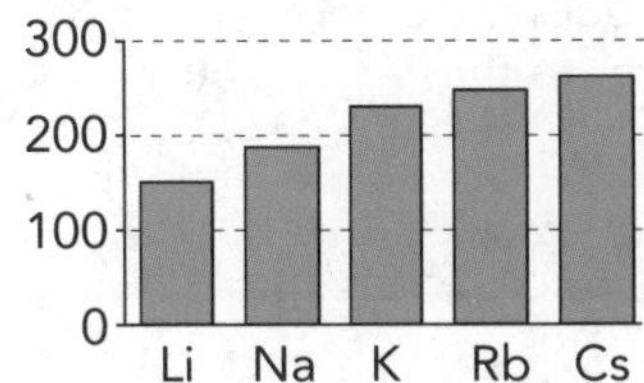

(12) **SEP Develop Models Show the periodicity of atomic size vs. atomic number by making a line graph that compares atomic radii across two periods.**

Explaining Ion Size

How does the **formation** of **cations** and **anions** relate to **atomic radius?**

Cation Formation in Metals When a metal atom, such as sodium, **loses one electron** it becomes a sodium **ion**, which has a **1+ charge.**

$-1e^-$

Na → Na

Sodium atom (Na)
11 protons
12 neutrons

Sodium ion (Na^+)
11 protons
12 neutrons

The **radius of the cation is smaller** due to an empty valence shell resulting as electrons were removed. For example the Li atom is 156 pm while the Li ion is 60 pm. Since the number of protons remains the same, there is a **higher Z_{eff}** per electron in a cation, which pulls the outer electrons closer to the nucleus.

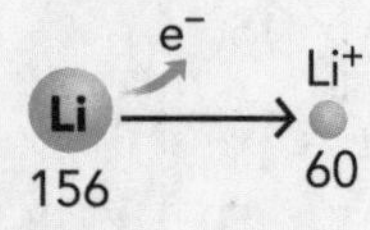

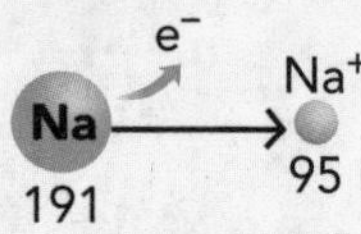

K 238 → K^+ 133

Anion Formation in Nonmetals When a nonmetal atom, such as flourine, **gains one electron** it becomes a fluoride **ion,** which has a **1− charge.**

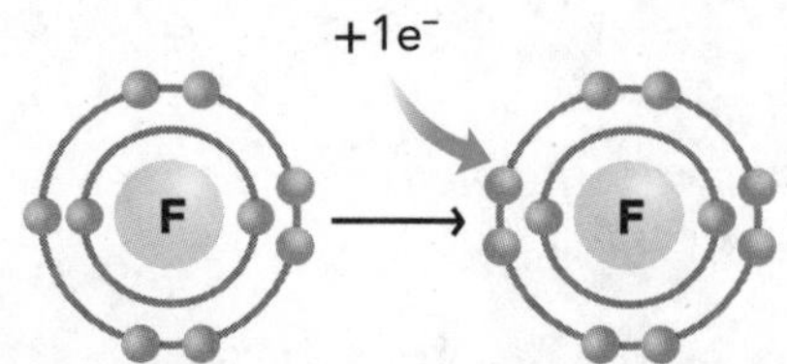

Fluorine atom (F)
9 protons
10 neutrons

Fluoride ion (F^-)
9 protons
10 neutrons

The **radius of the anion is bigger** due to more electron-electron repulsions as electrons were added. Since the number of protons remains the same, there is a **lower Z_{eff}** per electron, which allows the extra electrons to move farther from the nucleus. For example, the F atom is 62 pm while the F ion is 133 pm.

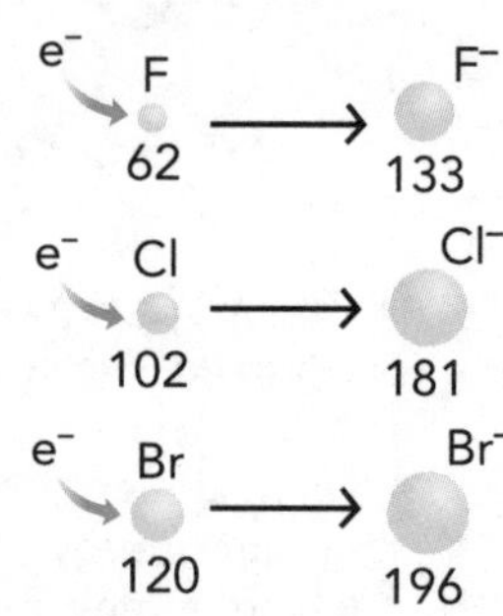

An **ion** is an atom or group of atoms that has a positive or negative charge. An atom that loses one or more electrons to form an ion with a net positive charge is called a **cation.** Cations are always smaller than their parent atoms. Metal atoms tend to lose electrons to become cations. An atom that gains one or more electrons to form an ion with a net negative charge is called an an **anion.** Anions are always larger than their parent atoms. Nonmetal atoms tend to gain electrons to become monatomic anions.

13 **SEP Use Models Explain why cations are always smaller than their parent atoms. Use a model to explain why this trend occurs.**

Ionization Energy

Ionization energy is the energy required to remove the outermost electron from the ground state of a gaseous atom. For example, 496 kJ/mol of energy is required to remove the outermost electrons from each atom of 1 mole of sodium vapor. (A mole, abbreviated "mol," is an amount of matter equal to the atomic mass in grams.) The size of an atom directly affects its ionization energy. Coulomb's law states that the closer an electron is to the nucleus, the stronger the force of attraction, and therefore the more energy required to remove the electron (i.e. higher ionization energy).

Small atoms tend to have high ionization energies, and large atoms have low ionization energies.

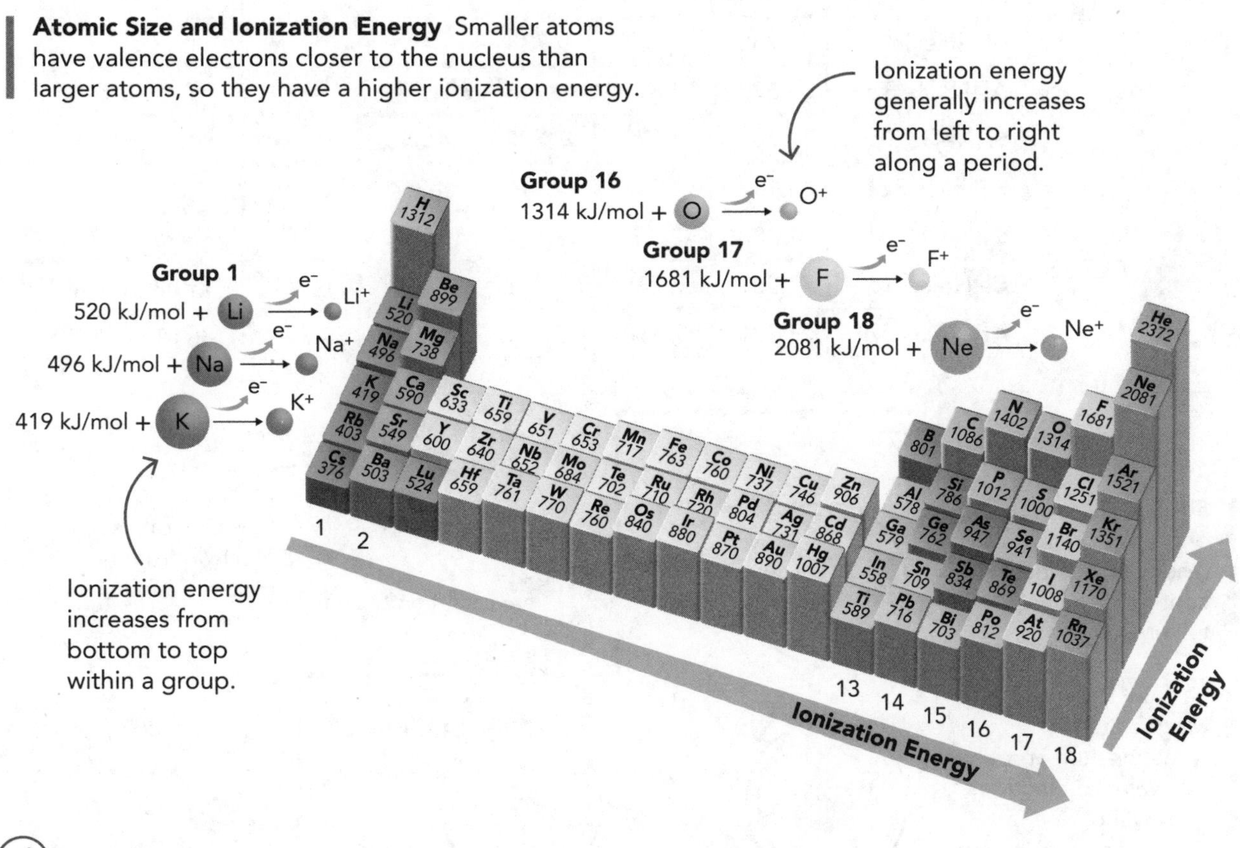

Atomic Size and Ionization Energy Smaller atoms have valence electrons closer to the nucleus than larger atoms, so they have a higher ionization energy.

(14) **CCC Patterns Compare the trends for atomic size and first ionization energy. Explain why these trends are related.**

....

....

....

....

Successive Ionization Energies

More than one electron may be removed from an atom to form an ion. The first ionization energy (I_1) is the energy required to remove the outermost electron. The second ionization energy I_2 is the energy needed to remove the second electron, and so on. Look for patterns in the relative values of ionization energies.

Ionization Energies Metals have a low Z_{eff}, lose electrons when forming ions, and have relatively low I_1. Nonmetals have higher Z_{eff}, gain electrons when forming ions, and have higher I_1. Noble gases have even higher I_1 because they experience a very high nuclear charge.

Ionization Energies for Sodium through Argon (kJ/mol)

Element	I_1	I_2	I_3	I_4	I_5	I_6	I_7
Na [Ne]$3s^1$	496	4,562					
Mg [Ne]$3s^2$	738	1,451	7,733				
Al [Ne]$3s^2 3p^1$	578	1,817	2,745	11,577			
Si [Ne]$3s^2 3p^2$	786	1,577	3,232	4,356	16,901		
P [Ne]$3s^2 3p^3$	1,102	1,907	2,914	4,964	6,274	21,267	
S [Ne]$3s^2 3p^4$	1,000	2,252	3,357	4,556	7,004	8,496	27,107
Cl [Ne]$3s^2 3p^5$	1,251	2,298	3,822	5,159	6,542	9,362	11,018
Ar [Ne]$3s^2 3p^6$	1,521	2,666	3,931	5,771	7,238	8,781	11,995

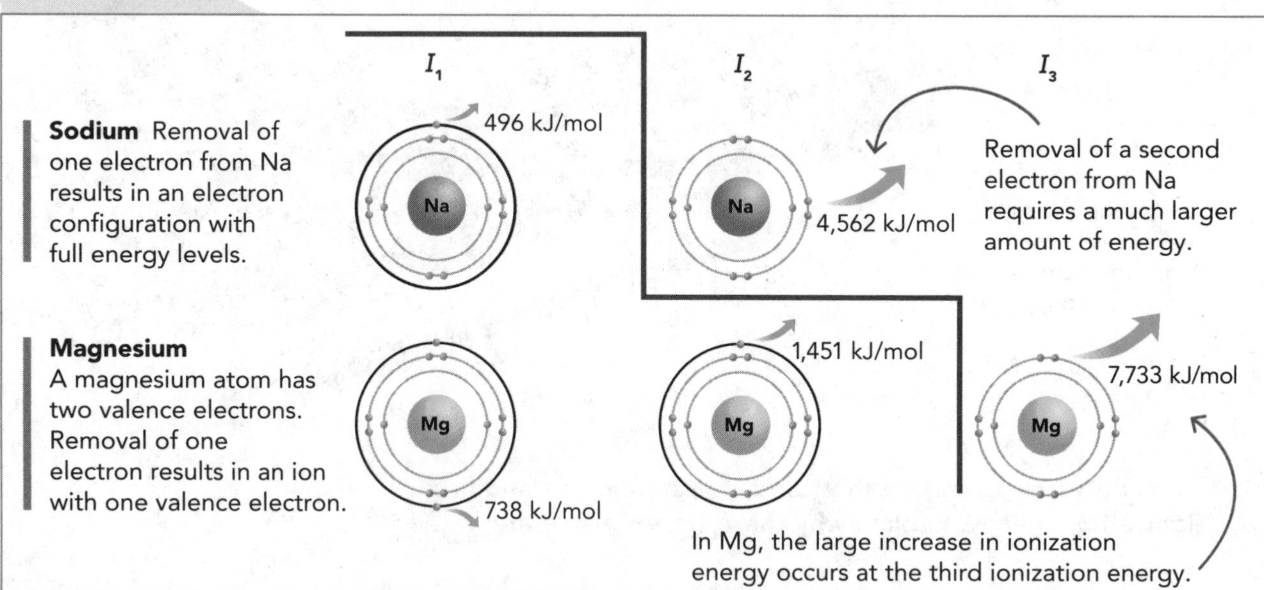

Sodium Removal of one electron from Na results in an electron configuration with full energy levels.

Magnesium A magnesium atom has two valence electrons. Removal of one electron results in an ion with one valence electron.

(15) **SEP Develop and Use Models** Draw a successive ionization energy diagram for aluminum.

Electron Affinity

Electron affinity is the energy change that happens when an atom gains an electron. For most atoms, energy is released when an electron is added to the atom. An atom with a higher electron affinity will release a greater amount of energy. A higher electron affinity has a more negative electron affinity value.

Identifying Trends for Electron Affinity Trends in electron affinity are not as regular across the periodic table as other trends.

Electron Affinity →

Electron affinity increases from left to right across a period in Groups 15 to 17.

1 1A	2 2A		13 3A	14 4A	15 5A	16 6A	17 7A	18 8A
1 **H** −73								2 **He** > 0
3 **Li** −60	4 **Be** > 0		5 **B** −27	6 **C** −122	7 **N** > 0	8 **O** −141	9 **F** −328	10 **Ne** > 0
11 **Na** −53	12 **Mg** > 0		13 **Al** −43	14 **Si** −134	15 **P** −72	16 **S** −200	17 **Cl** −349	18 **Ar** > 0
19 **K** −48	20 **Ca** −2		31 **Ga** −30	32 **Ge** −119	33 **As** −78	34 **Se** −195	35 **Br** −325	36 **Kr** > 0
37 **Rb** −47	38 **Sr** −5		49 **In** −30	50 **Sn** −107	51 **Sb** −103	52 **Te** −190	53 **I** −295	54 **Xe** > 0

Electron Affinity ↑

The high electron affinities in Groups 16 and 17 are due to the relatively high effective nuclear charge experienced by the valence electrons. An atom with a high effective nuclear charge readily attracts an electron to the valence shell. This is why nonmetal atoms tend to gain electrons and form anions.

16 **SEP Develop and Use Models Using the model of fluorine provided, draw a similar model for neon. Why do the noble gases have relatively low electron affinities? Use the models of fluorine and neon as evidence to support your answer.**

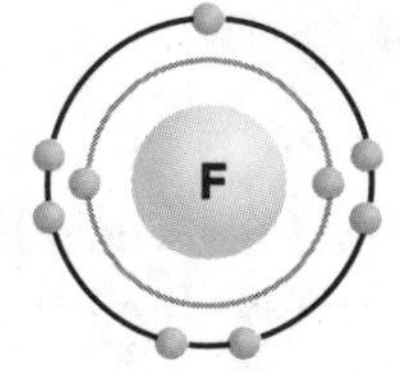

....

....

....

Common Charges in Representative Elements

Elements within a group tend to form ions with the same charge, for Groups 1, 2, 15, 16, and 17. These charges can be identified based on the location of the group in the periodic table and the group's electron configurations.

There are charges that are commonly formed for specific elements as they become ionized. Metals, such as Groups 1 and 2, tend to form cations. Metals lose electrons because of relatively low ionization energies. This tendency of an element to lose electrons and form cations is known as metallic character. Nonmetal atoms in Groups 15, 16, and 17 tend to form anions. Nonmetals gain electrons because of relatively high electron affinities. This tendency of an element to gain electrons and form anions is known as nonmetallic character.

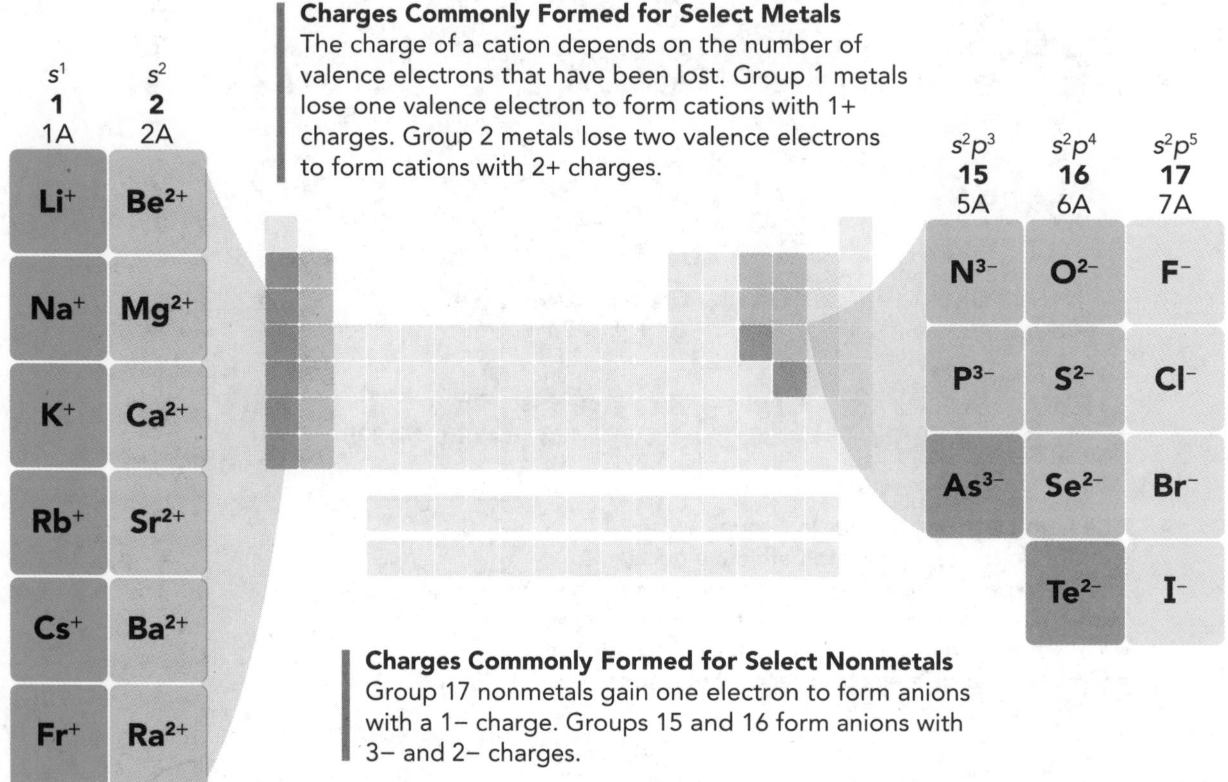

Charges Commonly Formed for Select Metals
The charge of a cation depends on the number of valence electrons that have been lost. Group 1 metals lose one valence electron to form cations with 1+ charges. Group 2 metals lose two valence electrons to form cations with 2+ charges.

Charges Commonly Formed for Select Nonmetals
Group 17 nonmetals gain one electron to form anions with a 1– charge. Groups 15 and 16 form anions with 3– and 2– charges.

(17) **CCC Patterns When asked why a chlorine atom gains one electron to form an anion with a 1– charge, a classmate answered, "Because noble gas configurations are stable." Is this statement generally true? Explain.**

....

....

....

Connecting the Trends

By arranging the elements according to atomic number, the periodic table becomes a powerful tool to predict an element's properties.

These properties include the effective nuclear charge, the number of electrons in the valence shell, the energy released when an electron is gained, and the tendency for an element to gain or lose electrons.

Periodic Trends Understanding periodic trends helps to predict properties of elements based on their location in the periodic table.

- **Metallic character** increases moving diagonally across the periodic table from the upper right corner to the lower left corner.
- **Nonmetallic character** increases moving diagonally across the periodic table from the lower left corner to the upper right corner.

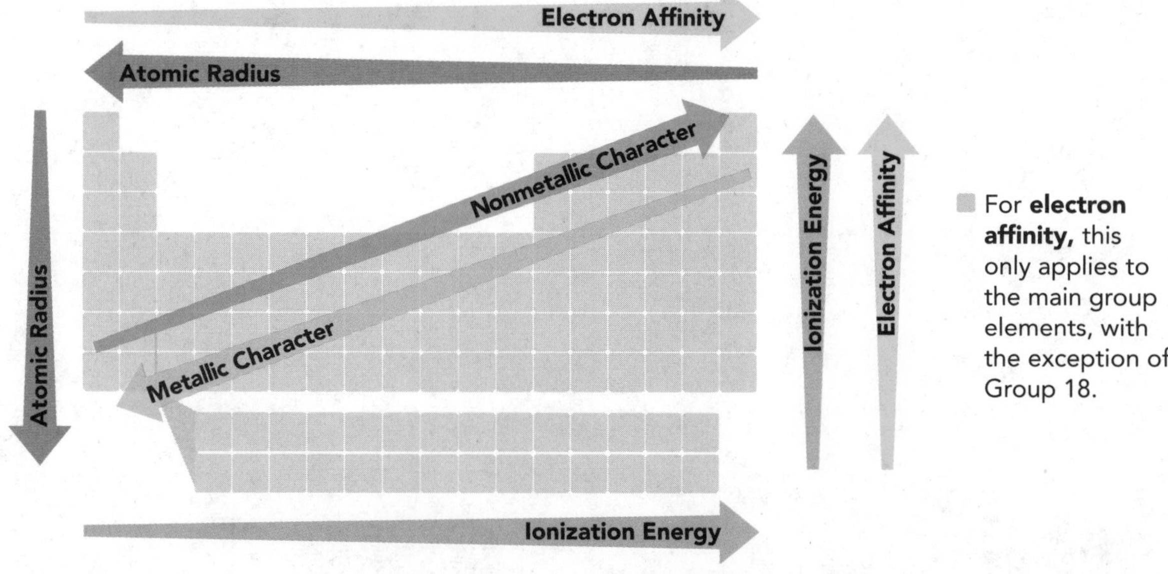

- For **electron affinity,** this only applies to the main group elements, with the exception of Group 18.
- The **atomic radius** increases moving down a group and increases moving within a period, from right to left.
- **Ionization energy** increases moving up a group and increases within a period, left to right.

18 **CCC Patterns Electron affinity and ionization energy appear to be opposing concepts. Explain, using main group elements only, why they both share similar periodic trends in a period and column.**

Revisit

INVESTIGATIVE PHENOMENON

GO ONLINE to Elaborate on and Evaluate your knowledge of periodic trends by completing the engineering design and class discussion activities.

In the CER worksheet, you constructed an argument to explain how electron shielding changes across a period or within a group. With a partner, reevaluate the evidence cited in your arguments.

19 **SEP Refine Your Argument** How could you expand your argument to support periodic trends? Explain.

GO ONLINE to Evaluate what you learned about patterns in the periodic table by completing the assessment resources.

In the Performance-Based Assessment, you analyzed data and predicted relative properties of elements based on the patterns of electrons in the valence shells of atoms. Wrap up your analysis by answering the following questions.

20 **SEP Engage in Argument** Of all the noble gases, helium and neon, are completely inert, as they do not form any chemical compounds. However, some of the heavier noble gases, such as Kr, Xe, and Rn, are capable of forming a few chemical compounds. Using periodic properties and electron configurations, explain how this can occur moving down this group of elements.

21 **Revisit the Anchoring Phenomenon** How does what you learned in this investigation help explain the chemistry of minerals?

INVESTIGATIVE PHENOMENON

GO ONLINE to Engage with real-world phenomena by watching a video and to complete a CER interactive worksheet.

Why do gems have different properties than metals?

INVESTIGATION 6

Chemical Bonding

Jewelers use gems in jewelry because of their appearances and how they can be shaped. The metals used in jewelry have different uses and properties than gems. Once you have viewed the Investigative Phenomenon video and worked on a first draft of a Claim-Evidence-Reasoning exercise to explain the phenomenon you observed, answer the following reflection questions about the physical properties of gems and metals.

1. **CCC Patterns Compare the properties of the gems and metals in the photo.**

Gems	Metals

2. **SEP Construct an Explanation Metals usually bend without breaking, while gems usually break in a specific pattern. What might be happening to the bonds between the atoms in these materials that can explain this difference?**

EXPERIENCE 1

Ionic Bonds

GO ONLINE to Explore and Explain the formation of ionic bonds and the properties of ionic compounds.

Ions and the Octet Rule

Stable Electron Configurations Atoms of noble gases, such as argon, rarely react to form bonds with other atoms. Each is stable because it has a full valence shell, which is energetically favorable compared to a partially filled valence shell. Except for helium, the highest occupied energy levels of the noble gases have electron configurations with ns^2np^6. Notice that they have eight valence electrons. Helium has two valence electrons.

Atoms of other elements tend to achieve the energetically stable electron configuration of a noble gas when they bond. The **octet rule** states that atoms tend to form bonds so that each atom has eight electrons in its valence shell. Atoms in most substances are arranged so that they have octets in their valence shells. Some atoms, such as hydrogen, are stable with two valence electrons.

Full Valence Shell All noble gases have full valence shells. Helium has two electrons in its valence shell. Others, such as argon, have an octet of valence electrons.

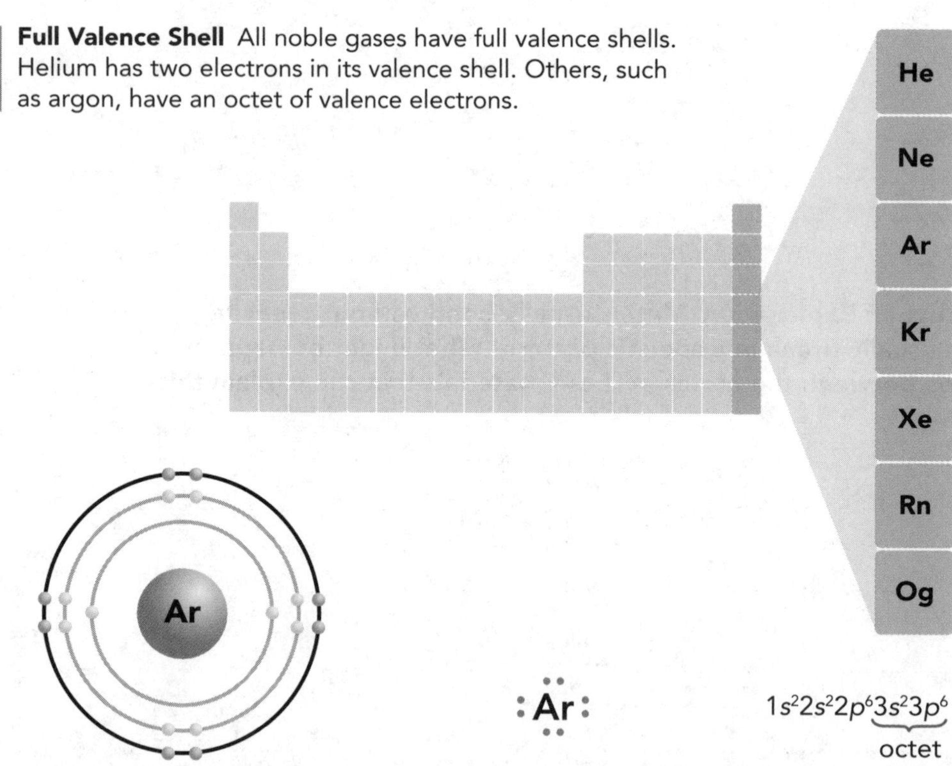

:Ar:

$1s^22s^22p^63s^23p^6$ (octet)

The Bohr model of an argon atom clearly shows that it has eight valence electrons. It also shows the core electrons.

The electron dot structure shows only the eight valence electrons.

The electron configuration shows that two electrons in the 3*s* subshell and six in the 3*p* subshell make up the octet.

Octets in Cations and Anions An atom can gain or lose electrons to achieve an octet in its valence shell. The resulting ion is more energetically favored than its parent atom because its electron configuration is more stable. The type of ion an element forms depends on how many valence electrons it has, which you can determine by examining its position in the periodic table.

Atoms in Groups 1 and 2 form cations with 1+ and 2+ charges when they lose electrons to get an octet. Each resulting ion has the electron configuration of the noble gas in the previous period. Atoms in Groups 15–17 tend to gain electrons to get an octet. Each tends to form an anion with a charge of 3−, 2−, or 1− to have an electron configuration of the noble gas in the same period.

Cations Metals in Groups 1 and 2 have one or two valence electrons, respectively. They lose these electrons to achieve an octet. For example, magnesium loses its two valence electrons to become a magnesium cation with a charge of 2+.

Anions Nonmetals in Groups 15, 16, and 17 have five, six, or seven valence electrons, respectively. They gain electrons to achieve an octet. For example, chlorine gains one electron to form a chloride anion with a charge of 1−.

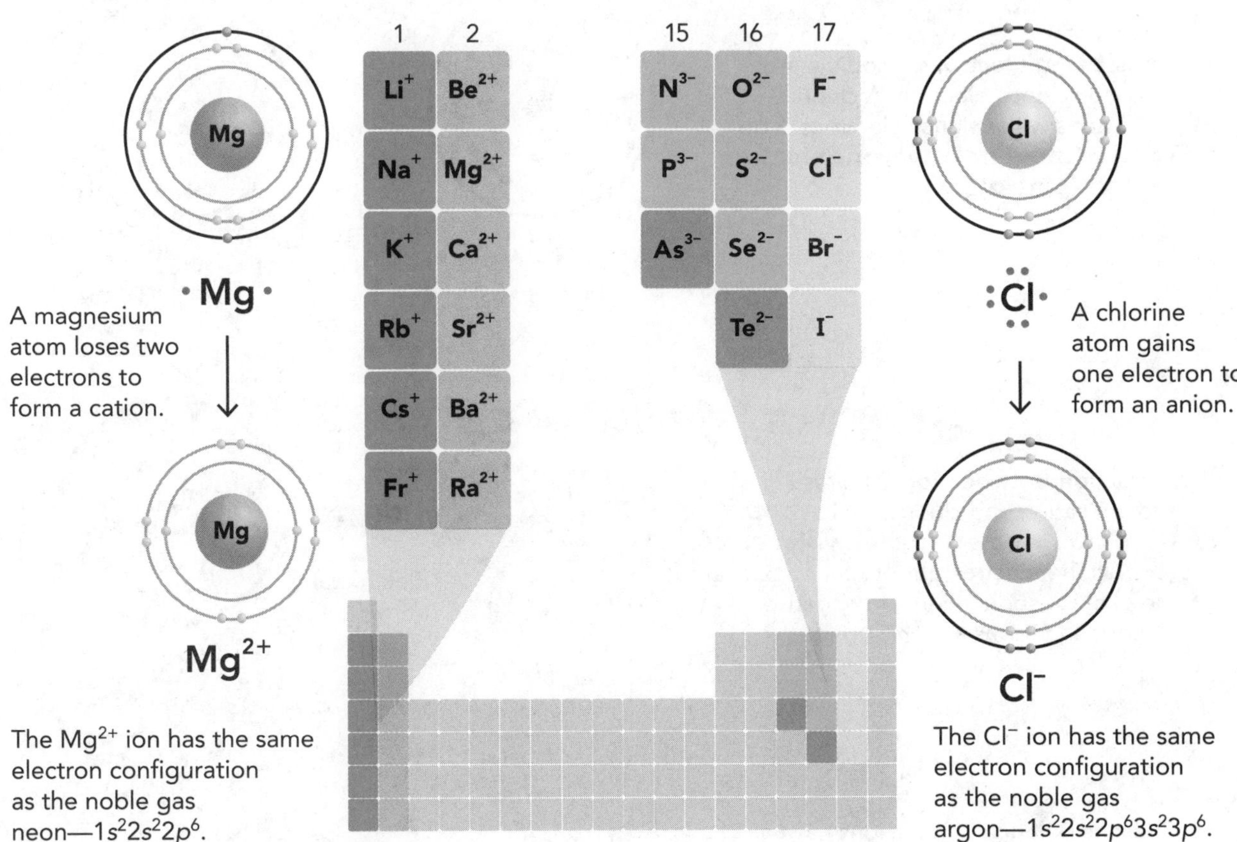

A magnesium atom loses two electrons to form a cation.

The Mg^{2+} ion has the same electron configuration as the noble gas neon—$1s^22s^22p^6$.

A chlorine atom gains one electron to form an anion.

The Cl^{-} ion has the same electron configuration as the noble gas argon—$1s^22s^22p^63s^23p^6$.

3 **CCC Patterns Draw the electron dot structures for the ions formed by nitrogen, oxygen, and fluorine atoms. Use a different colored pen or pencil for the electrons that the atoms gain to form these ions.**

Ionic Bonds

In sodium chloride, positive sodium ions and negative chloride ions are attracted to each other. An electrostatic attraction that holds oppositely charged ions together is called an **ionic bond.** Ionic bonds form when metals and nonmetals react to produce an **ionic compound,** which is an electrically neutral compound made of cations and anions. The positive and negative ions in an ionic compound both have energetically stable octets in their valence shells. The compound itself is electrically neutral because cations and anions combine in a ratio that balances the overall charge.

Ionic Bond Formation in Sodium Chloride

How does an **ionic bond form?**

Transferring Electrons A sodium atom has one valence electron. A chlorine atom has seven valence electrons. **The sodium atom transfers one electron to a chlorine atom.**

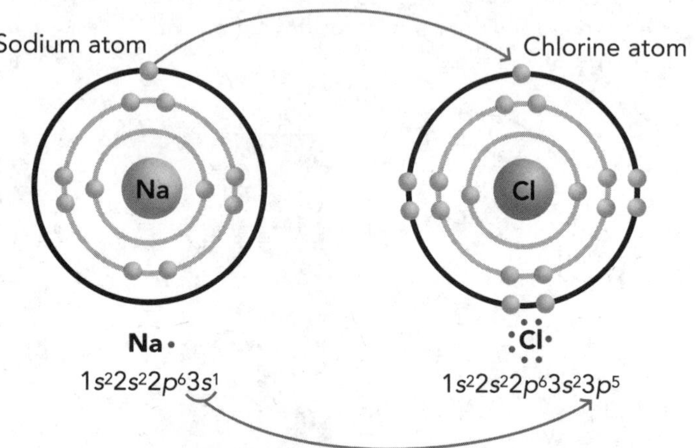

Attraction Between Ions The resulting sodium cation and chloride anion **both have stable octets in their valence shells.** The electrostatic attraction between the positive sodium ion and negative chloride ion forms an ionic bond.

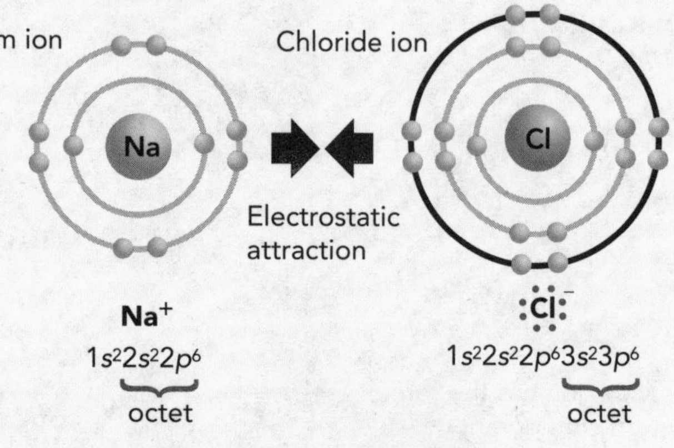

Charges Balance Sodium ions have a charge of 1+, and chloride ions have a charge of 1−. Therefore, they combine in a 1:1 ratio to **form an electrically neutral compound.**

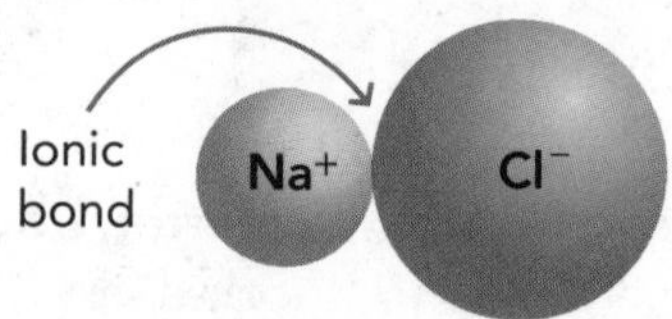

Electron Dot Structure The structure shows that sodium chloride has one sodium ion for every chloride ion. The positive ion does not have electron dots because it lost its electron. The negative ion has eight electron dots because it gained an electron.

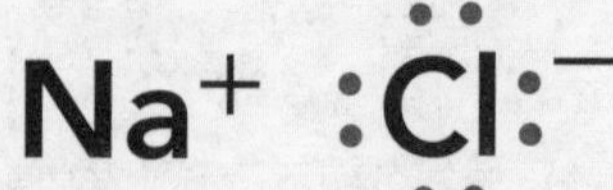

(4) **CCC Cause and Effect** **Magnesium ions form ionic bonds with fluoride ions in a 1:2 ratio. Explain how electrons are transferred between atoms and how the ionic bonds form in this compound.**

....

....

....

....

SAMPLE PROBLEM

Electron Dot Structures for Ionic Compounds

Draw the electron dot structures for the following ionic compounds.

a. lithium bromide (LiBr) **b.** calcium chloride ($CaCl_2$)

ANALYZE **Identify the relevant concepts.**

Atoms of metals lose valence electrons when forming an ionic compound. Atoms of nonmetals gain electrons. Enough atoms of each element must be used in the formula so that the overall charge is zero.

SOLVE **Apply the concepts to this problem.**

	a.	b.
Draw the electron dot structures for the atoms.	Li· and :Br· (with dots)	·Ca· and :Cl· (with dots)
Draw the electron dot structures for the ions, showing their ratio in the compound.	Li^+ $:\ddot{Br}:^-$	Ca^{2+} $:\ddot{Cl}:^-$ $:\ddot{Cl}:^-$

(5) **Draw the electron dot structure for magnesium oxide (MgO).**

GO ONLINE for more practice problems.

Ionic Compounds

Crystal Lattices Ionic compounds are not composed of individual molecules. Instead, each ion is attracted to all of the oppositely charged ions around it. In an ionic solid, a huge number of ions combine to form an extended structure called a crystal lattice. A **crystal lattice** is an orderly, repeating three-dimensional pattern of many ions, atoms, or molecules. In crystalline sodium chloride, each interior sodium ion is surrounded by six chloride ions, and each interior chloride ion is surrounded by six sodium ions. Each sodium ion is strongly attracted to its neighboring chloride ions, just as each chloride ion is strongly attracted to its neighboring sodium ions.

The strong attractive forces between ions in a crystalline ionic compound results in a very stable crystal.

Sodium Chloride Crystals Sodium chloride is also known as the mineral halite. The cube shape of halite crystals is the result of the repeating pattern of Na^+ ions and Cl^- ions in the crystal lattice. While there are many, many ions in the lattice, the ratio of Na^+:Cl^- is 1:1.

6 **SEP Construct an Explanation** Why is a crystal of strontium chloride ($SrCl_2$) described as an extended structure?

....

....

....

Coulomb's Law and Bond Strength Lattice energy is a measure of the strength of bonds in an ionic compound and depends on the electrostatic force between the ions. The strength of ionic bonds depends on the types of ions forming the bonds. According to Coulomb's law, both the charge of the ions and the distance between them affect the electrostatic force between ions.

Coulomb's Law and Ionic Bonds

How do charge and distance **affect ionic bond strength?**

Coulomb's Law The equation for Coulomb's law shows that **force (*F*) is proportional to the charge (*q*) of the ions and inversely proportional to the square of the distance (*d*²) between the ions.** The strength of the bonds increases as the charge on the ions increases and decreases as the distance between the ions increases.

$$F = \frac{k_e q_1 q_2}{d^2}$$

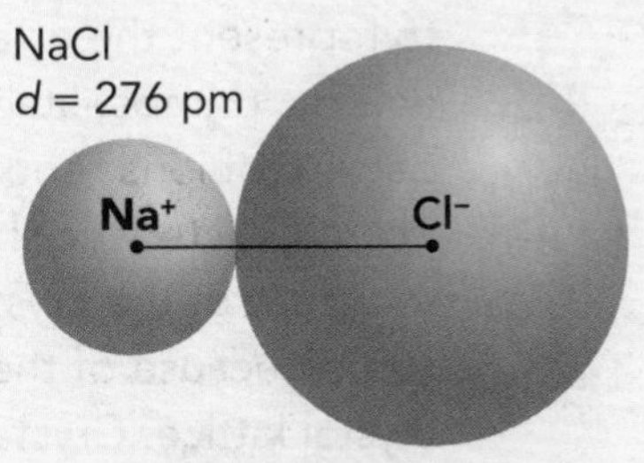

Sodium Chloride In NaCl, the charges of the ions are 1+ and 1–. The distance between the center of the ions is 276 picometers (pm).

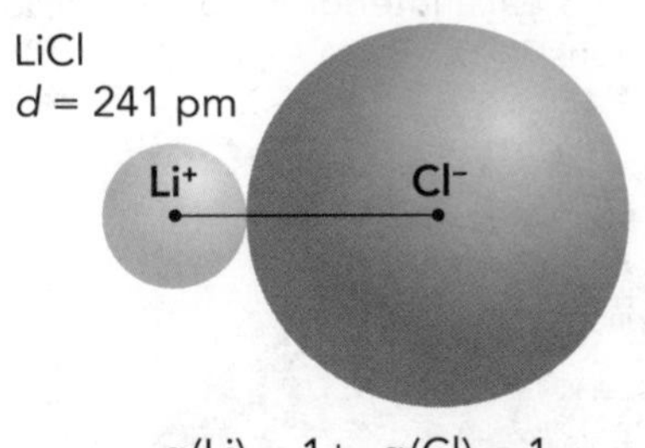

Lithium Chloride The product of the charges is the same as for the ions in sodium chloride. **However, the distance between the ions is smaller** because a Li^+ ion is smaller than a Na^+ ion. **Thus, the bonds** in LiCl **are stronger** than those in NaCl.

MgO
d = 205 pm
Mg^{2+} O^{2-}
q(Mg) = 2+, q(O) = 2–

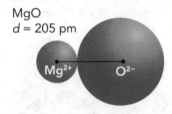

Magnesium Oxide The ionic bonds in magnesium oxide are stronger than in sodium chloride or lithium chloride. **The greater bond strength is a result of the larger ionic charge and the smaller distances between the ions.**

7. **CCC Matter and Energy Explain how you would expect the strength of the ionic bonds in potassium bromide (KBr) to compare with that of the bonds in lithium bromide (LiBr).**

Properties of Ionic Compounds

Crystals The properties of ionic compounds are a result of ionic bonding within the extended structure. Most ionic compounds are crystalline solids at room temperature. The structure of the crystal lattice depends on the size and charge of the ions in the compound. Ions with the same charge repel each other. However, ions in a crystal lattice are arranged in a way to minimize these repulsions.

A unit cell is a model that shows the smallest number of particles possible to represent the arrangement of ions. Each unit cell represents the lowest energy, or most stable, arrangement of the ions for a compound. This pattern of ions repeats in three dimensions throughout the crystal lattice. The characteristic shape of the crystals you can see depends on the structure of the crystal lattice. For example, sodium chloride crystals are cubic because of the way the sodium and chloride ions are arranged in the crystal lattice. Crystals of other minerals, such as rutile and fluorite, have different shapes because of the patterns of their ions.

Rutile Titanium dioxide (TiO_2) is also called rutile. It can form needle-like crystals. Throughout a crystal, each interior Ti^{4+} ion is surrounded by 6 O^{2-} ions. Each interior O^{2-} ion is surrounded by 3 Ti^{4+} ions.

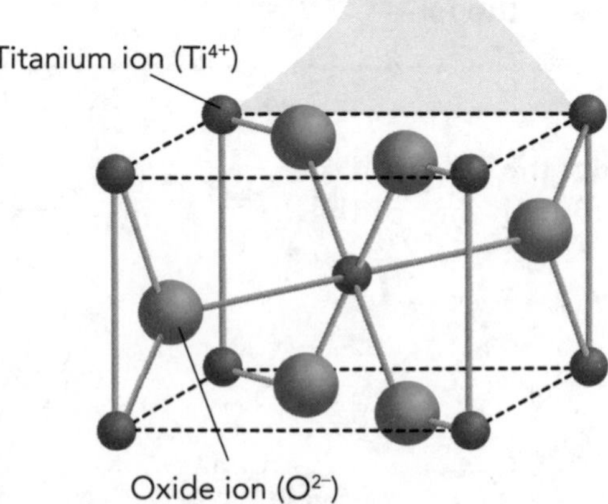

The unit cell for rutile shows how titanium and oxide ions are arranged. This pattern repeats throughout the entire rutile crystal.

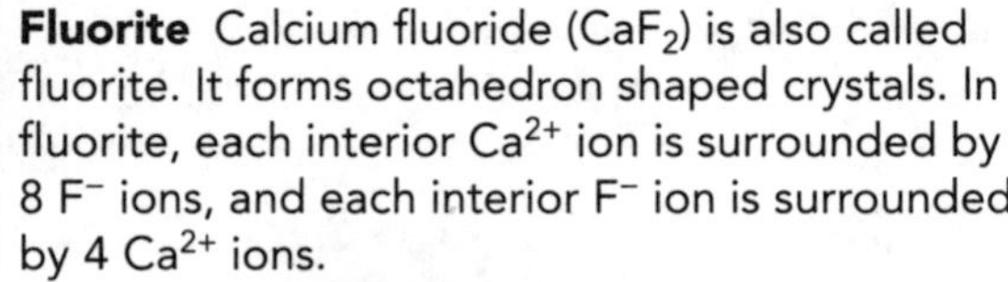
Fluorite Calcium fluoride (CaF_2) is also called fluorite. It forms octahedron shaped crystals. In fluorite, each interior Ca^{2+} ion is surrounded by 8 F^- ions, and each interior F^- ion is surrounded by 4 Ca^{2+} ions.

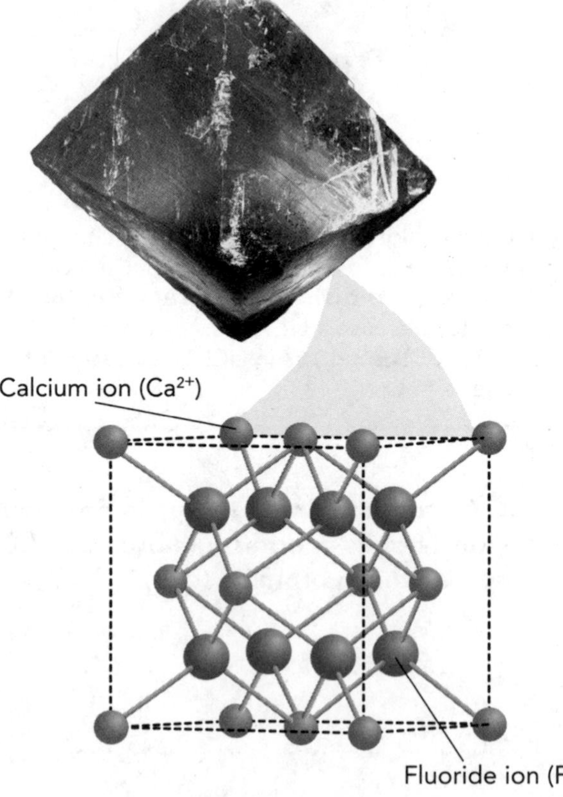

The unit cell for fluorite shows that the calcium and fluoride ions have a different pattern than the titanium and oxide ions in rutile.

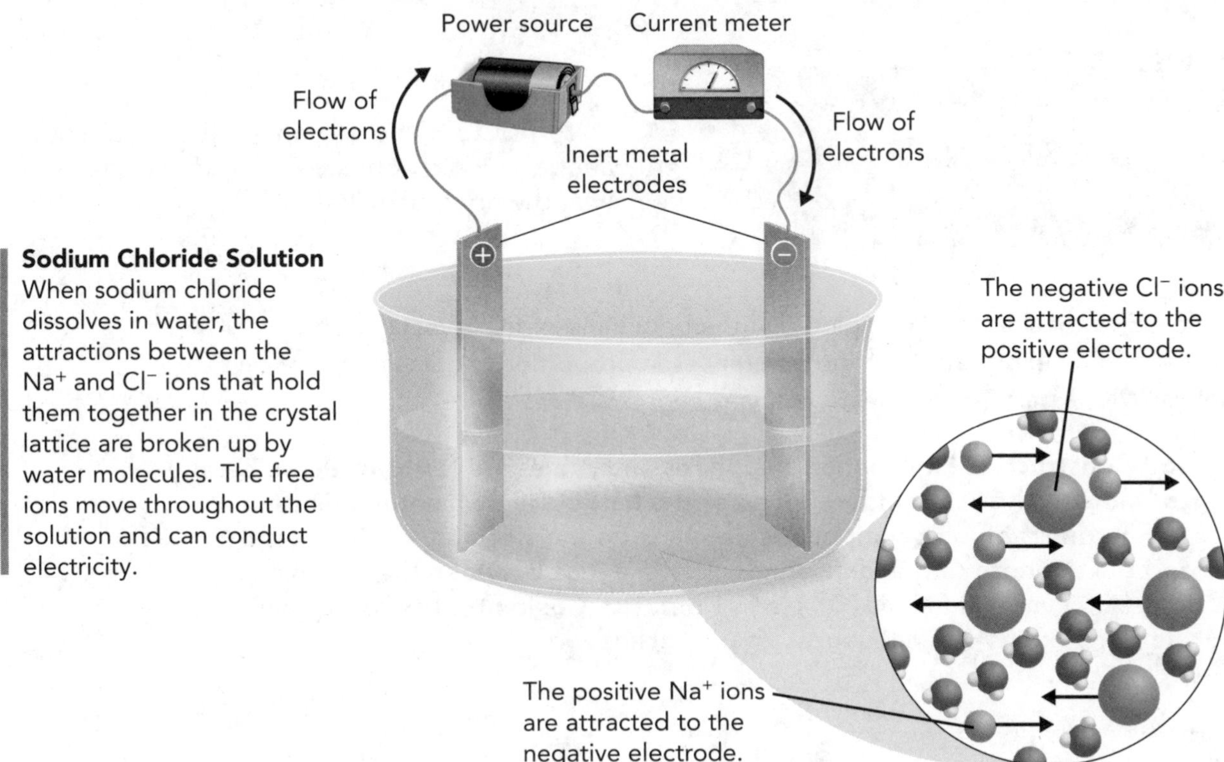
Power source
Current meter
Flow of electrons
Flow of electrons
Inert metal electrodes
The negative Cl⁻ ions are attracted to the positive electrode.
The positive Na⁺ ions are attracted to the negative electrode.

Sodium Chloride Solution When sodium chloride dissolves in water, the attractions between the Na^+ and Cl^- ions that hold them together in the crystal lattice are broken up by water molecules. The free ions move throughout the solution and can conduct electricity.

Conductivity and Solubility Many ionic compounds can dissolve in water. When an ionic compound dissolves, ions break away from the crystal as they are surrounded by water molecules. These ions are free to move in the solution. Thus, the resulting solutions can also conduct electric current. When a voltage is applied, anions move toward the positive electrode and cations move toward the negative electrode. The movement of ions allows electrons to flow through the wires that connect the electrodes. Liquid ionic compounds can also conduct electric current because the ions are mobile.

Melting Point Ionic compounds tend to be solids at room temperature because they have high melting points. For example, NaCl melts at about 800°C, and MgO has a melting point greater than 2800°C. The melting points of ionic compounds tend to be high because it takes a large amount of energy to overcome the strong attractive forces that hold the ions together throughout the solid.

8 **SEP Plan an Investigation Suppose you have samples of three unknown solids. Explain how you could use their properties to determine whether or not they are ionic solids.**

....

....

....

....

....

Revisit

INVESTIGATIVE PHENOMENON

GO ONLINE to Elaborate on and Evaluate your knowledge of ionic bonds by completing the peer review and writing activities.

In the CER worksheet you completed at the beginning of the investigation, you drafted an explanation for the differences in properties of gems and metals. With a partner, reevaluate your arguments.

9 **SEP Construct an Explanation** **Sapphires and rubies are forms of the mineral corundum, Al_2O_3. Corundum is one of the hardest known natural materials. The hardness of ionic compounds depends on the structure of the crystal and the strength of the ionic bonds. The distance between the aluminum ions (Al^{3+}) and oxide ions (O^{2-}) is 191 pm. Use Coulomb's law to explain how the bonding in Al_2O_3 influences its properties.**

EXPERIENCE 2

Metallic Bonds

GO ONLINE to Explore and Explain the properties of metals and to compare them to the properties of ionic compounds.

Sea of Electrons Model

Similar to the way ions form ionic compounds, metal atoms form cations to achieve stable electron configurations in pure metal substances. However, unlike in ionic compounds, the valence electrons are shared among all of the metal ions allowing them to move freely throughout the metal structure. A **metallic bond** is the electrostatic attraction between the free-moving valence electrons and the positively charged metal cations. Metallic bonding is modeled as a sea of electrons.

Metallic Bonding in Gold
The electrostatic attraction between the positive gold cations and the surrounding sea of electrons holds gold atoms together.

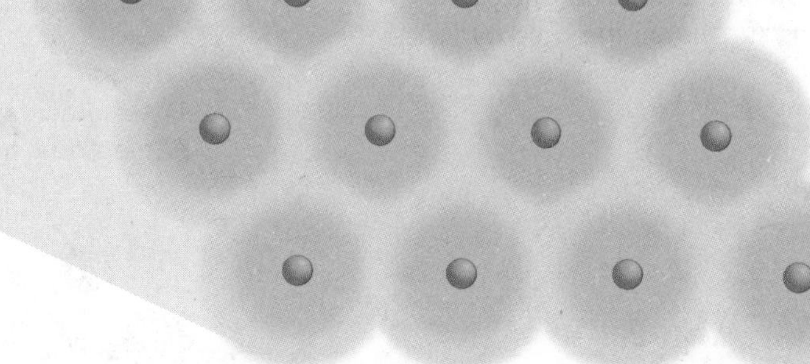

The core electrons and the nuclei make up the metal cations that are surrounded by the sea of electrons.

The orbitals in the valence shells of the metal atoms overlap. Valence electrons can travel throughout the metal, forming a sea of electrons.

(10) **SEP Compare Models Explain how the bonding model for sodium metal would differ from the bonding model for sodium chloride, NaCl.**

....

....

....

....

Properties of Metals

Extended Structures of Metals Like ionic compounds, metals are not composed of discrete molecules. The sea of electrons holds metal cations together in regular repeating structures throughout the entire solid. That is, solid metals have specific crystal structures.

The sea of electrons that extends in all directions results in specific properties of metals.

Metals can conduct electricity because their valence electrons are mobile. They are also malleable, meaning they can be hammered into shapes, and ductile, meaning they can be drawn into wires.

Malleability When a metal is hammered, it usually changes shape instead of breaking. As it changes shape, the metal cations slide past each other. Metallic bonds do not break when this happens because the surrounding valence electrons move, too.

Before being hammered, the sea of electrons surrounds the gold cations.

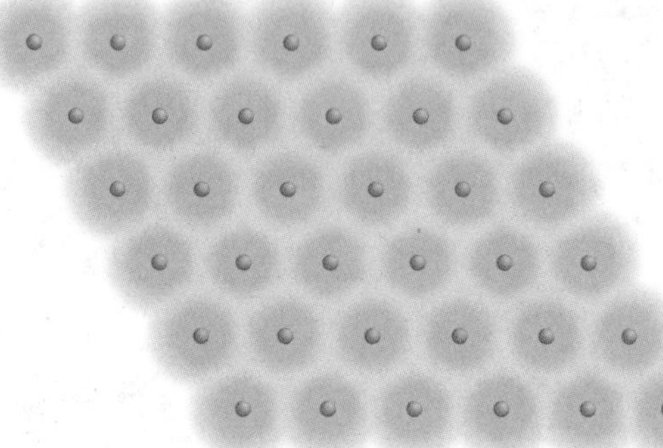

The gold cations move when gold is hammered. The metallic bonds are not broken because the sea of electrons moves with the gold cations.

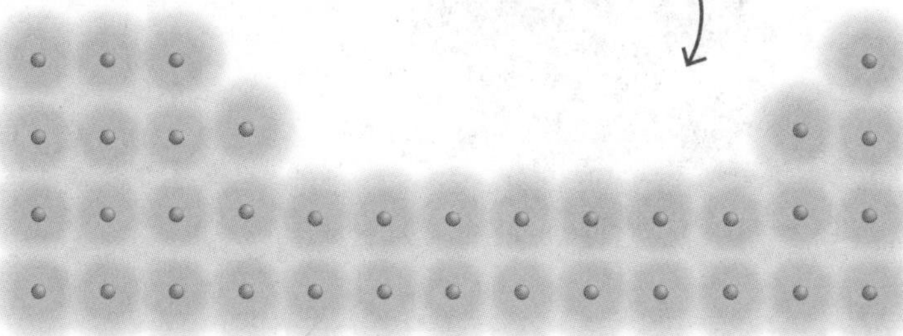

(11) **CCC Structure and Function** **When copper wires are made, a copper rod is pulled into a narrower wire. Explain how metallic bonding allows this to happen.**

Melting Point and Boiling Point Metals tend to have high melting points and boiling points. Iron, which is used to make steel, melts at 1535°C. Metals melt at high temperatures because of the strong electrostatic forces between the metal cations and surrounding valence electrons.

The melting point of a metal depends on the strength of the metallic bonds in the solid. For example, sodium melts at 98°C and boils at 883°C, while magnesium melts at 649°C and boils at 1107°C. Sodium melts at a lower temperature than magnesium because the melting point depends on the strength of the electrostatic attraction between the cations and the sea of electrons. This attractive force increases as the charge on the nucleus and the number of valence electrons increases.

Melting Point of Sodium The electrostatic attraction between sodium ions and the sea of electrons is strong.

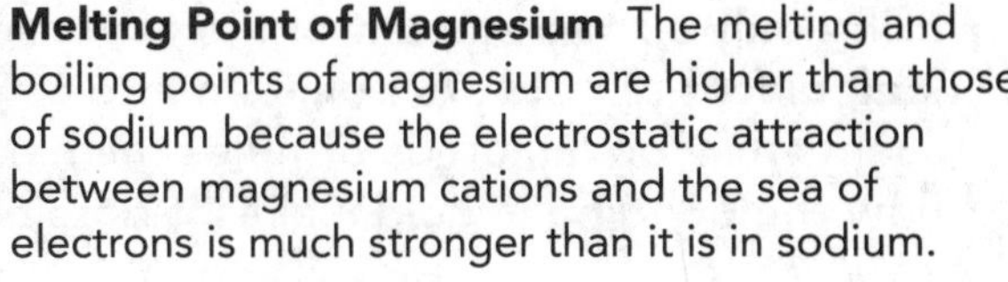
Melting Point of Magnesium The melting and boiling points of magnesium are higher than those of sodium because the electrostatic attraction between magnesium cations and the sea of electrons is much stronger than it is in sodium.

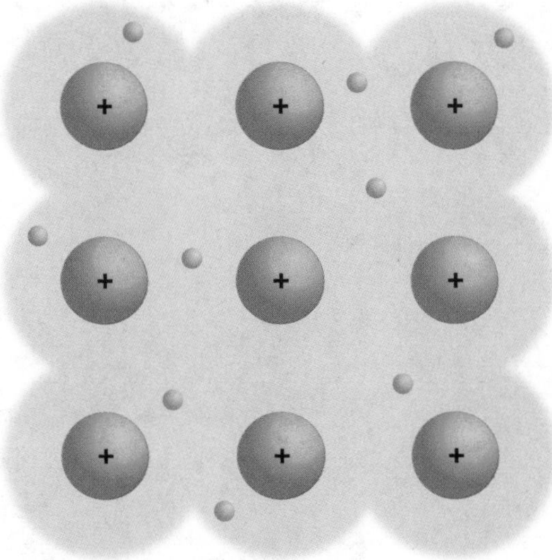

Sodium ions have a 1+ charge. Each ion contributes one electron to the electron cloud.

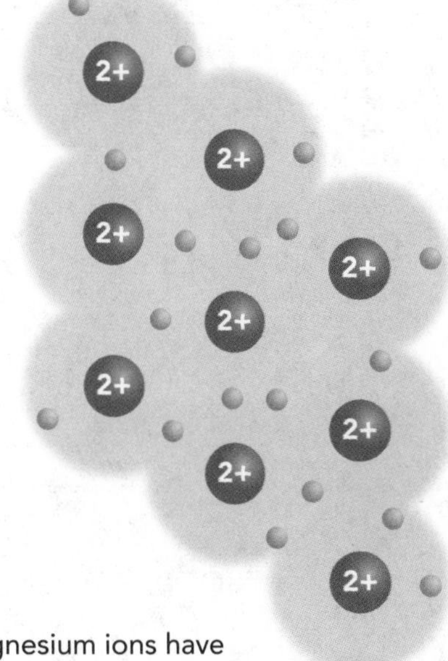

Magnesium ions have a 2+ charge. Each ion contributes two electrons to the electron cloud.

(12) **CCC Structure and Function Pots and pans that are used for cooking are often made of copper, aluminum, and iron. Explain how metallic bonding makes these metals suitable for this use.**

Revisit

INVESTIGATIVE PHENOMENON

GO ONLINE to Elaborate on and Evaluate your knowledge of metallic bonds by completing the class discussion and engineering design activities.

In the CER worksheet you completed at the beginning of the investigation, you drafted an explanation for the differences in properties of gems and metals. With a partner, reevaluate your arguments.

13 **SEP Construct an Explanation** **Gold leaf has been used by artisans since ancient times to cover objects with a decorative gold coating using only a small amount of the expensive metal. To make gold leaf, pieces of gold are pounded into extremely thin sheets. These sheets may be hundreds of times thinner than a human hair. Explain how the bonding in gold makes it possible to make gold leaf.**

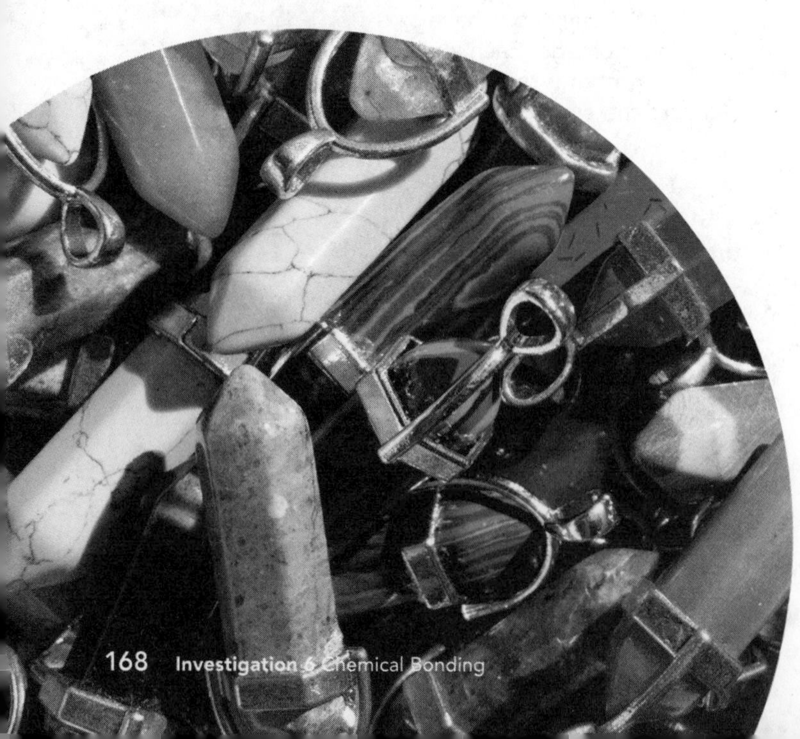

EXPERIENCE 3

Covalent Bonds

GO ONLINE to Explore and Explain covalent bonding and to analyze bond polarity.

Molecular Compounds

Nonmetal atoms share some or all of their valence electrons to form **covalent bonds.** These bonds hold the atoms together in discrete molecules. A **molecule** is a neutral group of atoms held together by one or more covalent bonds. Covalent bonds form when atoms of nonmetals get close enough for their orbitals to overlap. While electrons repel each other, the nuclei of the atoms pull on the electrons, and this force holds the atoms together.

In one model of covalent bonding, atomic orbitals mix, or hybridize, to form a new set of orbitals that form bonds in a molecule. These new orbitals help minimize the energy of the molecule. This model helps explain the shape of molecules and how atoms share pairs of electrons.

Hybrid Orbitals of Carbon The 2*s* and the three 2*p* atomic orbitals of the carbon atom hybridize to form four new $2sp^3$ orbitals in a methane molecule.

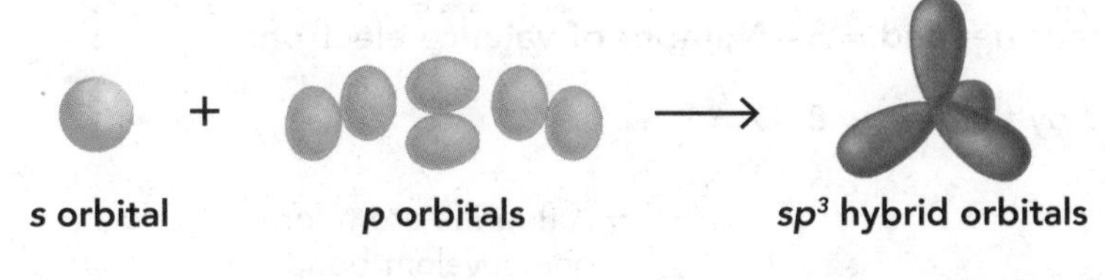

The hybrid orbitals that form the four bonds in methane have a different shape and orientation in space than *s* and *p* orbitals.

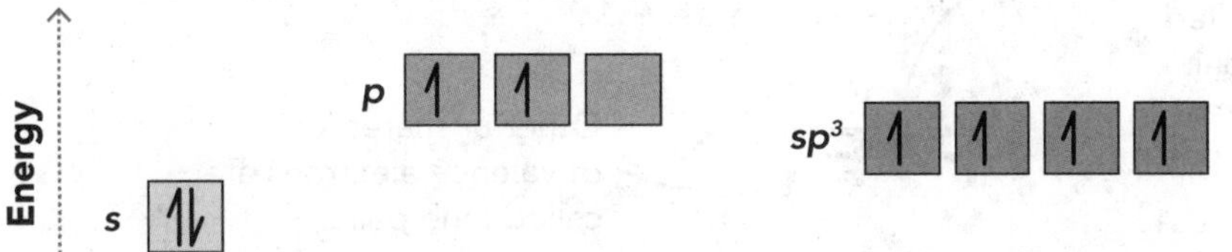

The sp^3 hybrid orbitals have a lower overall energy and are more stable than *p* orbitals when carbon forms bonds.

Bonding in a Methane Molecule When a carbon atom and four hydrogen atoms become close enough, the sp^3 orbitals of carbon and the *s* orbitals of hydrogen overlap to form the covalent bonds in a methane molecule.

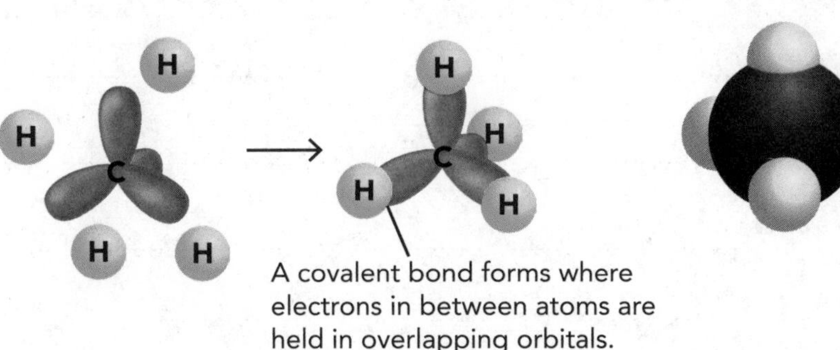

A covalent bond forms where electrons in between atoms are held in overlapping orbitals.

The shape of the hybrid orbitals can explain the shape of a methane molecule.

The Octet Rule in Molecules

Sharing Electrons Atoms of nonmetals form covalent bonds to become more stable by achieving the electron configuration of a noble gas. Instead of gaining or losing electrons, they share electrons. Hydrogen needs two valence electrons to have the electron configuration of helium. When two hydrogen atoms share a pair of electrons, both atoms attain the noble gas configuration. Most other nonmetal atoms share one or more pairs of electrons to attain eight electrons in their outermost energy levels.

Completing the Octet Nonmetal atoms, such as fluorine, share only some of their valence electrons to form covalent bonds. The number of bonding pairs of electrons equals the number of electrons needed for an octet, which can be determined from the group number in the periodic table.

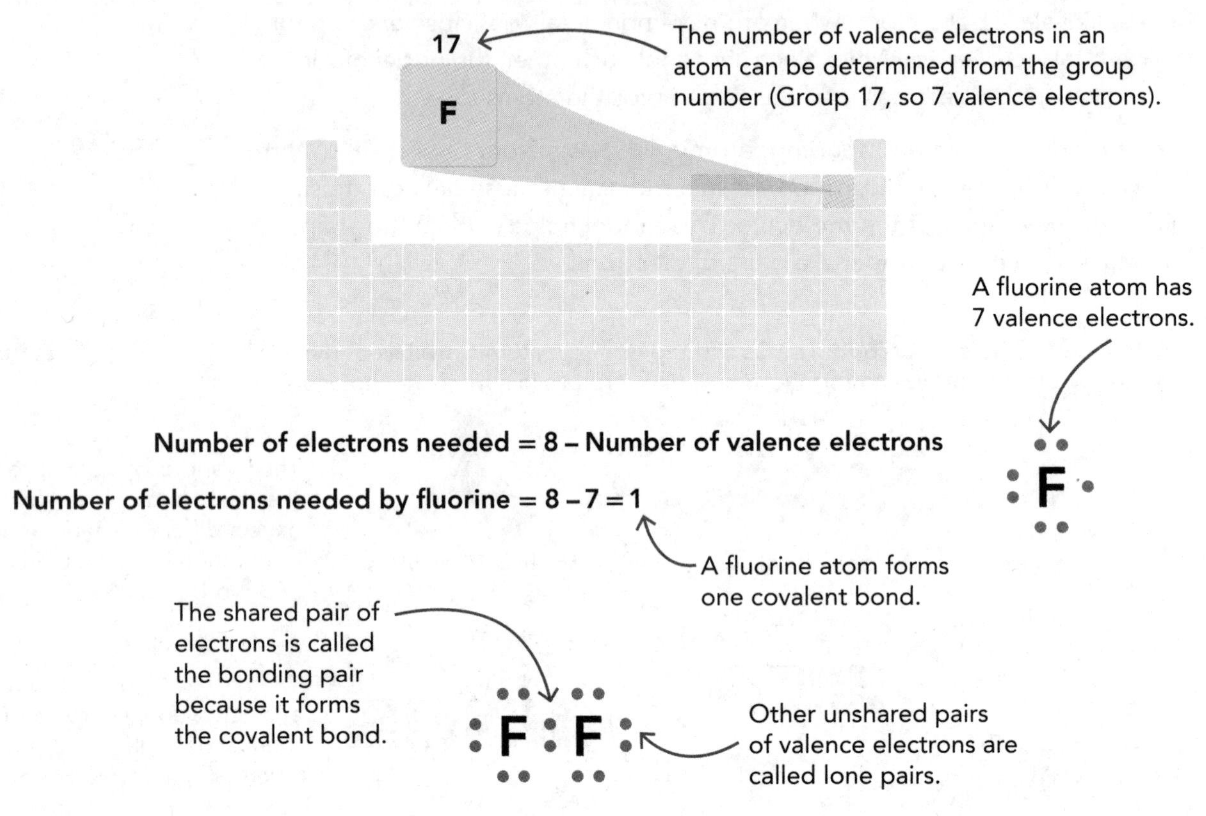

17
F
The number of valence electrons in an atom can be determined from the group number (Group 17, so 7 valence electrons).
A fluorine atom has 7 valence electrons.
Number of electrons needed = 8 – Number of valence electrons
Number of electrons needed by fluorine = 8 – 7 = 1
A fluorine atom forms one covalent bond.
The shared pair of electrons is called the bonding pair because it forms the covalent bond.
F F
Other unshared pairs of valence electrons are called lone pairs.

14 **CCC Patterns What is the relationship between the number of electrons an atom shares in covalent bonds and the number of valence electrons an atom has?**

Electron Dot Structures Electron dot structures show how atoms share electrons to meet the octet rule. A covalent bond may be modeled by a pair of dots located between the bonded atoms or by a line connecting the atoms. Lone pairs of electrons are also shown by dots. To draw a molecule's electron dot structure, determine how many bonds each atom will form. The central atom in the molecule must be able to form more than one bond. The total number of valence electrons in the atoms is the same as the total number of shared and unshared electrons in the molecule. Each atom, except for hydrogen, usually has an octet after electrons are shared. These electrons are grouped into four pairs, which may be either bonding pairs or lone pairs.

Drawing Electron Dot Structures The number of electrons an atom needs determines how many bonds it will form. Hydrogen and fluorine atoms form one bond because they each need one electron. Other atoms, such as nitrogen, form more bonds.

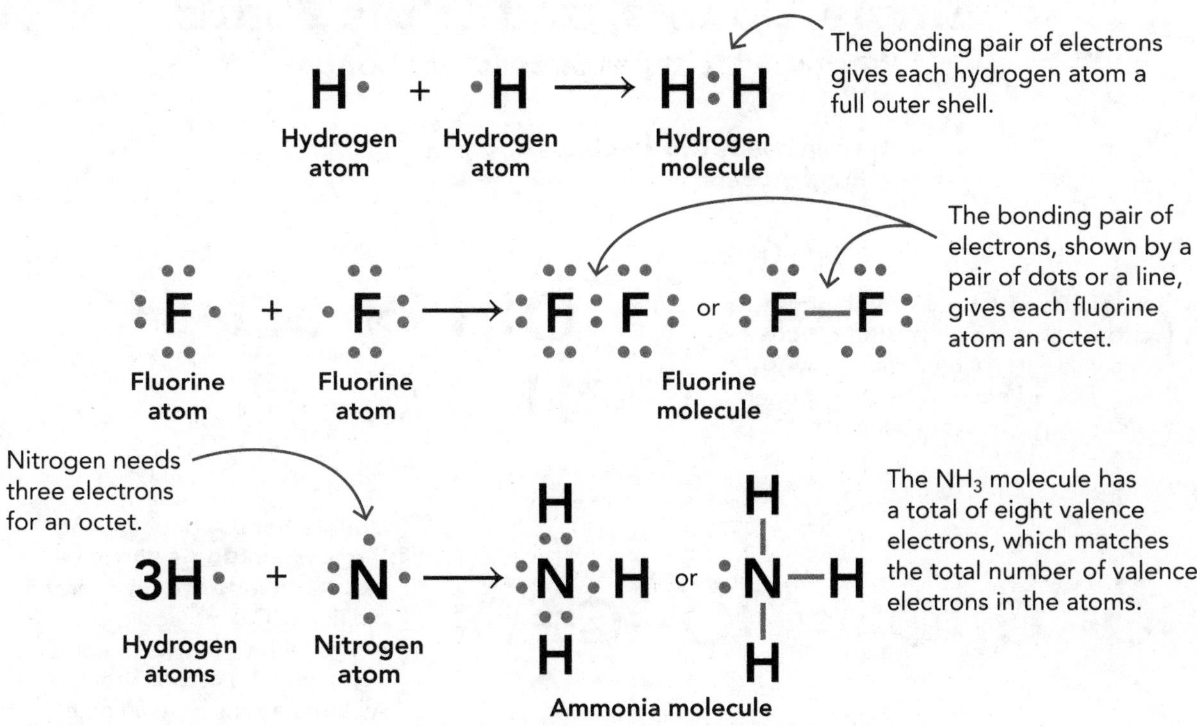

The bonding pair of electrons gives each hydrogen atom a full outer shell.
H• + •H ⟶ H:H
Hydrogen atom
Hydrogen atom
Hydrogen molecule
The bonding pair of electrons, shown by a pair of dots or a line, gives each fluorine atom an octet.
Fluorine atom
Fluorine atom
Fluorine molecule
or
Nitrogen needs three electrons for an octet.
3H• + N
Hydrogen atoms
Nitrogen atom
Ammonia molecule
The NH_3 molecule has a total of eight valence electrons, which matches the total number of valence electrons in the atoms.

Exceptions to the Octet Rule Hydrogen is an exception to the octet rule because it needs two electrons to achieve a stable electron configuration. It is better to think of the octet rule as a "guideline" rather than a rule because a number of other atoms may have fewer or more than eight valence electrons in a molecule. For example, boron may have only six valence electrons. Sulfur and phosphorus may have ten or twelve valence electrons.

Common Exceptions Boron forms three bonds in the boron trifluoride (BF_3) molecule. In a phosphorous pentachloride molecule (PCl_5), phosphorus forms five covalent bonds and has 10 valence electrons.

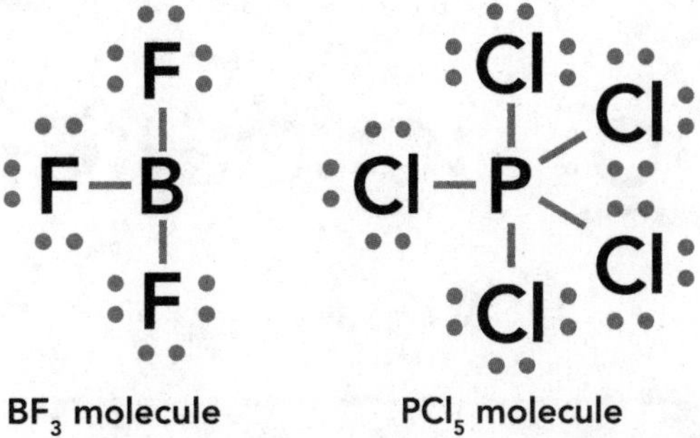

Types of Covalent Bonds

Atoms that need only one electron to attain a noble gas electron configuration, such as hydrogen and fluorine, form a single covalent bond. A **single covalent bond** is a bond made by one bonding pair of electrons. Atoms that need more than one electron for an octet, such as carbon and oxygen, can share more than one pair of electrons. A **double covalent bond** is a bond made by two bonding pairs of electrons. A **triple covalent bond** is a bond made by three bonding pairs of electrons. Sharing more electrons increases the strength of the force that holds two given atoms together. For example, a double bond between carbon and oxygen is stronger than a single bond between carbon and oxygen.

Single, Double, and Triple Bonds

What are the **types of covalent bonds?**

Oxygen needs two electrons to have an octet.

Single Bond A single bond forms when **atoms share one pair of electrons.** In a water (H_2O) molecule, there is a single bond between each hydrogen atom and the oxygen atom.

or

shared electrons

Double Bond A double bond forms when **atoms share two pairs of electrons.** In a carbon dioxide (CO_2) molecule, each oxygen atom forms a double bond with the carbon atom. All three atoms have an octet.

or

Triple Bond A triple bond forms when **atoms share three pairs of electrons.** In a carbon monoxide (CO) molecule, carbon and oxygen are held together by a triple bond. Both atoms have an octet.

or

Coordinate Covalent Bond In the CO molecule, the oxygen **atom donates an extra pair of electrons** to form the triple bond. In a molecule, it does not matter which atom the electrons in the bond come from.

SAMPLE PROBLEM

Electron Dot Structures for Molecular Substances

Draw the electron dot structures for the following molecular substances.

a. N_2 **b.** HOCl

ANALYZE Identify the relevant concepts.

The number of bonding pairs of electrons depends on how many electrons an atom needs to satisfy the octet rule. Atoms may form single, double, or triple bonds. Electron dot structures also show lone pairs of electrons.

SOLVE Apply the concepts to this problem.

	a.	b.
Draw the electron dot structures for the atoms.	:N· + ·N: **Nitrogen atom** **Nitrogen atom**	H· + ·Cl: + :O· **Hydrogen atom** **Chlorine atom** **Oxygen atom**
Determine how many electrons each atom needs.	3 electrons 3 electrons	1 electron 1 electron 2 electrons
Identify the central atom for molecules with more than two atoms. It must be able to form more than one single bond.	Diatomic molecules do not have a central atom.	O is the central atom. 
Draw the electron dot structure of the molecule so that each atom, except hydrogen, has an octet.	:N:::N: or :N≡N: **Nitrogen molecule**	H:O:Cl: or H–O–Cl: **Hypochlorous acid molecule**
Check that the total number of electrons in the structure is the same as the sum of the valence electrons in the atoms.	5 + 5 = 10	1 + 7 + 6 = 14

15 **Draw the electron dot structures for the molecular compounds.**

a. BrI **b.** CH_4

GO ONLINE for more practice problems.

Electronegativity and Bonding

Electronegativity and the Periodic Table Atoms pull on the electrons they share in bonds, and one atom often has a greater pull on the electrons. **Electronegativity** is the ability of an atom of an element to attract electrons toward itself in a chemical bond. Fluorine is the most electronegative element, which means it always pulls electrons away from an atom of another element when it forms a bond. For example, it pulls electrons away from carbon in the C—F bonds of carbon tetrafluoride (CF_4).

Electronegativity has predictable trends for the main-group elements in the periodic table.

Electronegativity Trends The electronegativity values given under the chemical symbols are from the Pauling scale. The highest value on this scale is 4.0. In the periodic table, values tend to increase from bottom to top within a group. For main-group elements, the values tend to increase from left to right across a period.

Electronegativity Increases (left to right)

Electronegativity Increases (bottom to top)

1 1A	2 2A		13 3A	14 4A	15 5A	16 6A	17 7A	18 8A
1 H 2.1								2 He
3 Li 1.0	4 Be 1.5		5 B 2.0	6 C 2.5	7 N 3.0	8 O 3.5	9 F 4.0	10 Ne
11 Na 0.9	12 Mg 1.2		13 Al 1.5	14 Si 1.8	15 P 2.1	16 S 2.5	17 Cl 3.0	18 Ar
19 K 0.8	20 Ca 1.0		31 Ga 1.6	32 Ge 1.8	33 As 2.0	34 Se 2.4	35 Br 2.8	36 Kr
37 Rb 0.8	38 Sr 1.0		49 In 1.7	50 Sn 1.8	51 Sb 1.9	52 Te 2.1	53 I 2.5	54 Xe

Metals have lower electronegativities than nonmetals. They have a weaker pull on electrons in bonds.

The electronegativity values of the noble gases are not shown because they rarely form bonds.

16 **CCC Patterns Rank the electronegativity values of lithium, oxygen, potassium, and selenium from lowest to highest. Explain their general electronegativity trends in the periodic table.**

Electron Tug-of-War Atoms are in a tug-of-war for bonding electrons, much like a knot in a rope is pulled toward opposite sides in a tug-of-war game.

The knot in the rope is in the middle of the two teams because they are pulling with equal force. Likewise, electrons are shared equally between atoms in a **nonpolar covalent bond.**

One team is pulling harder than the other. The knot is pulled to their side. In **polar covalent bonds,** electrons are pulled closer to the atom that has the higher electronegativity.

One team has pulled much harder than the other team and has won the game. In **ionic bonds**, the atom with higher electronegativity pulls the electron(s) away from the other atom.

Electronegativity and Bond Polarity The electronegativity difference between two bonded atoms helps characterize a bond as ionic, polar covalent, or nonpolar covalent. These bond types fall on a spectrum from increasingly ionic to decreasingly polar. Ionic bonds have an electronegativity difference greater than 2.0. A **polar covalent bond** is a bond in which electrons are shared but not shared equally between the atoms. The electronegativity difference of polar covalent bonds is between 0.4 and 2.0. A **nonpolar covalent bond** is a bond in which the electrons are shared equally. Nonpolar covalent bonds have minimal electronegativity differences (0.4 or less).

17 **SEP Use Math Calculate the electronegativity differences and determine the polarity for the bonds formed by the following pairs of atoms: K and F atoms and N and O atoms.**

Geometry and Polar Molecules

VSEPR Theory The electrostatic forces within a molecule help determine its shape. According to **VSEPR theory,** bonding pairs of electrons and lone pairs of valence electrons repel each other and push each other as far away as possible to minimize the electrostatic repulsions between them. These repulsions result in specific three-dimensional shapes. VSEPR stands for valence-shell electron-pair repulsion. The table shows common three-dimensional shapes that are predicted by VSEPR theory.

Examples of Common Molecular Shapes

Number of electron pairs	Number of lone pairs of electrons		
	0	1	2
2	linear		
3	trigonal planar	bent	
4	tetrahedral	pyramidal	bent

(18) **CCC Cause and Effect Why can molecules made of three atoms have a bent or linear shape?**

Polar Molecules In polar molecules, the electrons are not evenly distributed. One end of the molecule has a partial positive charge, and the other end has a partial negative charge. The polarity of bonds is modeled by different symbols. The lowercase Greek letter delta (δ) indicates which atoms have a partial charge of less than 1+ or 1−. An arrow also represents polarity. It points toward the more electronegative atom and has a "+" side next to the atom with partial positive charge.

The polarity of a molecule is determined by the polarity of the bonds and by the geometry of the molecule. Diatomic molecules have only one bond. If that bond is polar, then the molecule is polar. For other molecules, the geometry of a molecule may cancel out the polarity of different bonds to make the molecule nonpolar.

Diatomic Molecules All diatomic molecules with polar bonds, such as hydrogen fluoride (HF), are polar. In HF, fluorine is the more electronegative atom.

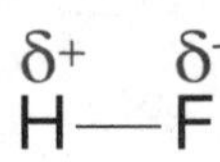

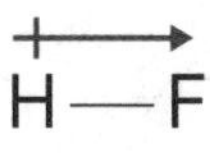

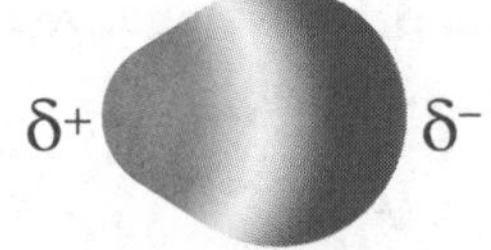

Polar Molecules Polar molecules, such as water, have polar bonds and a geometry that leads to an uneven electron density.

A water molecule has two bonding pairs and two lone pairs of electrons around the oxygen atom. Therefore, it has a bent shape.

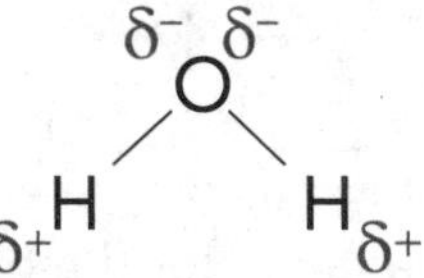

There are two polar bonds in a water molecule. The O atom has a partial negative charge because it is more electronegative.

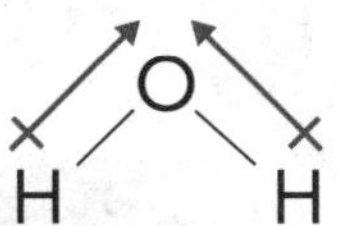

The arrows both point toward the O atom.

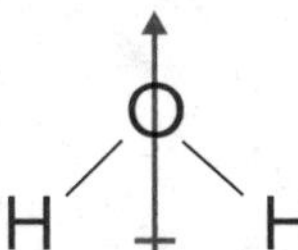

The polar bonds add together instead of canceling each other out, making water a polar molecule.

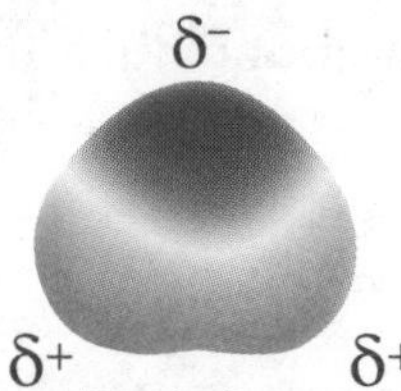

A polar molecule has an uneven electron density. In water, the O atom has a higher electron density than the side of the molecule with the H atoms.

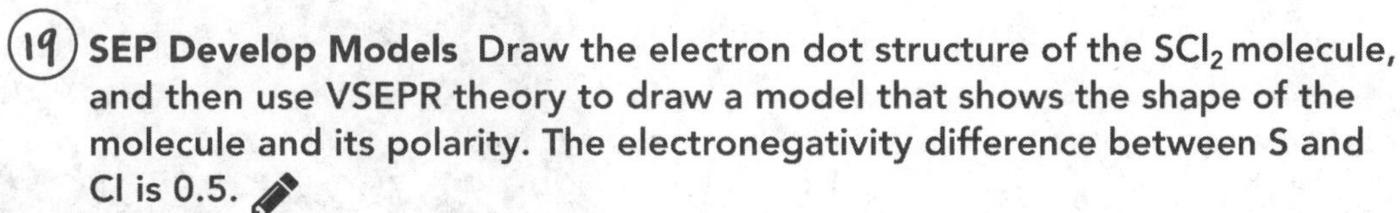

19 **SEP Develop Models Draw the electron dot structure of the SCl_2 molecule, and then use VSEPR theory to draw a model that shows the shape of the molecule and its polarity. The electronegativity difference between S and Cl is 0.5.**

Nonpolar Molecules Nonpolar molecules may have either nonpolar bonds or bond polarity that get cancelled due to the geometry of the molecule. Carbon dioxide molecules have two polar bonds, similar to water molecules. However, the molecules are nonpolar because of their shape.

Shape and Polarity of Carbon Dioxide Carbon dioxide is a linear molecule with two polar bonds. It is symmetrical because both halves are exactly the same.

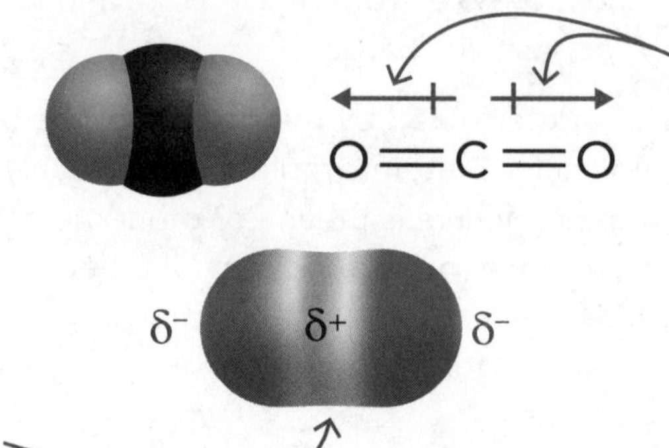

Both bonds are polar because the oxygen atoms pull on electrons more than the carbon atom does. However, they pull in opposite directions and cancel each other out.

The molecule doesn't have a positive end and a negative end. Instead it is like a sandwich of charge with a partially positive filling and partially negative ends.

Revisit

INVESTIGATIVE PHENOMENON

GO ONLINE to Elaborate on and Evaluate your knowledge of covalent bonding by completing the class discussion and data analysis activities.

In the CER worksheet you completed at the beginning of the investigation, you drafted an explanation for the differences in properties of gems and metals. With a partner, reevaluate your arguments.

20 Compare and Contrast Plastic beads used in jewelry making are made of long molecules usually consisting of carbon, hydrogen, and oxygen. Compare the bonding in these molecules to the bonding in gems.

....

....

....

....

....

....

....

....

EXPERIENCE 4

Intermolecular Attractions

GO ONLINE to Explore and Explain the differences in the properties of molecular substances as a result of intermolecular forces.

Van der Waals Forces

Attractions Between Molecules Molecules can be attracted to each other due to a variety of intermolecular forces. When comparing one to one, an intermolecular attraction is weaker than an ionic or covalent bond. However, many intermolecular attractions in a sample can result in a cumulative effect that is incredibly strong. The weakest types of attractions between molecules—dispersion forces and dipole interactions—are called **van der Waals forces.**

Dispersion Forces The weakest of all molecular interactions, called **dispersion forces** or London dispersion forces, are caused by the motion of electrons. Electron motion in a molecule results in a momentary uneven distribution of charges, which happens even in nonpolar molecules. Thus, dispersion forces occur between all molecules. Dispersion forces increase as the number of electrons increases because the electron cloud becomes easier to polarize, or cause temporary oppositely charged ends.

Nonpolar Molecules Hydrogen is a nonpolar molecule, and the electrons are evenly distributed. However, electrons shift around in molecules.

H — H

H — H

Electrons may be more concentrated momentarily on one side of the molecule than the other. This causes the molecule to form a temporary dipole.

The electric force of a temporarily polar molecule cause a dipole in a nearby molecule. A partial negative charge pushes electrons away. A partial positive charge pulls electrons toward it.

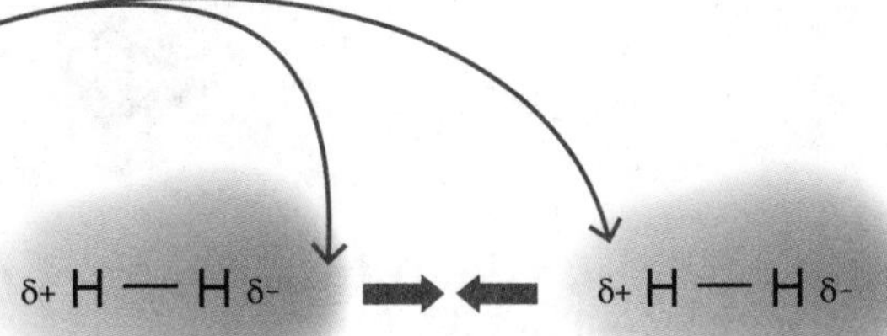

Temporary Forces A weak electrostatic attraction forms between partial positive and partial negative ends of the temporary dipoles. The attraction breaks up when electrons move again.

Dipole Interactions Because polar molecules have permanent partial positive and partial negative ends, they are attracted to one another by electrostatic attractions. **Dipole interactions** are intermolecular attractions between oppositely charged regions of polar molecules. The partially positive end of one molecule is attracted to the partially negative end of another molecule. These weak electrostatic forces hold molecules together in solids and liquids. Dipole interactions tend to be stronger than dispersion forces. However, they are still relatively weak compared to bonds between atoms and ions.

Dipole Interactions in ICl
Iodine monochloride (ICl) is a polar molecule because the chlorine atom has a stronger pull on the electrons. The partially positive iodine atom in one molecule is attracted to the partially negative chlorine atom in another molecule.

A dipole interaction is an electrostatic attraction between the partial positive and partial negative ends of polar molecules.

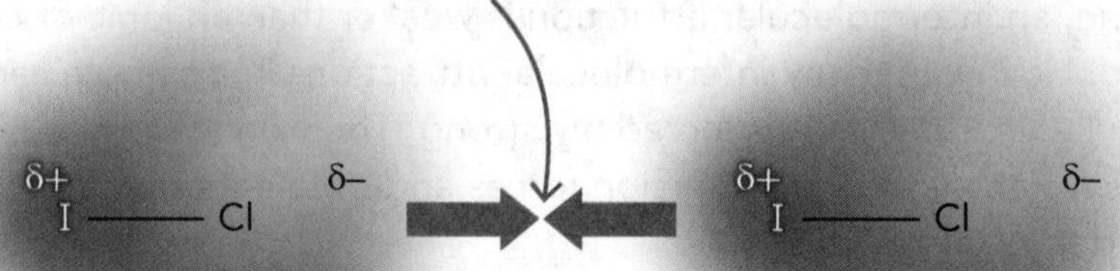

Each molecule can have several dipole interactions with other nearby molecules.

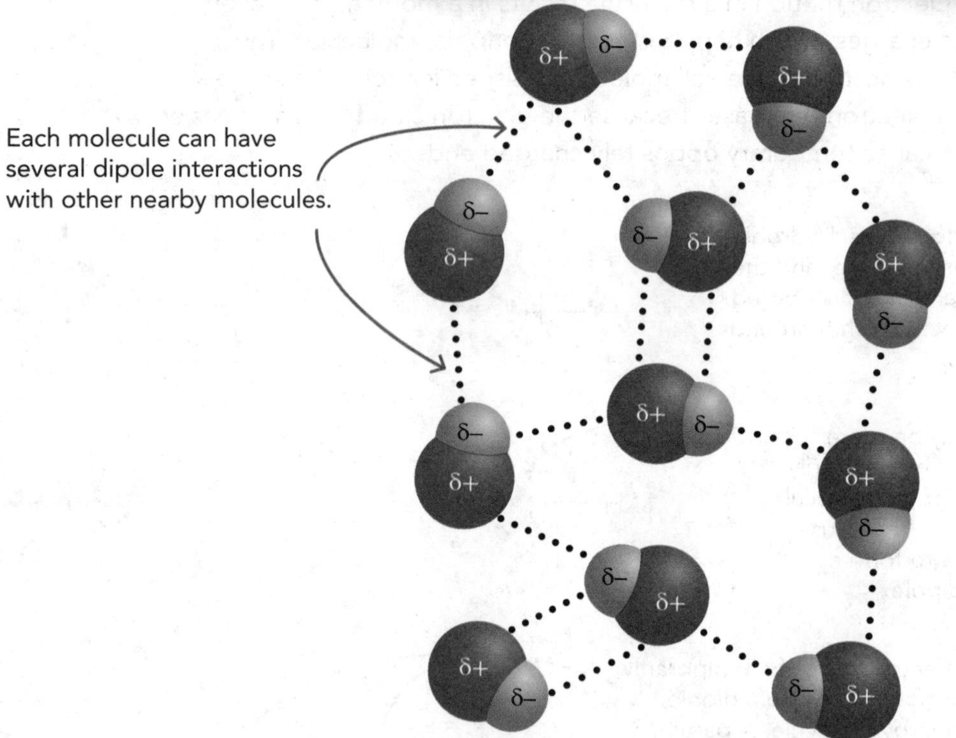

(21) **Predict** What type of van der Waals interactions occur between molecules of O_2, SCl_2, and CH_4 in liquids of these substances?

Hydrogen Bonds

Hydrogen bonds are intermolecular forces in which a hydrogen covalently bonded to a very electronegative atom is also weakly attracted to a lone electron pair of another electronegative atom. Hydrogen bonds always involve hydrogen, whose valence electrons are not shielded from the nucleus by other electrons. They form between molecules that have hydrogen bonded to a very electronegative atom, commonly fluorine, chlorine, oxygen, or nitrogen. These covalent bonds are strongly polar. The partially positive hydrogen atoms and the partially negative atoms in the molecules are attracted to each other to form hydrogen bonds between the molecules. Hydrogen bonds are a particularly strong type of dipole interaction and are the strongest of all the intermolecular forces. However, it is important to remember that hydrogen bonds are still a weak force, and they are not bonds.

Hydrogen Bonding in Water There are strong hydrogen bonds between water molecules. Each O—H bond in the water molecule is highly polar. The O has a slightly negative charge, and the H has a slightly positive charge. The positive region of one water molecule attracts the negative region of another water molecule, forming a hydrogen bond.

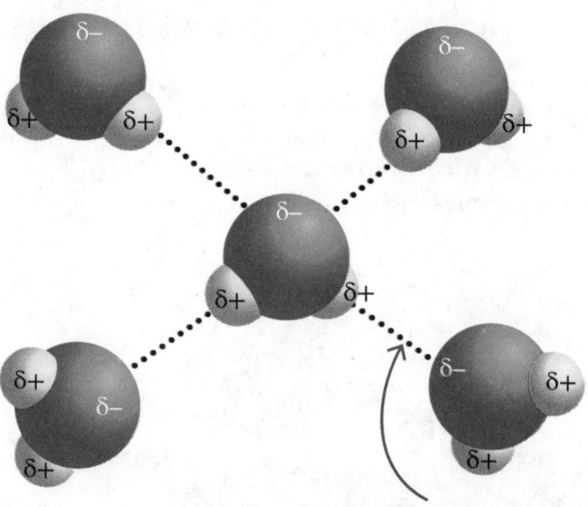

A hydrogen bond occurs between a partially positive hydrogen atom and the partially negative oxygen atom.

No Hydrogen Bonding Methane (CH_4) is a nonpolar molecule. Carbon is not highly electronegative, and the C—H bonds are not polar. Therefore, there is no hydrogen bonding between methane molecules.

22 **CCC Patterns Explain whether hydrogen bonding is present between hydrogen fluoride (HF) molecules.**

....

....

Properties of Molecular Substances

Intermolecular Force Effects on Macroscopic Properties Bulk properties such as melting point, boiling point, and volatility depend on intermolecular interactions. Strong intermolecular forces, such as hydrogen bonding and dipole interactions, hold the molecules together more tightly than weaker dispersion forces.

Volatility Volatility is a measure of how easily a liquid evaporates. Volatile liquids have a greater number of molecules in the gas phase above the liquid. The stronger the intermolecular forces, the lower the volatility because the molecules are held together strongly in the liquid phase, preventing them from going into the gas phase.

Volatility

How do **intermolecular forces affect volatility?**

Bromine Only dispersion forces hold bromine molecules together in liquid bromine. As a result, **bromine is highly volatile,** meaning there are many bromine molecules in the gas phase above the liquid.

Ethanol The forces between ethanol molecules are stronger than those between bromine molecules. Therefore, **ethanol is less volatile than bromine.**

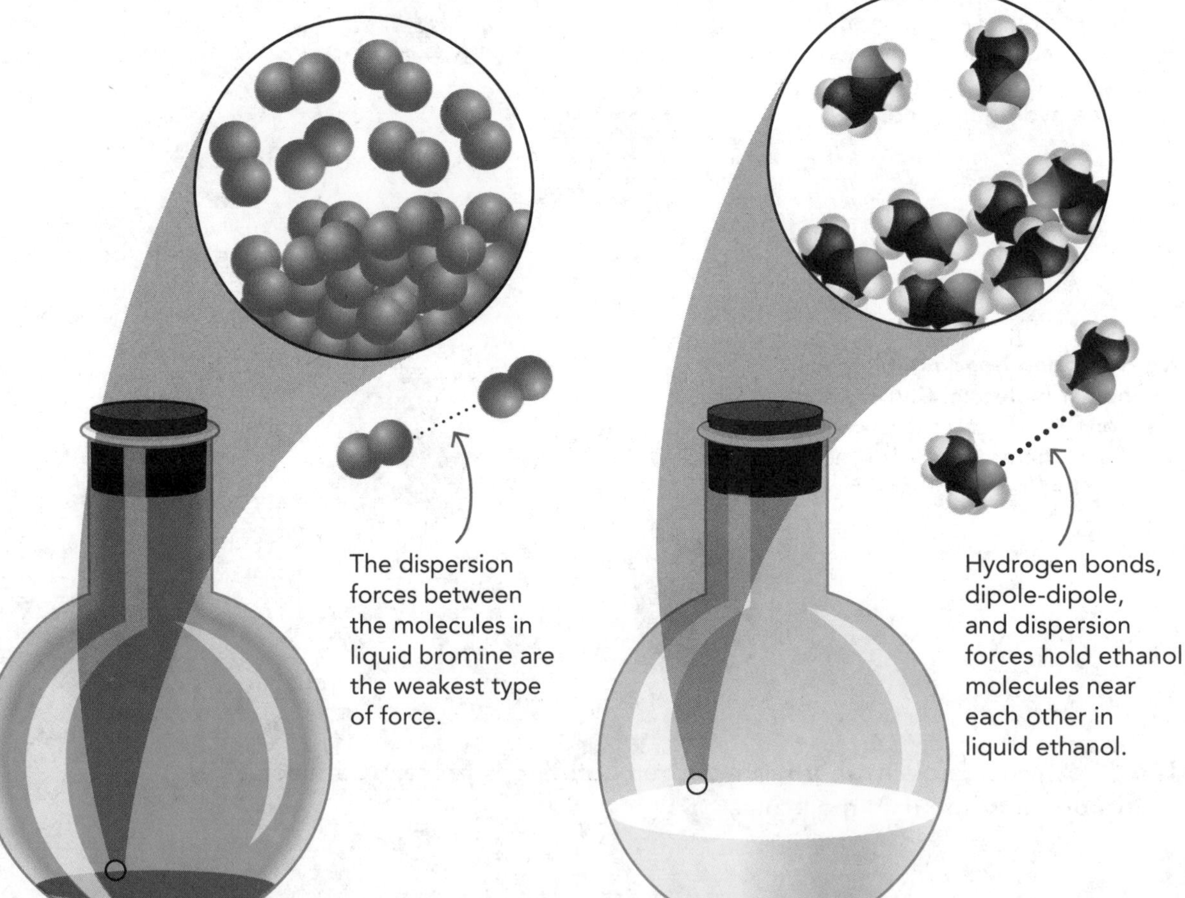

The dispersion forces between the molecules in liquid bromine are the weakest type of force.
Hydrogen bonds, dipole-dipole, and dispersion forces hold ethanol molecules near each other in liquid ethanol.

Gas in Air and Water
Nitrogen and oxygen are gases at even the coldest temperatures on Earth because they have low boiling points. Little energy is needed to break the weak dispersion forces that hold the molecules in these liquids together. Water exists as a solid, liquid, or gas on Earth. Below its melting point of 0°C, hydrogen bonds are strong enough to lock water molecules in place in a solid.

Melting Point and Boiling Point Molecular substances tend to melt and boil at lower temperatures than ionic compounds or metals because intermolecular attractions are weaker than ionic and metallic bonds. For molecular substances, melting and boiling points depend on the strength of intermolecular forces.

The stronger the intermolecular forces, the higher the melting and boiling points because it takes more energy to separate the molecules.

The relative strengths of different types of forces and the relative strengths of one type of force affects the properties of substances. For example, halogens exist at different states at room temperature and atmospheric pressure because of different strengths of dispersion forces. The number of electrons and size of the electron cloud increases from the top to the bottom of Group 17. Diatomic chlorine (Cl_2) molecules have 34 electrons, bromine (Br_2) molecules have 70 electrons, and iodine (I_2) molecules have 106 electrons. As a result, the dispersion forces are weakest in chlorine and strongest in iodine. This difference is observed on the macroscopic scale. Chlorine is a gas, bromine is a liquid, and iodine is a solid.

23 CCC Energy and Matter Identify the dominant intermolecular force in ammonia (NH_3). Given that ammonia is a gas at room temperature, what can you infer about the relative strengths of the intermolecular forces between ammonia molecules and between water molecules?

Revisit

INVESTIGATIVE PHENOMENON

GO ONLINE to Elaborate on and Evaluate your knowledge of intermolecular attractions by completing the peer review and writing activities.

In the CER worksheet you completed at the beginning of the investigation, you drafted an explanation for the differences in properties of gems and metals. With a partner, reevaluate your arguments.

24 SEP Evaluate Claims **Rock candy is composed of large sugar crystals, which are made of sugar molecules. Growing the crystals in water with food dyes makes colored crystals. A friend has a plan to make jewelry using rock candy and claims that the jewelry will look like and last as long as jewelry made from gemstones. Use evidence about the bonding in ionic and molecular compounds to evaluate this claim.**

EXPERIENCE 5

Names and Formulas of Compounds

GO ONLINE to Explore and Explain the names and chemical formulas for ionic and molecular compounds.

Naming Ions

Monoatomic Ions An ion that consists of a single atom with a positive or negative charge is called a **monoatomic ion.** Remember that main-group metal cations in Groups 1, 2, and 13 have charges of 1+, 2+, and 3+, respectively. Nonmetals form anions with charges that can be predicted from their group numbers (charge = group number − 18). Some metals, including transition metals such as iron and copper, can form more than one cation with different charges. The name of a monoatomic ion depends on whether it is a metal or nonmetal. The Stock system of naming is used for elements that can form more than one kind of cation. This system uses Roman numerals to indicate the charges of the ions.

General Rules for Naming Ions Ions are named differently, depending on whether they are metal ions, nonmetal ions, or ions of elements that can form more than one common ion.

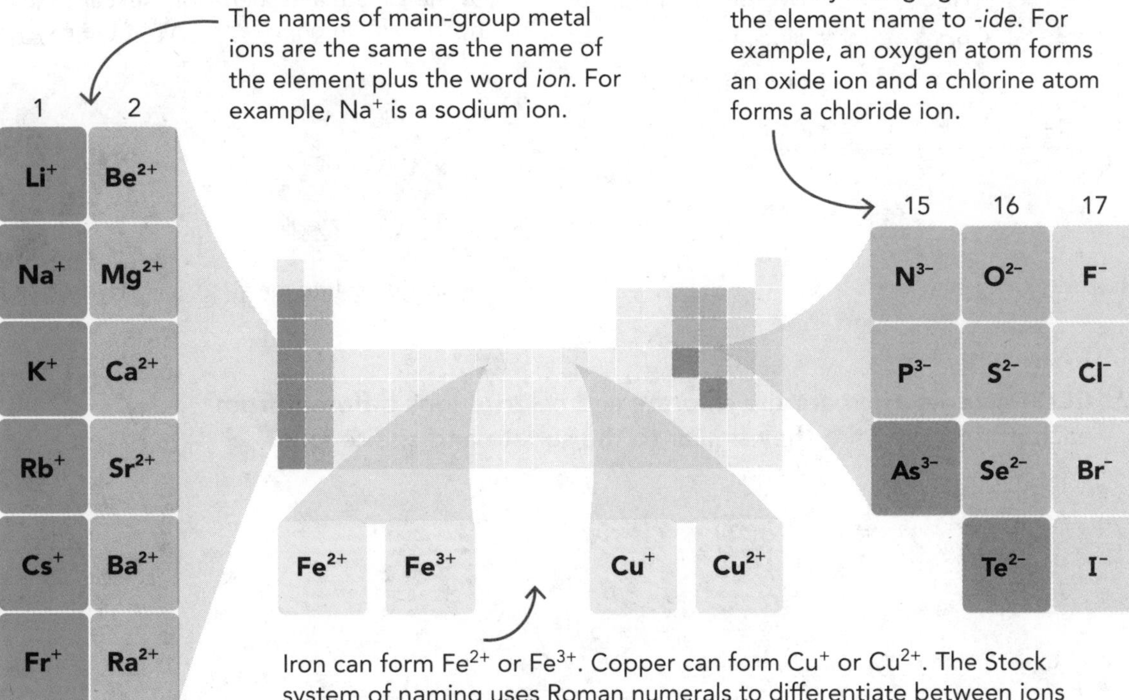

The names of main-group metal ions are the same as the name of the element plus the word *ion*. For example, Na^+ is a sodium ion.

Main-group nonmetal ions are named by changing the end of the element name to *-ide*. For example, an oxygen atom forms an oxide ion and a chlorine atom forms a chloride ion.

Iron can form Fe^{2+} or Fe^{3+}. Copper can form Cu^+ or Cu^{2+}. The Stock system of naming uses Roman numerals to differentiate between ions of the same element with different charges. In the Stock system, Fe^{2+} is named iron(II), which is read as *iron two*. Fe^{3+} is named iron(III), which is read as *iron three*.

Polyatomic Ions Ions that are made of a group of atoms that are covalently bonded together and have a charge are called **polyatomic ions.** These ions behave as a single unit, similar to a molecule. The name of a polyatomic ion depends on the types and number of atoms in the ion.

Polyatomic Ions The table and the models show several common polyatomic ions. The *-ite* and *-ate* endings in the names indicate that the polyatomic ions contains oxygen.

Common Polyatomic Ions

Charge	Formula	Name
1–	NO_2^-	Nitrite
	NO_3^-	Nitrate
	CN^-	Cyanide
	OH^-	Hydroxide
	HCO_3^-	Hydrogen carbonate
	$H_2PO_4^-$	Dihydrogen phosphate
	HSO_3^-	Hydrogen sulfite
	HSO_4^-	Hydrogen sulfate
	ClO_2^-	Chlorite
	ClO_3^-	Chlorate
2–	SO_3^{2-}	Sulfite
	SO_4^{2-}	Sulfate
	CO_3^{2-}	Carbonate
	CrO_4^{2-}	Chromate
	$Cr_2O_7^{2-}$	Dichromate
	HPO_4^{2-}	Hydrogen phosphate
3–	PO_3^{3-}	Phosphite
	PO_4^{3-}	Phosphate
1+	NH_4^+	Ammonium

The *-ite* ending indicates one less oxygen atom than the *-ate* ending.

Nitrite ion

Nitrate ion

The sulfite ion has one less oxygen atom than the sulfate ion. However, the sulfite ion has a different number of oxygen atoms than the nitrite ion.

Sulfite ion

Sulfate ion

Hydrogen sulfate and hydrogen sulfite are similar to the sulfate and sulfite ions, except they have a hydrogen ion bonded to one of the oxygen atoms.

Hydrogen sulfite ion

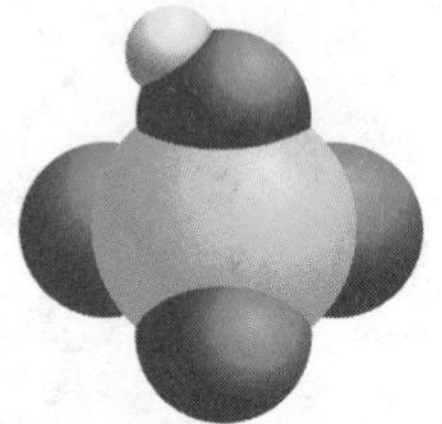
Hydrogen sulfate ion

25 CCC Patterns How are the chlorate and chlorite ions different from each other? How are they similar to the sulfate and sulfite ions?

Names of Ionic Compounds

A **chemical formula** shows the numbers of atoms of each element in the smallest representative unit of a substance. A **binary compound** is a compound composed of only two elements. To name a binary ionic compound, you combine the names of the cation and the anion, in that order, which is usually the way they are written in the chemical formula.

Compounds With Main-Group Elements To name ionic compounds with main-group elements, such as $CaCl_2$, put the cation name first and the anion name second.

The calcium ion, Ca^{2+}, is the cation.

The chloride ion, Cl^-, is the anion.

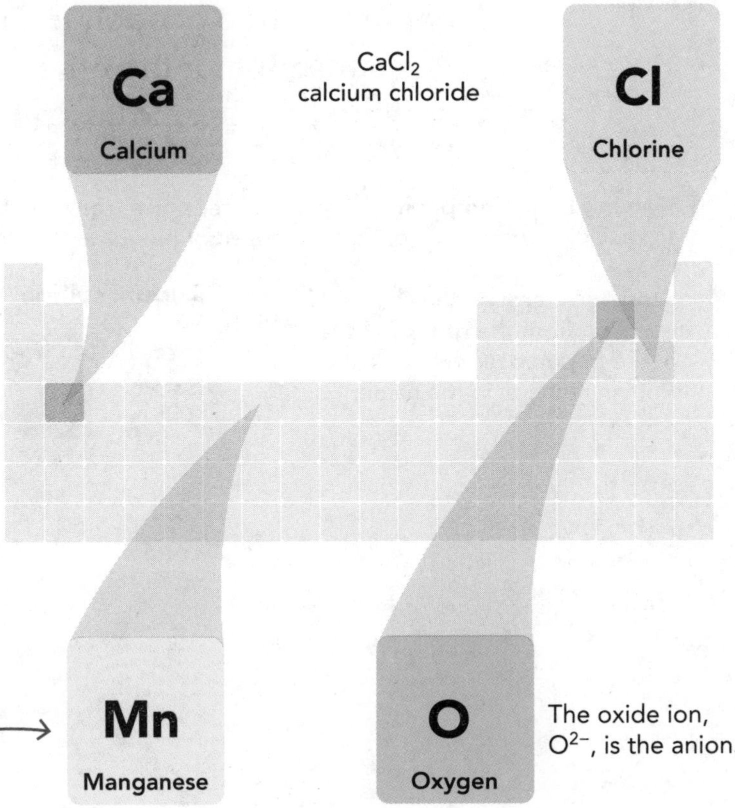

Ca
Calcium

$CaCl_2$
calcium chloride

Cl
Chlorine

Compounds That Use The Stock System The names of ionic compounds with metal cations that can form more than one cation, such as tin, lead, and many transition metals, include Roman numerals that indicate the charge of the cation. Use the charge of the anion to find the charge of the cation. Then, put the name of the cation before the name of the anion.

Mn
Manganese

O
Oxygen

The oxide ion, O^{2-}, is the anion.

The manganese cation can have different charges. For MnO_2 to be neutral, it must have a 4+ charge: $1(4+) + 2(2-) = 0$.

MnO_2
manganese(IV) oxide

The IV indicates that the compound contains Mn^{4+}.

26 **SEP Use Models Other than the names of the ions, how does the name of CaS differ from the name of CdS?**

Formulas for Ionic Compounds

The name of a binary ionic compound is the name of the cation followed by the name of the anion. You can use the periodic table to find the symbols for the chemical formula. After writing the symbol for the metal cation followed by the symbol for the nonmetal anion, find the subscripts to complete the formula. To find the subscripts, you must balance the charges of the cations and anions.

The crisscross method is one way to find the subscripts for a binary ionic compound. In this method, the number for the charge of each ion is crossed over and becomes the subscript for the other ion. The subscripts are then reduced to the smallest whole-number ratio.

Naming Ionic Compounds Use these steps to determine the formulas for ionic compounds composed of monoatomic ions.

Step 1 Determine the charge of each ion from the group number in the periodic table or the Roman numeral in the name.

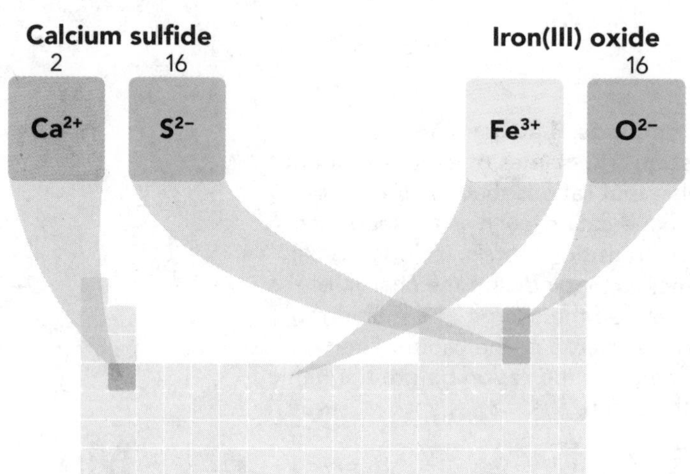

Step 2 Balance the charges with subscripts in the formula using the crisscross method.

Ca 2+ 2 S 2− 2

Step 3 Reduce the subscripts to the smallest whole-number ratio.

Ca_2S_2 reduces to CaS **Fe_2O_3**

Step 4 Confirm that the charges are balanced.

1(2+) + 1(2−) = 0 **2(3+) + 3(2−) = 0**

27 **SEP Construct an Explanation** Explain whether the formula CuO can be used to represent both copper(I) oxide and copper(II) oxide.

Compounds With Polyatomic Ions

Compounds containing polyatomic ions are named in the same order as binary ionic compounds. Use a reference table of polyatomic ions to find the name or formula of the ion. To find the subscripts for the chemical formula, you must balance the charges of the cations and anions. When using the crisscross method, remember that the charge and subscript apply to the entire polyatomic ion. Add parentheses to the chemical formula to indicate which atoms are part of a polyatomic ion.

Writing Chemical Formulas Shells of marine organisms are made of calcium carbonate. Follow the steps to determine the formula.

	Calcium carbonate
Step 1 Write the symbol for each ion.	Ca^{2+} CO_3^{2-}
Step 2 Use the crisscross method to determine the subscripts needed to balance the charges.	Ca^{2+} ✕ CO_3^{2-} $Ca_2\ CO_{3\ 2}$
Step 3 Add parentheses around the polyatomic ion to show that the subscript applies to the entire ion.	$Ca_2(CO_3)_2$
Step 4 Reduce the subscripts to the smallest whole-number ratio.	$CaCO_3$
Step 5 Check that the charges are balanced.	$1(2+) + 1(2-) = 0$

Naming Polyatomic Compounds Baking soda is the common name of the compound $NaHCO_3$. You can name the compound just as you name binary compounds, except you cannot find the name of the polyatomic ion by referencing the periodic table. Instead, use a reference table to find its name.

Cation	**Anion**
Na^+	HCO_3^-
sodium	hydrogen carbonate

sodium hydrogen carbonate

SAMPLE PROBLEM

Identifying Ionic Compounds

Write the chemical formula or name for the following compounds.

a. magnesium hydroxide **b.** $Fe(ClO_3)_3$

ANALYZE Identify the relevant concepts.

In a chemical formula, each ion is represented by its chemical symbol or formula, and subscripts show the lowest whole-number ratio of ions that balances the charge. The name of a compound includes a Roman numeral for a charge if an element can form different ions.

SOLVE Apply the concepts to this problem.

Write the symbol or formula for the cation first, then the anion.

a. cation: Mg^{2+} anion: OH^-

Use subscripts to balance the formula. Make sure that the formula expresses the lowest whole-number ratio of ions.

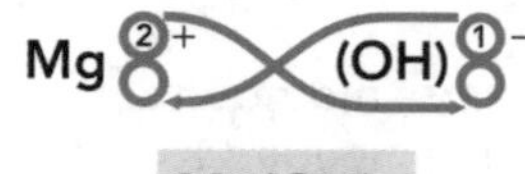

$Mg(OH)_2$

Check that the charges of the two ions add up to zero.

$1(2+) + 2(1-) = 0$

Identify any polyatomic ions.

b. Chlorate is ClO_3^-.

If any metal ions in the compound have more than one common ionic charge, use the nonmetal anion to determine which charge is indicated by the formula.

Iron forms Fe^{2+} and Fe^{3+}.

Three ClO_3^- ions give a charge of 3−. So the iron ion is Fe^{3+} to balance the charge.

Write the name of the cation, then the name of the anion. Include a Roman numeral as needed.

iron(III) chlorate

(28) What is the chemical formula for copper(II) nitrate?

(29) What is the name of $(NH_4)_2S$?

GO ONLINE for more practice problems.

Names of Molecular Compounds

Nonmetals can combine in different ratios to form binary molecular compounds. For example, carbon and oxygen can combine to form CO and CO_2. These compounds have very different properties—CO is poisonous, while you exhale CO_2. Rather than calling both compounds carbon oxide, prefixes are used in the name to indicate the number of atoms of each element in a molecule. If just one atom of the first element is in the formula, the prefix *mono-* is omitted for that element. Also, the vowel at the end of a prefix is sometimes dropped when the name of the element begins with a vowel. For example, tetroxide (instead of tetraoxide) is used for a compound with four oxygen atoms.

Prefixes Molecules of CO have a different number of oxygen atoms than molecules of CO_2. Prefixes in the names of these molecular compounds indicate how they differ from each other. The steps show how to name these compounds.

Prefixes Used in Naming Binary Molecular Compounds

Prefix	Number
mono-	1
di-	2
tri-	3
tetra-	4
penta-	5
hexa-	6
hepta-	7
octa-	8
nona-	9
deca-	10

Step 1 Write the names in the order they are listed.

CO	CO_2
carbon oxygen	**carbon oxygen**

Step 2 Use prefixes to indicate the number of each type of atom. Do not add the *mono-* prefix to the first element.

carbon **mono**xygen   carbon **di**oxygen

Step 3 Change the ending of the second substance so that it ends in *-ide*.

carbon monox**ide**   carbon diox**ide**

30 **SEP Use Models Chlorine and oxygen form many different compounds, including ClO_2 and Cl_2O_3. How do the names of these compounds differentiate one chlorine oxide from another?**

Rocket Fuel
Dinitrogen tetroxide is a compound in some types of liquid rocket fuel.

Formulas for Molecular Compounds

If you know the name of a binary molecular compound, you can use the prefixes and the periodic table to write its chemical formula. To write a chemical formula for a binary molecular compound, find the symbols for the two nonmetal elements in the periodic table. Combine the symbols with the subscripts that indicate the number of each element. Follow these steps to write the formula for dinitrogen tetroxide.

Step 1 Use the name to identify symbols of the elements. **dinitrogen** → **N**; **tetroxide** → **O**

Step 2 Use prefixes to determine the number of each type of atom. ***di-* = 2**; ***tetra-* = 4**

Step 3 Write the number of each element as the subscript after its symbol. N_2O_4

31 **CCC Patterns There are many compounds composed of nitrogen and oxygen. Compare the formulas for nitrogen monoxide and nitrogen dioxide.**

SAMPLE PROBLEM

Identifying Molecular Compounds

Write the formula or name of the following molecular compounds.

a. disulfur dichloride **b.** N_2O

ANALYZE Identify the relevant concepts.

In the name of a binary compound composed of two nonmetals, prefixes indicate the number of each kind of atom. The prefixes in the name indicate the subscript of each element in the formula.

SOLVE Apply the concepts to this problem.

Use the prefixes to determine how many atoms of each element are in the compound.

a. The prefix *di-* means two. So each molecule of disulfur dichloride has 2 sulfur atoms and 2 chlorine atoms.

Write the formula using symbols and subscripts for the number of atoms.

S_2Cl_2

Identify the elements and the number of atoms of each element in a molecule of the compound.

b. N_2O is composed of two nonmetals, nitrogen and oxygen.

Each molecule of N_2O has

2 nitrogen atoms and 1 oxygen atom.

Write the names of the elements in the order they are written in the formula.

nitrogen oxygen

Include prefixes to show how many atoms of each element are in the compound. Use the suffix *-ide* with the name of the second element.

dinitrogen monoxide

(32) **Name the compound P_4S_3.**

....

(33) **Write the formula for carbon tetrachloride.**

....

GO ONLINE for more practice problems.

Revisit

INVESTIGATIVE PHENOMENON

GO ONLINE to Elaborate on and Evaluate your knowledge of naming and writing chemical formulas for compounds by completing the class discussion and data analysis activities.

In the CER worksheet you completed at the beginning of the investigation, you drafted an explanation for the differences in properties of gems and metals. With a partner, reevaluate your arguments.

34 SEP Develop Models Many gemstones are silicate minerals, meaning they contain polyatomic ions composed of silicon and oxygen atoms. Peridot is a yellowish green gemstone containing the orthosilicate ion (SiO_4^{4-}). In the form of peridot called forsterite, the orthosilicate ion bonds with magnesium, while in the form called fayalite, iron(II) bonds with the orthosilicate ion. Write the chemical names and formulas for these two forms of peridot.

....

....

....

....

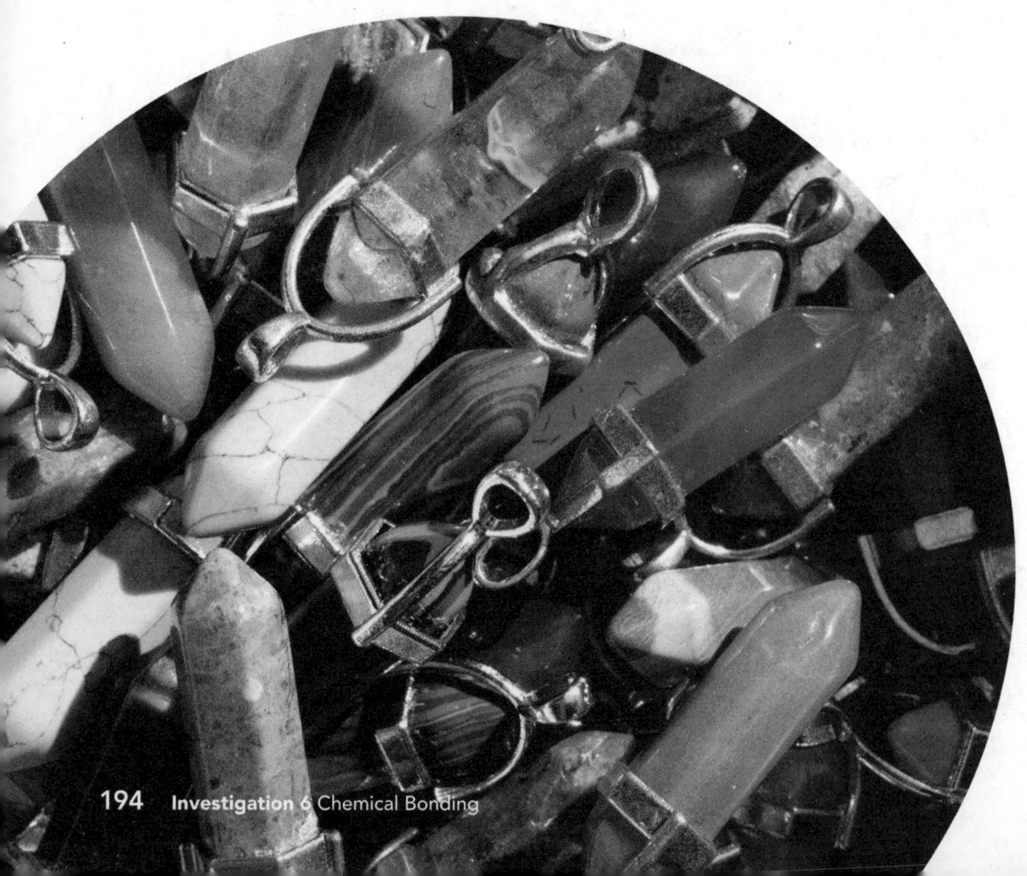

GO ONLINE to Evaluate what you learned about chemical bonding by using the available assessment resources.

In the Performance-Based Assessment, you investigated and constructed explanations for the varying properties of substances with different types of bonding. Wrap up your explanations by answering the following questions.

35 **SEP Identify Limitations of a Model You built a yes/no flowchart that could be used to characterize the chemical bonds of an unknown solid. Reevalute your flowchart, identify any limitations it may have, and explain how you might revise it to correct or mitigate for those limitations.**

Revisit

ANCHORING PHENOMENON

36 **Apply what you learned in Instructional Segment 2 to answer the Anchoring Phenomenon question "What distinguishes the minerals in this mountain?"**

GO ONLINE for a **problem-based learning** activity that you can tackle after completing Instructional Segment 2.

Understanding Chemical Reactions

Investigation 7
Physical Properties of Materials

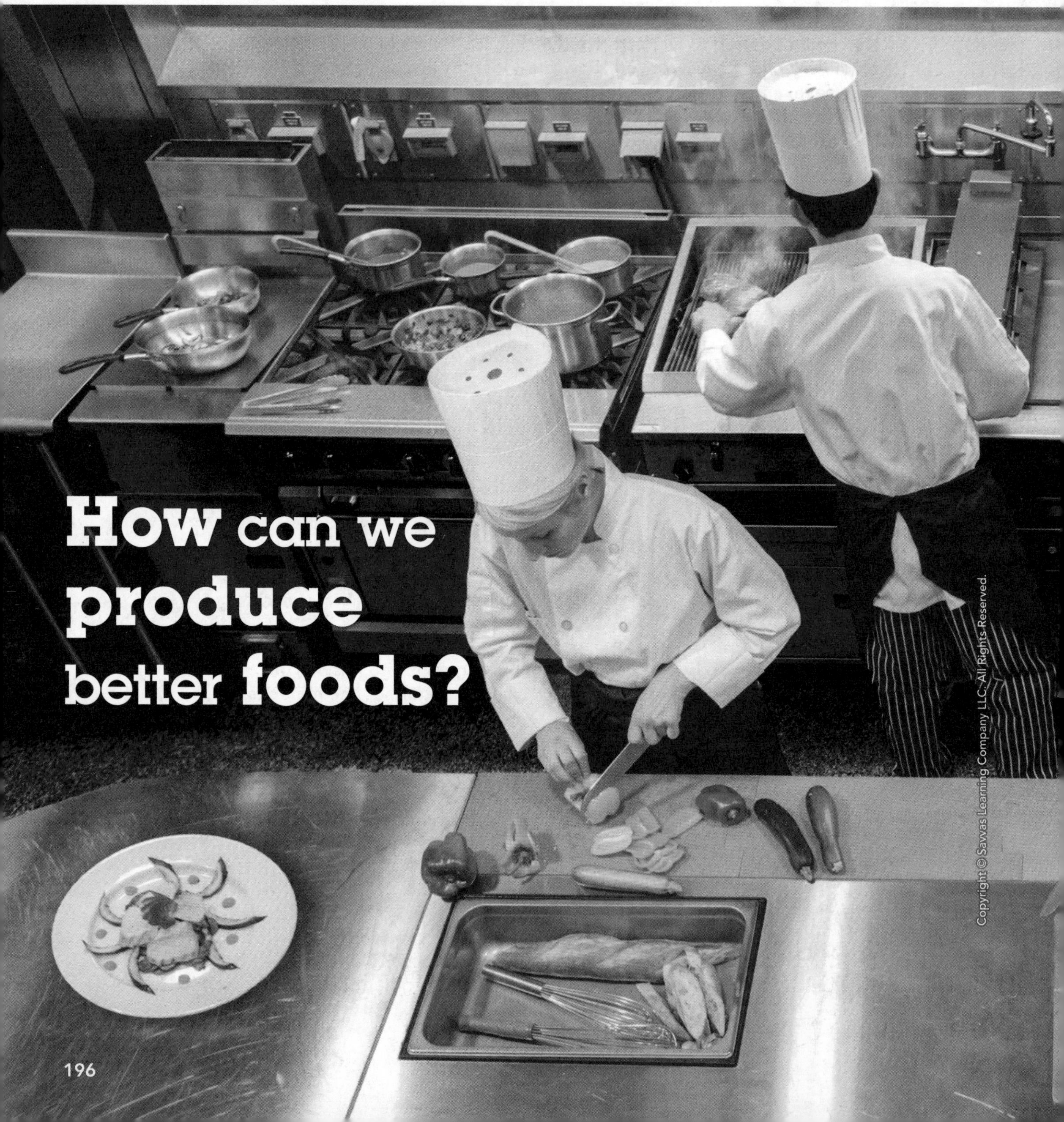

How can we produce better foods?

Investigation 8
Chemical Quantities

Investigation 9
Chemical Reactions

Investigation 10
Stoichiometry

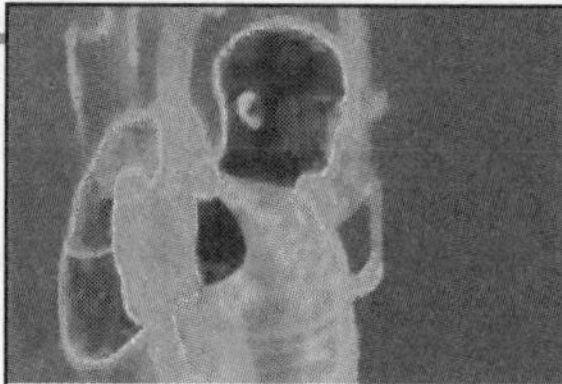
Investigation 11
Thermochemistry

ANCHORING PHENOMENON

Inquiry Launch Preparing and cooking foods involves a knowledge of food chemistry. Like chemists in a lab investigating a chemical reaction, chefs need to know lots of information before they begin their work. Look at the image of chefs preparing food in a restaurant kitchen. What types of information might they need in order to prepare a perfect meal?

Write a series of questions you think a chef would need and want answered to properly prepare a meal.

....

....

....

....

....

....

....

GO ONLINE to Engage with real-world phenomena. Watch the anchoring phenomenon video and preview the optional **problem-based learning experience**.

INVESTIGATIVE PHENOMENON

GO ONLINE to Engage with real-world phenomena by watching a video and to complete a CER interactive worksheet.

How do we design materials for a specific function?

INVESTIGATION 7

Physical Properties of Materials

The peak of Mount Everest is 8,848 meters above sea level, or about 5.5 miles. There is less oxygen in the air, and the temperature is always below freezing. Mountain climbers depend on reliable equipment to survive in these conditions. Choosing which materials to use when designing the equipment requires a great deal of thought. Once you have viewed the investigative phenomenon video and completed the claim-evidence-reasoning exercise, answer these reflection questions.

1. **CCC Structure and Function Ice and water are made out of the same molecule, but they have very different properties. List two physical properties of both ice and water and describe how their structures result in those properties.**

2. **SEP Plan Your Investigation Ice axes and carabiners are important tools used by mountaineers summiting snowy peaks. These objects need to be strong and reliable in cold temperatures. Engineers have choices of materials to use in making these tools. Plan an investigation that could provide the evidence needed to decide which material is best to use.**

EXPERIENCE 1

States of Matter

GO ONLINE to Explore and Explain the properties of different states of matter.

Kinetic Theory and a Model for Gases

The word *kinetic* refers to motion. The energy an object has because of its motion is called **kinetic energy.** Scientists explain some of the properties of matter in terms of the kinetic energy of the particles that make up the substance. The model scientists use, called the **kinetic theory,** describes all matter as tiny particles that are in constant motion.

Gases in Kinetic Theory The particles in a gas are small, hard spheres with insignificant volume. They are all in motion and colliding at room temperature.

There are no attractive forces between particles, so all **collisions are perfectly elastic,** meaning there is no loss of kinetic energy in the collision.

The motion of the particles is rapid, constant, and random, and **particles move in straight lines** until they collide with other particles or the container walls.

3 **SEP Develop a Model** **In the cube of gas particles, draw in extra particles so that there are twice as many particles. Show how those particles interact with each other and the container. Consider the three main principles of the kinetic theory when drawing the particles.**

Common Gases

The particles in a gas can be individual atoms, diatomic molecules, or even more complex molecules. **Standard temperature and pressure (STP)** is a standard set of conditions used for comparing properties of different gases and corresponds to a temperature of 0°C and approximately atmospheric pressure at sea level (100 kPa). The elements that exist as gases under STP are indicated on periodic tables.

Common Gases Gases can be elements in pure form or compounds. The elements that occur naturally as gases at STP typically populate the right side of the periodic table.

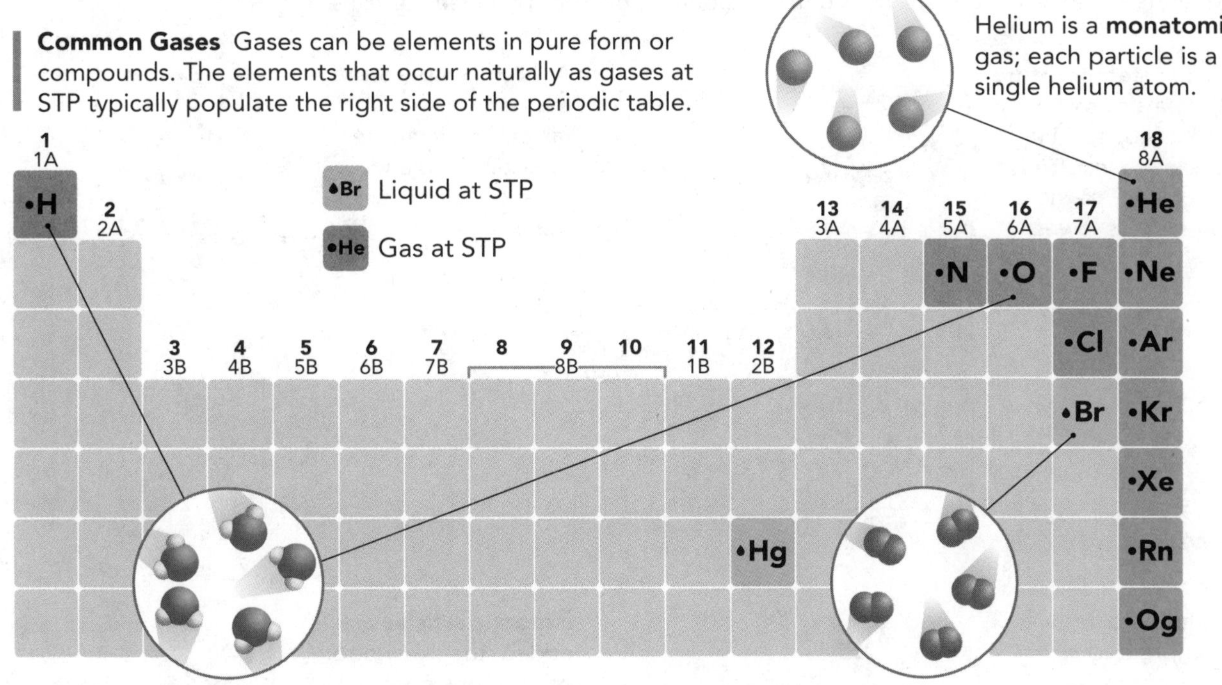

The particles in steam are molecules of the **compound** H_2O (water). At temperatures at or above 100°C, H_2O is a gas.

The particles in bromine gas are **diatomic**, composed of two bromine atoms. At temperatures at or above 58.8°C, Br_2 is a gas.

4 **CCC Patterns The table shows a list of compounds that are gases at STP. Identify the type of bonding (ionic, covalent, or metallic) for each compound listed.**

Gas	Type of Bonding
hydrogen sulfide (H_2S)	
ammonia (NH_3)	
methane (CH_4)	
nitrous oxide (N_2O)	

5 **CCC Patterns What bonding pattern do you observe that you could use to predict whether a compound will be a gas at STP?**

....

....

Gas Pressure

Gas pressure is the result of forces between the molecules of gas and the container walls. These forces result from collisions. Pressure can be increased by increasing the number of collisions. This can be done by shrinking the container, adding more particles, or speeding up the particles.

Temperature, Volume, and Pressure Changes in temperature and volume affect the speed of the particles and the number of collisions between particles.

At **low temperature**, the particles of a gas move slowly. They are much less likely to collide, so the pressure is lower.

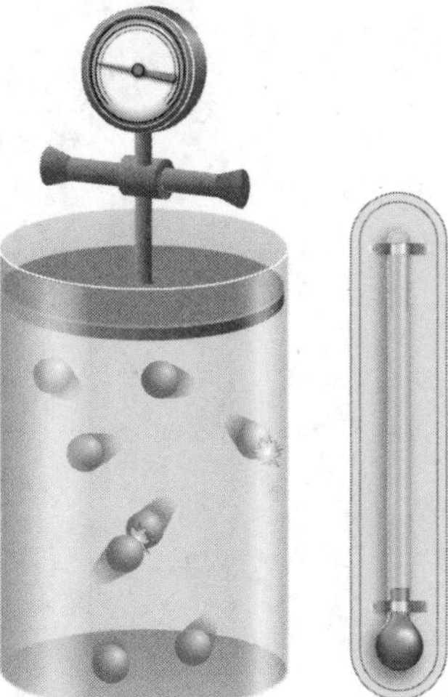

At **high temperature**, the particles move faster. This increases the likelihood and force of collisions, so the pressure is higher.

If the particles are compressed into a **smaller space**, they get closer. This increases the likelihood of collisions, so the pressure is higher.

If **more particles** are added, the likelihood of collisions goes up, so the pressure is higher.

6 **SEP Construct an Explanation** When it gets cold outside, a car's tire pressure can decrease. What might be happening to the gas molecules in the tire to cause the decrease in pressure?

Units of Pressure

What units can you use to show pressure?

PSI and kPa The pressure of gas can be expressed in pounds per square inch, or PSI. The SI unit of pressure is the pascal (Pa), which is a newton per square meter. 1 kPa = 1,000 Pa.

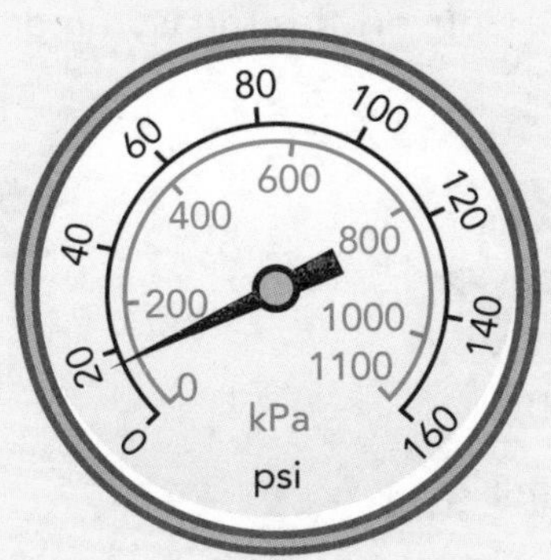

mm Hg A mercury barometer measures the pressure of the air pushing down on the mercury, which forces the mercury up a tube. The height of the mercury in the tube is read as a unit of pressure, millimeters of mercury (mm Hg).

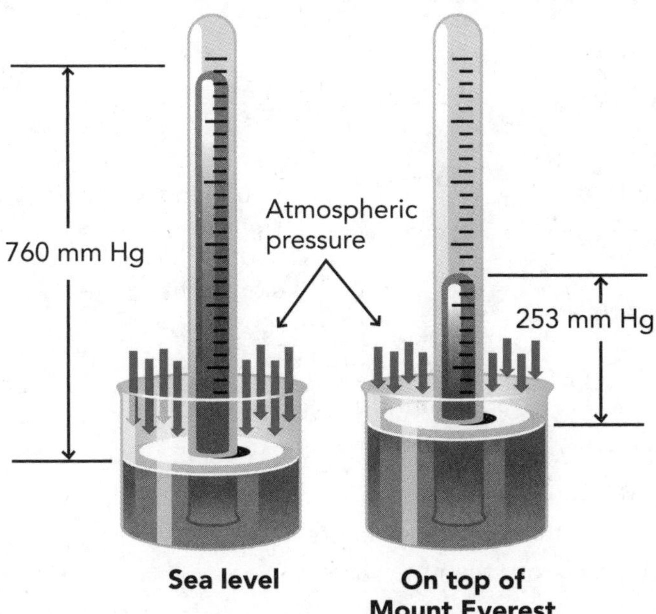

Comparing units Conversion factors are used to convert between different units of pressure.

1 atm = 760 mm Hg
1 atm = 101.3 kPa

Atmospheres Air is a mixture of gases that are pulled toward Earth's surface by gravity. Over each square meter of Earth's surface is a column of air that is more than 200 km high at sea level. The weight of the gases pressing on this square meter is pressure.

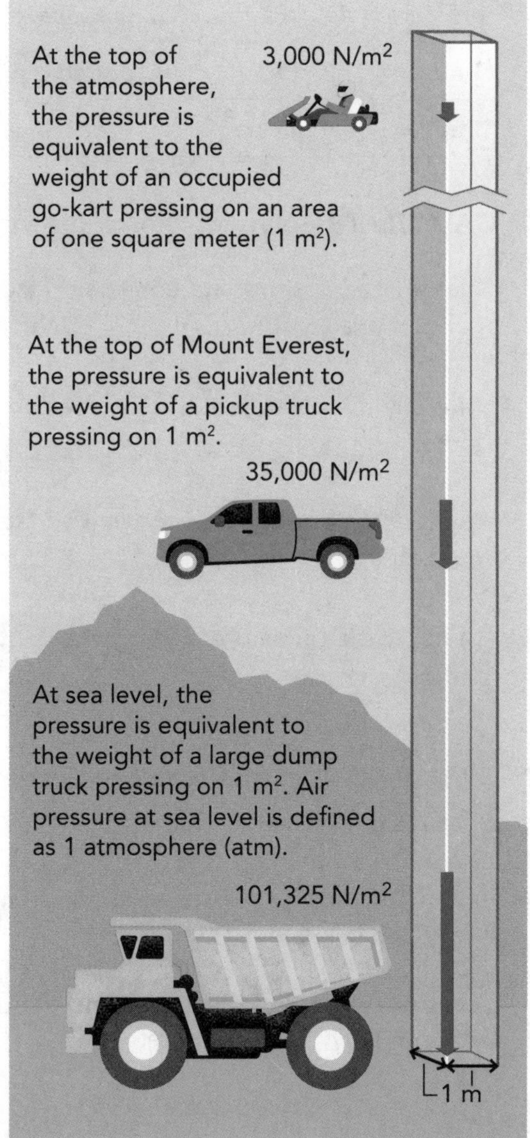

At the top of the atmosphere, the pressure is equivalent to the weight of an occupied go-kart pressing on an area of one square meter (1 m²).
3,000 N/m²
At the top of Mount Everest, the pressure is equivalent to the weight of a pickup truck pressing on 1 m².
35,000 N/m²
At sea level, the pressure is equivalent to the weight of a large dump truck pressing on 1 m². Air pressure at sea level is defined as 1 atmosphere (atm).
101,325 N/m²
1 m

SAMPLE PROBLEM

Converting Between Units of Pressure

A pressure gauge records a pressure of 450 kPa. Convert this measurement to **a.** atmospheres and **b.** millimeters of mercury.

ANALYZE List the knowns and unknowns.

Knowns	Unknowns
pressure = 450 kPa	pressure = ? atm
1 atm = 101.3 kPa	pressure = ? mm Hg
1 atm = 760 mm Hg	

CALCULATE Solve for the unknowns.

Identify the appropriate conversion factor to convert kPa to atm.

a. $\frac{1\ \text{atm}}{101.3\ \text{kPa}}$

The units in the known should be in the denominator so that the units will cancel.

Multiply the given pressure by the conversion factor.

$$450\ \cancel{\text{kPa}} \times \frac{1\ \text{atm}}{101.3\ \cancel{\text{kPa}}} = 4.4\ \text{atm}$$

Identify the appropriate conversion factor to convert kPa to mm Hg.

b. $\frac{760\ \text{mm Hg}}{101.3\ \text{kPa}}$

Multiply the given pressure by the conversion factor.

$$450\ \cancel{\text{kPa}} \times \frac{760\ \text{mm Hg}}{101.3\ \cancel{\text{kPa}}} =$$

$$3376\ \text{mm Hg} = 3.4 \times 10^3\ \text{mm Hg}$$

Round the answer to two significant figures because 450 kPa has only two significant figures.

EVALUATE Does the result make sense?

Because the conversion factor for kPa to atm is much less than 1 and for kPa to mm Hg is much greater than 1, it makes sense that the values expressed in atm and mm Hg are, respectively, smaller and larger than the value expressed in kPa.

7 **What pressure, in kilopascals and in atmospheres, does a gas exert at 385 mm Hg?**

8 **The pressure at the top of Mount Everest is 33.7 kPa. Is that pressure greater or less than 0.25 atm?**

GO ONLINE for more practice problems.

Kinetic Energy and Particle Motion in Solids, Liquids and Gases

As a substance's temperature increases, energy is transferred to particles in the substance and the motion of the particles increases. This motion can be translational, rotational, or vibrational. In **translation,** a body shifts from one point in space to another. In **rotation,** a body spins around a fixed point. In **vibration,** an object moves rapidly back and forth but stays in a fixed place.

Motion of Particles
Molecules can translate, rotate, vibrate, or some combination of the three types of motion.

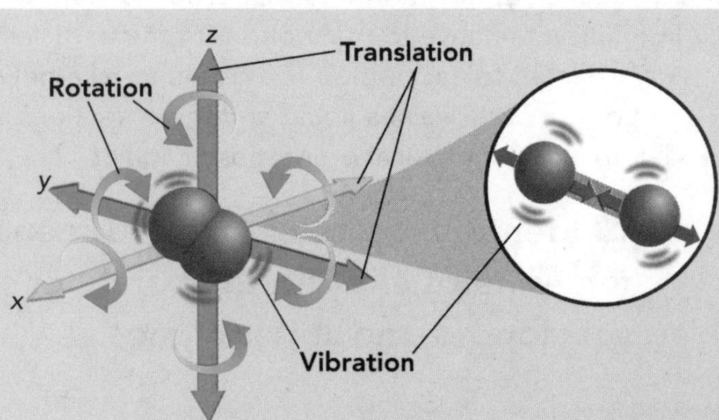

In a **gas**, the particles are free to move in all three ways.

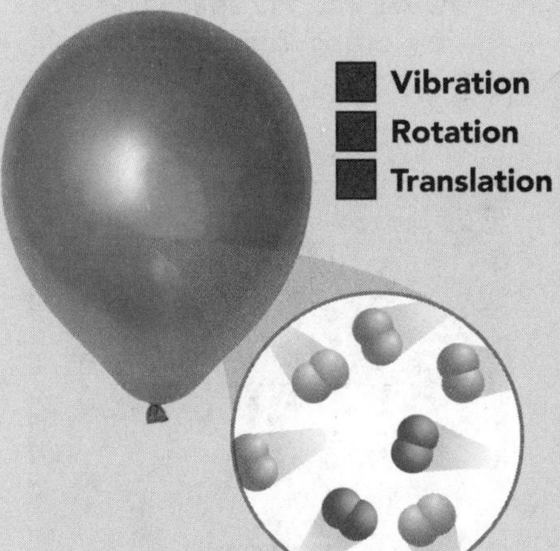

In a **liquid**, close proximity and attractions between the particles limit translational motion.

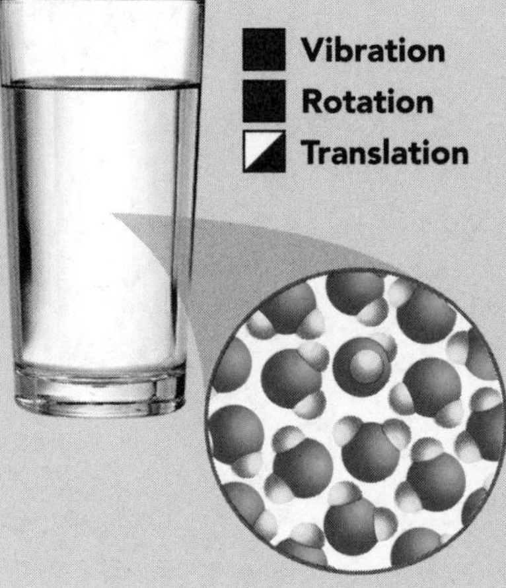

In a **solid**, the particles are close together and have strong attraction to each other, resulting in only vibrational energy.

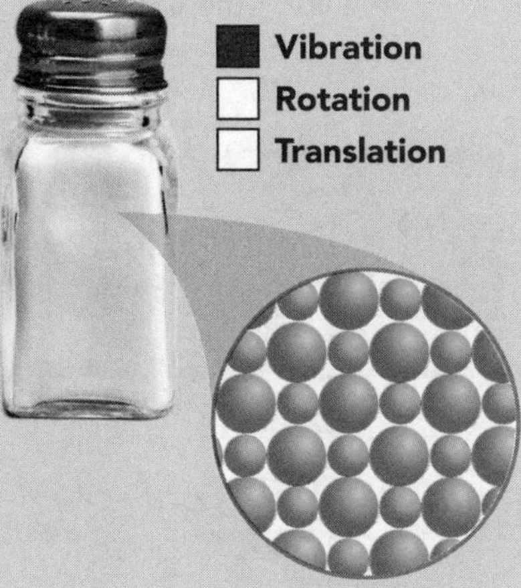

9 **SEP Argue from Evidence Will the average vibrational energy of nitrogen gas (N_2) at 22°C be greater than, less than, or equal to the average vibrational energy of NaCl at 22°C? Make a claim and support it with evidence.**

....

....

....

....

Liquids and Intermolecular Forces

Any substance that flows is considered a **fluid.** Both liquids and gases can be considered fluids because both conform to the shape of a container. But flow by itself doesn't help distinguish the differences between fluids and gases.

The strength of the attractive forces between particles that bring the particles closer together are what distinguish a liquid from a gas. In the kinetic theory, the intermolecular attractions between particles in a gas are insignificant relative to the motions of the particles. In a liquid, the particles are attracted to each other. The give-and-take between the disruptive motions of particles in a liquid and the attractions among the particles determines the physical properties of liquids.

Identifying patterns in the strength of attractive forces helps explain the behavior of different substances and states of matter.

Fluids When particles have relative freedom of motion, one particle can move rapidly to replace another particle.

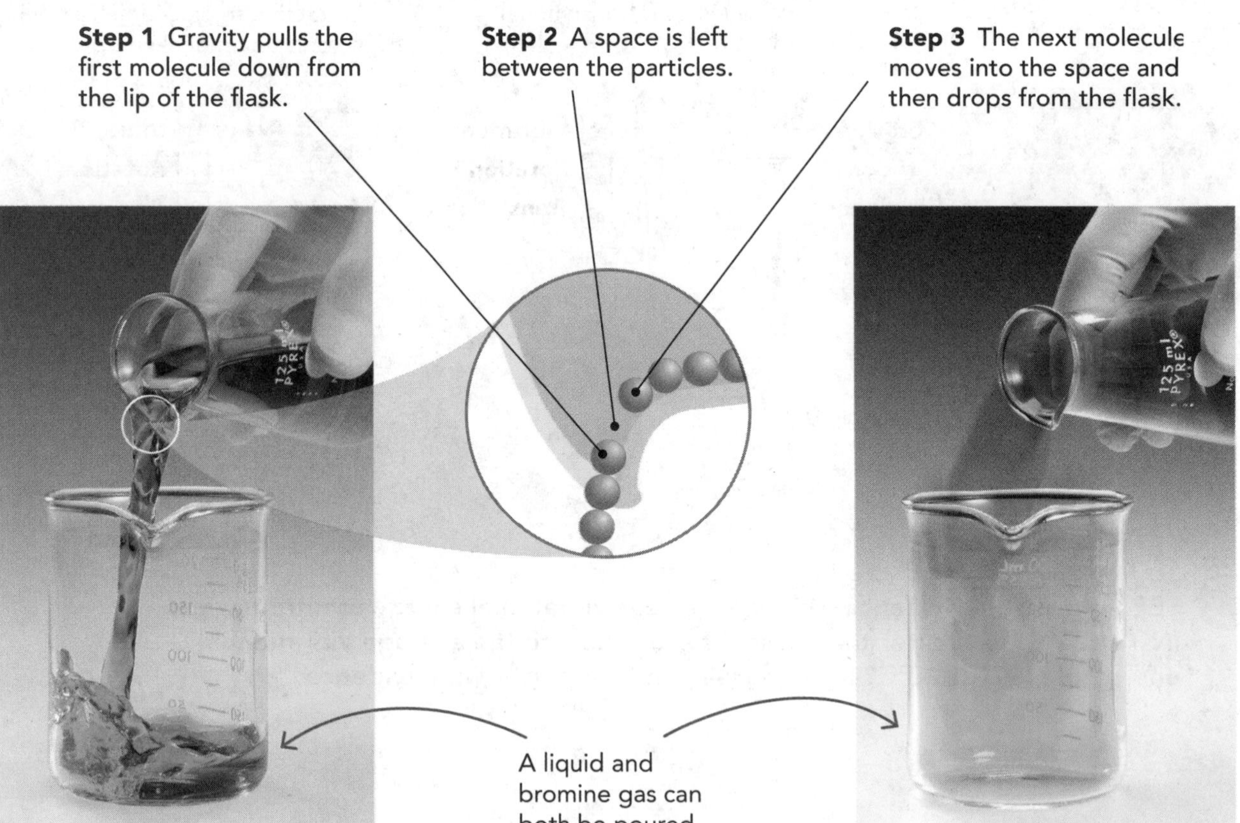

Step 1 Gravity pulls the first molecule down from the lip of the flask.
Step 2 A space is left between the particles.
Step 3 The next molecule moves into the space and then drops from the flask.
A liquid and bromine gas can both be poured.

Intermolecular Forces

What types of **electrical forces** occur **between atoms?**

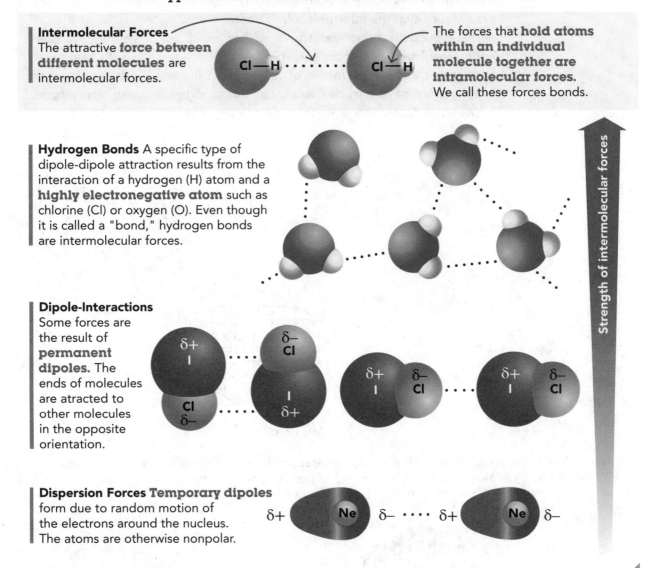

Intermolecular Forces
The attractive **force between different molecules** are intermolecular forces.

Cl—H ········ Cl—H

The forces that **hold atoms within an individual molecule together are intramolecular forces.** We call these forces bonds.

Hydrogen Bonds A specific type of dipole-dipole attraction results from the interaction of a hydrogen (H) atom and a **highly electronegative atom** such as chlorine (Cl) or oxygen (O). Even though it is called a "bond," hydrogen bonds are intermolecular forces.

Dipole-Interactions
Some forces are the result of **permanent dipoles.** The ends of molecules are atracted to other molecules in the opposite orientation.

δ+ I ···· δ– Cl
Cl δ– ···· I δ+
δ+ I δ– Cl ···· δ+ I δ– Cl

Dispersion Forces Temporary dipoles form due to random motion of the electrons around the nucleus. The atoms are otherwise nonpolar.

δ+ Ne δ– ···· δ+ Ne δ–

Strength of intermolecular forces

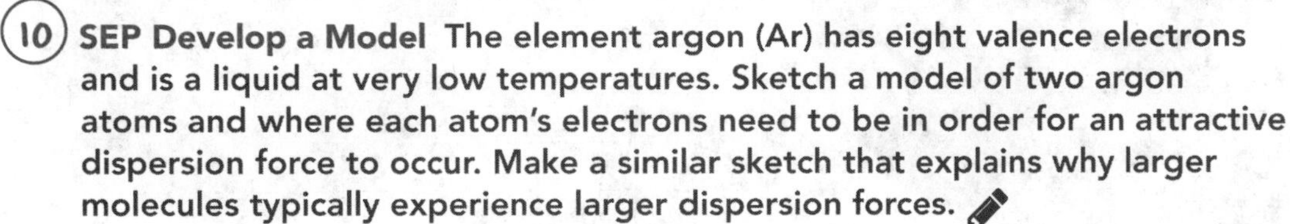

10 **SEP Develop a Model** The element argon (Ar) has eight valence electrons and is a liquid at very low temperatures. Sketch a model of two argon atoms and where each atom's electrons need to be in order for an attractive dispersion force to occur. Make a similar sketch that explains why larger molecules typically experience larger dispersion forces.

Solids and Attractive Force

Motions of Particles in Solids In solids, the particles are packed together closely such that the intermolecular forces are very strong, or all of the particles are actually bonded together. The molecules can neither translate nor rotate. The only motion available to molecules in a solid is vibration back and forth. The properties of solids reflect the orderly arrangement and fixed location of its particles, as well as the strength of the attractive force between particles. There are four main types of solids.

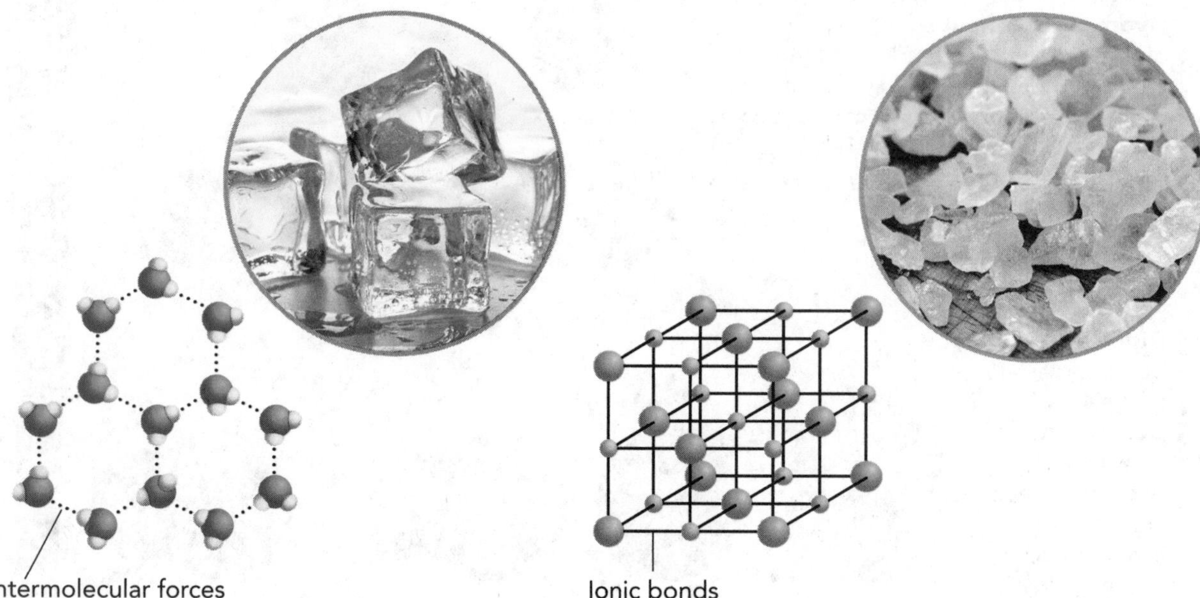

Molecular Solid The water molecules in ice are held together by relatively weak dipole-dipole intermolecular forces in the form of hydrogen bonds.

Ionic Solid Table salt (sodium chloride) consists of positively and negatively charged sodium and chlorine ions held together by ionic bonds.

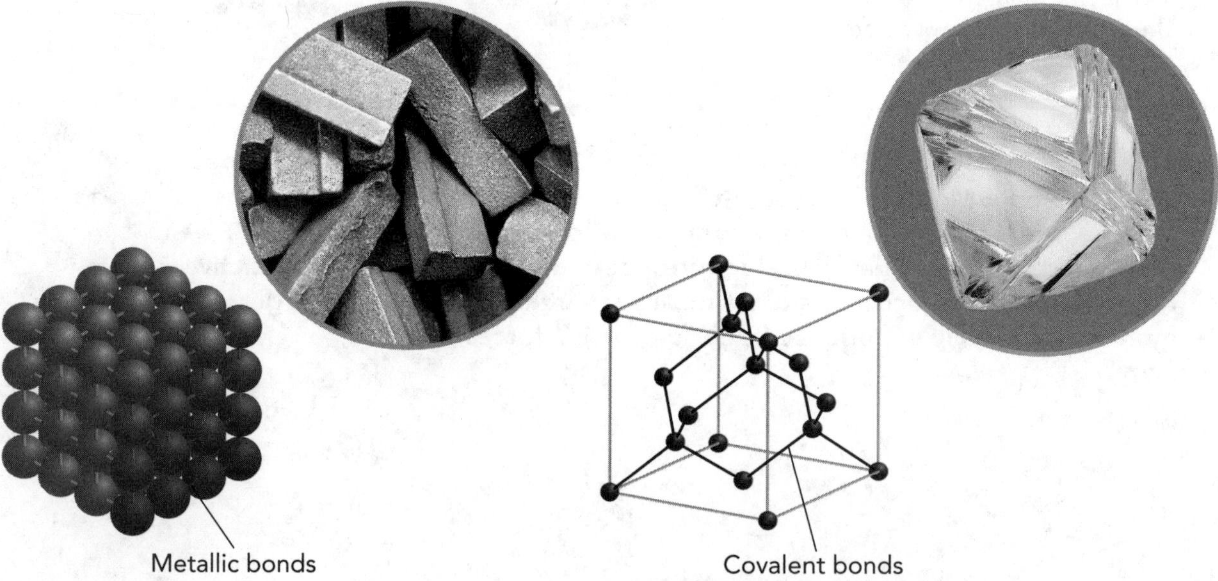

Metallic Solid Solid iron is a network of iron atoms held together by metallic bonds.

Covalent Network Solid Diamond is a network of carbon atoms held together by covalent bonds.

Properties of Solids The four types of solids are classified by how the particles are held together. **Molecular solids** consist of molecules that are held together by the relatively weak intermolecular forces. Because of these weak molecular connections, molecular solids tend to be soft and have low melting points. **Ionic solids** consist of positively and negatively charged ions held together by ionic bonds. This relatively strong attraction results in high melting points and hardness. Similarly, **metallic solids** are formed via strong metallic bonds. However, the properties of metallic solids are highly variable and depend on exactly how the electrons are arranged. **Covalent network solids** consist of networks of atoms held together by covalent bonds. Covalent solids are very hard and tend to have the highest melting points.

Types of Crystalline Solids

Type of Solid	Forces	Structural Units	Melting Point	Hardness	Electrical Conductivity	Examples
Molecular	Dispersion, dipole-dipole, hydrogen bonding	Atoms, molecules	Low	Soft	Nonconducting	H_2 H_2O CO_2
Ionic	Ionic bonding	Ions	High to very high	Hard	Nonconducting	NaCl $CaCl_2$ MgO
Metallic	Metallic bonding	Atoms	Variable	Variable hardness	Conducting	Al Cu Fe
Covalent network	Covalent bonding	Atoms	Very high	Very hard	Variable	C (graphite) C (diamond) SiO_2 (quartz)

11 SEP Construct an Explanation Explain why carbon dioxide is a gas, water is a liquid, and salt is solid at room temperature based on how the particles are held together.

Crystal Structure

Most solid substances are crystalline. In a **crystal,** the particles are arranged in an orderly, repeating, three-dimensional pattern called a crystal lattice. Not all solids are crystalline. An **amorphous solid** lacks an ordered internal structure. Rubber, plastic, and asphalt are examples of amorphous solids.

Crystalline Solid Crystals have an orderly internal structure, with bonds found along flat planes. Facets are the flat faces on bulk crystals. The facets result from the underlying structure of the microscopic bonds.

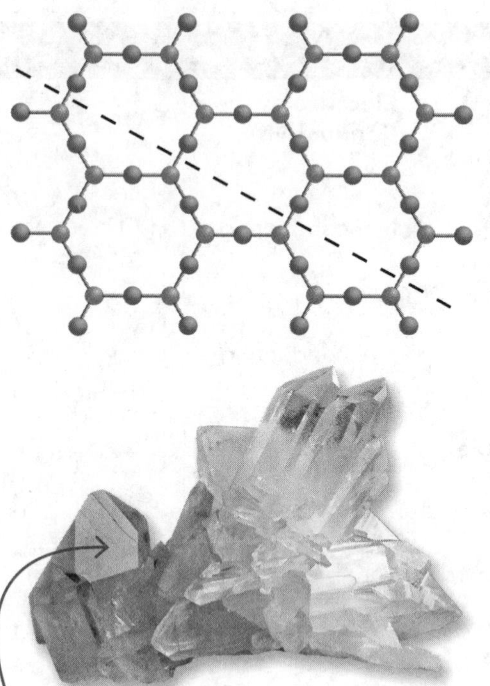

Cleavage is the tendency of a material to break along smooth planes parallel to a plane of bonds.

Amorphous Solid Amorphous materials have no orderly internal structure, with neighboring bonds found along curved paths. An amorphous solid does not have facets, and the shape of the bulk material does not reflect any underlying structure.

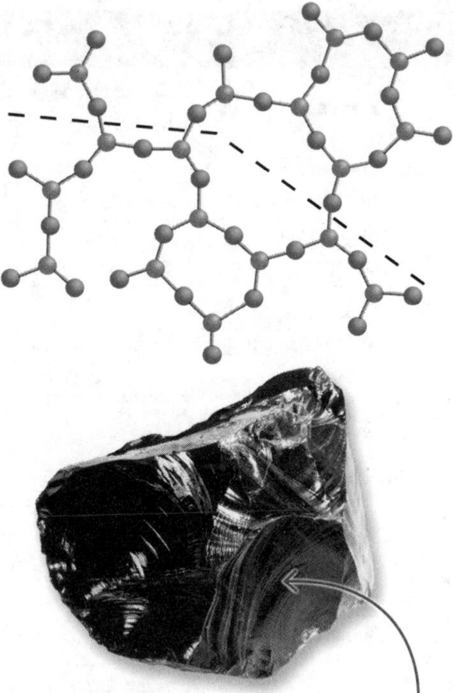

Fracture is the tendency of a solid to break along curved surfaces without definite shape due to a lack of a flat bonding plane.

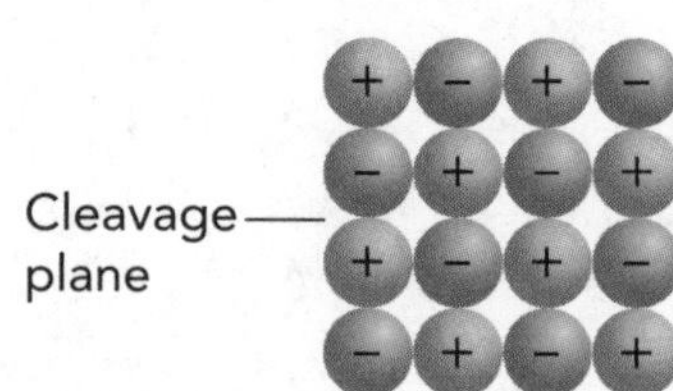

In **ionic crystalline solids,** ions with opposite charges align to form a crystal with strong attraction between planes.

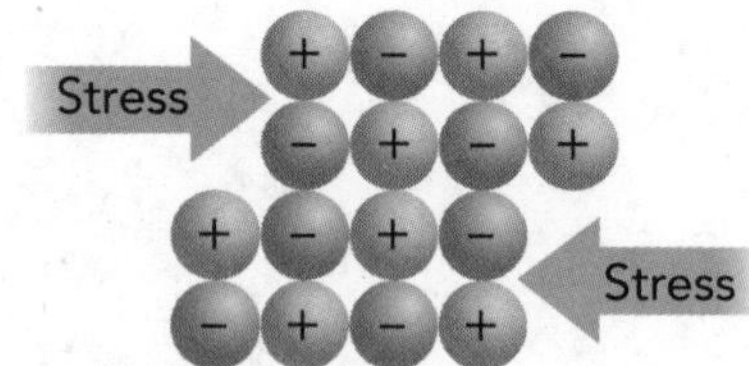

When shear forces are applied to the crystal, the ions shift. Ions with the same charge end up next to each other.

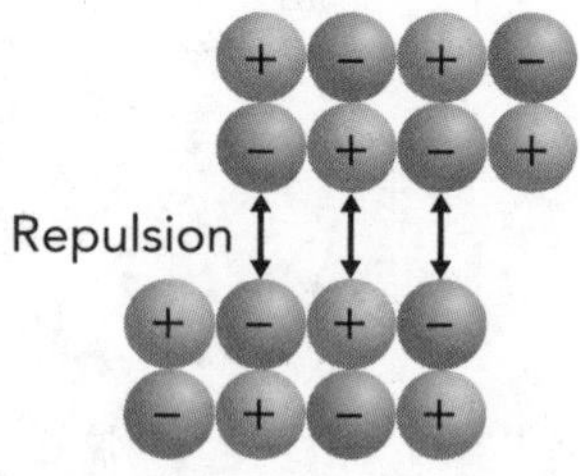

Ions of the same charge repel each other. This repulsion causes the ionic bonds to break along the entire plane.

Unit Cells The orderly structure of crystalline solids consists of groups of atoms that repeat in space. The smallest group of particles within a crystal that retains the overall symmetry of the crystal is called a *unit cell.* An entire crystal lattice is built from repetition of the unit cell in three dimensions. How closely atoms are packed within a crystal unit cell affects the physical, electrical, and mechanical properties of a material.

Crystal Systems Crystals can be classified into seven crystal systems. Two crystals are in the same crystal system if they have similar symmetries, although they could have different unit cells.

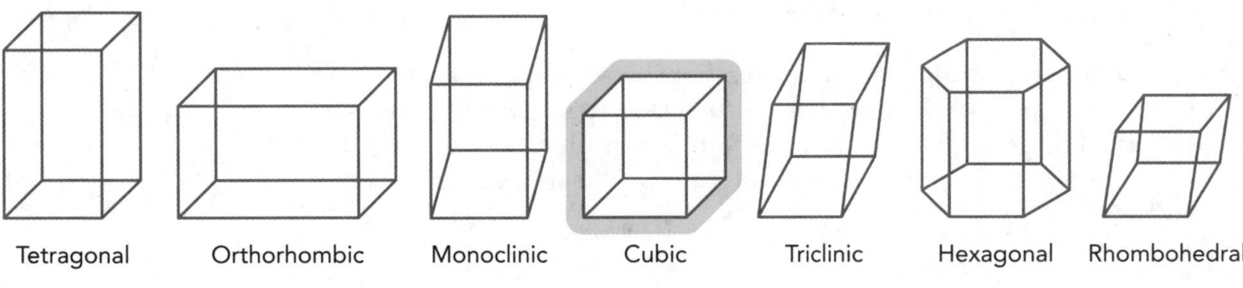

Cubic Systems There are three different types of unit cells for cubic systems.

In a **simple cubic** unit cell, the atoms or ions are arranged at the corners of an imaginary cube.

In a **body-centered cubic** unit cell, atoms or ions are arranged at the corners and in the center of an imaginary cube. Materials with this structure tend to be harder and less malleable than face-centered materials.

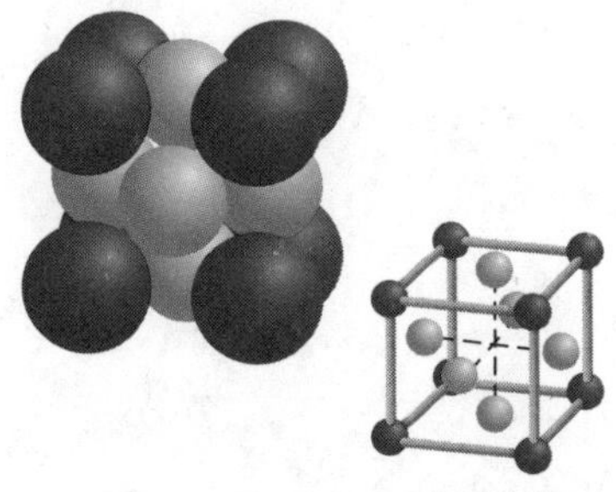

In a **face-centered** cubic unit cell, atoms or ions are arranged at the corners and in the center of each face of the imaginary cube. Materials with this structure tend to be more ductile than more loosely packed materials.

12 **CCC Structure and Function Why is the arrangement of the constituent atoms or molecules more important in determining the properties of a solid than a liquid or a gas? Why are the structures of solids usually described in terms of the positions of the constituent atoms rather than their motion?**

....

....

....

....

Revisit

INVESTIGATIVE PHENOMENON

GO ONLINE to Elaborate and Evaluate your knowledge of states of matter by completing the class discussion and writing task activities.

In the CER worksheet, you drafted a scientific argument to explain how materials used on mountaintops are engineered. With a partner, reevaluate the evidence cited in your arguments.

13 **SEP Develop a Model** **Mountain climbers need really warm clothing because it gets colder at higher altitudes. Sketch molecular models for equal-mass samples of air at different altitudes. Use your models to show why there might be less energy in the samples at higher altitudes.**

EXPERIENCE 2

Modeling Phase Changes

GO ONLINE to Explore and Explain the changes in energy during phase changes.

Phase Changes

Energy and Phase Change As energy is added to a material, the temperature of the material changes. However, there are certain points where the temperature stops increasing. Instead, the added energy is used to convert the material from one state of matter to another. This transformation from one state of matter to another is called a **phase change.** The temperature remains constant during a phase change because all the added energy goes into breaking attractive forces holding particles together instead of increasing the kinetic energy of the particles.

Increasing Kinetic Energy of Liquid Water Molecules Added energy is absorbed by the water molecules and turned into increased molecular motion, increasing the temperature.

Breaking Intermolecular Forces Added energy goes into breaking the hydrogen bonds between water molecules, and not into increasing molecular motion. The temperature remains constant.

Increasing Kinetic Energy of Gaseous Water Molecules Once all hydrogen bonds are broken, added energy goes into molecular motion, increasing temperature.

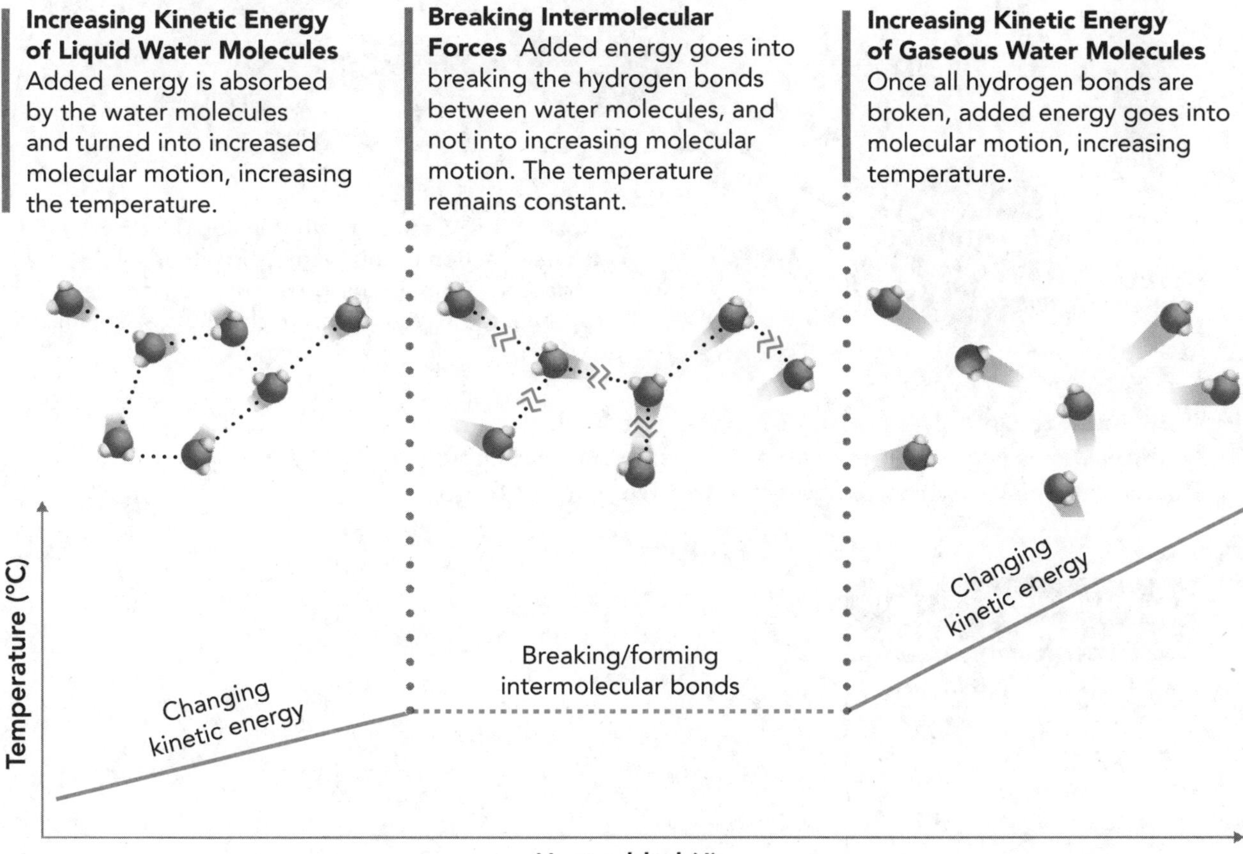

Types of Phase Changes When a material changes from solid to liquid, the material is melting. When going from liquid to solid, the material is freezing. Similarly, changing from liquid to gas is called **vaporization.** Changing from gas to liquid is called **condensation.** Some solids can change directly into gas through a process called **sublimation.** Going from gas to solid is called **deposition.** The properties of the material can change significantly from one phase to another, even though all the actual particles remain the same.

Heat Energy in Materials The heat energy in a material increases as it transitions from solid to liquid, and liquid to gas.

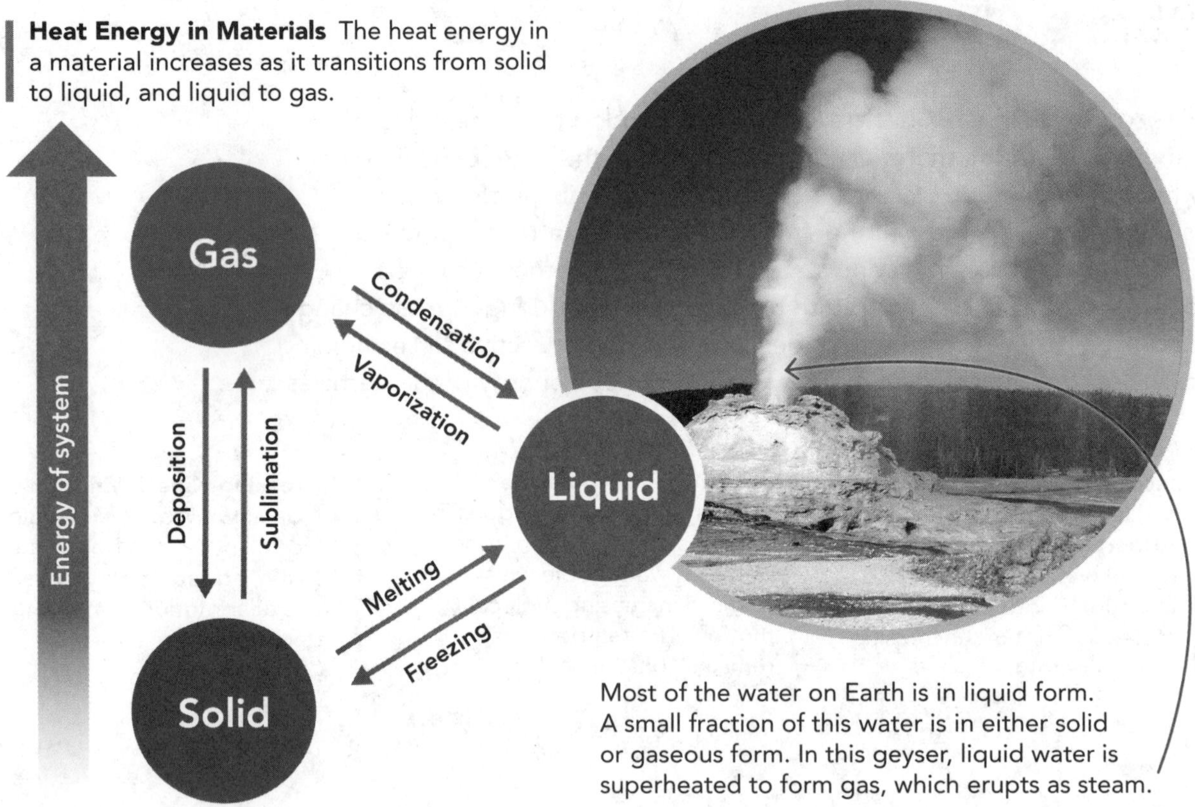

Most of the water on Earth is in liquid form. A small fraction of this water is in either solid or gaseous form. In this geyser, liquid water is superheated to form gas, which erupts as steam.

(14) **SEP Analyze Data The density of oxygen at 1 atm and various temperatures is given in the table. Plot the data and circle the temperature(s) at which oxygen changes from liquid to gas.**

Temperature (T) and Density (d) of Oxygen	
T (K)	**d (mol/L)**
60	40.1
70	38.6
80	37.2
90	35.6
100	0.123
120	0.102
140	0.087

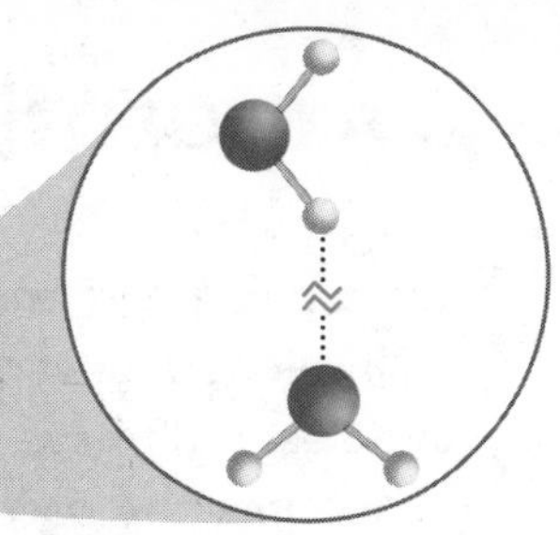

Breaking Bonds The intermolecular hydrogen bonds in water are broken during boiling. But the intramolecular covalent bonds that hold a molecule together do not break, so the actual particles remain the same.

Heating a Liquid

As a liquid is heated, the particles gain vibrational and rotational energy. When enough energy is gained, the remaining attractive forces between particles are broken, and the liquid becomes gas. The temperature at which the attractive forces break is the boiling point.

The relative strength of intermolecular forces can be used to predict differences in bulk properties like boiling point. Stronger intermolecular forces result in higher boiling points. The strength of intermolecular forces is related to the type of force and the size and weight of the molecules.

Intermolecular Force Affects Bulk Properties

Substance	Intermolecular Force	Molar Mass (g/mol)	Boiling Point (K)
Fluorine (F_2)	Dispersion	38.0	85
Hydrogen chloride (HCl)	Dipole-dipole	38.5	188
Hydrogen sulfide (H_2S)	Hydrogen bond	34.1	213

15 **SEP Interpret Data The table shows the atomic radii and boiling points of five halogens that experience intermolecular dispersion forces. Plot the boiling point vs. the atomic radius and use the resulting pattern to predict the boiling point of astatine.**

Atomic Radius and Boiling Point

Halogen	Atomic radius (pm)	Boiling point (K)
Fluorine (F_2)	72	85
Chlorine (Cl_2)	99	238
Bromine (Br_2)	114	332
Iodine (I_2)	133	457
Astatine (At_2)	150	

Evaporation and Condensation

Kinetic Energy and Attractive Forces A liquid doesn't have to be boiling for some vaporization to occur. Below the boiling point, most of the particles don't have enough energy to overcome the attractive forces and escape into the gaseous state. However, since the individual kinetic energies of particles fall within a distribution, some particles may have enough energy to break free and become gas in a process called **evaporation.**

Some Particles Have More Energy Than Others The particle energies within a liquid have a wide distribution. The average kinetic energy is well below the energy needed for molecules to break free and evaporate. However, a small number of the particles do have enough energy to break free.

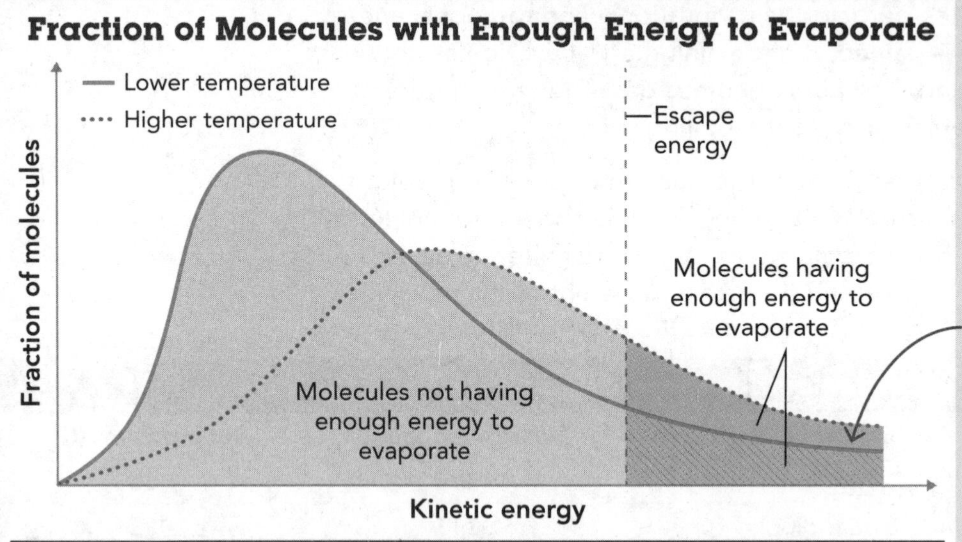

Increasing the temperature of a liquid results in more particles having enough energy to evaporate.

In the process of **condensation,** some of the molecules in a gas will have lower energy than the rest and can transition to the liquid phase.

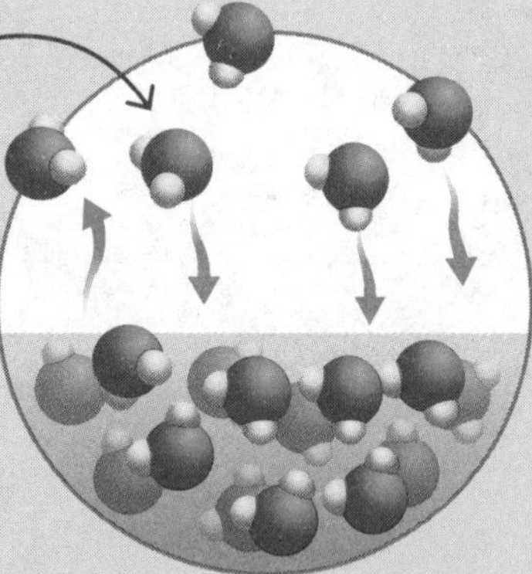

In the process of **evaporation,** those particles at the surface that have enough energy can escape the liquid and enter the gas phase.

Evaporation and Condensation with Changing Temperature

Increasing the temperature of the liquid increases the average kinetic energy of the molecules and broadens the distribution. This means even more individual molecules will have enough energy to break away from the liquid. This process happens at the surface of liquids, where, for example, the sun slightly heats the surface of a lake, allowing a small fraction of the particles at the surface to escape into the gaseous state. This process of evaporation is one type of vaporization.

Condensation is the reverse process. Some of the particles in a gas have a low enough energy within the distribution to change from a gas to a liquid. For example, at the surface of a cold glass, the water vapor in the air is cooled just enough that the kinetic energy of some of the particles is lowered enough to form liquid water on the glass surface.

Evaporation Is Not Boiling Water evaporates from the surface of Earth's oceans and turns to gaseous water vapor, which is an important step in the water cycle that allows life to flourish. The oceans are certainly not boiling, though.

16 **SEP Ask Questions The process of evaporation has a different outcome in an open system versus a closed system. What happens to the water level in a closed water bottle compared to an open water bottle if you set them both out in the sun?**

Vapor Pressure and Boiling

When liquid is sealed in a closed container, some of the particles will vaporize due to evaporation. These particles collide with the container walls and each other, producing pressure. The pressure of the gas above the liquid in this situation is called **vapor pressure.** In a system of constant vapor pressure, a dynamic equilibrium occurs between the vapor and liquid, where when one particle is released into the gas, another condenses back into the liquid.

In a system of variable vapor pressure, several factors, including temperature and atmospheric pressure, affect the boiling point of the liquid. The boiling point can be defined as the temperature at which the vapor pressure is equal to the external pressure on a fluid, allowing for the escape of the transitioning gas.

Vapor Pressure and Altitude

How does **air pressure** affect the **boiling point** of liquids?

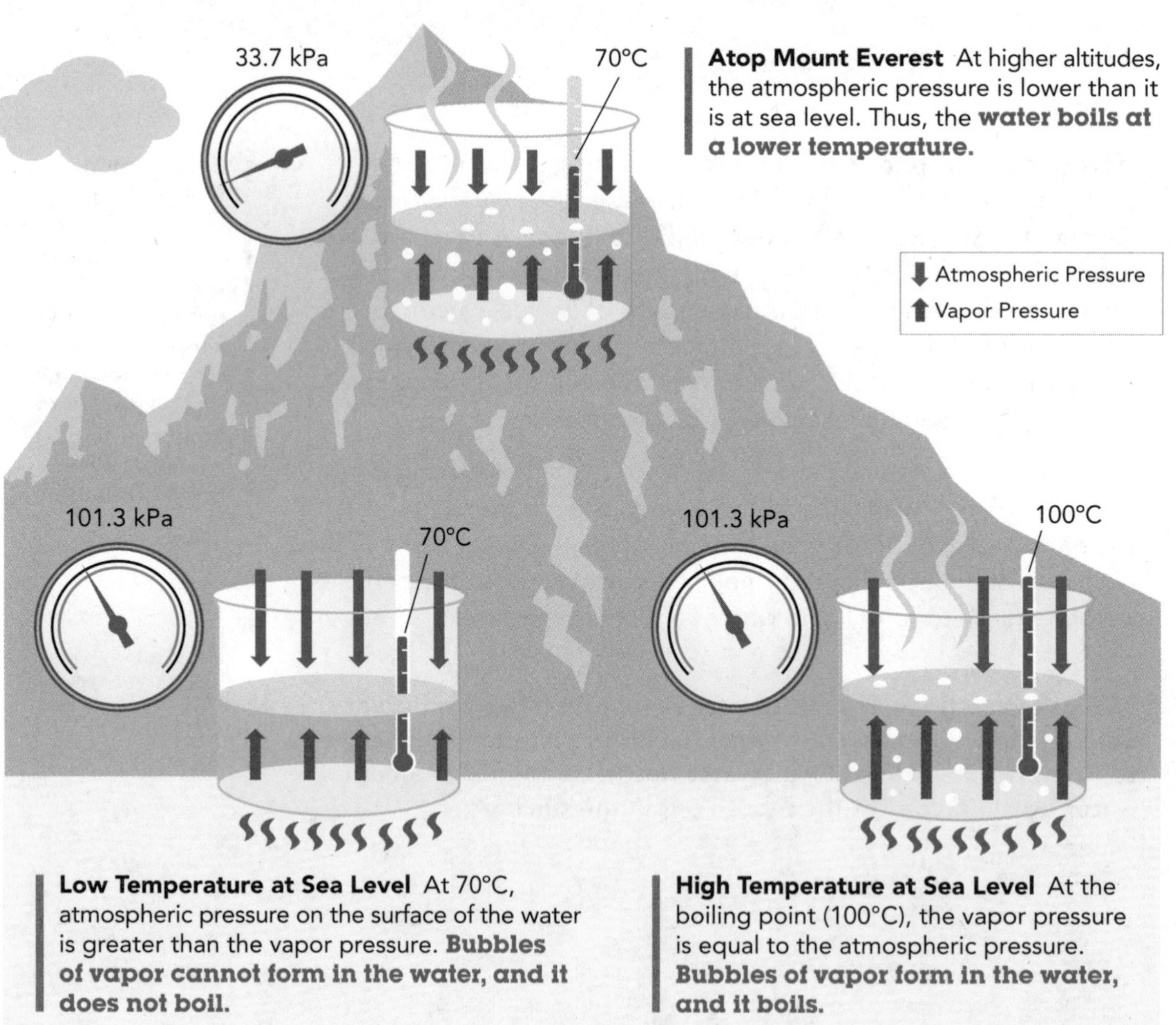

Atop Mount Everest At higher altitudes, the atmospheric pressure is lower than it is at sea level. Thus, the **water boils at a lower temperature.**

Low Temperature at Sea Level At 70°C, atmospheric pressure on the surface of the water is greater than the vapor pressure. **Bubbles of vapor cannot form in the water, and it does not boil.**

High Temperature at Sea Level At the boiling point (100°C), the vapor pressure is equal to the atmospheric pressure. **Bubbles of vapor form in the water, and it boils.**

Boiling Points The normal boiling point is defined as the boiling point of a liquid at 101.3 kPa, which is approximately atmospheric pressure at sea level. If the surrounding external pressure is greater, then the boiling point will also be higher.

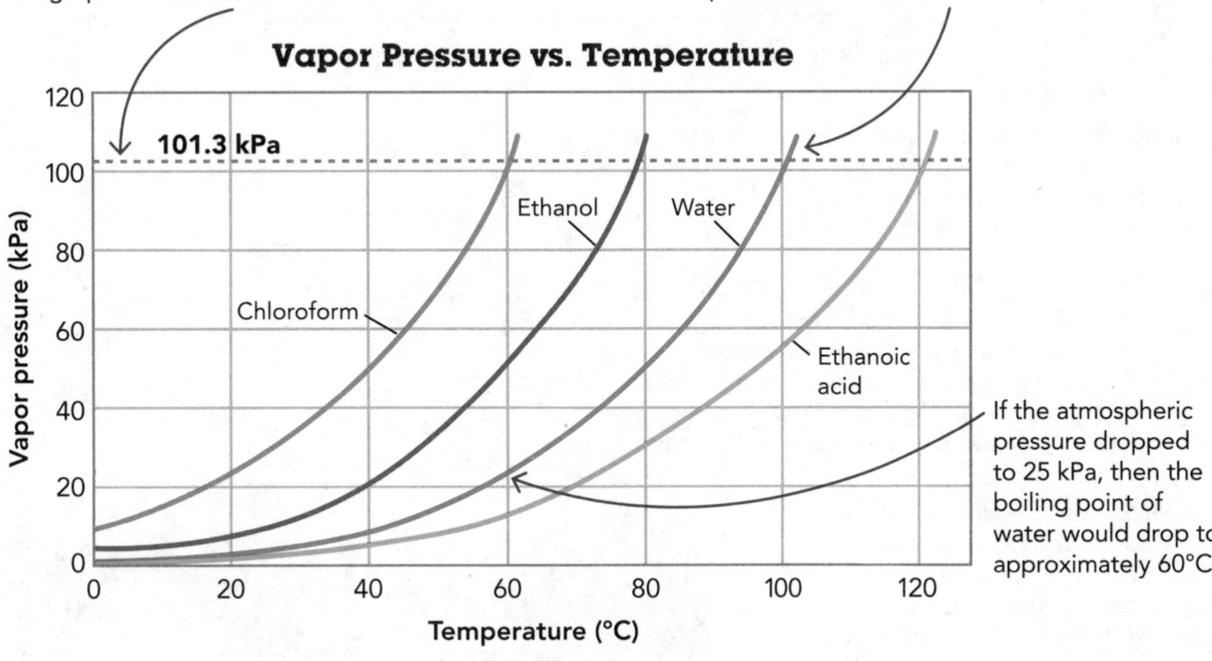

The dashed line marks 101.3 kPa which is where the normal boiling point is read on the graph for each substance.
At 100°C, the vapor pressure of water equals 101.3 kPa, so the normal boiling point of water is 100°C.
Vapor Pressure vs. Temperature
101.3 kPa
Chloroform
Ethanol
Water
Ethanoic acid
Vapor pressure (kPa)
0
20
40
60
80
100
120
Temperature (°C)
If the atmospheric pressure dropped to 25 kPa, then the boiling point of water would drop to approximately 60°C.

17 **SEP Interpret Data** The table compares vapor pressure values for water, ethanol, and diethyl ether at six temperatures. Determine the approximate normal boiling point for each substance. What do the data suggest about the relative strength of attraction between particles in each substance?

Vapor Pressure (in kPa) of Three Substances at Different Temperatures

Substances	0°C	20°C	40°C	60°C	80°C	100°C
Water	0.61	2.33	7.37	19.92	47.34	101.33
Ethanol	1.63	5.85	18.04	47.02	108.34	225.75
Diethyl ether	24.70	58.96	122.80	230.65	399.11	647.87

Heating a Solid

As a solid is heated, the particles gain vibrational energy. If enough energy is supplied, the particles can no longer absorb all the energy and they begin to move away from each other, weakening the attractive forces between them. With weakened attraction, the uniform structure of the solid can change and the solid transitions into a liquid. The temperature at which a solid becomes a liquid is called the **melting point.**

Molecular Solids Molecules of water are attracted to each other via intermolecular hydrogen bonds. These forces hold the molecules together in a regular geometric pattern.

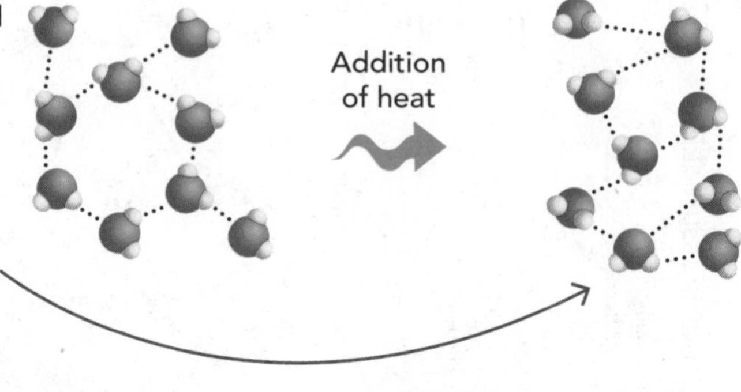

When heat is added, some of the intermolecular forces are broken, and molecules move apart into a less orderly arrangement. The covalent bonds within molecules remain intact.

Ionic Solids In sodium chloride crystals, ions of sodium and chlorine are held together in a regular geometric pattern via strong ionic bonds. For ionic and metallic solids to change phase, the chemical bonds between the atoms must break for the structure to change.

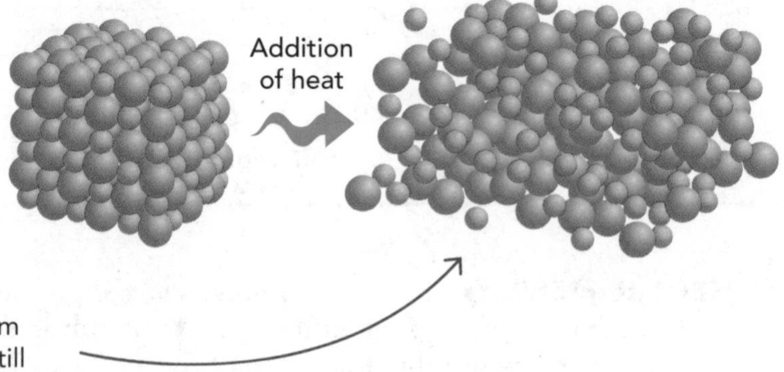

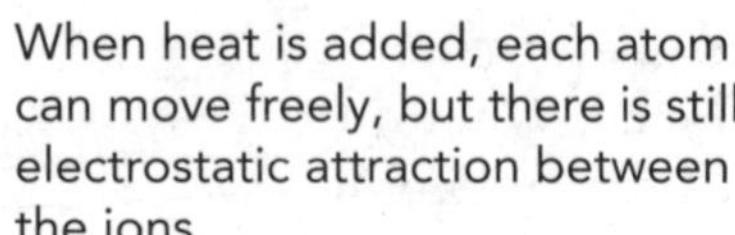

When heat is added, each atom can move freely, but there is still electrostatic attraction between the ions.

(18) **SEP Analyze and Interpret Data The table shows several ionic solids, their average bond energies in electron volts (eV), and their melting points. Use the pattern indicated in the table to predict the average bond energy of calcium fluoride (CaF_2), which has a melting point of 1420°C.**

Bond Energy and Melting Point of Selected Compounds

Material	Bond energy (eV/bond)	Melting point (°C)
Cesium chloride (CsCl)	6.747	646
Sodium chloride (NaCl)	7.96	801
Lithium fluoride (LiF)	10.45	870
Copper fluoride (CuF_2)	26.85	1360
Aluminum oxide (Al_2O_3)	157.46	3500

Dry Ice Carbon dioxide gas is pressurized and rapidly cooled to produce solid "dry ice." At atmospheric pressure, this substance skips the liquid phase and immediately begins to sublimate.

Sublimation

The change of a substance from solid to vapor without passing through the liquid state is called **sublimation.** Sublimation at STP typically occurs in materials held together by very weak intermolecular forces. For example, carbon dioxide (CO_2) is nonpolar and is therefore held together in solid, "dry ice" form via very weak dispersion forces. Since these intermolecular forces are very weak, it does not take much energy to completely break them versus weakening them. Therefore, the liquid phase is completely skipped. Because of this, solids will also have a vapor pressure. Sublimation occurs in solids with vapor pressures that exceed atmospheric pressure.

Noticing patterns can be a first step to organizing phenomena and exploring why and how the patterns occur.

19 **CCC Stability and Change** **Predict whether or not the substances in the table will sublime at STP. Base your predictions only on the type of force holding the solid together.**

Will It Sublime?		
Compound	**Type of Intermolecular Forces**	**Sublime at STP?**
Carbon dioxide (CO_2)		
Hydrogen fluoride (HF)		
Calcium chloride ($CaCl_2$)		
Naphthalene ($C_{10}H_8$)		
Iodine (I_2)		
Sodium chloride (NaCl)		
Water (H_2O)		

Phase Diagrams

The relationships among the solid, liquid, and vapor states of a substance in a sealed container can be represented in a single graph. A **phase diagram** is a graph that describes the conditions of temperature and pressure at which a substance exists as a solid, liquid, or gas.

Reading a Phase Diagram A phase diagram shows the pressure as a function of the temperature and outlines in what phase a material will be found at a specific temperature and pressure.

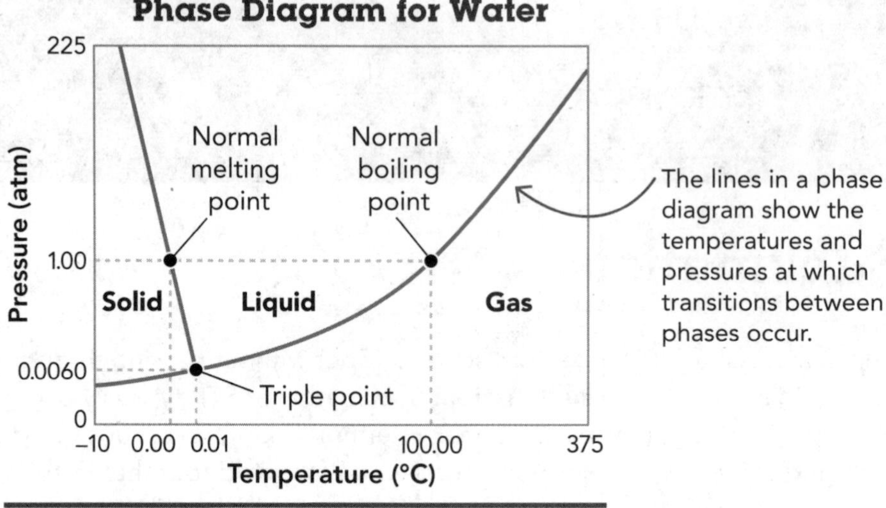

The lines in a phase diagram show the temperatures and pressures at which transitions between phases occur.

The **normal melting point** is the temperature at which water melts at 101.3 kPa (1 atm). The normal melting point of water is 0°C.

The **triple point** describes the only set of conditions under which all three phases can exist in equilibrium with each other.

The **normal boiling point** is the temperature at which water boils at 101.3 kPa. For water, this temperature is 100°C.

20 **SEP Interpret Data Use the phase diagram for carbon dioxide (CO_2) to determine in which phase CO_2 would be at STP. Similar to the normal boiling point for water, CO_2 will have a normal sublimation point. Identify the normal sublimation temperature of carbon dioxide.**

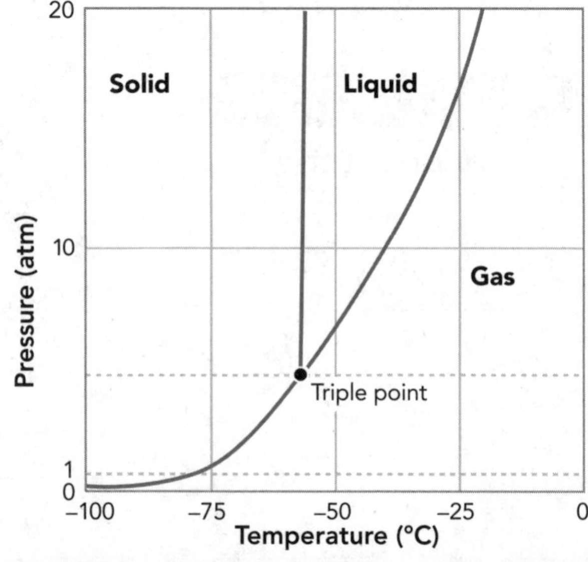

Revisit

INVESTIGATIVE PHENOMENON

GO ONLINE to Elaborate and Evaluate your knowledge of phase changes by completing the peer review and data analysis activities.

In the CER worksheet, you drafted a scientific argument to explain how materials used on mountaintops are engineered. With a partner, reevaluate the evidence cited in your arguments.

21 **SEP Construct an Explanation** **At high altitude, the boiling point of water changes. Does it go up or down? Why? How would this affect cooking on a mountain? Explain why the boiling point changes at higher altitude and design a solution to this cooking problem.**

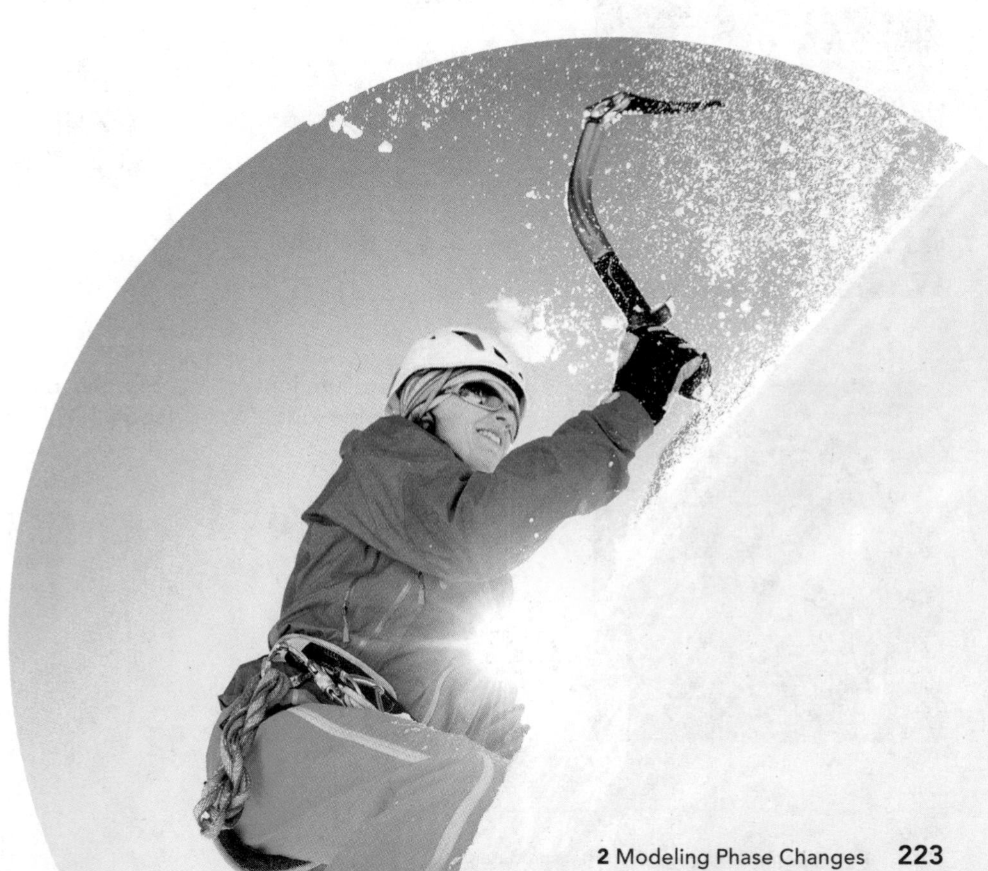

EXPERIENCE 3

Comparing Ionic and Molecular Compounds

GO ONLINE to Explore and Explain the properties of ionic and molecular compounds.

Representative Units

A molecular compound is a compound whose atoms share electrons through covalent bonds. Ionic compounds, on the other hand, are composed of positively and negatively charged ions held together by electrostatic forces. The representative unit of a molecular compound is a molecule. A molecule is made up of two or more atoms that act as a single unit. No such discrete units exist in an ionic compound, where ions are arranged in a repeating three-dimensional pattern. The representative unit for an ionic compound is called a formula unit.

Representative Units The representative unit of a molecular compound, such as water, is a molecule. For an ionic compound, such as salt, the representative unit is a formula unit.

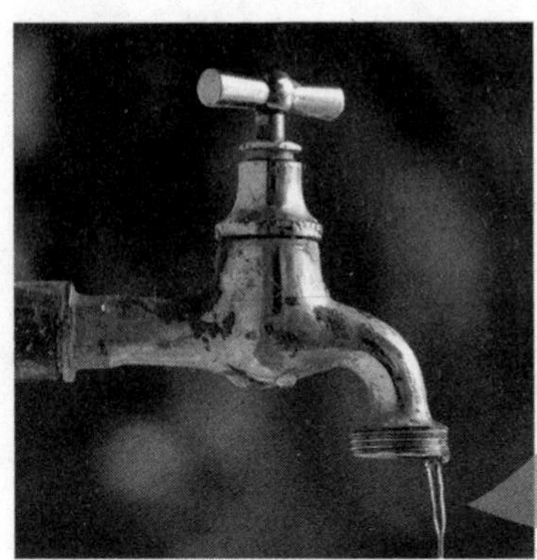

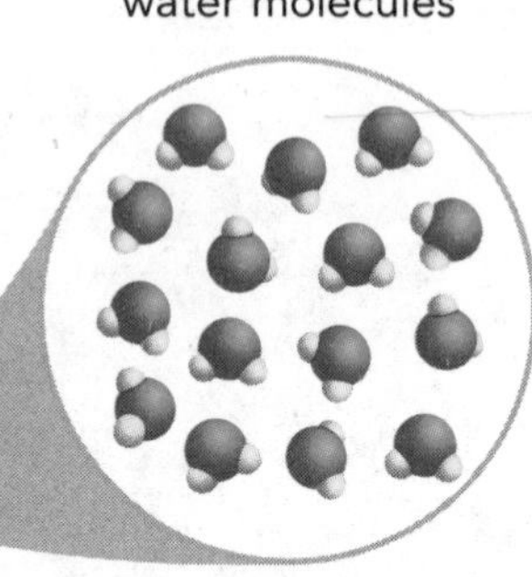

Molecule of water

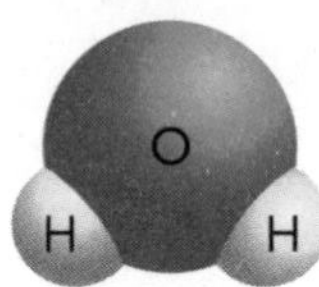

Chemical formula

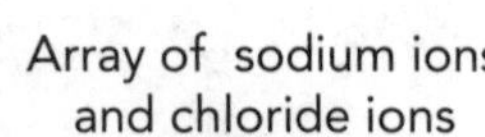

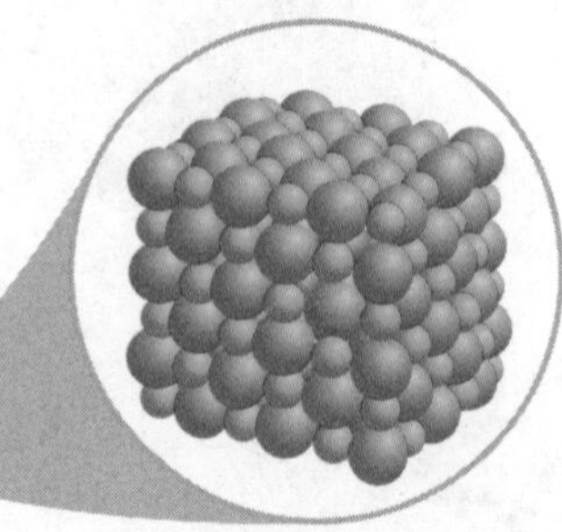

Formula unit of sodium chloride

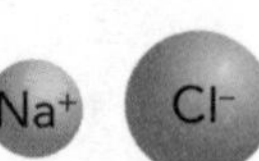

Chemical formula

Determining Compound Type

The periodic table can be divided up into metal elements and nonmetal elements. The metal elements are on the left and middle of the periodic table. The nonmetal elements are on the right. Elements along the boundary, such as boron or silicon, are considered metalloids but their bonding patterns are similar to nonmetals.

Ionic compounds are made up of a combination of metal and nonmetal atoms. Molecular compounds, on the other hand, are made up of only nonmetals. Ionic compounds include lithium fluoride (LiF), calcium chloride ($CaCl_2$), and sodium chloride (NaCl). Molecular compounds include water (H_2O), carbon dioxide (CO_2), and carbon monoxide (CO).

Ionic Compound The ionic compound sodium chloride (NaCl) is a combination of metal sodium (Na) atoms and nonmetal chlorine (Cl) atoms. When naming ionic compounds, the metals are listed first.

Molecular Compound The molecular compound carbon monoxide (CO) is a combination of nonmetal carbon (C) and nonmetal oxygen (O) atoms.

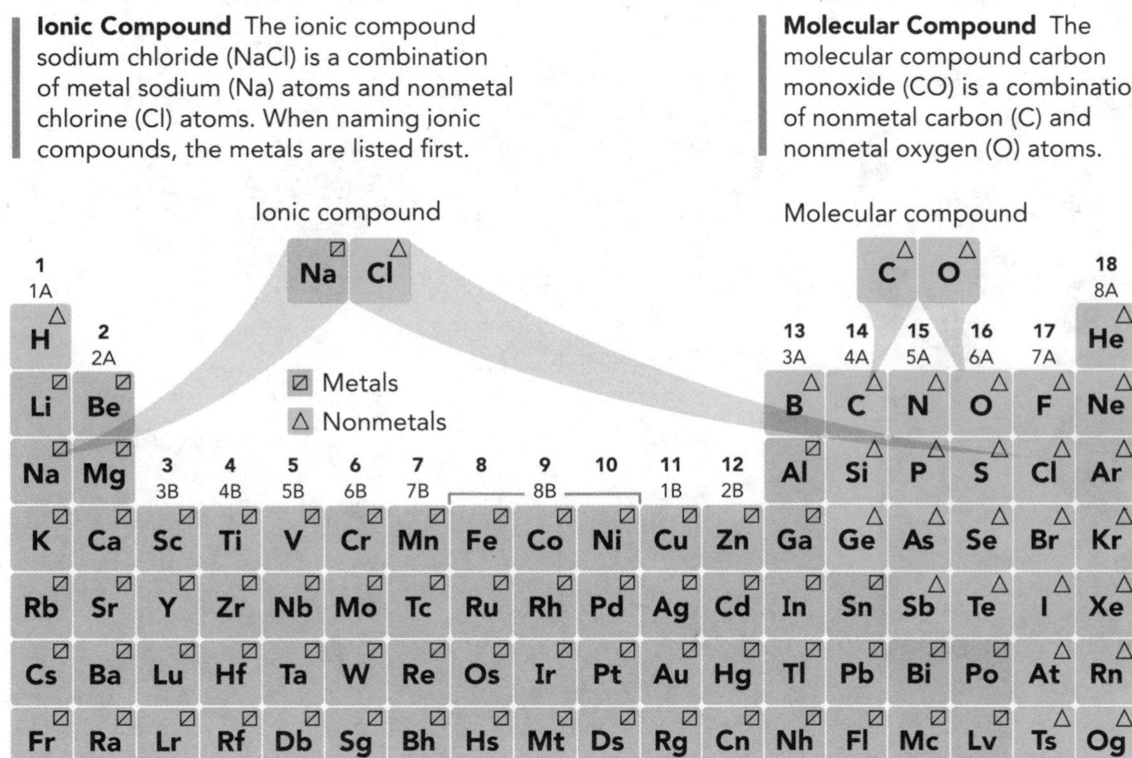

22 **SEP Use a Model Complete the table using the model for differentiating ionic compounds from molecular compounds.**

Ionic and Molecular Compounds			
Compounds	**Metal Elements**	**Nonmetal Elements**	**Ionic or Molecular?**
NaCl	Na	Cl	Ionic
CaO			
$MgSO_4$			
CH_4			
H_2SO_4			
NH_4			

Properties of Ionic and Molecular Compounds

Molecular compounds tend to have lower normal melting and boiling points than ionic compounds. This difference is due to the strength of attractive forces between molecules or atoms. For example, carbon dioxide (CO_2) molecules are held together by very weak dispersion forces, while water (H_2O) molecules are connected by stronger hydrogen bonds. Sodium chloride (NaCl) atoms are held together by a network of ionic bonds that are significantly stronger than hydrogen bonds.

Molecular Compounds | **Ionic Compounds**

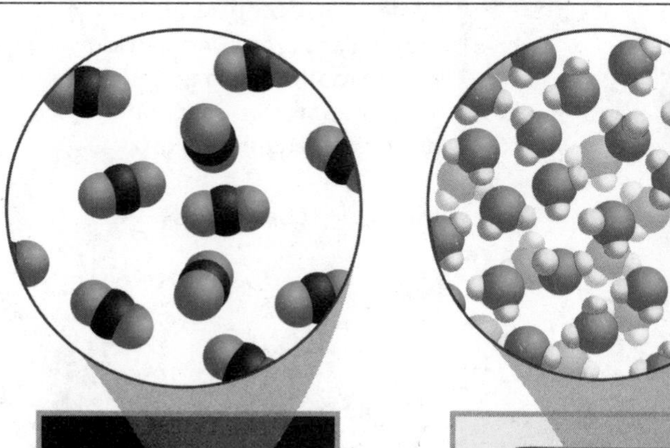

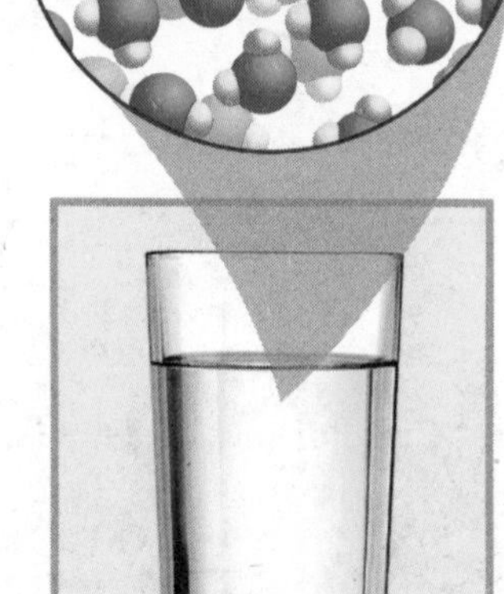

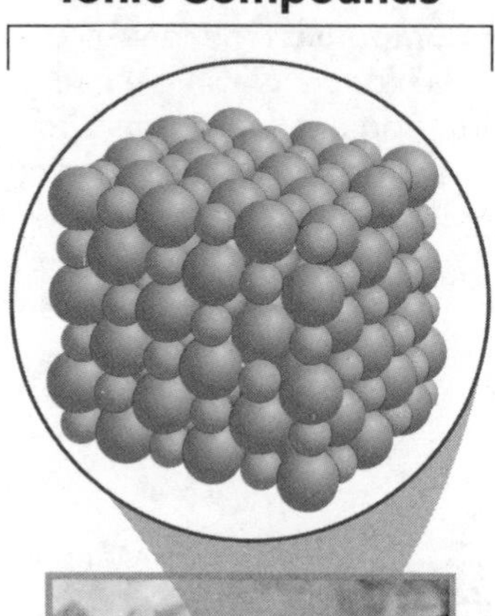

- Weak dispersion forces
- Typically gases at STP
- Lower melting points
- Volatile

- Strong hydrogen bonds
- Typically liquids at STP
- Lower melting points
- Volatile

- Very strong ionic bonds
- Hard solid at STP
- Higher melting points
- Not volatile

23 **SEP Construct an Explanation** **Use compound type to infer the relative boiling points of the following compounds: NaF, N_2O, and H_2O. Rank them in order from lowest to highest boiling point. Explain how you made your ranking. Then look up the boiling points and check your answer.**

Covalent Network Solids

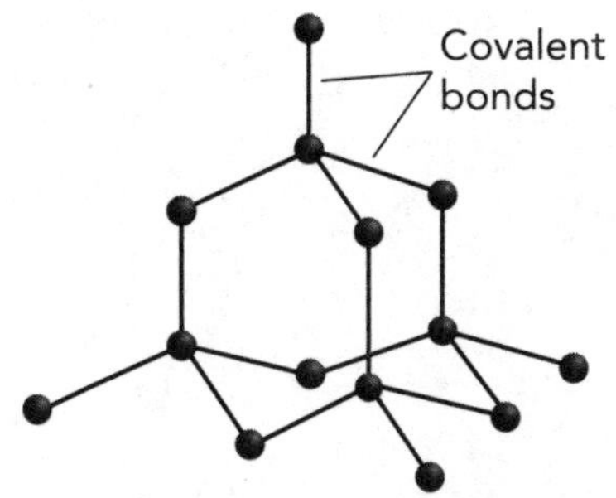

Diamond Each carbon (C) atom in diamond is covalently bonded to four other carbon atoms, forming a strong three-dimensional network.

In most molecular compounds, the molecules are held together by weak intermolecular forces. This explains why molecular compounds have lower boiling and melting points compared to ionic compounds. However, some molecular compounds do not melt until far above 1,000°C. These interesting exceptions are called **covalent network solids.** A covalent network solid is a molecular compound made up of networks of atoms or molecules held together by strong covalent bonds, not weak intermolecular forces.

The carbon atoms in diamond form what is called a tetrahedral structure. This unique structure makes diamond one of the hardest substances on Earth.

Allotropes are different physical forms of the same element. Although all allotropes of an element are composed of the same kinds of atoms, they have very different properties based on their structure.

Other Crystalline Forms of Carbon Diamond is one crystalline form of carbon, but it is not the only one. Other forms, or allotropes, include carbon nanotubes, graphite, and fullerenes.

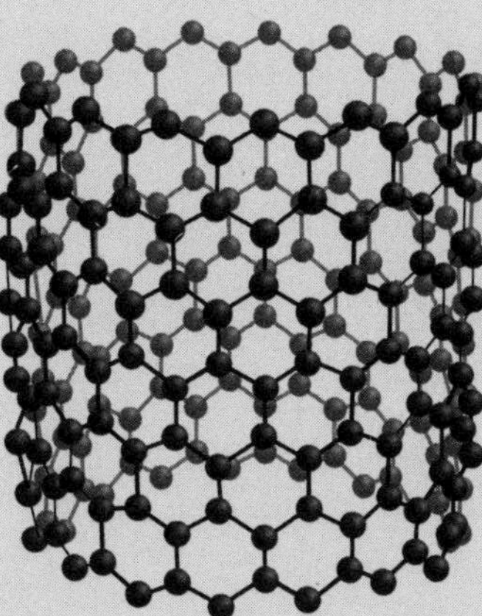

Carbon nanotubes are hollow, cylindrical tubes of carbon atoms in a honeycomb framework. Each carbon atom forms very strong covalent bonds with its neighbors, producing the strongest and stiffest material ever discovered.

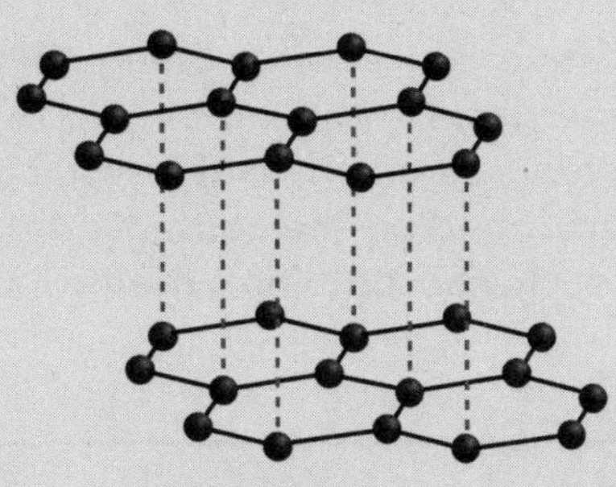

In **graphite**, the carbon atoms are linked in widely spaced layers of hexagonal (six-sided) arrays. The atoms in a layer are covalently bonded, but the layers are held together by very weak dispersion forces.

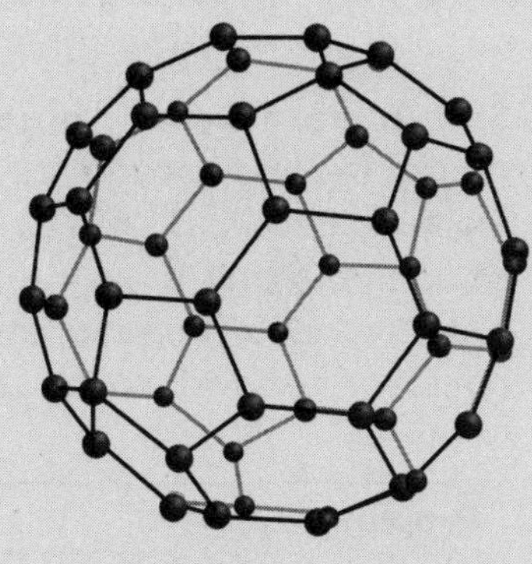

In a buckminsterfullerene (also called a buckyball), 60 carbon atoms are arranged in pentagons and hexagons to form a hollow ball. **Fullerenes** are used in medicine and in solar cells.

(24) **SEP Evaluate Information** Graphite is a soft substance used in writing instruments like pencils. Carbon nanotubes are the hardest substance known to humans. Both are made entirely of carbon atoms. Explain why each allotrope has such different properties.

Revisit

INVESTIGATIVE PHENOMENON

GO ONLINE to Elaborate and Evaluate your knowledge of ionic and molecular compounds by completing the class discussion and engineering design activities.

In the CER worksheet, you drafted a scientific argument to explain how materials used on mountaintops are engineered. With a partner, reevaluate the evidence cited in your arguments.

(25) **SEP Analyze Data** Designing materials requires being able to recognize and categorize properties. On the lab bench, there are three vials labeled A, B, and C. The table summarizes the results of a series of analyses that have been performed on the contents. Interpret the data and determine whether each vial contains a molecular, ionic, or covalent network solid.

Property	Vial A	Vial B	Vial C
Melting point	High	Low	Very high
Electrical conductivity	Moderate	Poor	Poor
Hardness	Hard	Soft	Very hard

EXPERIENCE 4

Comparing Metals and Nonmetals

GO ONLINE to Explore and Explain the properties of metals and nonmetals.

Delocalized Electrons

Metals have very different properties than nonmetals. This is largely due to the unique arrangement of their electrons. Unlike other elements, metals have too few electrons in their outer shell to form covalent bonds with their neighbors. Instead, metals consist of closely packed cations and loosely held, delocalized valence electrons that provide the attractive force holding the atoms together. In ionic and covalent compounds, which contain nonmetals, the electrons involved in bonding have to stay close to their atoms. In metals, they do not.

Electrons in Metals In metals, including zinc, electrons are not bound to individual atoms. Instead, they move around the atoms freely, holding them together in a crystalline structure.

Two zinc atoms by themselves do not form a chemical bond.

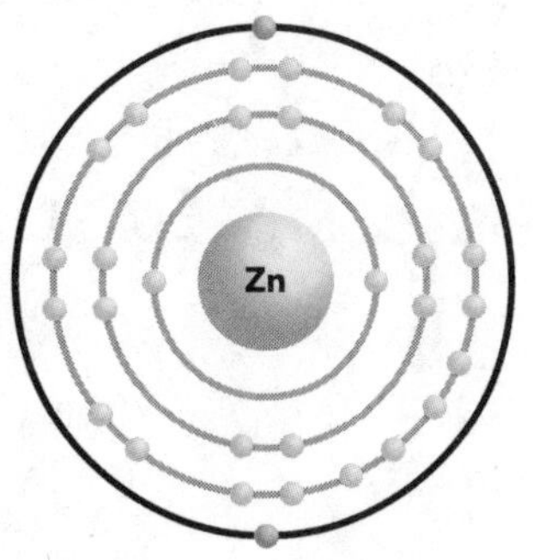

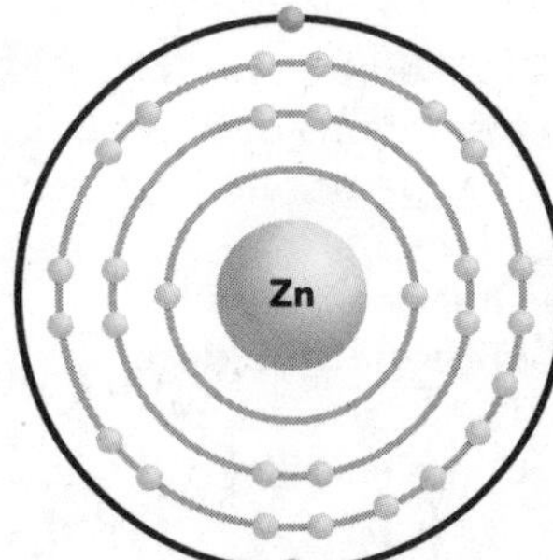

When enough zinc atoms come together in a cluster, their two valence electrons become delocalized. This means the electrons can move around the cluster from one atom to the next. Positive Zn^{2+} cations are left behind.

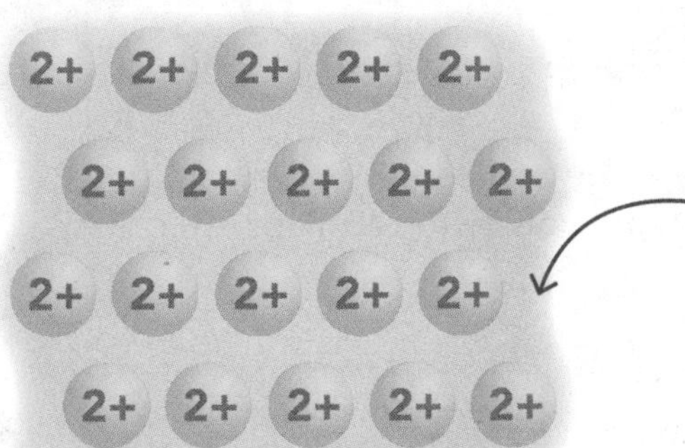

With enough atoms, the Zn^{2+} cations form a crystal structure held together by a swarm of delocalized electrons that surround the metal ions.

Ductility and Malleability

Two very important properties of metals are ductility and malleability. **Ductility** is the ability to be drawn into wires. **Malleability** is the ability to be hammered or pressed into shapes. Both ductility and malleability can be explained by the mobility of delocalized valence electrons in a metal.

Metals vs. Ionic Compounds A sea of valence electrons allows metals to be squeezed into wire or hammered without breaking. Ionic compounds do not behave the same way.

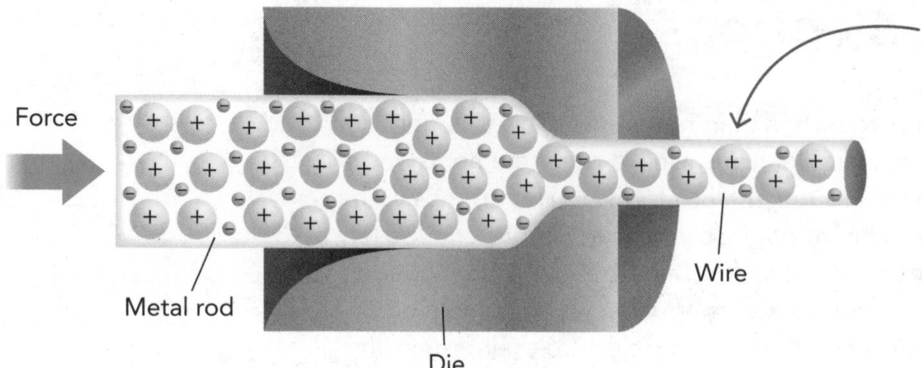

Drifting electrons insulate metal cations from each other. When **metal** is forced through a die, the cations easily slide past one another, **allowing the metal to be formed into wire**. This is an example of **ductility**.

When pressure is applied to a **metal,** the cations easily change position, so the **metal changes shape without breaking.** This is an example of **malleability.**

External force

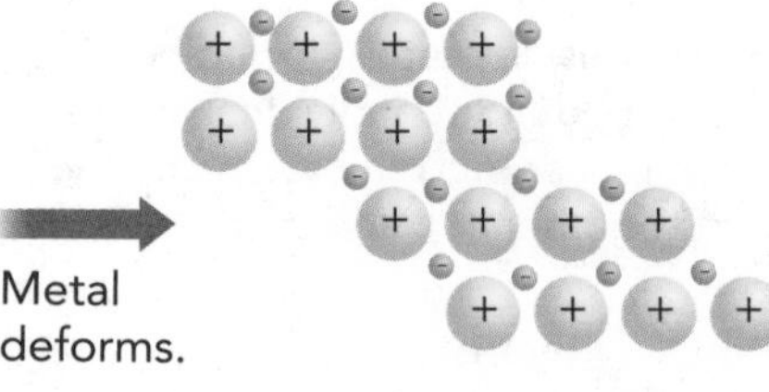

In contrast, applying pressure to an **ionic compound** tends to push the ions close together. The positive ions repel each other, and the **crystal shatters.**

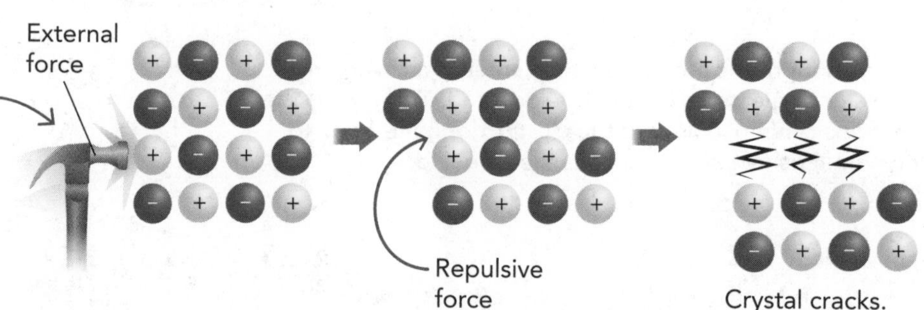

26 **SEP Plan an Investigation You want to compare the malleability of two metals. Plan an investigation that would allow you to determine which metal is more malleable.**

Conductivity and Luster

Metals are good conductors of both heat and electricity. **Thermal conductivity** is a material's ability to conduct heat. **Electrical conductivity** is a material's ability to conduct electricity. These properties make metals highly useful for cookware (pots and pans) and electronics. Another unique property of metals is their shiny appearance. The way light interacts with a material's surface is called **luster.** Light causes the free electrons in metals to move and then the excited electrons re-emit the light, which is why metals aren't transparent and look shiny. This property makes metals highly valued in jewelry making.

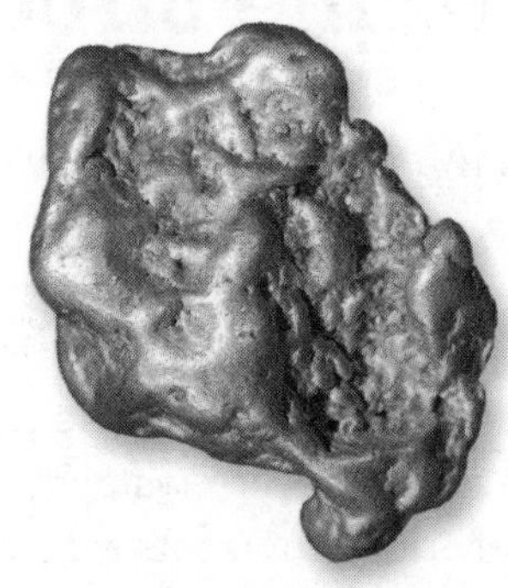

Luster Much of the light that hits the surface of a metal such as gold is reflected. This makes metals appear shinier than nonmetals.

Thermal Conductivity Electrons can carry energy in the form of heat. Because the electrons in metal can move around, they conduct heat more easily than ionic solids or covalent network solids.

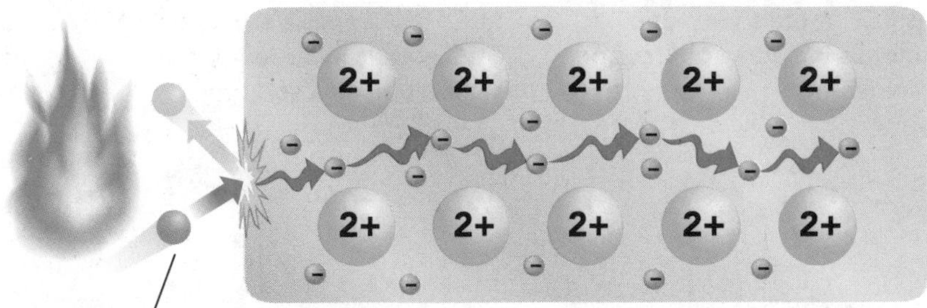

2+
A warm air molecule transfers energy to the metal.

Electrical Conductivity Electric current is the movement of electrons. The delocalized electrons in metals can easily move, making metals more conductive than ionic solids.

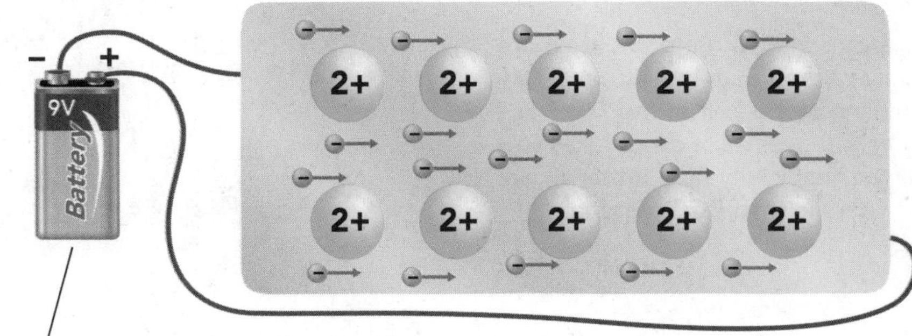

–
+
9V
Battery
2+
The battery "pushes" the electrons in one direction, creating an electric current in the metal.

27 **SEP Develop a Model** Does a rumor spread faster in a gym where all of the students can move around freely, or in a classroom where students are confined to desks? Develop an analogy for the difference in conductivity between metals and ionic solids.

....

....

....

Crystalline Structure and Properties of Metals

Pure metal is a crystalline solid with atoms arranged in repeating patterns. Metals usually adopt one of three packing arrangements: body-centered cubic (BCC), face-centered cubic (FCC), or hexagonal close-packed (HCP). The microscopic crystal structure of a metal largely determines its macroscopic bulk properties. For example, when the planes of atoms in a metal crystal are closely packed, it tends to be easier for them to slide past each other. Therefore, cubic structures with closely packed planes (such as FCC) are more ductile than those that are less closely packed (such as BCC).

Crystalline Packing Structures The three packing arrangements for atoms in a metal crystal are FCC, BCC, and HCP.

In **FCC structure,** every atom has 12 neighbors arranged as shown. This **tightly-packed** structure makes FCC metals very ductile. FCC metals include gold, copper, and aluminum.

In **BCC structure,** every atom has eight neighbors. Because BCC is **less closely packed** than FCC, BCC metals are less ductile. BCC metals include lithium, potassium, and sodium.

In **HCP structure,** each atom has 12 neighbors, like FCC. However, HCP metals tend to be brittle since its **non-cubic geometry** means it has fewer planes across which atoms can slip past each other. HCP metals include zinc, cobalt, and cadmium.

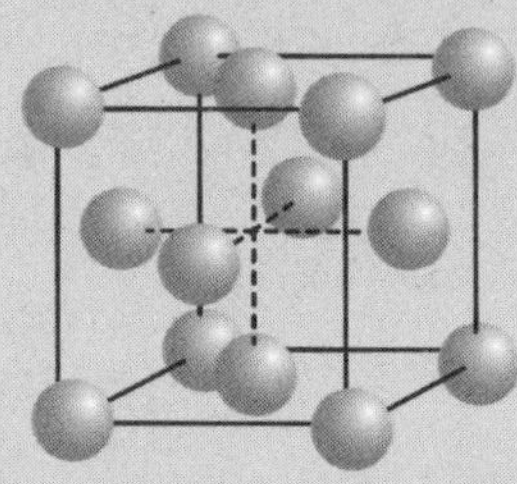

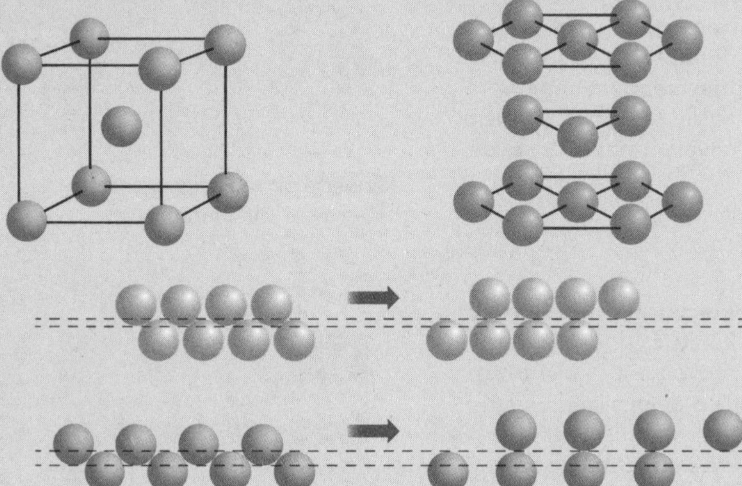

The atoms in FCC materials are more closely packed than in BCC materials, so pulling atoms out of the "dip" as the planes slip over each other takes less energy. That's why FCC materials are more ductile than BCC materials.

(28) **CCC Cause and Effect Young's modulus is a measure of a solid material's stiffness. A highly ductile material will typically have a very low modulus. The table shows several different metals, their crystalline structure, and their Young's modulus. Describe the pattern you observe and explain the connection between structure and stiffness.**

Young's Modulus

Metal	Structure	Young's Modulus (GPa)
Chromium	BCC	279
Iron	BCC	210
Tungsten	BCC	411
Copper	FCC	110
Silver	FCC	83
Aluminum	FCC	70
Lead	FCC	16

Defects and Properties of Metals

Crystal Dislocations Natural crystals are almost never perfect. All have some defects in their lattice structure. Atoms may be missing, or an extra atom might get stuck where it doesn't belong. Sometimes, an atom gets substituted for another type of atom.

"Errors" in the crystal structure are called point defects. A **point defect** is a defect or irregularity within a crystal that occurs at a point in the lattice. The presence of defects can strongly influence many of a crystal's properties, including its color.

Types of Point Defects Defects in crystal structure can take a variety of forms.

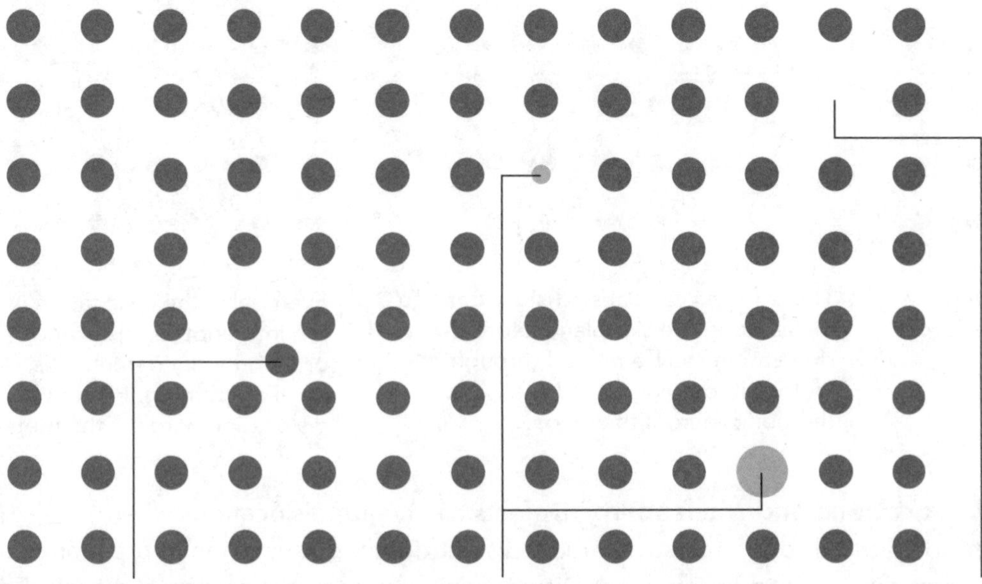

In an **interstitial** defect, extra atoms are stuck where they don't belong.

In a **substitution** defect, different atoms take the place of existing atoms in the crystal lattice.

In a **vacancy** defect, atoms are missing from the lattice structure.

Colorful Defects All of these gemstones contain defects of aluminum oxide, which is clear and colorless in its pure form. Blue sapphires result from substitutions of titanium and iron atoms. Green sapphires result from iron impurities. Chromium atom substitutions result in the formation of red rubies.

Work Hardening
Swordsmiths hammer and fold metal blades to increase their strength. These actions create a dense network of dislocations throughout the metal structure, hardening the blade.

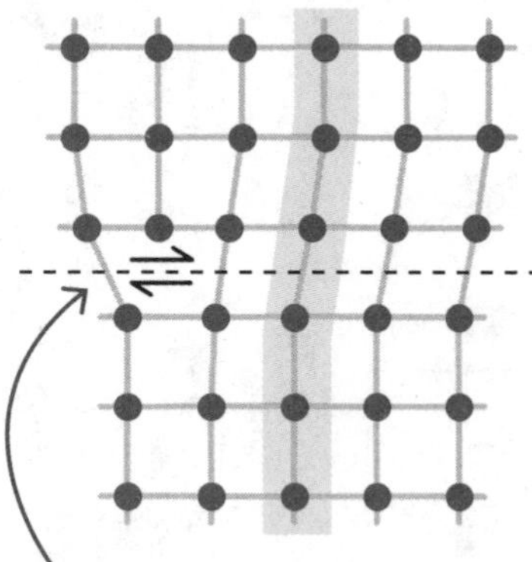

Folding or hammering the metal creates **shear forces** along the slip plane.

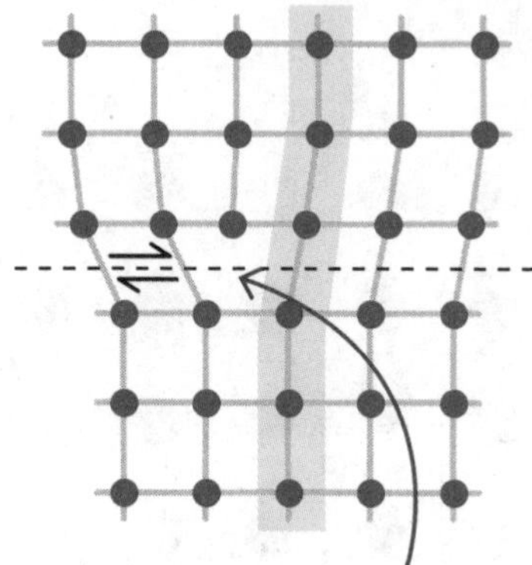

These forces can cause **dislocations** to move along the slip plane. Note that a dislocation can be moved through the metal without having to break all of the bonds across the plane.

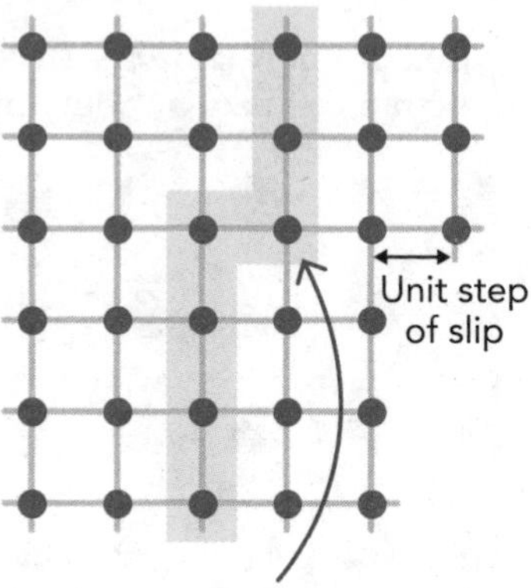

Eventually, the dislocation will run into another dislocation or a boundary defect. This is called **pinning**. Pinning a dislocation hardens the metal.

Dislocations and Malleability Defects can create dislocations when propagated through the structure. A **dislocation** happens when entire planes of atoms get inserted or removed. Dislocations affect the properties of metals. For example, the more dislocations in a metal structure, the lower its malleability.

The intentional introduction of dislocations in metal is called work hardening. When a metal is bent or shaped repeatedly, the number of dislocations increases. These dislocations get tangled, preventing further movement and making it harder to deform the metal. Work hardening also results in the movement of dislocations, which leads to hardening through a process called pinning. Work-hardened metals are stronger than unworked metals, but they are also more brittle.

29 SEP Conduct an Investigation Unbend a paper clip such that you have a long, straight piece of metal. Bend one of the initially straight sections back and forth several times. Does it become easier or harder to bend the paper clip in the same spot? What happens if you keep bending the paper clip back and forth?

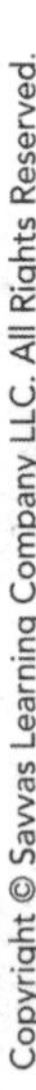

Alloys

Most of the metals you encounter every day are alloys. Alloys are mixtures of two or more elements, at least one of which is a metal. Alloys are important because their properties are often superior to those of their constituent elements. Steel is a combination of a metal element (iron) and up to 2% by weight of a nonmetal element (carbon). The carbon atoms are a type of point defect that makes steel less malleable than iron. That's why support structures in buildings are made from steel and not iron.

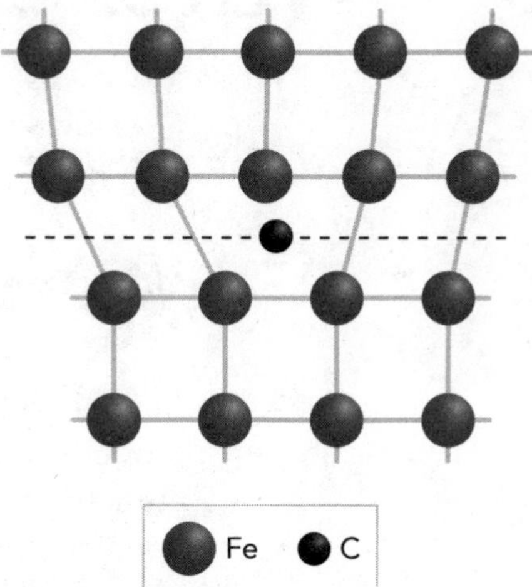

Structure of Steel Carbon occupies interstitial sites in iron's structure. These carbon atoms get trapped at dislocation sites, preventing the movement of the dislocation (pinning). This makes steel stronger than pure iron.

30 **SEP Define a Problem** **You are designing a metal bicycle frame. What properties should the frame have?**

Revisit

INVESTIGATIVE PHENOMENON

GO ONLINE to Elaborate and Evaluate your knowledge of metals and nonmetals by completing the class discussion and engineering design activities.

In the CER worksheet, you drafted a scientific argument to explain how materials used on mountaintops are engineered. With a partner, reevaluate the evidence cited in your arguments.

31 **SEP Design a Solution** **Mountain climbers rely on permanently installed ropes to help them ascend steep, slippery rock faces safely. Fiber ropes are not hardy enough to be left on the side of a mountain for years. Steel cables are stronger than ropes, but they are also very heavy and not very flexible. Use your understanding of metal strength and malleability to design a rope system that will be both strong and flexible.**

EXPERIENCE 5

Water and Aqueous Systems

GO ONLINE to Explore and Explain the properties of water and aqueous systems.

Water and Hydrogen Bonding

Compared with other molecular compounds, water has some pretty unusual properties. Because water molecules are highly polar, they are strongly attracted to each other. This intermolecular attraction is known as hydrogen bonding, though the attractive force is not actually a true bond. Hydrogen bonds are the strongest kind of intermolecular forces, and many of water's important properties—including those that make it essential to life—are the result of this strong attraction.

Polarity and Hydrogen Bonds Because water is a polar molecule, its molecules are attracted to each other. Hydrogen bonds hold water molecules together.

Oxygen (O) has greater electronegativity than hydrogen (H), so the oxygen atom attracts the electron pair of the covalent O—H bond more than the hydrogen atom. This gives the hydrogen atoms a partially positive charge.

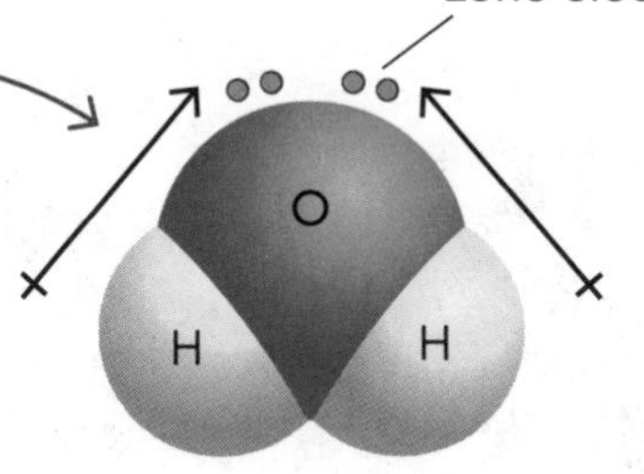

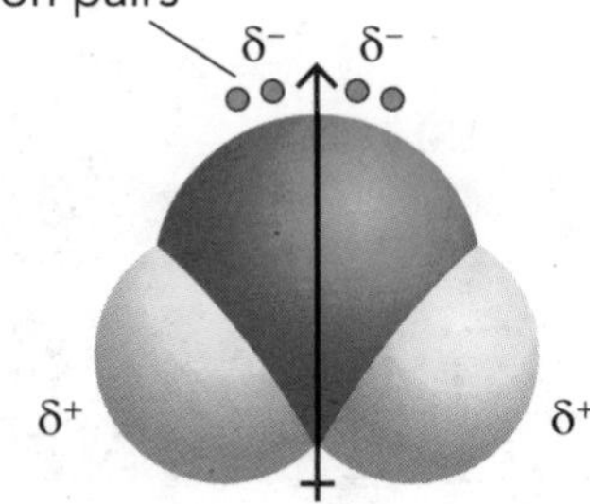

The hydrogen bond forms due to the attraction between the partially positive hydrogen and the negative lone pairs on the oxygen molecule.

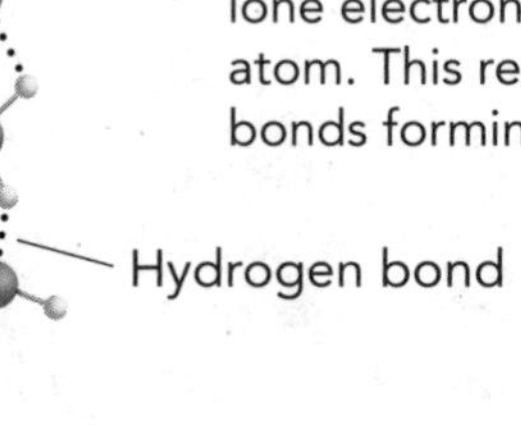

Liquid water

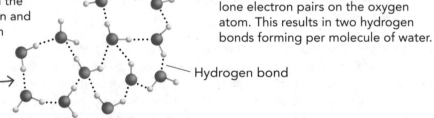

Hydrogen bonding in water is particularly strong due to the two lone electron pairs on the oxygen atom. This results in two hydrogen bonds forming per molecule of water.

32 **SEP Construct an Explanation** **Why is water (H_2O) a liquid at room temperature while carbon dioxide (CO_2) is a gas? What's different about their structures that results in very different properties?**

Surface Tension

If you've ever seen dew sitting on a leaf in the early morning, you know that, unlike other liquids, water tends to form nearly spherical drops. Once again, hydrogen bonding is responsible. Within the body of the drop, the attractive forces between molecules are balanced. However, molecules at the surface of the liquid experience an unbalanced attraction as they are pulled on from below, but not from above. As a result, the molecules at the surface tend to be drawn inward. This inward force creates tension along the surface of the drop, causing it to act as though it were covered by an elastic membrane. This tension on the surface of the water drop is known as **surface tension.** Water has a higher surface tension than most other liquids thanks to hydrogen bonding.

Beaded Water Unbalanced forces pulling inward on a drop of water cause it to minimize the amount of surface area by beading up on some surfaces.

A **molecule at the surface** of the drop will experience only attractive forces from below. Because these attractive forces are **unbalanced,** there is a net pull on the molecule into the drop.
A **molecule in the middle** of the drop will experience attractive forces from all sides. Because these attractive forces are **balanced,** there is no net pull on the molecule.

Surface Tension Variations Surface tension is affected by the type of substrate, or surface, water is resting on. Nonpolar substrates do not pull very hard on water molecules, so the drops remain rounded. Polar substrates pull on water molecules more, making the drops flatter. This is called wetting. Surface tension can also be reduced by introducing a surfactant to water. A **surfactant** is a substance that reduces surface tension and increases wetting. Surfactants are commonly used in detergents to allow the detergent to mix with water.

Substrates and Surfactants

What factors affect **surface tension?**

Type of Substrate Water molecules are attracted by a polar substrate, and the drop flattens. When a drop rests on a nonpolar substrate, the substrate does not pull very hard on the water molecules, so the attraction between water molecules is not interrupted and the drop remains rounded.

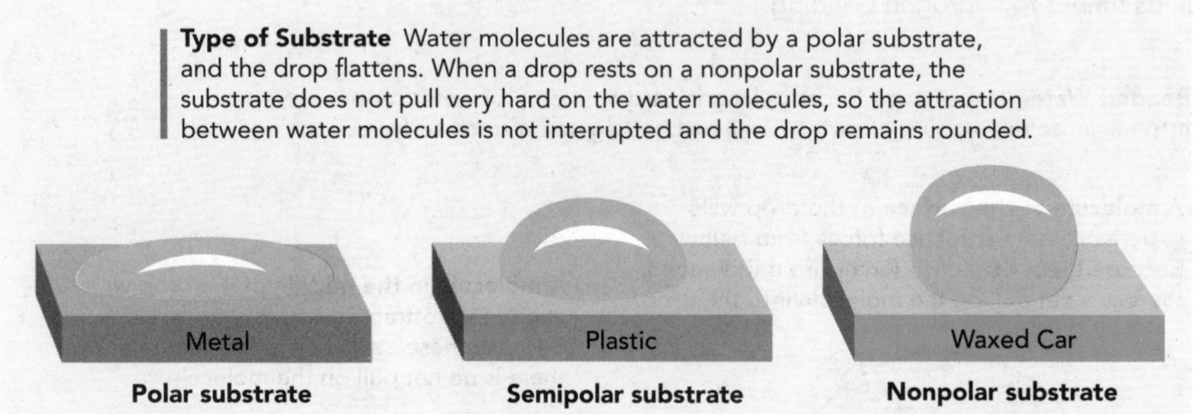

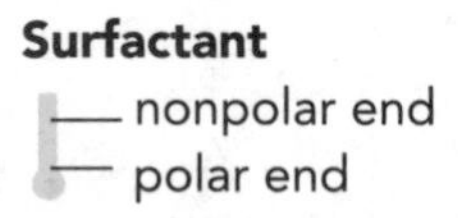

Amount of Surfactant Surfactants have a polar end and a nonpolar end. When added to water, they move to the surface and the water molecules hydrogen bond with the polar end of the surfactant instead of each other, reducing surface tension. The more surfactant is added, the flatter the drop will be.

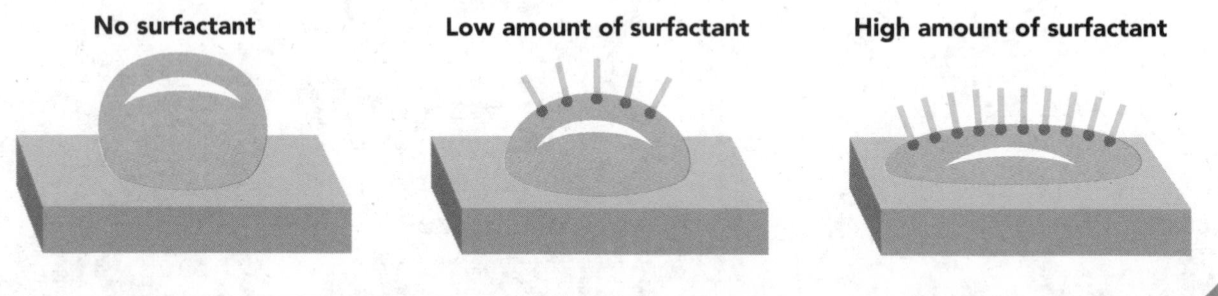

(33) **SEP Construct an Explanation** Printers often use surfactants in the printing of paper with ink. Explain why this might be.

....

....

....

Hydrogen Bonding and Boiling Point

Molecular compounds that have low molar mass are usually gases at STP. For example, ammonia (NH_3) has a molar mass of 17.0 g/mol and boils at −33°C. Water has a similar molar mass of 18.0 g/mol, but it has a boiling point of 100°C, so it is liquid at STP. The difference is due to the fact that water has stronger hydrogen bonds and forms more bonds per molecule, which raises the temperature at which it turns into gas. The reason that water forms more hydrogen bonds is because its oxygen atom has two lone pairs of electrons, while the nitrogen atom in ammonia has only one pair. This results in two hydrogen bonds per molecule of water versus one per molecule of ammonia. The individual hydrogen bonds in water are also slightly stronger because oxygen is more electronegative than nitrogen, which results in a larger partial positive charge on the hydrogen atoms in water molecules.

Hydrogen Bonds Affect Boiling Point Water has a much higher boiling point than ammonia because water forms stronger hydrogen bonds with neighboring molecules than ammonia does.

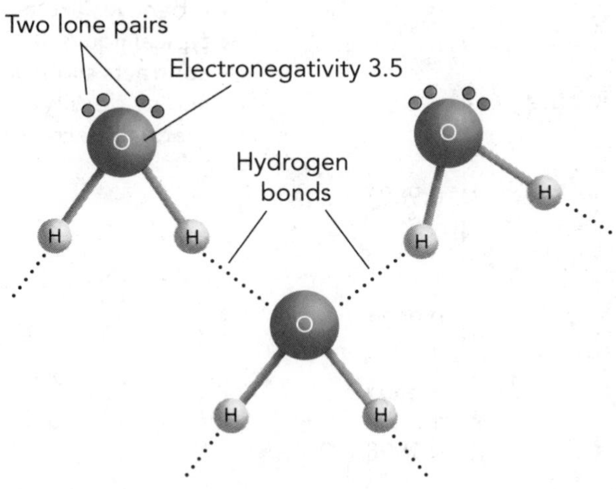

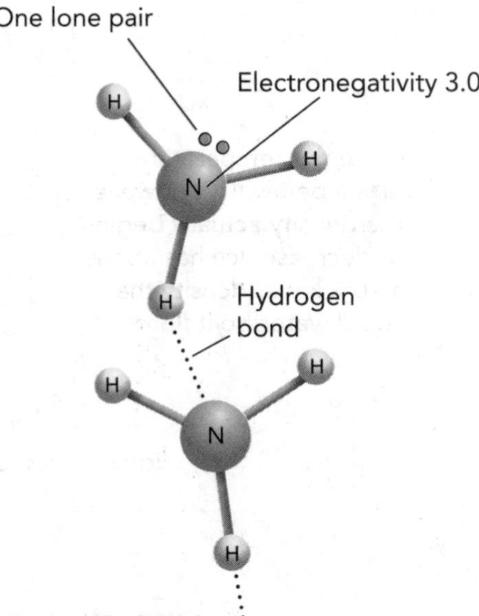

Water (H_2O)
- Low molar mass
- Strong hydrogen bonds
  - High electronegativity of O
  - Both Hs involved in hydrogen bonding
- Low vapor pressure
- High boiling point
- Liquid at STP

Ammonia (NH_3)
- Low molar mass
- Weak hydrogen bonds
  - Lower electronegativity of N
  - Only one H involved in hydrogen bonding at any one time
- High vapor pressure
- Low boiling point
- Gas at STP

34 **SEP Construct an Explanation Hydrogen fluoride (HF) has a lower boiling point than water (H_2O), even though fluoride (F) has a greater electronegativity than oxygen (O). Why do you think that is?**

....

....

Structure Affects Properties of Ice

Water in its solid state—ice—also exhibits some unique properties. For example, most other substances get more dense as they cool down and turn from liquid to solid. That's because their molecules contract together as they lose energy, so they take up less space. And, because the density of the solid is greater than the liquid, most solids sink in their own liquid. But if you've ever ice-skated on a frozen pond, you may have noticed that ice does something quite different—it floats in its own liquid! That's because, unlike other substances, water expands to become less dense as it freezes.

Water Density This thermometer shows how the density of water changes with temperature.

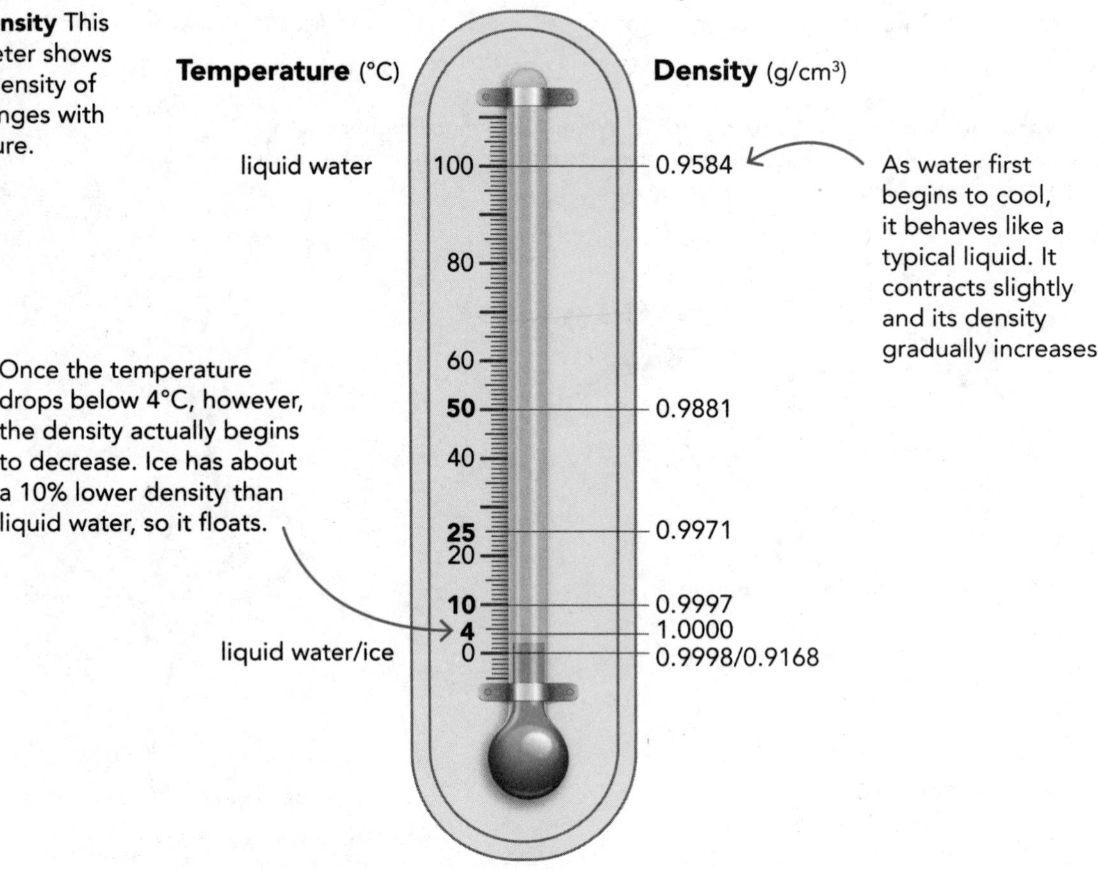

Temperature (°C)
Density (g/cm³)
liquid water
100
0.9584
As water first begins to cool, it behaves like a typical liquid. It contracts slightly and its density gradually increases.
80
60
50
0.9881
Once the temperature drops below 4°C, however, the density actually begins to decrease. Ice has about a 10% lower density than liquid water, so it floats.
40
25
0.9971
20
10
0.9997
4
1.0000
liquid water/ice
0
0.9998/0.9168

(35) **SEP Analyze Data Using data from the figure, graph the density as a function of the temperature for liquid water from 100°C to 4°C.**

The unique property of flotation can be explained by ice's structure. In liquid water, hydrogen bonds attract water molecules together but don't hold them in any set pattern. In ice, these same hydrogen bonds link water molecules together in a repeating pattern of linked hexagons. Because the molecules in this pattern are not packed in tightly, ice is less dense than liquid water. When ice melts, the open framework collapses, and the water molecules pack closer together again.

Insulating Ice A layer of ice on top of a body of water acts as an insulator for the water beneath, preventing it from freezing solid. This allows aquatic life to survive even during winter.

Structure of a Snowflake All snowflakes are six-sided because they are made up of different combinations of microscopic hexagonal ice crystals.

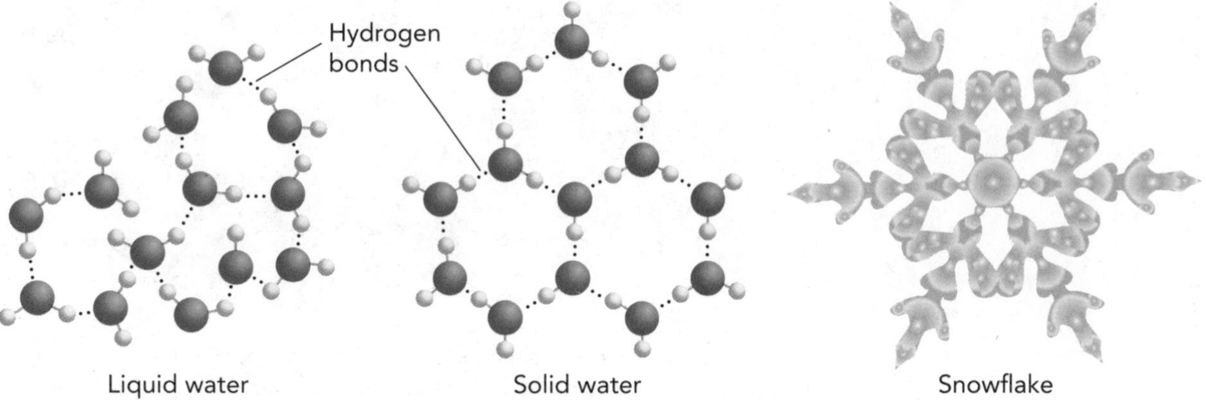

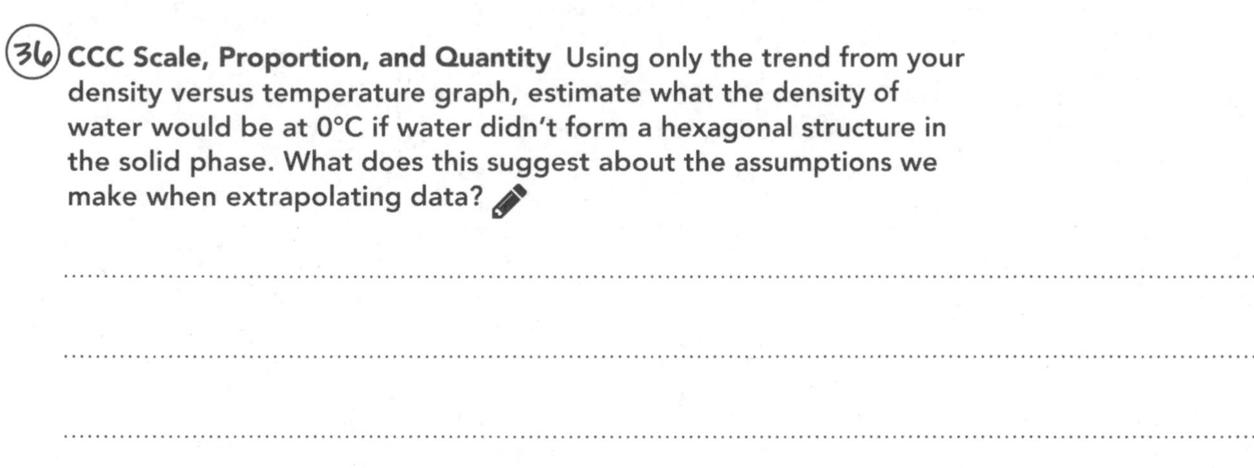

36 **CCC Scale, Proportion, and Quantity** Using only the trend from your density versus temperature graph, estimate what the density of water would be at 0°C if water didn't form a hexagonal structure in the solid phase. What does this suggest about the assumptions we make when extrapolating data?

Aqueous Solutions

Some substances dissolve readily into other substances to form a solution. Others do not. In any solution, the dissolving medium is called the **solvent.** The dissolved particles (usually ions, but also polar molecules) are called the **solute.** The process of ion capture by the solvent is called **solvation.** Solvents and solutes may be gases, liquids, or solids. An **aqueous solution** is defined as a solution where water is the solvent. Substances that dissolve most readily in water include ionic and polar covalent compounds, due to water's own high polarity.

Polar Compounds in Water Sodium chloride (NaCl) is an ionic compound made up of sodium (Na^+) and chloride (Cl^-) ions.

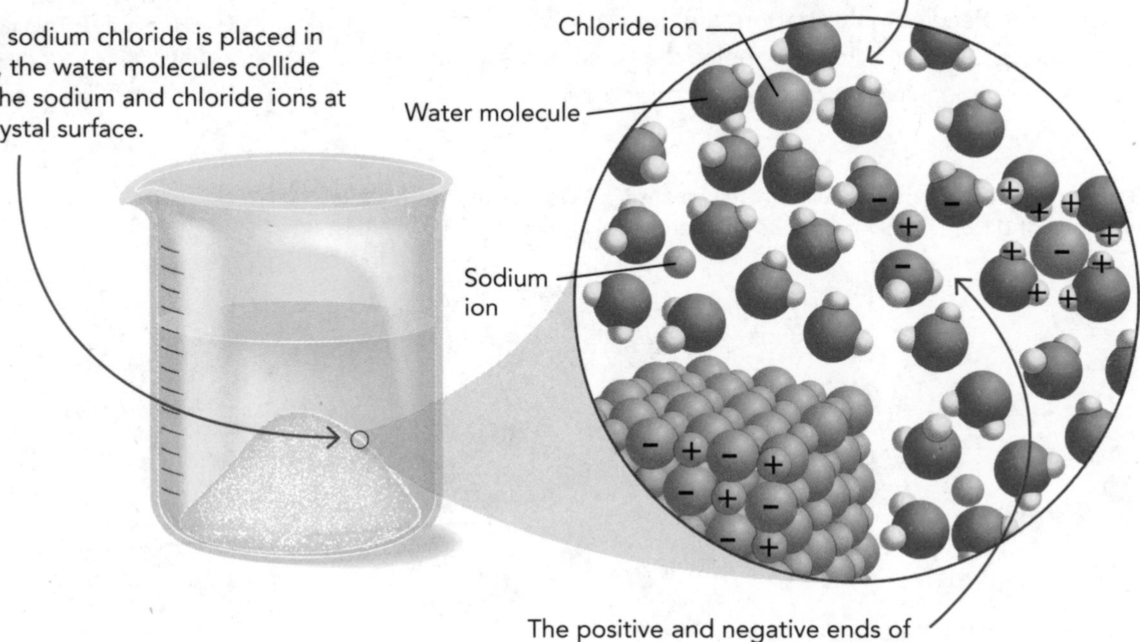

When sodium chloride is placed in water, the water molecules collide with the sodium and chloride ions at the crystal surface.
As individual solute ions break away from the crystal surface, they become surrounded by the polar water molecules.
Chloride ion
Water molecule
Sodium ion
The positive and negative ends of the polar water molecules attract the solute ions (Na^+, Cl^-).

37 **SEP Develop a Model Draw a model showing the solvation of potassium chloride in water.**

Nonpolar compounds typically do not dissolve in water. You may know that oil and water don't mix. Oils are made up of large, mostly nonpolar molecules. Because oil is generally nonpolar and does not form ions, it is not solvated by polar water molecules and so does not dissolve in water. Nonpolar compounds tend to dissolve only in other nonpolar compounds.

How a compound behaves in water is directly related to the structure of its atoms or molecules. If the atoms or molecules are polar, the substance will dissolve.

Nonpolar Compounds in Water Much like oil, hexane (C_6H_{14}) is a nonpolar molecule. The carbon atoms in hexane are more electronegative than the hydrogen atoms, so the outside surface of the hexane molecules have a positive charge. However, the molecule is symmetric so the charge is uniformly distributed, making the molecule nonpolar.

If a water molecule were placed in the hexane layer it would be forced back down into the water layer by gravity, the repulsion between positive hexane hydrogen atoms and positive water hydrogen atoms, and the strong attraction of the water hydrogen atoms to the oxygen atoms in the other water molecules.

The negatively charged oxygen atoms in the water molecules tend to align towards the positively charged hydrogen atoms in the hexane molecules at the interface.

38 CCC Structure and Function Consider the following list of compounds: $MgSO_4$, C_2H_2, CH_4, CaO. Circle the compounds that are most likely to dissolve in water. What information did you use to make your prediction?

....

....

....

Electrolytes and Nonelectrolytes

An **electrolyte** is a compound that conducts electric current when dissolved in an aqueous solution or in the molten state. Conduction of an electric current requires ions that are mobile and able to carry charge through a liquid. All ionic compounds are electrolytes because they dissociate, or separate, into ions. In a solution that contains a strong electrolyte, all or nearly all of the solute exists as ions. In a solution that contains a weak electrolyte, only a fraction of the solute exists as ions.

A **nonelectrolyte** is a compound that does not conduct electric current in either an aqueous solution or in the molten state. Many molecular compounds are nonelectrolytes because they are not composed of ions. For example, glucose (a simple sugar) and 2-propanol (rubbing alcohol) are nonelectrolyte molecular compounds.

Electrolyte Conduction When an electrolyte is placed in water, it disassociates into positive and negative ions. The positively charged ions move toward the negative electrode while the negatively charged ions move toward the positive electrode, carrying electric current to the light bulb.

Sodium chloride (NaCl) is a **strong electrolyte** that dissociates nearly completely into ions in water. An aqueous solution of sodium chloride is very conductive. **The bulb shines brightly**.

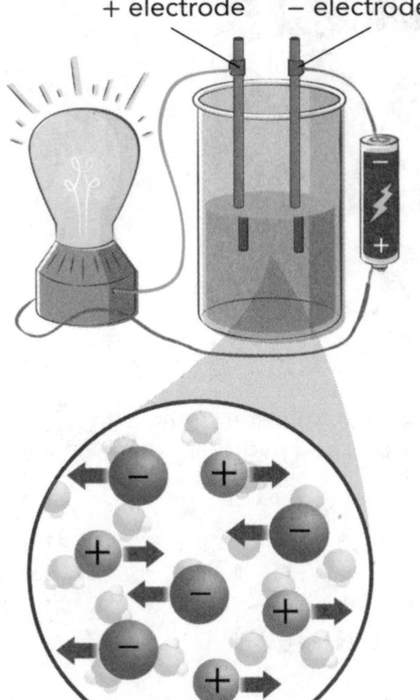

Mercury(II) chloride ($HgCl_2$) is a **weak electrolyte** that dissociates only partially in water. An aqueous solution of mercury(II) chloride is weakly conductive. **The bulb shines dimly**.

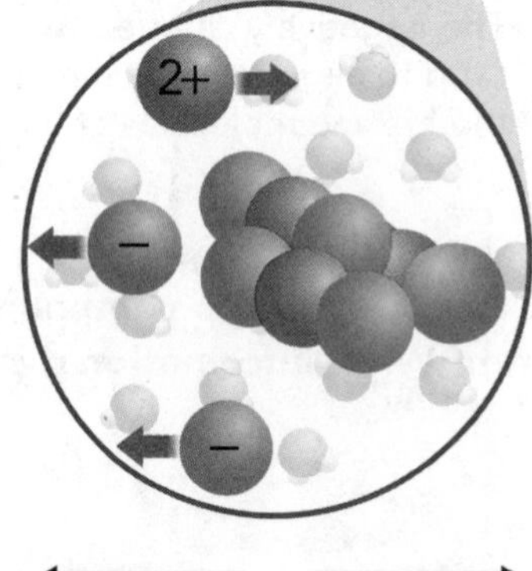

Glucose ($C_6H_{12}O_6$) is a **nonelectrolyte** that does not dissociate in water. An aqueous solution of glucose is not conductive. **The bulb does not shine at all**.

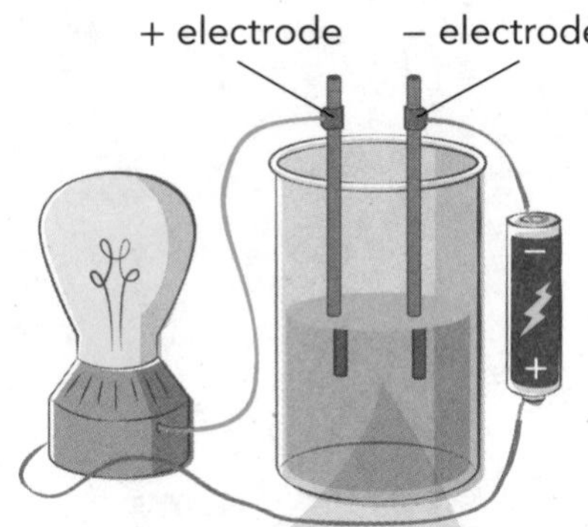

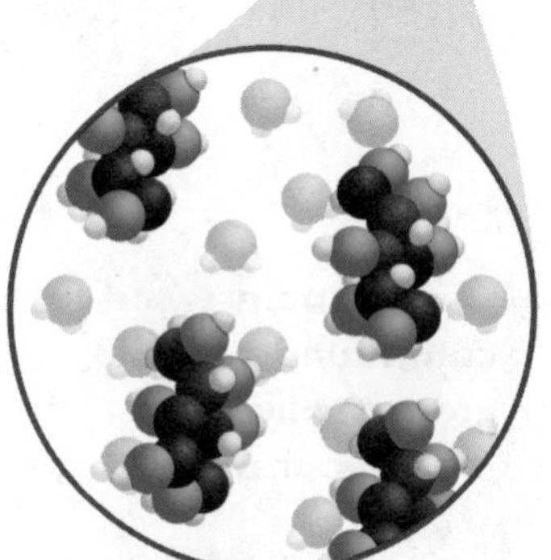

Some familiar liquids are actually strong electrolytes. Lemons contain citric acid, a polar covalent compound that disassociates into ions in the watery interior of the fruit. If you stick an electrode into either end of a lemon and attach it to an electric circuit, current will flow through the lemon. A pickle could also be used. Pickle brine is made by dissolving large amounts of salt in water. The dissolved salt turns the brine into a strong electrolyte.

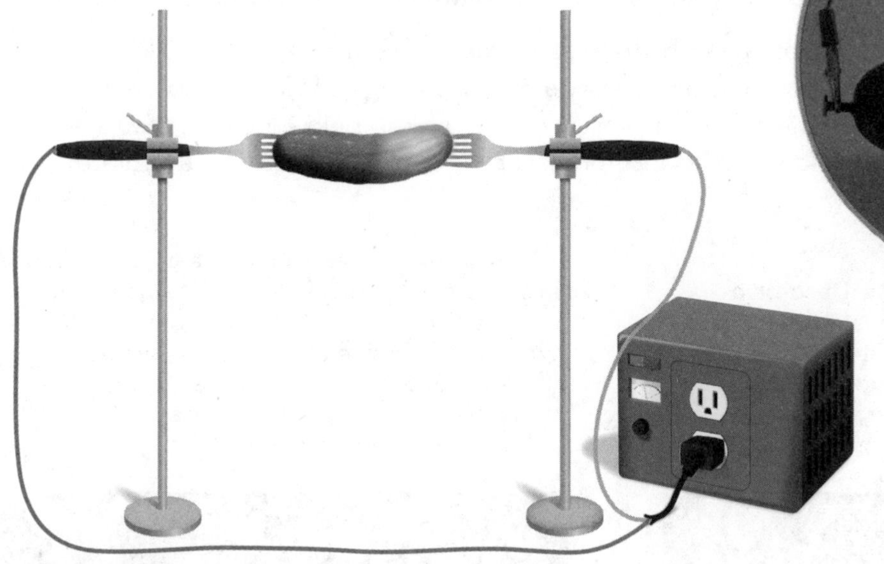

Pickle Light A pickle is made by saturating a cucumber in a brine. The interior of the pickle is mostly salty water and is therefore a strong electrolyte. When the pickle is placed into an electric circuit, current can flow through the pickle.

39 **SEP Evaluate Information** **Your body's cells use electrolytes to carry electrical impulses to other cells. These electrolytes are crucial to nerve and muscle function. Sports drinks were designed to replenish electrolytes lost through sweat during exercise. Circle the compounds in the ingredients list that are electrolytes.**

Nutrition Facts

Serving Size 1 Bottle (591 mL)

Amount Per Serving
Calories 50

	% Daily Value
Total Fat 0g	0%
Sodium 270mg	11%
Potassium 75mg	2%
Total Carbohydrate 13g	4%
Sugars 12g	
Protein 0g	

Ingredients: Water, Sugar, Citric Acid, Sodium Citrate, Salt, Natural and Artificial Flavor, Monopotassium Phosphate, Sucralose, Acesulfame Potassium.

Hydrates

A **hydrate** is a solid, crystalline compound that contains water molecules as an integral part of its crystal structure. For example, when an aqueous solution of copper(II) sulfate is allowed to evaporate, deep-blue crystals of copper(II) sulfate pentahydrate ($CuSO_4 \bullet 5H_2O$) are deposited. The water contained in a crystal is called the water of hydration or water of crystallization.

Copper(II) sulfate pentahydrate has a vapor pressure of about 1.0 kPa at room temperature, whereas the average partial pressure of water vapor in the air is 1.3 kPa. If the partial air pressure were to drop below 1.0 kPa, then the hydrate would effloresce. **Efflorescence** is the loss of water by a hydrate.

Pentahydrate Copper Sulfate Deep-blue crystals of copper(II) sulfate pentahydrate have water (H_2O) molecules integrated into the structure. The intermolecular forces holding water molecules in hydrates are not very strong, so the water is easily lost and regained.

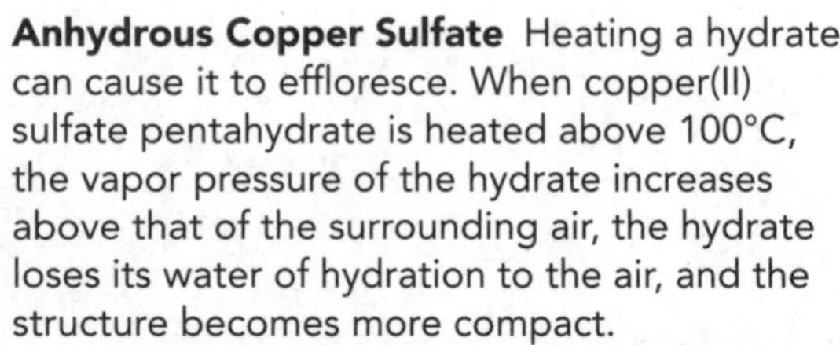

Anhydrous Copper Sulfate Heating a hydrate can cause it to effloresce. When copper(II) sulfate pentahydrate is heated above 100°C, the vapor pressure of the hydrate increases above that of the surrounding air, the hydrate loses its water of hydration to the air, and the structure becomes more compact.

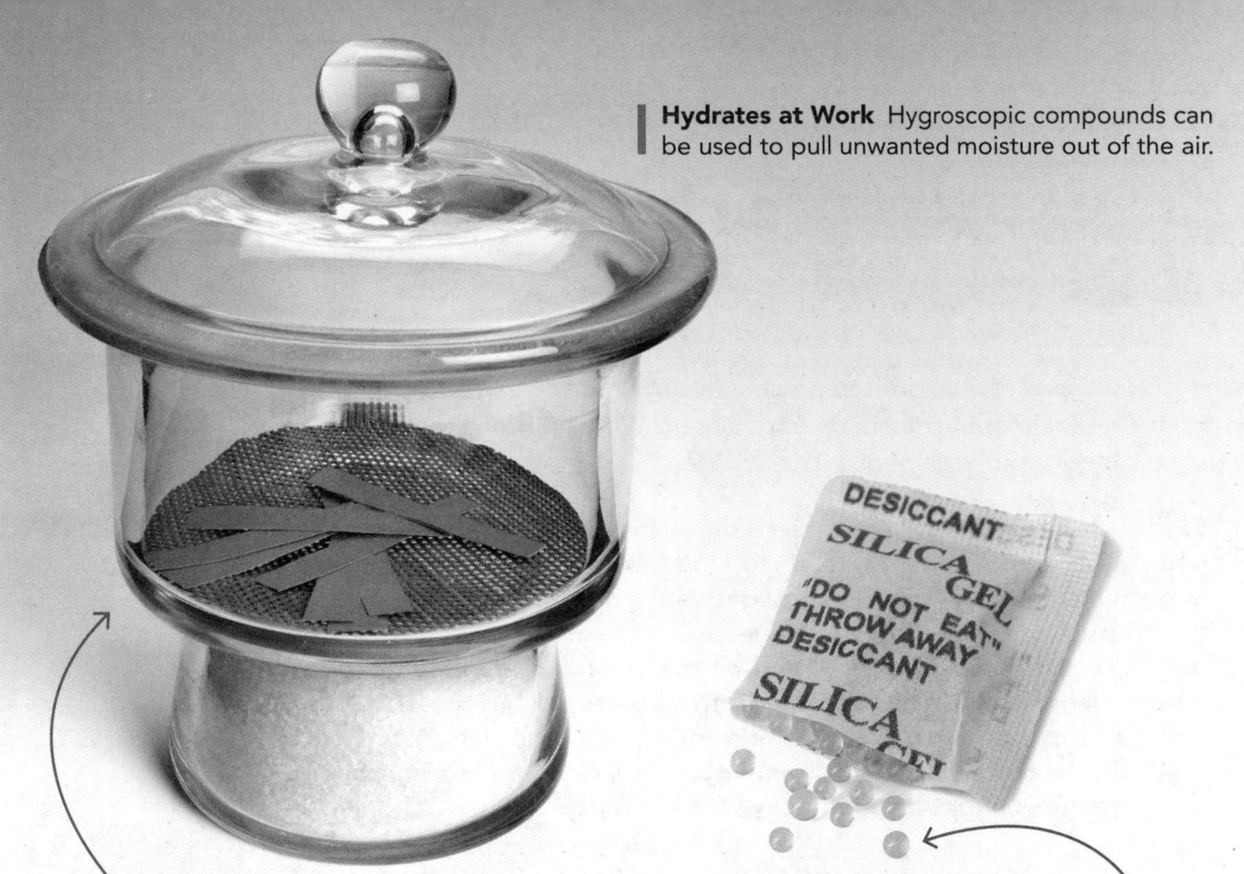

Hydrates at Work Hygroscopic compounds can be used to pull unwanted moisture out of the air.

A **desiccator** is a chamber used for maintaining a dry environment in chemistry labs. The chamber is sealed and contains a hygroscopic compound that pulls any moisture out of the air. Moisture can be detrimental to many laboratory substances.

You are probably familiar with **silica gel packs** that come with new shoes, electronics, or medicines. The packs contain the hygroscopic chemical silica, which absorbs moisture from the air. Excess moisture can damage packaged items.

Hydrates have practical uses in the real world. Hydrates with a low vapor pressure (below 1.3 kPa) will actually remove water from moist air to form higher hydrates (hydrates that contain more water molecules). These types of compounds are called hygroscopic. Often, hygroscopic compounds are used as desiccants in the laboratory. A desiccant is a substance used to absorb moisture from the air.

Engineers use their understanding of the chemical properties of different kinds of substances to devise practical uses for those substances in everyday life.

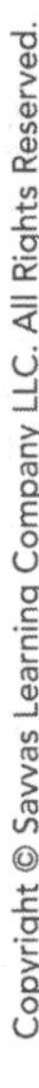

40 **CCC Systems and System Models** Describe how the processes of boiling, sublimation, and efflorescence are similar.

Revisit

INVESTIGATIVE PHENOMENON

GO ONLINE to Elaborate and Evaluate your knowledge of water and aqueous systems by completing the peer review and data analysis activities.

In the CER worksheet, you drafted a scientific argument to explain how materials used on mountaintops are engineered. With a partner, reevaluate the evidence cited in your arguments.

41 **SEP Design a Solution** **When it's cold outside, it's very important that you stay dry. Your outer layer of clothing has to keep water out. It's also important that gases can circulate between your body and the outside air, because otherwise your sweat will be trapped inside your clothing, making you wet. The material used on the outside of mountaineering jackets needs to take into account both of these design criteria. Draw a diagram of a small section of fabric and describe how the fabric could be designed to keep water out and let air still circulate. What other jacket features might help you stay warm and dry?**

EXPERIENCE 6

Properties of Solutions

GO ONLINE to Explore and Explain the properties of solutions.

Solution Formation

The rate at which a solute dissolves is called the **dissolution rate.** The dissolution rate depends on the structure of the solute (particle size) and processing (heating and agitating). Have you noticed when making tea that granulated sugar dissolves faster than sugar cubes and that both dissolve faster in hot tea or when you stir the tea?

Dissolution Rate How quickly a solute dissolves into solution depends on the temperature of the system and the structure of the solute. It also depends on whether or not the solution is agitated.

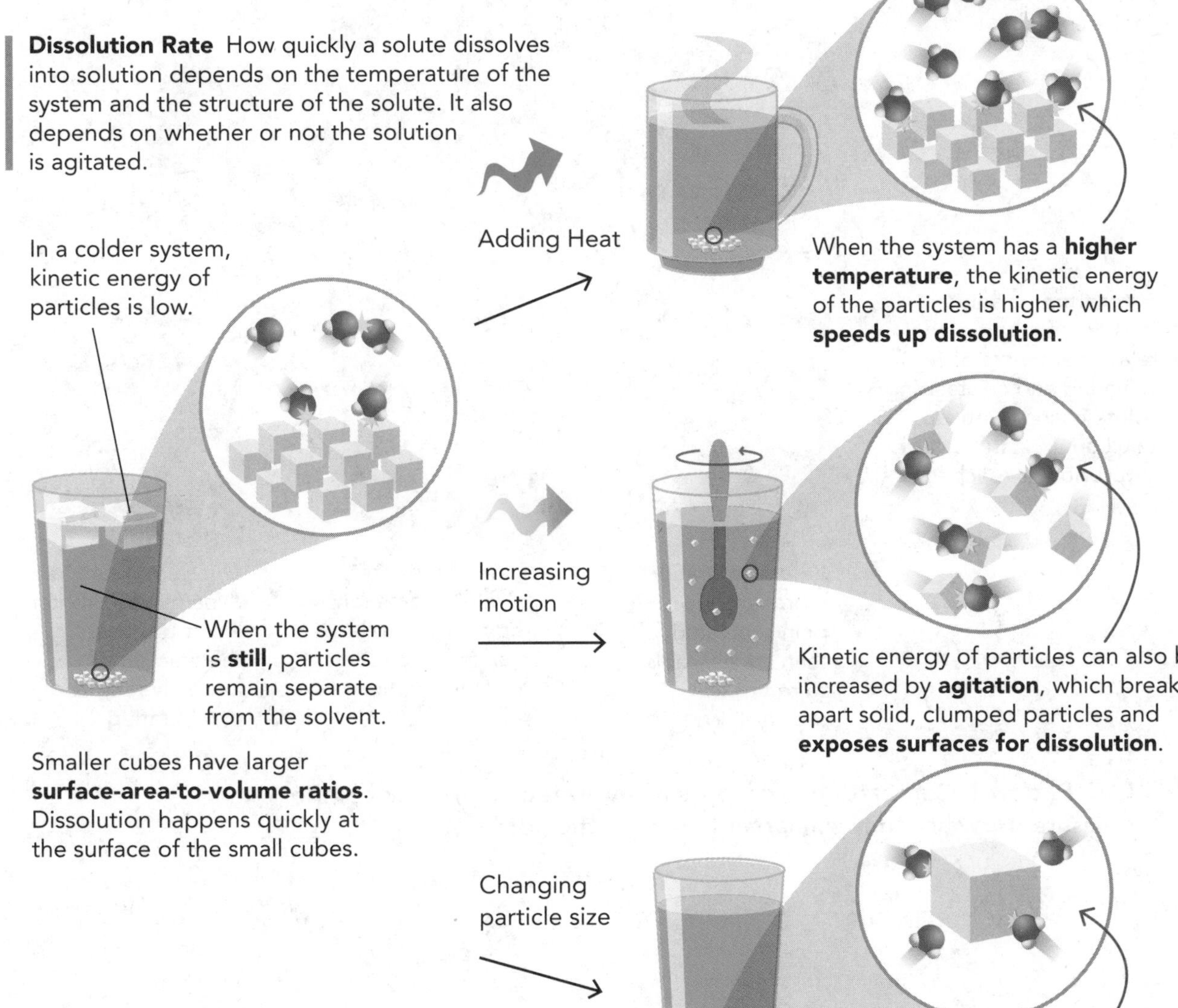

In a colder system, kinetic energy of particles is low.
When the system is **still**, particles remain separate from the solvent.
Smaller cubes have larger **surface-area-to-volume ratios**. Dissolution happens quickly at the surface of the small cubes.
Adding Heat
When the system has a **higher temperature**, the kinetic energy of the particles is higher, which **speeds up dissolution**.
Increasing motion
Kinetic energy of particles can also be increased by **agitation**, which breaks apart solid, clumped particles and **exposes surfaces for dissolution**.
Changing particle size
A single large cube has a **lower surface-to-area-volume ratio**, which **slows dissolution**.

Solubility

If you add 36.2 g of sodium chloride to 100 g of water at 25°C, all of the salt dissolves. However, if you add one more gram of salt, then the extra gram will never dissolve. The saltwater solution is saturated. A **saturated solution** contains the maximum amount of solute for a given quantity of solvent at a constant temperature and pressure. The **solubility** of a substance is the amount of solute that dissolves in a given quantity of a solvent at a specified temperature and pressure to produce a saturated solution.

Solvation Water molecules continuously bombard excess solid, solvating and removing the solute ions from the crystal. However, at the same time, already dissolved ions can return to the crystal.

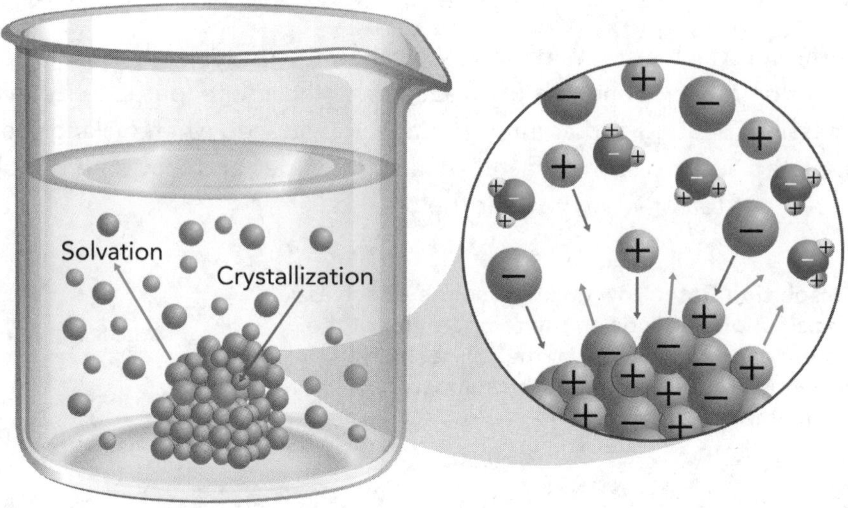

Saturation As solute ions enter solution, the relative amounts of solvating and crystallizing solute change until an equilibrium state, called **saturation**, is reached.

Before saturation, more ions are being solvated than are available to return to the crystal.

As more ions are solvated, some ions begin to precipitate back to the crystal from the solution.

Once saturated, a dynamic equilibrium exists between the amount of ions solvating and precipitating.

42 **CCC Patterns Compare the concepts of saturated solution and vapor pressure. How are they similar and how are they different?**

Solubility and Temperature

A **solubility curve** is a graph of the solubility as a function of temperature. You can use the solubility curve to predict whether a given solution will be unsaturated, saturated, or supersaturated for a given temperature based on the amount of solute dissolved in the solution. The solubility of most solid substances increases as the temperature of the solvent increases. For a few substances, such as ytterbium sulfate ($Yb_2(SO_4)_3$), the solubility actually decreases with increasing temperature.

Solubility Curves The solubility of several substances is shown as a function of temperature. The solubility of solids is expressed in grams of solute per 100 g of solvent (g/100 g H_2O).

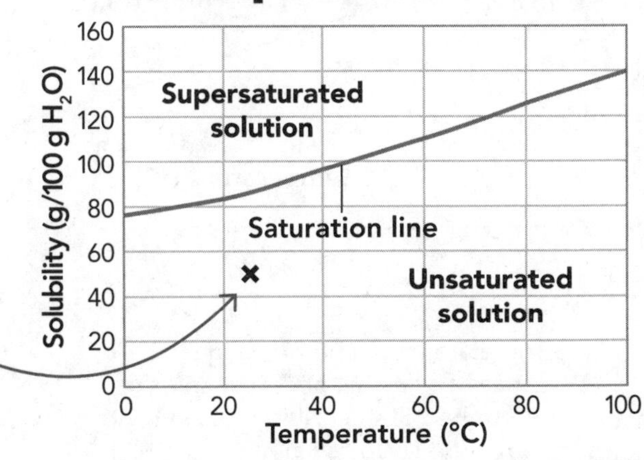

At conditions below the solubility line, the solution will be unsaturated. For example, at 25°C, an aqueous solution containing 50 g sodium acetate to 100 g H_2O will be unsaturated.

Solubility Varies with Temperature

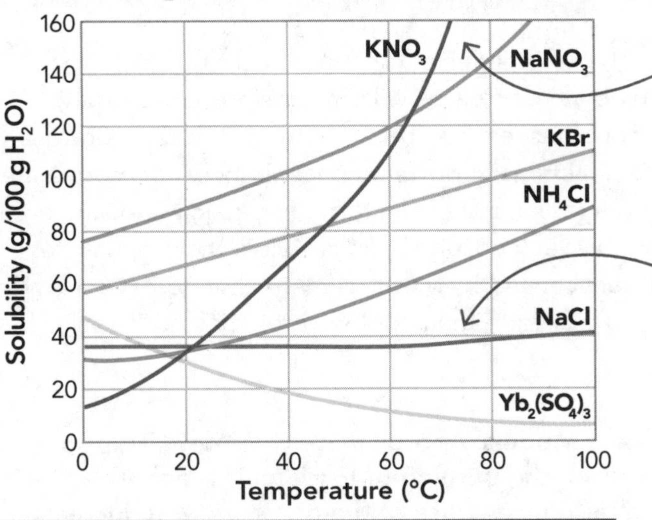

Potassium nitrate (KNO_3) experiences a dramatic increase in solubility with increasing temperature.

For sodium chloride (NaCl), the solubility does not change much at all for increasing temperature.

43 SEP Interpret Data **Suppose you added some solid potassium nitrate (KNO_3) to a saturated solution of KNO_3 at 20°C and then warmed the mixture to 40°C. What would happen to the added KNO_3? What would happen if you repeated the procedure, except with sodium chloride (NaCl)?**

Solubility Curve for Oxygen This figure shows solubility of oxygen (O_2) as a function of temperature. Solubility of gases is expressed in grams per liter of solution (g/L).

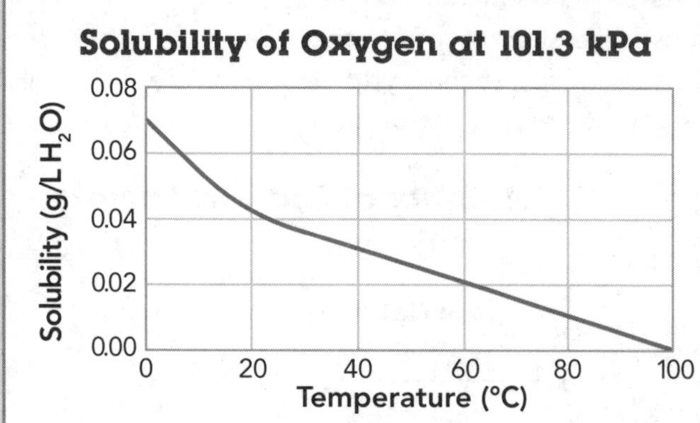

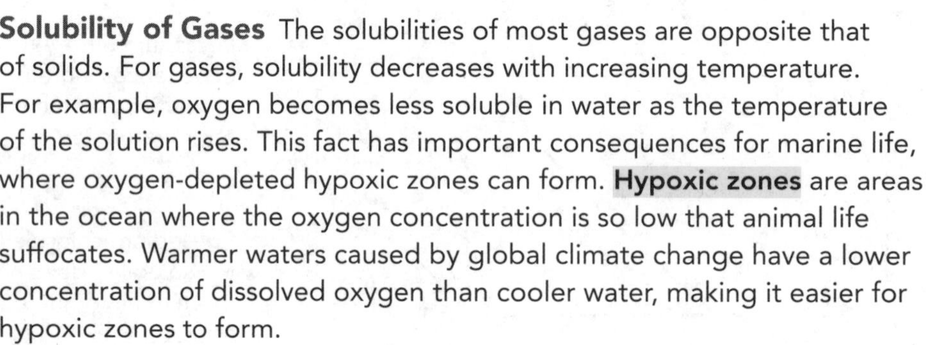

There are large and growing hypoxic zones off the east and west coast of the United States, which are associated with large-scale fish kills.

Solubility of Gases The solubilities of most gases are opposite that of solids. For gases, solubility decreases with increasing temperature. For example, oxygen becomes less soluble in water as the temperature of the solution rises. This fact has important consequences for marine life, where oxygen-depleted hypoxic zones can form. **Hypoxic zones** are areas in the ocean where the oxygen concentration is so low that animal life suffocates. Warmer waters caused by global climate change have a lower concentration of dissolved oxygen than cooler water, making it easier for hypoxic zones to form.

44 CCC Systems and System Models Approximately 26% of all carbon dioxide (CO_2) released from the burning of fossil fuels is absorbed by the oceans. If the average temperature of the ocean were to increase, how would this affect the ocean's ability to absorb carbon dioxide?

Supersaturation

A **supersaturated solution** contains more solute than it can theoretically hold at a given temperature. The crystallization of a supersaturated solution can be initiated by adding a small crystal, called a seed crystal, of solute. The rate at which excess solute deposits upon the surface of the seed crystal can be very rapid.

Crystallization of a Supersaturated Solution When a seed crystal is added to a supersaturated solution, a precipitate forms.

Step 1: In a saturated solution, solvation and precipitation are balanced.

Step 2: When the saturated solution is heated, more solute can dissolve.

Step 3: When the saturated solution is then cooled, the solution becomes supersaturated.

Step 4: Adding a seed crystal causes rapid precipitation from a supersaturated solution.

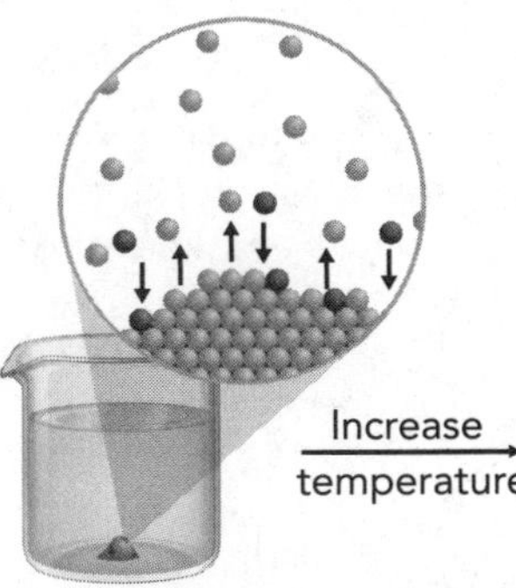

Saturated solution at 25°C

Increase temperature

Saturated solution at 30°C

Decrease temperature

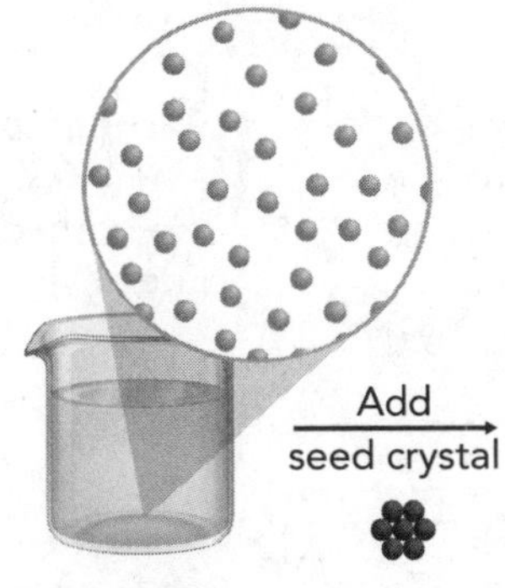

Supersaturated solution at 10°C

Add seed crystal

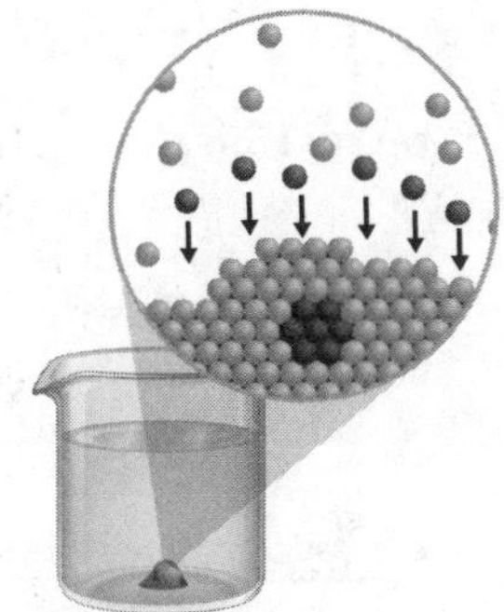

Precipitate forms at 10°C

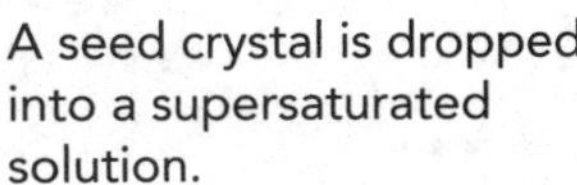

A seed crystal is dropped into a supersaturated solution.

The seed crystal causes crystallization of the excess solute.

45 **SEP Plan an Investigation Describe a procedure for making rock candy using sucrose. At 20°C, the solubility of sucrose is 230.9 g/100 g H_2O. At 50°C, it is 260.4 g/100 g H_2O. At 100°C, it is 487 g/100 g H_2O.**

Solubility and Pressure

Changes in pressure have little effect on the solubility of solids and liquids. However, pressure strongly influences the solubility of gases. Gas solubility increases as the partial pressure of the gas above the solution increases. The relationship between solubility and pressure is described by **Henry's law,** which states that at a given temperature, solubility (S) of a gas in a liquid is directly proportional to the pressure (P) of that gas above the liquid. The mathematical expression of Henry's law is as follows:

$$\frac{S_1}{P_1} = \frac{S_2}{P_2}$$

S_1 is the solubility of a gas at one pressure, P_1.

S_2 is the solubility of the same gas at another pressure, P_2.

Pressure on the System If gas pressure increases, gas molecules are "forced" into the solution. This decreases the net pressure applied by the gas on the solution.

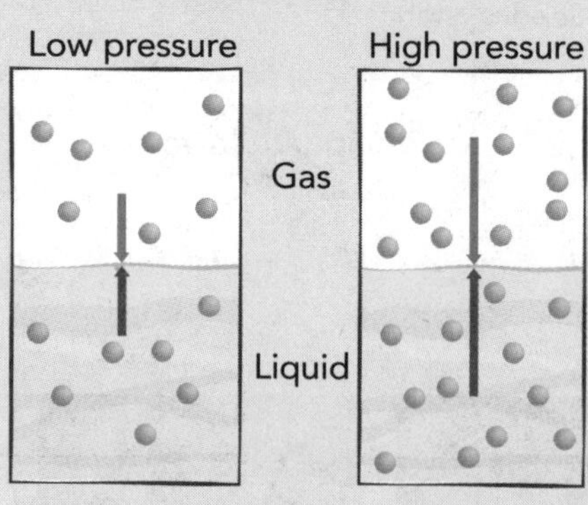

Carbonated Beverages Carbonated beverages contain large amounts of carbon dioxide (CO_2) gas dissolved in water. The drinks are bottled under high pressure, which forces large amounts of gas into solution.

When the cap is on, the partial pressure of the gas above the solution keeps the gas (CO_2) dissolved in the liquid.

When the cap is removed, the pressure of the gas above the liquid decreases. Bubbles of CO_2 form in the liquid, rise to the surface, and escape from the open bottle.

46 **SEP Develop a Model** **Decompression sickness happens when divers return to the surface too quickly, and nitrogen bubbles form in the bloodstream. Apply Henry's law to sketch a model that can explain how nitrogen bubbles could form during a rapid ascent from depth.**

SAMPLE PROBLEM

Using Henry's Law

If the solubility of a gas in water is 0.77 g/L at 3.5 atm of pressure, what is its solubility (in g/L) at 1.0 atm of pressure? (The temperature is held constant at 25°C.)

ANALYZE List the knowns and unknown.

Knowns	Unknown
$P_1 = 3.5$ atm	$S_2 = ?$ g/L
$S_1 = 0.77$ g/L	
$P_2 = 1.0$ atm	

CALCULATE Solve for the unknown.

Write the equation for Henry's law.

$$\frac{S_1}{P_1} = \frac{S_2}{P_2}$$

Solve Henry's law for S_2. Isolate S_2 by multiplying both sides by P_2.

$$P_2 \times \frac{S_1}{P_1} = \frac{S_2}{P_2} \times P_2$$

Substitute the known values into the equation and solve.

$$S_2 = \frac{S_1 \times P_2}{P_1} = \frac{0.77 \text{ g/L} \times 1.0 \text{ atm}}{3.5 \text{ atm}}$$

$$= 0.22 \text{ g/L}$$

EVALUATE Does the result make sense?

The new pressure is approximately one third of the original pressure, so the new solubility should be approximately one third of the original. The answer is correctly expressed to two significant figures.

47 **The solubility of a gas in water is 0.16 g/L at 104 kPa. What is the solubility when the pressure of the gas is increased to 288 kPa? Assume the temperature remains constant.**

48 **A gas has a solubility in water at 0°C of 3.6 g/L at a pressure of 1.0 atm. What pressure is needed to produce an aqueous solution containing 9.5 g/L of the same gas at 0°C?**

GO ONLINE for more practice problems.

Colloids and Suspensions

Solutions are called **homogeneous mixtures** because they have a uniform appearance and composition. **Heterogeneous mixtures** are not uniform in composition and are not considered solutions. A **colloid** is a heterogeneous mixture containing particles, called the dispersed phase, that are spread throughout another substance, called the dispersion medium. A **suspension** is a heterogeneous mixture from which particles settle out upon standing.

Comparing Solutions to Heterogeneous Mixtures

How do solutions differ from colloids and suspensions?

Solution (salt water) In a solution, individual molecules and ions of the solute and solvent are mixed together.

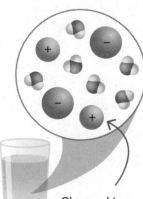

Charged ions less than 10^{-7} cm in size

Colloid (milk) Most colloids contain charged particles of clumped molecules or ions that are spread throughout the dispersion medium.

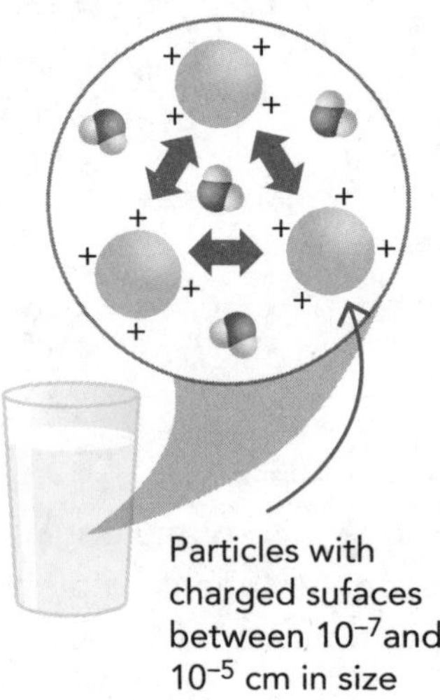

Particles with charged sufaces between 10^{-7} and 10^{-5} cm in size

Suspension (flour in water) A suspension is a mixture from which particles settle out upon standing.

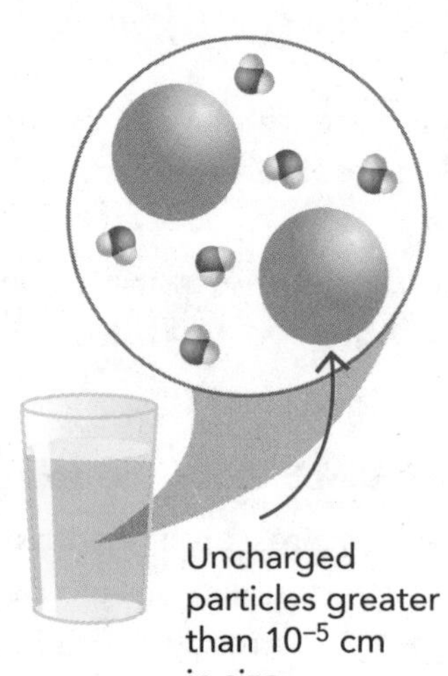

Uncharged particles greater than 10^{-5} cm in size

Tyndall effect Different types of particles reflect light differently. The scattering of visible light by particles is called the Tyndall effect.

Solution is transparent and homogeneous. Particles do not reflect light.

Particles reflect light. Beam is visible and homogeneous.

Particles reflect light. Beam is visible but cloudy and heterogeneous.

Difference Between Colloids and Suspensions The main physical difference between colloids and suspensions is the particle size. The smaller particle sizes of colloids typically means that the particles cannot be filtered out using filter paper. They also do not settle out with time.

Colloids typically do not settle like suspensions because their particle surfaces become charged by absorbing ions from the dispersion medium. All the colloidal particles in a particular colloidal system will have the same charge. The repulsion between like-charged colloid particles prevents the particles from forming heavier aggregates that would have a greater tendency to settle out.

Some Colloidal Systems

System			
Dispersed Phase	**Dispersion Medium**	**Type**	**Example**
Gas	Liquid	Foam	Whipped cream
Gas	Solid	Foam	Marshmallow
Liquid	Liquid	Emulsion	Milk, mayonnaise
Liquid	Gas	Aerosol	Fog, aerosol
Solid	Gas	Smoke	Dust in air
Solid	Liquid	Sols, gels	Egg white, jelly, paint, blood, starch in water, gelatin

Destabilization of Colloidal Systems Milk is a colloid composed of butterfat dispersed in water. The butterfat is surrounded by charged membranes made of phospholipids and proteins, which prevent the fat in milk from pooling together into chunks called curds. Cheese is made by separating the curds from the water-based whey in milk. Pouring lemon juice into milk will cause the colloid particles to come together and form heavier aggregates that can be collected as cheese curds.

49 **SEP Construct an Explanation** **Explain why cheese curds form when lemon juice is added to milk. Consider the mechanism that keeps colloid particles suspended and how that mechanism could be interrupted.**

Revisit

INVESTIGATIVE PHENOMENON

GO ONLINE to Elaborate and Evaluate your knowledge of solutions by completing the peer review and writing activities.

In the CER worksheet, you drafted a scientific argument to explain how materials used on mountaintops are engineered. With a partner, reevaluate the evidence cited in your arguments.

50 **SEP Design a Solution** **Acute mountain sickness (AMS) is caused by low amounts of oxygen in the bloodstream at high elevation. The decrease in the amount of oxygen at high altitude can be easily corrected by using oxygen tanks and masks. However, simply breathing more oxygen doesn't prevent AMS. Why? Explain using Henry's law and design a solution for emergency treatment of AMS at high altitude.**

GO ONLINE to Evaluate what you learned about the properties of different types of molecules and substances by completing the assessment resources.

In the Performance Based Assessment, you investigated the effectiveness of several compounds used as deicers on roadways. Wrap up your analysis by answering the following questions.

51 **SEP Define Problems When evaluating solutions to engineering problems, it is useful to define the problem by identifying criteria and constraints to which the solution must conform. With your group, generate a list of at least 3 criteria and 3 constraints that could be used to evaluate a design solution for a road deicing program.**

Criteria	Constraints

52 **Revisit the Anchoring Phenomenon How does what you learned in this investigation help predict how to design better food products?**

GO ONLINE to Engage with real-world phenomena by watching a video and to complete a CER interactive worksheet.

Why do we quantify matter in different ways?

INVESTIGATION 8

Chemical Quantities

Avocados are typically sold by the count. Eggs and bread rolls are often packaged in groups of 12 we call a dozen. Some items, like apples and nuts, are sold by weight. Liquid items like milk are usually sold by volume. In chemistry, we quantify matter in the same way: by count, mass, and volume. Once you have viewed the Investigative Phenomenon video and used the claim-evidence-reasoning worksheet to draft an explanation, answer these reflection questions about quantifying matter.

1. **CCC Scale, Proportion, and Quantity** **Estimate how long it would take you to count a dozen eggs. Now estimate how long it would take you to count the number of atoms in a single egg. If you knew how many atoms were in a single egg, how would you use that information to estimate the number of atoms in a dozen eggs?**

2. **SEP Identify Unknowns** **While eating from a can of mixed nuts, you wonder about the ratio of almonds to cashews. Describe how you would determine the percentage of almonds and the percentage of cashews in the can.**

EXPERIENCE 1

The Mole Concept

GO ONLINE to Explore and Explain moles and atomic mass.

Measuring Matter

Chemistry is a quantitative science, which means we have to quantify how much matter we have. There are three basic ways to quantify matter: by count, by mass, and by volume. Knowing how the count, mass, and volume of an item relate to a common unit allows you to convert among these units.

Converting Among Units Apples can be quantified by their count, volume, or mass. You can use conversion factors to convert between these quantities of apples.

Count
1 dozen apples = 12 apples

Mass
1 dozen apples = 2.0 kg

Volume
1 dozen apples = 0.20 bushels

$$\frac{\text{1 dozen apples}}{\text{12 apples}} \qquad \frac{\text{1 dozen apples}}{\text{2.0 kg apples}} \qquad \frac{\text{1 dozen apples}}{\text{0.20 bushel apples}}$$

These conversion factors relate the count, mass, and volume of apples. The conversion factors for count and mass can be used to calculate the mass of one apple.

Mass of One Apple

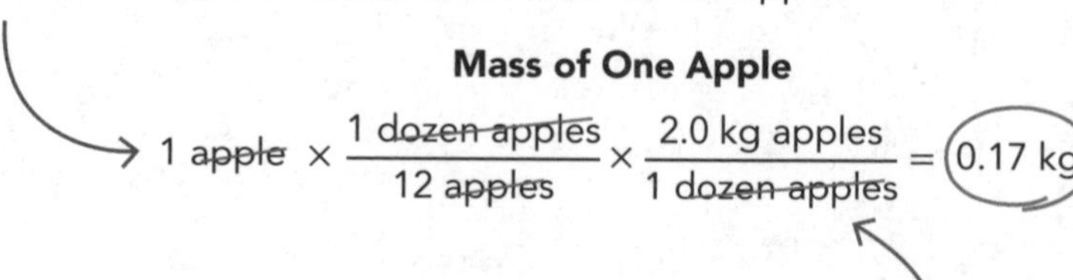

$$1\ \cancel{\text{apple}} \times \frac{\text{1 }\cancel{\text{dozen apples}}}{12\ \cancel{\text{apples}}} \times \frac{\text{2.0 kg apples}}{1\ \cancel{\text{dozen apples}}} = 0.17\text{ kg}$$

In order for the units to cancel, dozen apples must be in the denominator.

3 **SEP Interpret Data** The graph shows the total mass as a function of the number of grapefruits. What is the slope of the best-fit line? What does this value mean? Predict the mass of 8 grapefruits.

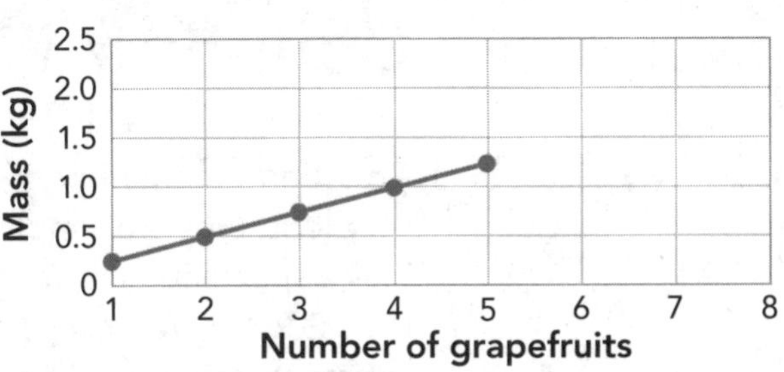

SAMPLE PROBLEM

Finding Mass From a Count

What is the mass of 90 apples if 1 dozen of the apples has a mass of 2.0 kg?

ANALYZE List the knowns and the unknown.

Knowns	Unknown
number of apples = 90	mass of 90 apples = ? kg
12 apples = 1 dozen apples	
1 dozen apples = 2.0 kg apples	

CALCULATE Solve for the unknown.

Identify the steps to convert from number, or count, to mass.

number of apples → dozens of apples → mass of apples

Multiply the number of apples by the two conversion factors needed to convert from number of apples to mass of apples.

$$90 \text{ apples} \times \frac{1 \text{ dozen apples}}{12 \text{ apples}} \times \frac{2.0 \text{ kg apples}}{1 \text{ dozen apples}} = 15 \text{ kg apples}$$

EVALUATE Does the result make sense?

A dozen apples has a mass of 2.0 kg, and 90 apples is less than 10 dozen apples, so the mass should be less than 20 kg of apples (10 dozen × 2.0 kg/dozen).

4 **SEP Use Mathematics** Assume 2.0 kg of apples is 1 dozen and that each apple has 8 seeds. How many seeds are in 14 kg of apples?

GO ONLINE for more practice problems.

Counting With Moles

Counting the number of atoms in a gram of substance would take a very long time. To simplify the counting of atoms, chemists group them into a specified number called a mole. A **mole** (mol) of a substance is 6.02×10^{23} representative particles of that substance. The term **representative particle** refers to the species present in a substance, usually atoms, molecules, or formula units. In compounds, each molecule or formula unit is a representative particle, but they are made of multiple elements. For example, in every water molecule there is one oxygen atom and two hydrogen atoms. The number of representative particles in a mole, 6.02×10^{23}, is called **Avogadro's number** after the Italian scientist Amedeo Avogadro.

Representative Particles Representative particles are usually atoms, molecules, or formula units. Other items, such as eggs or sandwiches, can also be representative particles.

Grouping eggs in a dozen is similar to grouping atoms where each atom is a representative particle. One egg is the representative particle in a dozen eggs.

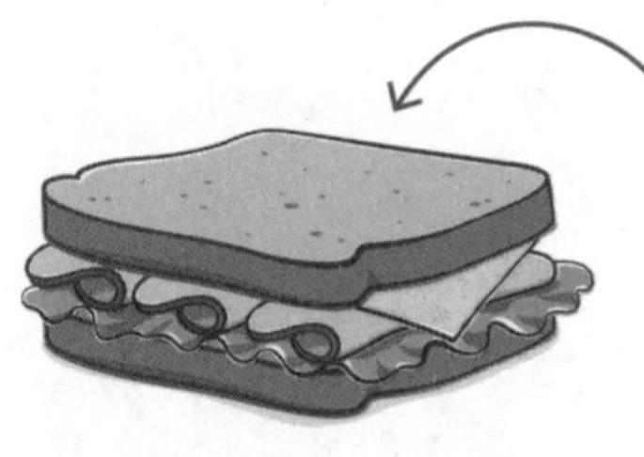

This entire sandwich is similar to a representative particle of a compound because it is made of certain amounts of each ingredient. One sandwich is a representative particle made of 2 slices of bread, 3 pieces of ham, 1 slice of cheese, and 1 leaf of lettuce. To make a dozen identical sandwiches, you need 24 slices of bread. To make a mole of identical sandwiches, you need 1.20×10^{24} slices of bread.

5 **SEP Develop Models The table shows examples of representative particles for several types of substances. Develop a mental model for the concept of representative particles and use your model to complete the table.**

Representative Particles and Moles

Substance	Representative Particle	Chemical Formula	Representative Particles in 1.00 mol
Copper	Atom	Cu	6.02×10^{23}
Atomic nitrogen			
Nitrogen gas	Molecule	N_2	6.02×10^{23}
Water			
Calcium fluoride	Formula unit	CaF_2	6.02×10^{23}
Sodium chloride			

SAMPLE PROBLEM

Converting Number of Atoms to Moles

Magnesium is a light metal used in the manufacture of aircraft and tools. How many moles of magnesium is 1.25×10^{23} atoms of magnesium?

ANALYZE List the knowns and the unknown.

Knowns	Unknown
number of atoms = 1.25×10^{23} atoms Mg	moles = ? mol Mg

CALCULATE Solve for the unknown.

Identify the relationship between moles and number of representative particles.

$$1 \text{ mol Mg} = 6.02 \times 10^{23} \text{ atoms Mg}$$

Write the conversion factors based on this relationship.

$$\frac{1 \text{ mol Mg}}{6.02 \times 10^{23} \text{ atoms Mg}} \text{ and } \frac{6.02 \times 10^{23} \text{ atoms Mg}}{1 \text{ mol Mg}}$$

Identify the conversion factor needed to convert from atoms to moles.

$$\frac{1 \text{ mol Mg}}{6.02 \times 10^{23} \text{ atoms Mg}}$$

The units in the known should be in the denominator so that the units will cancel.

Multiply the number of atoms of Mg by the conversion factor.

$$1.25 \times 10^{23} \cancel{\text{atoms Mg}} \times \frac{1 \text{ mol Mg}}{6.02 \times 10^{23} \cancel{\text{atoms Mg}}} = 0.208 \text{ mol Mg}$$

EVALUATE Does the result make sense?

The given number of atoms is less than one fourth of Avogadro's number, so the answer should be less than one fourth (0.25) mol of atoms. The answer should have three significant figures.

6 **SEP Use Math** How many moles is 2.17×10^{23} representative particles of bromine gas?

7 **SEP Use Math** How many moles is 2.80×10^{24} atoms of silicon?

GO ONLINE for more practice problems.

Volume and Mass of a Mole

A dozen roses, a dozen bagels, and a dozen eggs all have 12 representative particles. Because roses, bagels, and eggs are different representative particles, their respective masses and volumes are different. Similar to the number of representative particles in a dozen, a mole is 6.02×10^{23} representative particles of a substance, no matter what the substance.

Representative particles can come in different masses and sizes. Therefore, a mole of a substance will have a mass and volume dependent on the properties of the representative particle.

A Mole of Common Substances
Common substances may have atoms, molecules, or formula units as their representative particles. A water molecule is the representative unit of water. Aluminum and copper both have atoms as their representative particles. The volume of these substances depends on the properties of these particles.

A water molecule is composed of one oxygen atom and two hydrogen atoms.

Therefore, 1 mole of water has 3 moles of atoms.

1 mole of H_2O = 1 mole of O + 2 moles of H

A mole of water takes up less space than a mole of sucrose (sugar, $C_{12}H_{22}O_{11}$).
A mole of copper takes up less space than a mole of aluminum because copper is denser than aluminum.
A mole of table salt (NaCl) takes up less space than a mole of sugar ($C_{12}H_{22}O_{11}$).

A mole of water has less mass than a mole of sugar or a mole of copper. The mass of 1 mole of a substance is called the **molar mass** and is expressed in units of g/mol. Similarly, the atomic mass is the mass of a mole of the element expressed in grams. Therefore, the molar mass of elements can be read directly from the periodic table.

Molar Mass

How do you obtain the molar mass from the periodic table?

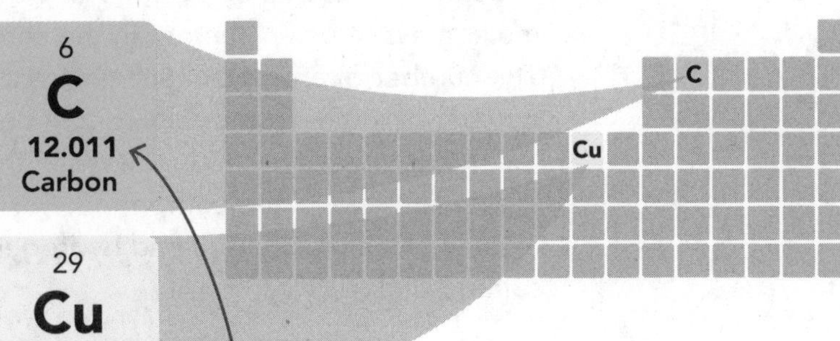

Atomic Weight The periodic table gives the atomic weight of each element. Atomic weight is a dimensionless quantity that represents the **average mass of atoms of an element divided by 1/12 the atomic mass of a carbon-12 atom.**

Molar Mass The **molar mass is the mass of 1 mole of an element.** It is the atomic weight multiplied by 1 g/mol. To obtain the molar mass, read the atomic weight from the periodic table and add the unit g/mol.

1 mole of carbon

Molar mass of carbon
= 12.011 g/mol

1 mole of copper

Molar mass of copper
= 63.546 g/mol

Molar Mass as Conversion Factor
The **molar mass can be represented as a fraction and used as a conversion factor** to convert a known mass into moles or known moles into mass. The molar mass is often rounded to 1 decimal place to simplify calculations.

$$\frac{\textbf{12.0 g C}}{\textbf{1 mol C}} \text{ or } \frac{\textbf{1 mol C}}{\textbf{12.0 g C}}$$

$$\frac{\textbf{63.5 g Cu}}{\textbf{1 mol Cu}} \text{ or } \frac{\textbf{1 mol Cu}}{\textbf{63.5 g Cu}}$$

8 **CCC Scale, Proportion, and Quantity** **The table shows how many moles are in 6 grams of four elements. The equation shows how to use carbon's molar mass to find the moles of carbon. Complete the table.**

$$6.0 \text{ g C} \times \frac{1 \text{ mol C}}{12.0 \text{ g C}} = 0.50 \text{ mol C}$$

Converting Mass to Moles			
Substance	**Mass (g)**	**Molar Mass (g/mol)**	**Moles (mol)**
Carbon	6.0	12.0	0.50
Sulfur	6.0		
Aluminum	6.0		
Boron	6.0		

Molar Mass of Compounds

The molar mass of a compound depends on the number of moles and the molar mass of each element in the compound's representative particle. The number of atoms of each element in the chemical formula is also the number of moles of that element in one mole of the compound. Therefore, the molar masses of the elements in the compound are used to determine the molar mass of the compound. For example, you can use the molar masses of sulfur, oxygen, and hydrogen to determine the molar mass of sulfuric acid (H_2SO_4).

Molar Mass of Sulfuric Acid Adding the masses of 2 moles of hydrogen, 1 mole of sulfur, and 4 moles of oxygen gives the molar mass of H_2SO_4.

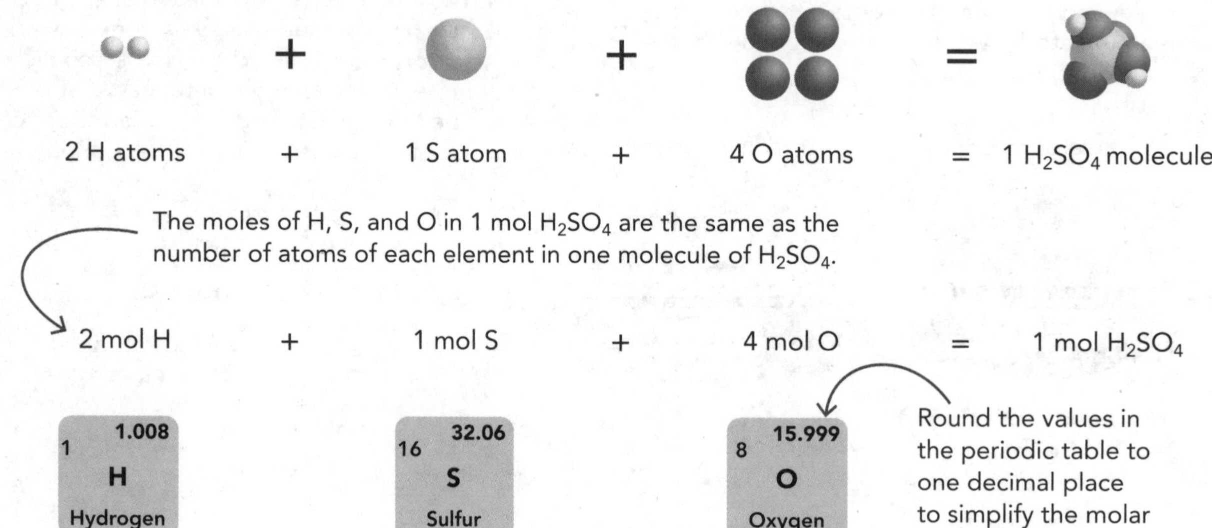

Multiply the moles of each element by its molar mass.

$$\left(2\ \cancel{\text{mol H}} \times \frac{1.0\text{ g H}}{1\ \cancel{\text{mol H}}}\right) + \left(1\ \cancel{\text{mol S}} \times \frac{32.1\text{ g S}}{1\ \cancel{\text{mol S}}}\right) + \left(4\ \cancel{\text{mol O}} \times \frac{16.0\text{ g O}}{1\ \cancel{\text{mol O}}}\right) = 98.1\text{ g/mol}$$

CCC Scale, Proportion, and Quantity The table shows the total mass of carbon dioxide (CO_2) as a function of the number of moles of CO_2. Complete the table.

Mass of CO_2

CO_2 (mol)	C (mol)	O (mol)	Total mass CO_2 (g)
1	1	2	44.0
2			
3			
4			

SAMPLE PROBLEM

Find the Molar Mass of a Compound

The decomposition reaction of hydrogen peroxide (H_2O_2) provides sufficient energy to launch a rocket. What is the molar mass of hydrogen peroxide?

ANALYZE **List the knowns and the unknown.**

Knowns	Unknown
molecular formula = H_2O_2	molar mass = ? g/mol
mass of 1 mol H = 1.0 g H	
mass of 1 mol O = 16.0 g O	

CALCULATE **Solve for the unknown.**

Multiply the molar mass of each element by its subscript in the chemical formula to find the total mass of the element.

Convert moles of atoms to grams using conversion factors (g/mol) based on the molar mass of each element.

$$2\ \cancel{\text{mol H}} \times \frac{1.0\ \text{g H}}{1\ \cancel{\text{mol H}}} = 2.0\ \text{g H}$$

$$2\ \cancel{\text{mol O}} \times \frac{16.0\ \text{g O}}{1\ \cancel{\text{mol O}}} = 32.0\ \text{g O}$$

Add the masses of the elements to determine the molar mass of the compound.

mass of 1 mol H_2O_2 = 2.0 g H + 32.0 g O = 34.0 g

molar mass of H_2O_2 = 34.0 g/mol

EVALUATE **Does the result make sense?**

There are two hydrogen atoms and two oxygen atoms in H_2O_2, so the answer should be two times the molar mass of hydrogen and oxygen. The answer is expressed to the tenths place because the numbers being added are expressed to the tenths place.

10 **SEP Use Mathematics** **Phosphorus trichloride (PCl_3) is used as a reactant in the production of many other chemicals that contain phosphorus, including pesticides and herbicides. Find the molar mass of PCl_3.**

11 **SEP Use Mathematics** **Baking soda is also known as sodium hydrogen carbonate. What is the mass of 1.00 mol of sodium hydrogen carbonate ($NaHCO_3$)?**

GO ONLINE for more practice problems.

Revisit

INVESTIGATIVE PHENOMENON

GO ONLINE to Elaborate on and Evaluate your knowledge of moles as a counting unit by completing the discussion and writing activities.

In the CER worksheet you completed at the beginning of the investigation, you drafted an explanation for the ways in which matter is quantified. With a partner, reevaluate your arguments.

12. **SEP Construct an Explanation** **A mole of table sugar (sucrose, $C_{12}H_{22}O_{11}$) is 342.3 g. A mole of table salt (sodium chloride, NaCl) is 58.45 g. What does the difference in macroscopic size of a mole of sugar and a mole of salt suggest about their microscopic representative particles? Considering the size of a mole of these materials, why do you think chemists use the concept of moles when dealing with macroscopic quantities?**

EXPERIENCE 2

Molar Relationships

GO ONLINE to Explore and Explain how the mole relates to mass, volume, and the number of particles.

The Mole Roadmap

When you convert between mass, volume, and representative particles, you must use the mole as an intermediate step. The mole roadmap provides the path to convert one quantity to another, just as a real roadmap shows you how to get from Point A to Point B. It shows how the conversion factor you need to use depends on what you know and what you want to calculate. Including the appropriate units in the conversion factors will help keep you on the right path in your calculations. You know you have chosen the correct conversion factor(s) if the units cancel to give the desired unit for the answer.

The Mole Roadmap Follow the arrows on the roadmap to determine which conversion factors you need to use to convert between mass, volume, and number of representative particles.

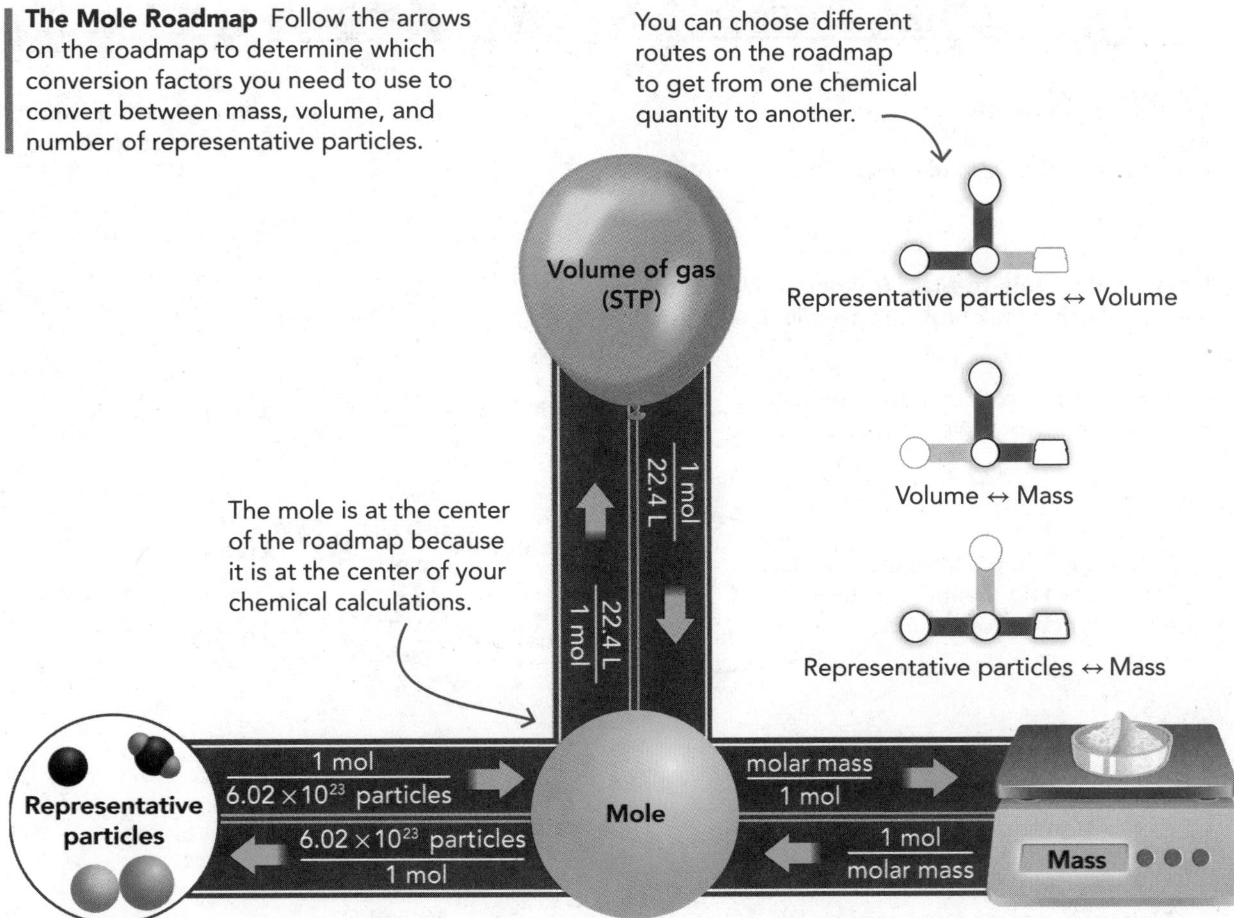

The Mole-Mass Relationship

The molar mass of a substance can be used to convert between the number of moles of a substance and its mass. The conversion factors for these calculations are based on this relationship: molar mass = 1 mol. The molar mass can be used as a conversion factor for individual elements or compounds.

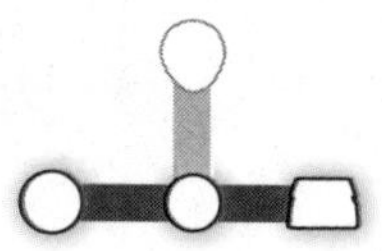

Converting Between Mass, Moles, and Particles The mole-mass relationship can be used to convert from mass to moles or from moles to mass. The relationship between the mole and Avogadro's number can also be used to convert between representative particles and mass.

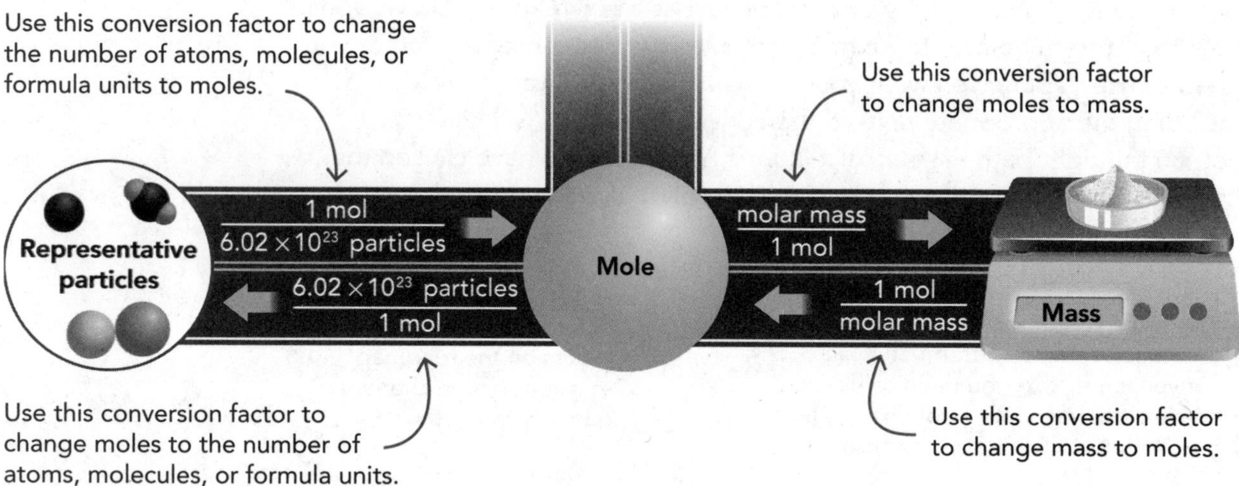

Applying the Mole-to-Mass Roadmap What is the mass, in grams, of 3.2 mol nitrogen dioxide (NO_2)?

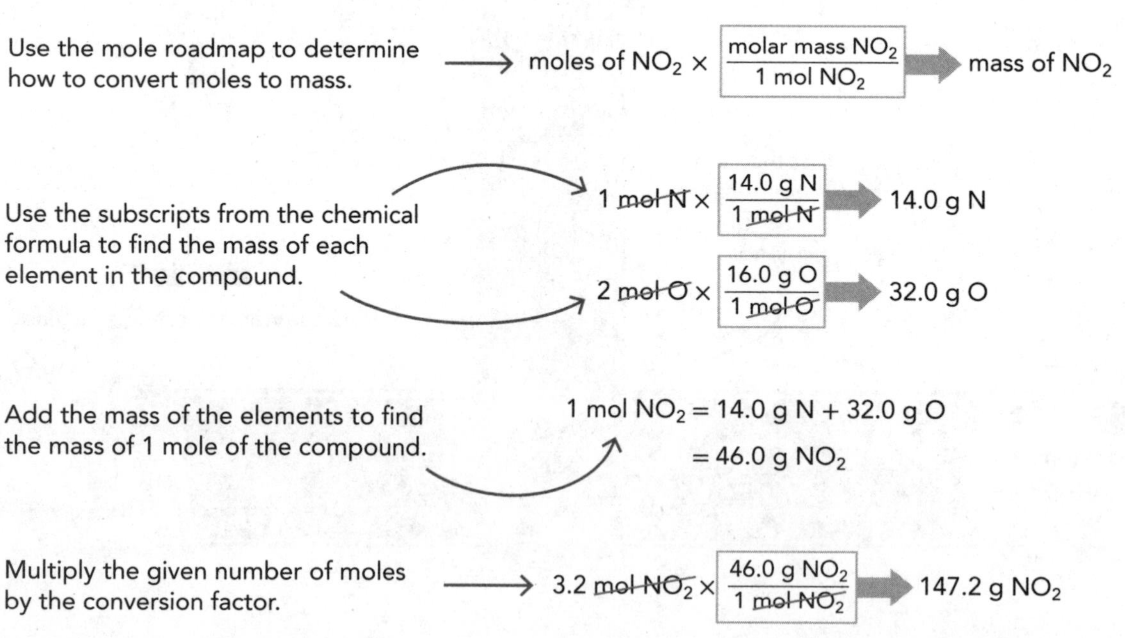

Use the mole roadmap to determine how to convert moles to mass.
moles of NO2 × molar mass NO2 / 1 mol NO2 → mass of NO2
Use the subscripts from the chemical formula to find the mass of each element in the compound.
1 mol N × 14.0 g N / 1 mol N → 14.0 g N
2 mol O × 16.0 g O / 1 mol O → 32.0 g O
Add the mass of the elements to find the mass of 1 mole of the compound.
1 mol NO2 = 14.0 g N + 32.0 g O
= 46.0 g NO2
Multiply the given number of moles by the conversion factor.
3.2 mol NO2 × 46.0 g NO2 / 1 mol NO2 → 147.2 g NO2

SAMPLE PROBLEM

Converting Moles to Mass

Items made of aluminum, such as aircraft parts and cookware, are resistant to corrosion because the aluminum reacts with oxygen in the air to form a coating of aluminum oxide (Al_2O_3). This tough, resistant coating prevents any further corrosion. What is the mass, in grams, of 9.45 mol aluminum oxide?

ANALYZE **List the knowns and the unknown.**

Knowns	Unknown
number of moles = 9.45 mol Al_2O_3	mass = ? g Al_2O_3

CALCULATE **Solve for the unknown.**

Identify the necessary conversion.

moles → mass

Multiply the moles by the molar masses to determine the mass of each element in the compound.

$$2\ \cancel{\text{mol Al}} \times \frac{27.0\ \text{g Al}}{1\ \cancel{\text{mol Al}}} = 54.0\ \text{g Al}$$

$$3\ \cancel{\text{mol O}} \times \frac{16.0\ \text{g O}}{1\ \cancel{\text{mol O}}} = 48.0\ \text{g O}$$

Use the subscripts to determine the moles of each element in the compound.

Add the mass of the elements to find the mass of 1 mole of the compound.

$$1\ \text{mol Al}_2\text{O}_3 = 54.0\ \text{g Al} + 48.0\ \text{g O} = 102.0\ \text{g Al}_2\text{O}_3$$

Identify the conversion factor for converting from moles to mass.

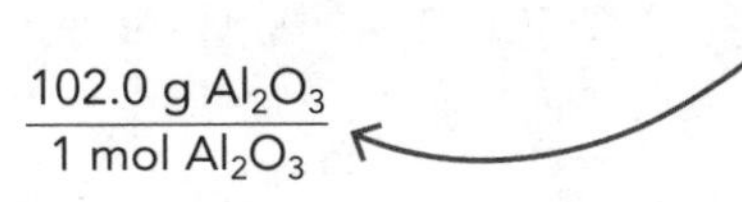

$$\frac{102.0\ \text{g Al}_2\text{O}_3}{1\ \text{mol Al}_2\text{O}_3}$$

The known unit (mol) is in the denominator and the unknown unit (g) is in the numerator.

Multiply the given number of moles by the conversion factor.

$$9.45\ \cancel{\text{mol Al}_2\text{O}_3} \times \frac{102.0\ \text{g Al}_2\text{O}_3}{1\ \cancel{\text{mol Al}_2\text{O}_3}} = 964\ \text{g Al}_2\text{O}_3$$

EVALUATE **Does the result make sense?**

The number of moles of Al_2O_3 is approximately 10, and each mole has a mass of approximately 100 g. The answer should be close to 1000 g. The answer has been rounded to the correct number of significant figures.

13 **SEP Use Mathematics** **Calculate the mass, in grams, of 2.50 mol of iron(II) hydroxide.**

GO ONLINE for more practice problems.

SAMPLE PROBLEM

Converting Mass to Moles

When iron is exposed to air, it undergoes a corrosion reaction to form a red-brown rust. Rust is iron(III) oxide (Fe_2O_3). How many moles of iron(III) oxide are contained in 92.2 g of pure Fe_2O_3?

ANALYZE List the knowns and the unknown.

Knowns	Unknown
mass = 92.2 g Fe_2O_3	number of moles = ? mol Fe_2O_3

CALCULATE Solve for the unknown.

Identify the necessary conversion.

mass → moles

Use the subscripts to determine the moles of each element in the compound. Multiply the moles by the molar masses to determine the mass of each element in the compound.

$$2\ \cancel{\text{mol Fe}} \times \frac{55.8\text{ g Fe}}{1\ \cancel{\text{mol Fe}}} = 111.6\text{ g Fe}$$

$$3\ \cancel{\text{mol O}} \times \frac{16.0\text{ g O}}{1\ \cancel{\text{mol O}}} = 48.0\text{ g O}$$

Add the mass of the elements to find the mass of 1 mole of the compound.

$$1\text{ mol }Fe_2O_3 = 111.6\text{ g Al} + 48.0\text{ g O} = 159.6\text{ g }Fe_2O_3$$

Identify the conversion factor for converting mass to moles.

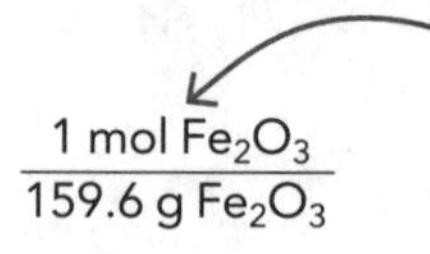

$$\frac{1\text{ mol }Fe_2O_3}{159.6\text{ g }Fe_2O_3}$$

Note that the known unit (g) is in the denominator and the unknown unit (mol) is in the numerator.

Multiply the given mass by the conversion factor.

$$92.2\ \cancel{\text{g }Fe_2O_3} \times \frac{1\text{ mol }Fe_2O_3}{159.6\ \cancel{\text{g }Fe_2O_3}} = 0.578\text{ mol }Fe_2O_3$$

EVALUATE Does the result make sense?

The given mass is slightly larger than the mass of one-half mole of Fe_2O_3, so the answer should be slightly larger than one-half mol.

14 **SEP Use Mathematics Calculate the number of moles in 75.0 g of dinitrogen trioxide.**

GO ONLINE for more practice problems.

Avogadro's Hypothesis

Avogadro's hypothesis states that any two samples of gas with an equal number of particles will have the same volume when they are held at the same pressure and temperature. It was proposed in 1811 by Amedeo Avogadro. The volume of a gas is usually measured at standard temperature and pressure (STP)—0°C and 101.3 kPa, or 1 atm. The **molar volume** is the volume of 1 mole of a gas at STP and is 22.4 L/mol for any ideal gas. The molar volume does not depend on the size of the representative particles in the gas.

Volume of Gas The kinetic theory states that gas particles have negligible volume in comparison to the volume of their containers. Since a gas expands to fill the container, each gas has the same volume, even though their masses can be very different.

Gas particles move around rapidly in the empty space inside their container.

One mole of any ideal gas has a volume of approximately 22.4 L, which is about the volume inside three basketballs.

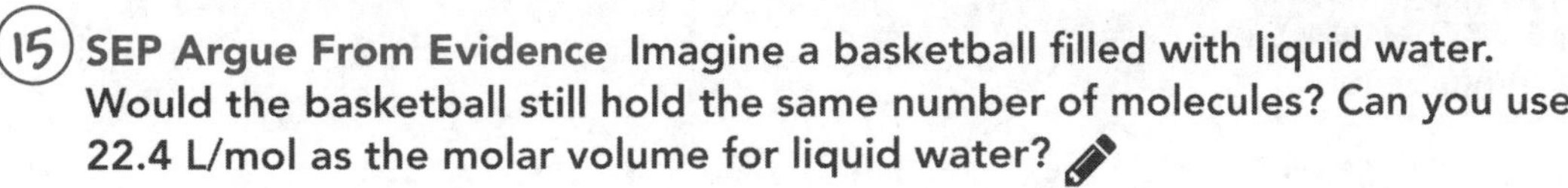

15 **SEP Argue From Evidence Imagine a basketball filled with liquid water. Would the basketball still hold the same number of molecules? Can you use 22.4 L/mol as the molar volume for liquid water?**

The Mole-Volume Relationship

The molar volume of a gas is used to convert between the number of moles of a gas and the volume of a gas. The conversion factors are based on this relationship: molar volume = 1 mol. The molar volume can be used as a conversion factor for individual gaseous elements or compounds.

Converting Between Moles and Volume The mole-volume relationship can be used to convert moles to volume or volume to moles. The relationship between moles and Avogadro's number can be included to convert between the number of representative particles and the volume.

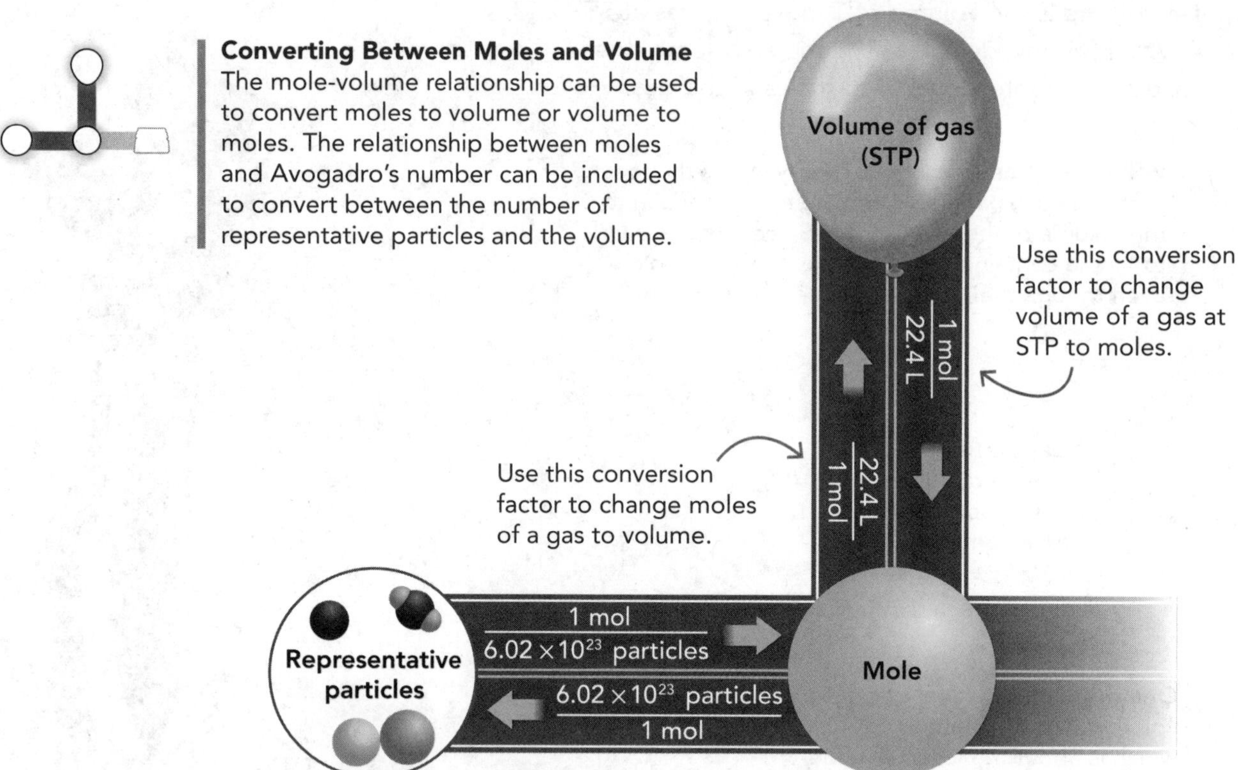

16 **SEP Analyze Data** The table shows experimental data for the volume as a function of the number of moles for nitrous oxide (N_2O) gas, a sedative known as laughing gas. The slope of the best-fit line for these data can be used to convert volume to moles. Graph the volume as a function of moles, draw a best-fit line on the graph, and determine its slope.

Volume and Moles of N_2O

Moles (mol)	Volume (L)
0.15	3.4
0.25	5.6
0.35	7.8
0.45	10.1
0.55	12.3

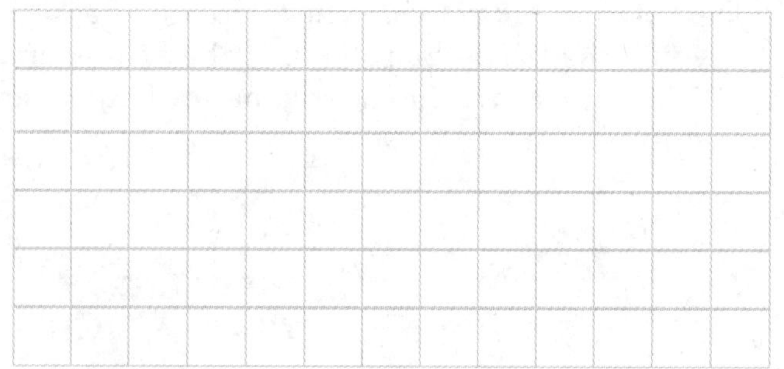

SAMPLE PROBLEM

Calculating Gas Quantities at STP

Sulfur dioxide (SO_2) is a gas produced by burning coal. It is an air pollutant and one of the causes of acid rain. Determine the volume, in liters, of 0.60 mol SO_2 gas at STP.

ANALYZE **List the knowns and the unknown.**

Knowns	Unknown
number of moles = 0.60 mol SO_2	volume = ? L SO_2
1 mol SO_2 = 22.4 L SO_2 at STP	

CALCULATE **Solve for the unknown.**

Identify the conversion factor relating moles of SO_2 gas to volume of SO_2 gas at STP.

$$\frac{22.4\ \text{L}\ SO_2}{1\ \text{mol}\ SO_2}$$

Multiply the given number of moles by the conversion factor.

$$0.60\ \cancel{\text{mol}\ SO_2} \times \frac{22.4\ \text{L}\ SO_2}{1\ \cancel{\text{mol}\ SO_2}} = 13\ \text{L}\ SO_2$$

EVALUATE **Does the result make sense?**

One mole of any gas at STP has a volume of 22.4 L, so 0.60 mol should have a volume slightly larger than one-half of this value. The answer should have two significant figures.

17 **SEP Use Mathematics** **At STP, how many moles are in the given volumes of the following gases?**

a. 67.2 L SO_2

b. 0.880 L He

c. 1.00×10^3 L C_2H_6

GO ONLINE for more practice problems.

Mass and Density

A gas-filled balloon will either sink or float in the air depending on whether the density of the gas inside the balloon is greater or less than the density of the surrounding air. **Density** is the ratio of the mass of a substance to its volume. Although the molar volumes of gases are approximately the same (22.4 L/mol) at STP, different gases will have different densities. The density of a gas at STP can be determined using one of the following expressions:

$$\text{density} = \frac{\text{mass}}{\text{volume}} \quad \text{or} \quad \text{density} = \frac{\text{molar mass}}{\text{molar volume}}$$

Density, Mass, and Volume Density can be calculated from mass and volume. For example, what is the density of 2.0 mol He?

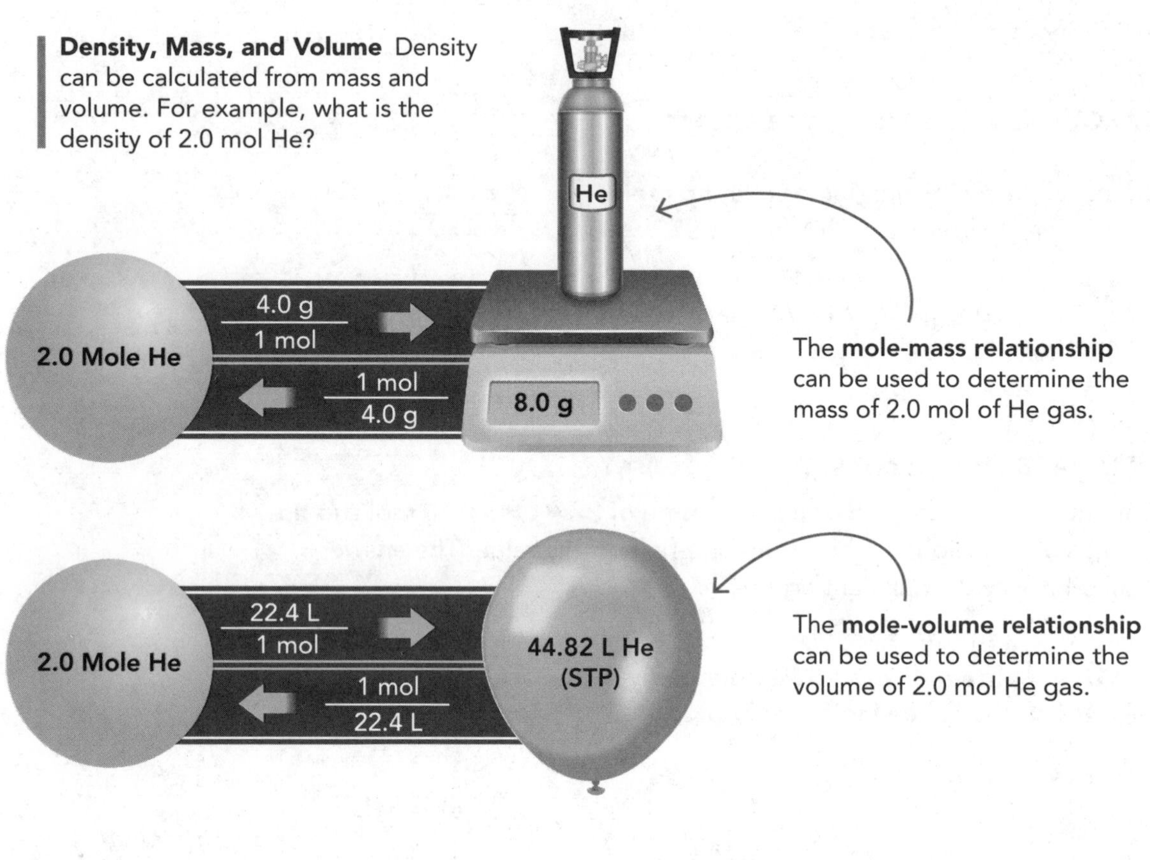

$$\text{density He} = \frac{\text{mass}}{\text{volume}} = \frac{8.0 \text{ g He}}{44.82 \text{ L He}} = 0.18 \text{ g/L He}$$

Helium has a density of 0.18 g/L at STP, which is less than the density of air (1.23 g/L). Therefore, a helium-filled balloon floats.

$$\text{density He} = \frac{\text{molar mass He}}{\text{molar volume He}} = \frac{\frac{4.0 \text{ g He}}{1 \cancel{\text{mol He}}}}{\frac{22.4 \text{ L He}}{1 \cancel{\text{mol He}}}} = 0.18 \text{ g/L He}$$

Since density is a ratio, you can also calculate it directly from the molar mass and molar volume. The moles cancel!

(18) **SEP Interpret Data** The table shows several gases, their molar masses, and their densities at STP. Complete the table by determining whether or not a balloon filled with the gas will float in air. The density of air is 1.23 g/L.

Density of Gases			
Gas	**Molar Mass (g/mol)**	**Density (g/L)**	**Does It Float?**
He	4.0	0.18	Yes
CH_4	16.0	0.71	
CO_2	44.0	1.96	
C_6H_6	78.1		
NH_3	17.0		

Revisit INVESTIGATIVE PHENOMENON

GO ONLINE to Elaborate on and Evaluate your knowledge of mole-mass and mole-volume relationships by completing the peer review and data analysis activities.

In the CER worksheet you completed at the beginning of the investigation, you drafted an explanation for the ways in which matter is quantified. With a partner, reevaluate your arguments.

(19) **SEP Design a Solution** A simple bread recipe calls for 400 g of flour, 7 g of salt (NaCl), 1 g of yeast, and 0.3 L of water (H_2O). You have exactly 0.6 mol of salt. If you want to use all of the salt, how many loaves of bread could you make? How much of each of the other ingredients would you need?

EXPERIENCE 3

Percent Composition and Empirical Formulas

GO ONLINE to Explore and Explain percent composition and molecular formulas.

Percent Composition of a Compound

In a given compound, the ratio of the atoms of each element is fixed. Therefore, the ratio of the masses of the elements is also fixed. The **law of definite proportions** states that a compound contains its component elements in a fixed ratio by mass. For example, in carbon dioxide (CO_2), the ratio of C:O is 1 mol:2 mol. The ratio of the mass is 12.0 g C:32.0 g O, or 0.38 g C:1.0 g O. This ratio is the same for any amount of CO_2.

The relative amounts of the elements in the compound are expressed as the **percent composition,** or the percent by mass of each element in the compound. The mathematical expression for the percent by mass of an element in a compound is as follows:

$$\% \text{ by mass of element} = \frac{\text{mass of element}}{\text{mass of compound}} \times 100\%$$

Fertilizer The relative amounts, or the percent composition, of nitrogen, phosphorus, and potassium (N-P-K) in fertilizer is important.

In spring, a fertilizer high in nitrogen with an N-P-K ratio of 10-1-4 may be used to help grass grow.
Nitrogen (N) 10%
Phosphorus (P) 1%
Other 85%
Potassium (K) 4%
Lawn Fertilizer
N-P-K
10 1 4
A fertilizer with a high percentage of phosphorus with an N-P-K ratio of 5-20-10 may be used when seedlings are planted to help roots grow.
Nitrogen (N) 5%
Phosphorus (P) 20%
Other 65%
Potassium (K) 10%
Planting Fertilizer
N-P-K
5 20 10

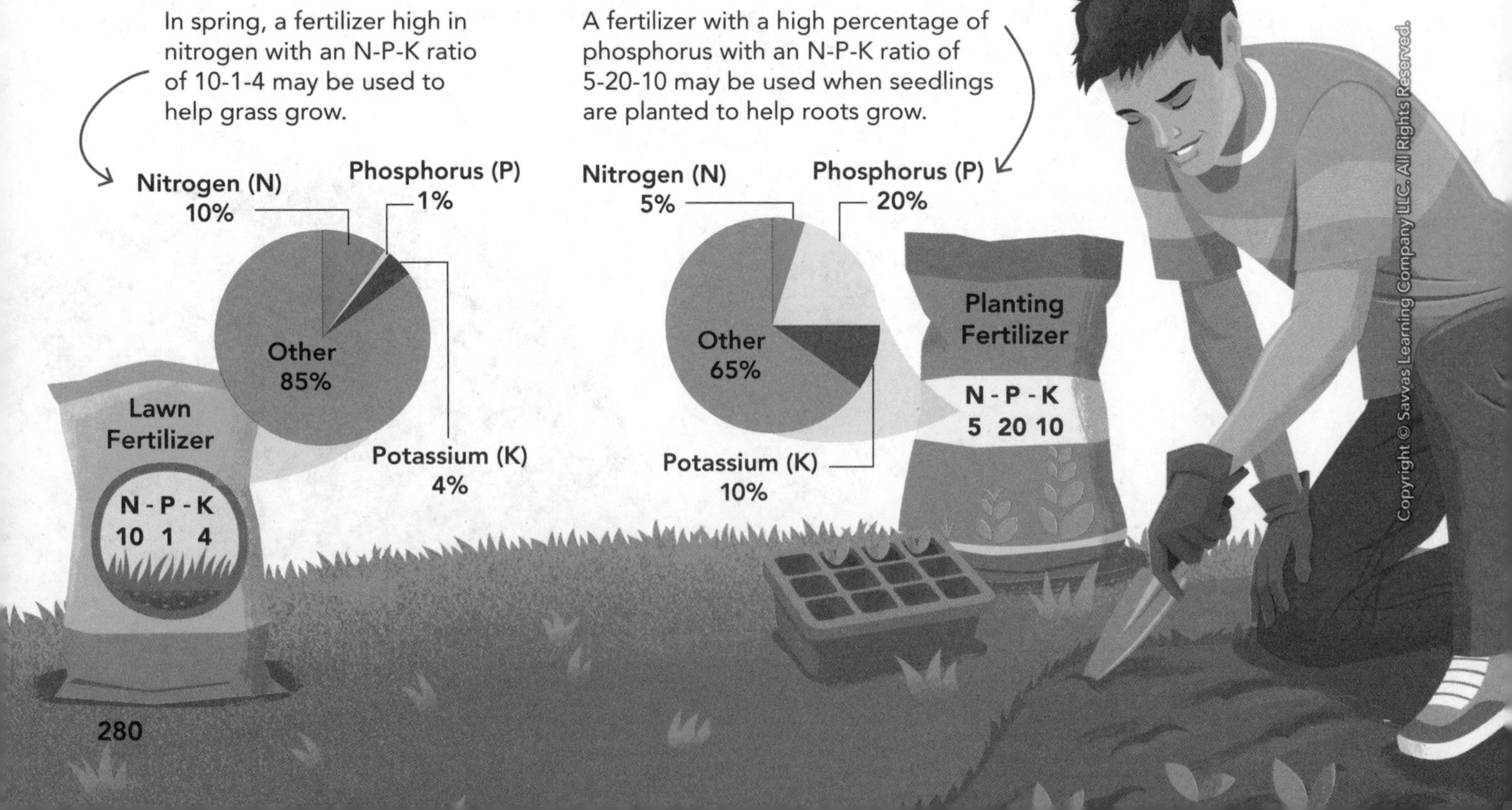

20 **SEP Plan an Investigation** Plan an investigation to determine the percentage by mass of cashews and almonds in a jar of mixed nuts.

SAMPLE PROBLEM

Percent Composition From Mass Data

When a 13.60-g sample of a compound containing only magnesium and oxygen is decomposed, 5.40 g of oxygen is obtained. What is the percent composition of this compound?

ANALYZE List the knowns and the unknowns.

Knowns	Unknowns
mass of compound = 13.60 g	percent by mass of Mg = ?% Mg
mass of oxygen = 5.40 g O	percent by mass of O = ?% O
mass of magnesium = 13.6 g − 5.40 g O = 8.20 g Mg	

CALCULATE Solve for the unknowns.

Determine the percent by mass of Mg in the compound.

$$\%Mg = \frac{\text{mass of Mg}}{\text{mass of compound}} \times 100\%$$
$$= \frac{8.20\ \cancel{g}}{13.60\ \cancel{g}} \times 100\% = 60.3\%\ Mg$$

Determine the percent by mass of O in the compound.

$$\%O = \frac{\text{mass of O}}{\text{mass of compound}} \times 100\%$$
$$= \frac{5.40\ \cancel{g}}{13.60\ \cancel{g}} \times 100\% = 39.7\%\ O$$

EVALUATE Does the result make sense?

The percents of the elements add up to 100%.

21 **SEP Use Mathematics** When a 14.2-g sample of mercury(II) oxide is decomposed into its elements by heating, 13.2 g Hg is obtained. What is the percent composition of this compound?

GO ONLINE for more practice problems.

Percent Composition From Chemical Formulas

The **law of constant composition** states that any sample of a compound will be made up of the same elements in the same ratio. Because of this, you can calculate the percent composition of a compound using its chemical formula. The mathematical expression for the percent by mass of an element in a compound is as follows:

$$\% \text{ by mass of element} = \frac{\text{mass of element in 1 mol of compound}}{\text{molar mass of compound}} \times 100\%$$

Percent Composition of Water Any sample of pure water will have the same proportions of hydrogen and oxygen. To determine the percent composition of each element in water, calculate its proportion by mass.

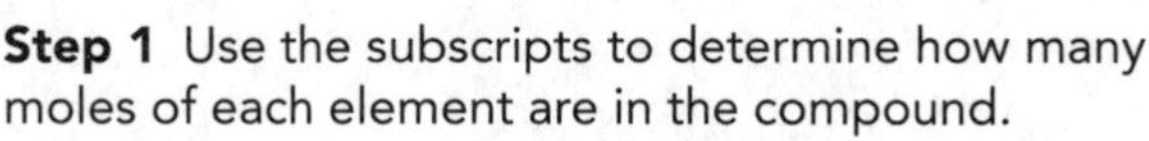

Step 1 Use the subscripts to determine how many moles of each element are in the compound.

1 mol H_2O = 2 mol H + 1 mol O

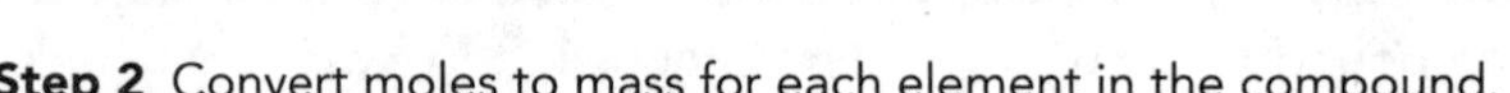

Step 2 Convert moles to mass for each element in the compound.

$2 \text{ mol H} \times \frac{1.0 \text{ g H}}{1 \text{ mol H}} \rightarrow 2.0 \text{ g H}$ $\quad$ $1 \text{ mol O} \times \frac{16.0 \text{ g O}}{1 \text{ mol O}} \rightarrow 16.0 \text{ g O}$

Step 3 Calculate the percent composition of each element.

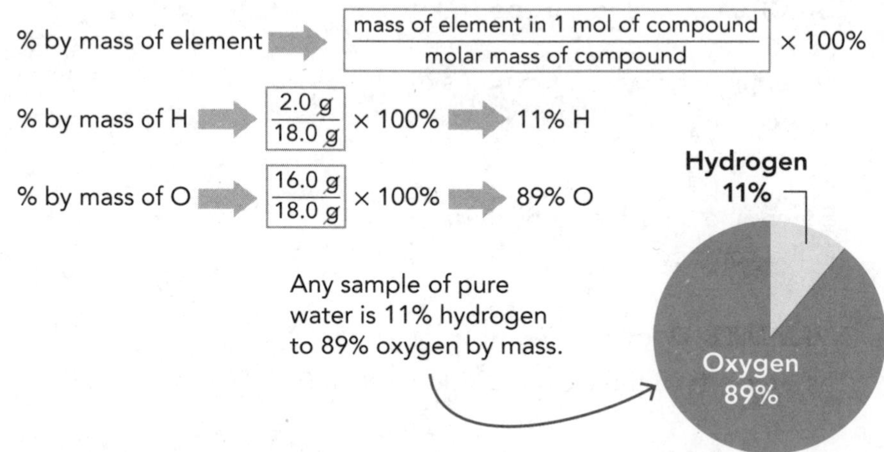

$\% \text{ by mass of element} \rightarrow \frac{\text{mass of element in 1 mol of compound}}{\text{molar mass of compound}} \times 100\%$

$\% \text{ by mass of H} \rightarrow \frac{2.0 \text{ g}}{18.0 \text{ g}} \times 100\% \rightarrow 11\% \text{ H}$

$\% \text{ by mass of O} \rightarrow \frac{16.0 \text{ g}}{18.0 \text{ g}} \times 100\% \rightarrow 89\% \text{ O}$

Any sample of pure water is 11% hydrogen to 89% oxygen by mass.

22 SEP Use Mathematics In the "heavy water" that is used in nuclear reactors, the hydrogen in water is replaced with deuterium. Deuterium is a hydrogen atom with a neutron. It has a molar mass twice that of hydrogen. Sketch the percent composition pie chart for heavy water.

SAMPLE PROBLEM

Calculating Percent Composition From a Chemical Formula

Propane (C_3H_8), the fuel commonly used in gas grills, is one of the compounds obtained from petroleum. Calculate the percent composition of propane.

ANALYZE List the knowns and the unknowns.

Knowns	Unknowns
mass of C in 1 mol C_3H_8 = 3 mol × 12.0 g/mol = 36.0 g	percent by mass of C = ?% C
mass of H in 1 mol C_3H_8 = 8 mol × 1.0 g/mol = 8.0 g	percent by mass of H = ?% H
molar mass of C_3H_8 = 36.0 g/mol + 8.0 g/mol = 44.0 g/mol	

CALCULATE Solve for the unknown.

Determine the percent by mass of C in the C_3H_8 by dividing the mass of C in 1 mole of the compound by the molar mass of the compound and multiplying by 100%.

$$\%C = \frac{\text{mass of C in 1 mol } C_3H_8}{\text{molar mass of } C_3H_8} \times 100\%$$

$$= \frac{36.0\ \cancel{g}}{44.0\ \cancel{g}} \times 100\% = 81.8\%\ C$$

Determine the percent by mass of H in C_3H_8.

$$\%H = \frac{\text{mass of H in 1 mol } C_3H_8}{\text{molar mass of } C_3H_8} \times 100\%$$

$$= \frac{8.0\ \cancel{g}}{44.0\ \cancel{g}} \times 100\% = 18\%\ H$$

EVALUATE Does the result make sense?

The percents of the elements add up to 100% when the answers are expressed to two significant figures (82% + 18% = 100%).

(23) **SEP Use Mathematics What is the percent by mass of nitrogen in the following fertilizers?**

a. NH_3

b. NH_4NO_3

GO ONLINE for more practice problems.

Percent Composition as a Conversion Factor

You can use percent composition to calculate the number of grams of any element in a specific mass of a compound. The percent composition can be used as a conversion factor. For example, if you wanted to know the mass of hydrogen in 20 g of water, you would use the percent composition of hydrogen as a conversion factor. Because water is 11.1% hydrogen by mass, there are 11.1 g of hydrogen in 100 g of water.

$$20 \text{ g } \cancel{H_2O} \times \frac{11.1 \text{ g H}}{100 \text{ g } \cancel{H_2O}} = 2.2 \text{ g H}$$

Percent Composition of Propane
Trucks deliver propane (C_3H_8) to homes, where it is used as fuel.

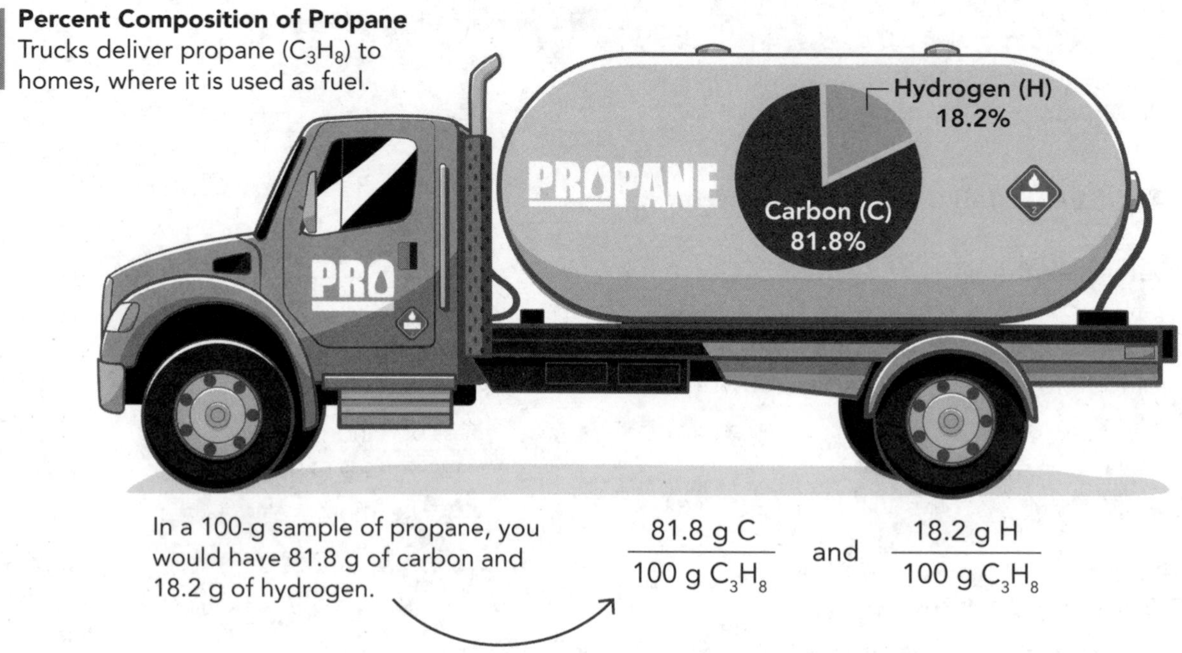

In a 100-g sample of propane, you would have 81.8 g of carbon and 18.2 g of hydrogen.

$$\frac{81.8 \text{ g C}}{100 \text{ g } C_3H_8} \text{ and } \frac{18.2 \text{ g H}}{100 \text{ g } C_3H_8}$$

(24) **SEP Plan an Investigation** **Plan an investigation to determine the percent by mass of water that makes up a sample of hydrated copper(II) sulfate ($CuSO_4 \cdot 5H_2O$). Identify the steps you would take in your investigation.**

SAMPLE PROBLEM

Calculating the Mass of an Element in a Compound Using Percent Composition

Calculate the mass of carbon and the mass of hydrogen in 82.0 g of propane (C_3H_8).

ANALYZE List the known and the unknowns.

Knowns	Unknowns
mass of C_3H_8 = 82.0 g	mass of carbon = ? g C
	mass of hydrogen = ? g H

CALCULATE Solve for the unknowns.

Write the conversion factor to convert from mass of C_3H_8 to mass of C. The percent by mass of C in C_3H_8 is 81.8%.

$$\frac{81.8 \text{ g C}}{100 \text{ g } C_3H_8}$$

Multiply the mass of C_3H_8 by the conversion factor.

$$82.0 \text{ g } \cancel{C_3H_8} \times \frac{81.8 \text{ g C}}{100 \text{ g } \cancel{C_3H_8}} = 67.1 \text{ g C}$$

Write the conversion factor to convert from mass of C_3H_8 to mass of H. The percent by mass of H in C_3H_8 is 18.2%.

$$\frac{18.2 \text{ g H}}{100 \text{ g } C_3H_8}$$

Multiply the mass of C_3H_8 by the conversion factor.

$$82.0 \text{ g } \cancel{C_3H_8} \times \frac{18.2 \text{ g H}}{100 \text{ g } \cancel{C_3H_8}} = 14.9 \text{ g H}$$

EVALUATE Does the result make sense?

The sum of the two masses equals 82.0 g, the sample size.

25 SEP Use Mathematics **Calculate the grams of nitrogen in 125 g of each fertilizer.**

a. NH_3

b. NH_4NO_3

GO ONLINE for more practice problems.

Empirical Formulas

The **empirical formula** of a compound gives the lowest whole-number ratio of the atoms or moles of elements in a compound. For example, there are two atoms each of hydrogen and oxygen in one molecule of hydrogen peroxide (H_2O_2). The lowest ratio of hydrogen to oxygen is 1:1, so the empirical formula is HO.

An empirical formula may or may not be the same as the molecular formula, which gives the actual number of atoms in a molecule.

Empirical Formula From Data If you know the percent composition or the masses of the elements in a sample of an unknown compound, such as hydrogen peroxide, then you can determine the empirical formula. For example, suppose a sample of hydrogen peroxide contains 6% hydrogen and 94% oxygen.

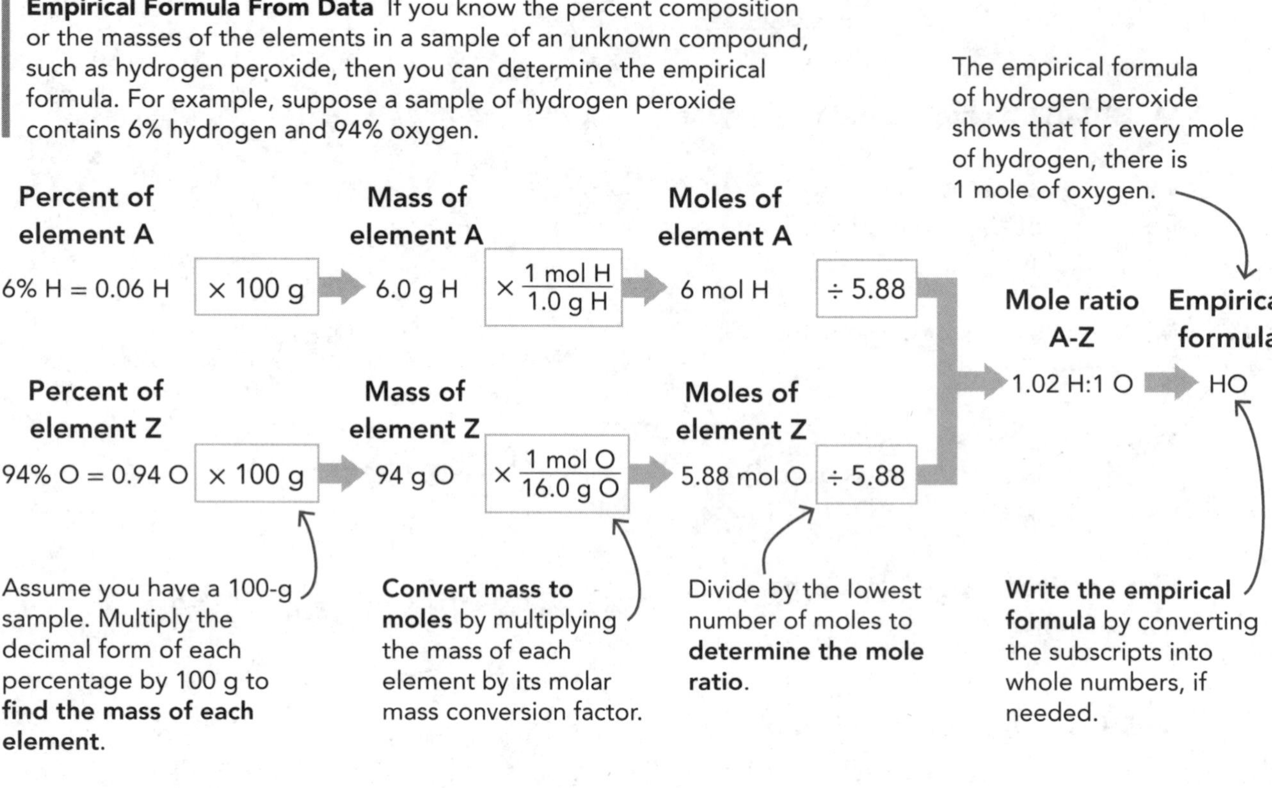

The empirical formula of hydrogen peroxide shows that for every mole of hydrogen, there is 1 mole of oxygen.
Percent of element A
6% H = 0.06 H
× 100 g
Mass of element A
6.0 g H
× 1 mol H / 1.0 g H
Moles of element A
6 mol H
÷ 5.88
Percent of element Z
94% O = 0.94 O
× 100 g
Mass of element Z
94 g O
× 1 mol O / 16.0 g O
Moles of element Z
5.88 mol O
÷ 5.88
Mole ratio A-Z
1.02 H:1 O
Empirical formula
HO
Assume you have a 100-g sample. Multiply the decimal form of each percentage by 100 g to find the mass of each element.
Convert mass to moles by multiplying the mass of each element by its molar mass conversion factor.
Divide by the lowest number of moles to determine the mole ratio.
Write the empirical formula by converting the subscripts into whole numbers, if needed.

26 CCC Structure and Function **Acetylene (C_2H_2) is a flammable gas used in welders' torches. Styrene (C_8H_8) is used to make packing peanuts. What is the empirical formula for each? Describe why the empirical formula might be useful in the lab setting but not useful for predicting the properties and/or functions of materials.**

....

....

....

....

SAMPLE PROBLEM

Determining the Empirical Formula

An unknown compound is analyzed and found to contain 25.9% nitrogen and 74.1% oxygen. What is the empirical formula of the compound?

ANALYZE **List the knowns and the unknown.**

Knowns	Unknown
percent by mass of N = 25.9% N	empirical formula = $N_?O_?$
percent by mass of O = 74.1% O	

CALCULATE **Solve for the unknown.**

Convert the percent by mass of each element to moles to determine the mole ratio.

$$25.9\ \cancel{g\,N} \times \frac{1\ \text{mol N}}{14.0\ \cancel{g\,N}} = 1.85\ \text{mol N}$$

$$74.1\ \cancel{g\,O} \times \frac{1\ \text{mol O}}{16.0\ \cancel{g\,O}} = 4.63\ \text{mol O}$$

The mole ratio is $N_{1.85}$:$O_{4.63}$.

Divide each molar quantity by the smaller number of moles to get 1 mol from the element with the smaller number of moles.

$$\frac{1.85\ \text{mol N}}{1.85} = 1\ \text{mol N}$$

$$\frac{4.63\ \text{mol O}}{1.85} = 2.5\ \text{mol O}$$

The mole ratio becomes N_1:$O_{2.5}$.

Reduce the mole ratio to the lowest whole-number ratio by multiplying each part of the ratio by the smallest whole number that will convert both subscripts to a whole number.

1 mol N × 2 = 2 mol N

2.5 mol O × 2 = 5 mol N

The empirical formula is N_2O_5.

EVALUATE **Does the result make sense?**

The subscripts are whole numbers, and the percent composition of this empirical formula equals the percentages given in the original problem.

27 **SEP Use Mathematics Calculate the empirical formula for a compound that contains 67.6% Hg, 10.8% S, and 21.6% O.**

GO ONLINE for more practice problems.

Molecular Formulas

The **molecular formula** of a compound is either the same as its experimentally-determined empirical formula, or it is a simple whole-number multiple of its empirical formula. The molecular formula gives the actual number of atoms in the structure of the molecule, as opposed to just the ratio. For example, methanal, ethanoic acid, and glucose have the same empirical formula—CH_2O. However, they have different molecular formulas and very different properties.

You can determine the molecular formula of a compound from its empirical formula and its experimentally determined molar mass. Calculate the empirical formula mass (EFM) of a compound from its empirical formula. Then divide the molar mass by the empirical formula mass to find the number of empirical formula units in a molecule of the compound.

Empirical vs. Molecular Formula The empirical formula of methanal, ethanoic acid, and glucose shows that they have the same percent composition of C, H, and O. However, their molecular formulas show that the actual number of atoms in each molecule are different.

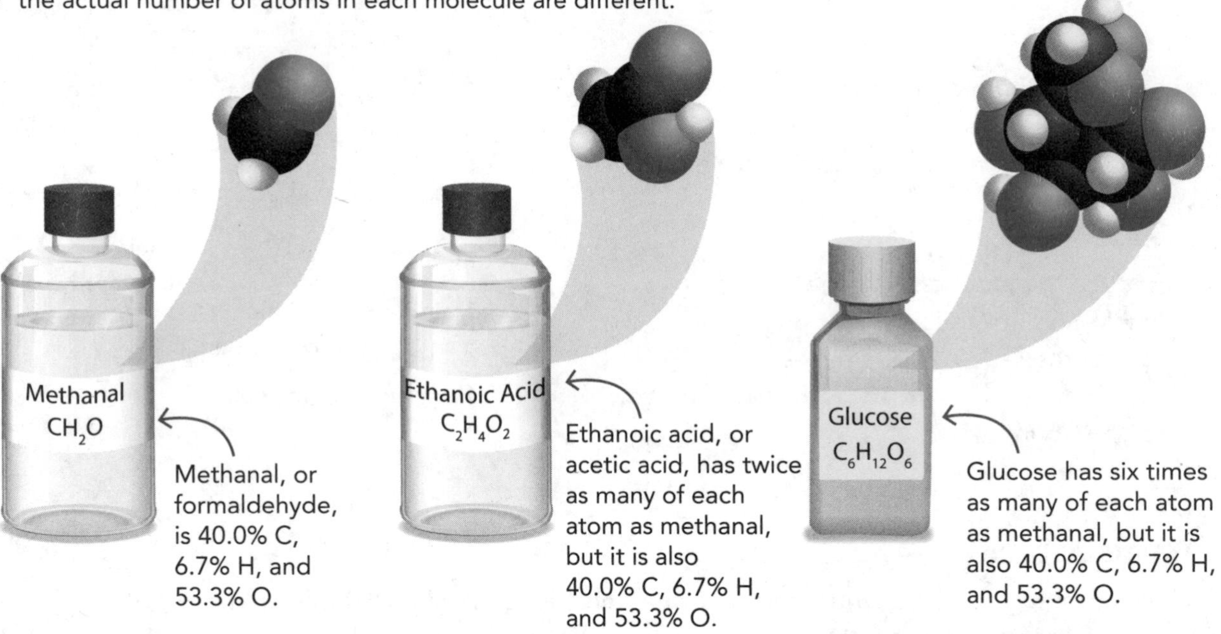

Methanal
CH_2O
Methanal, or formaldehyde, is 40.0% C, 6.7% H, and 53.3% O.
Ethanoic Acid
$C_2H_4O_2$
Ethanoic acid, or acetic acid, has twice as many of each atom as methanal, but it is also 40.0% C, 6.7% H, and 53.3% O.
Glucose
$C_6H_{12}O_6$
Glucose has six times as many of each atom as methanal, but it is also 40.0% C, 6.7% H, and 53.3% O.

28 **SEP Interpret Data If you know the molar mass of methanal, how could you determine the molar mass of ethanoic acid and glucose? Complete the table.**

Formula (name)	Molar mass (g/mol)
CH	13
C_2H_2 (ethyne)	26 (2 × 13)
C_6H_6 (benzene)	78 (6 × 13)
CH_2O (methanal)	30
$C_2H_4O_2$ (ethanoic acid)	
$C_6H_{12}O_6$ (glucose)	

SAMPLE PROBLEM

Determining the Molecular Formula

Calculate the molecular formula of a compound whose molar mass is 60.0 g/mol and empirical formula is CH_4N.

ANALYZE **List the knowns and the unknown.**

Knowns	Unknown
empirical formula = CH_4N	molecular formula = $C_?H_?N_?$
molar mass = 60.0 g/mol	

CALCULATE **Solve for the unknown.**

Calculate the empirical formula mass (EFM). It is the molar mass of the empirical formula.

EFM of CH_4N =
$12.0 \text{ g/mol} + 4(1.0 \text{ g/mol}) + 14.0 \text{ g/mol} = 30.0 \text{ g/mol}$

Divide the molar mass by the empirical formula mass to obtain a whole number.

$$\frac{\text{molar mass}}{\text{EFM}} = \frac{60.0 \cancel{\text{g/mol}}}{30.0 \cancel{\text{g/mol}}} = 2$$

Multiply the empirical formula subscripts by this value to get the molecular formula.

$(CH_4N) \times 2 = C_2H_8N_2$

EVALUATE **Does the result make sense?**

The molecular formula has the molar mass of the compound.

29 **SEP Use Mathematics** **Find the molecular formula of ethylene glycol, which is used in antifreeze. The molar mass is 62.0 g/mol, and the empirical formula is CH_3O.**

30 **SEP Use Mathematics** **What is the molecular formula of a compound with the empirical formula CClN and a molar mass of 184.5 g/mol?**

GO ONLINE for more practice problems.

Revisit

INVESTIGATIVE PHENOMENON

GO ONLINE to Elaborate on and Evaluate your knowledge of percent composition and the conservation of mass by completing the peer review and engineering design activities.

In the CER worksheet you completed at the beginning of the investigation, you drafted an explanation for the ways in which matter is quantified. With a partner, reevaluate your arguments.

31 **SEP Obtain and Evaluate Information** **Monosaccharides are the basic units of carbohydrates called "simple sugars." Two such monosaccharides are glucose, found in plants and animals, and fructose, found in fruits and honey. Both glucose and fructose have the same empirical formula and the same molecular formula ($C_6H_{12}O_6$). However, they have different structures, which is why they have different names. What are the empirical formulas for glucose and fructose? Research and compare their structures and list two other carbohydrates that have the chemical formula $C_6H_{12}O_6$. How do their structures affect their functions?**

EXPERIENCE 4

Concentrations of Solutions

GO ONLINE to Explore and Explain concentration and molarity.

Molarity

Concentration of a Solution The **concentration** of a solution is a measure of the amount of solute that is dissolved in a given quantity of solvent. You can describe the amount of a solute in solution qualitatively using the terms *dilute* and *concentrated.* A solution with a small amount of solute is a **dilute solution.** By contrast, a **concentrated solution** contains a large amount of solute. A solution with 5 g copper sulfate per 100 mL water might be described as dilute compared to a solution with 10 g copper sulfate per 100 mL water.

Amount of Solute The more solute particles in a given amount of solution, the greater the concentration of the solute.

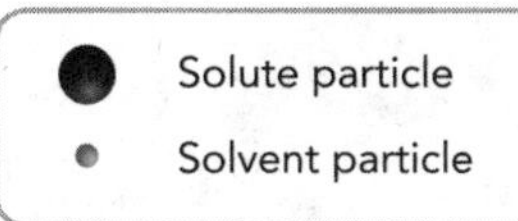

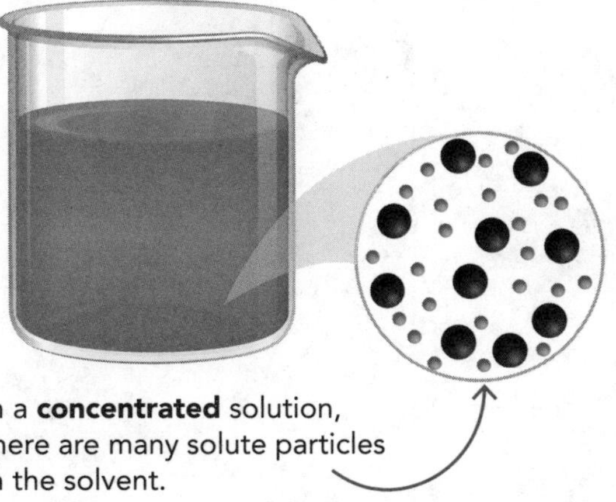

In a **concentrated** solution, there are many solute particles in the solvent.

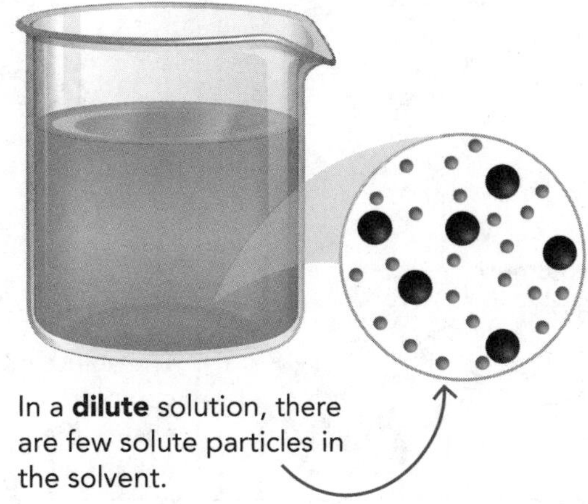

In a **dilute** solution, there are few solute particles in the solvent.

32 SEP Define a Problem The test tubes contain water (A) and three copper sulfate solutions (B–D) with increasing concentration. Why is it difficult to say whether solution C is a concentrated solution or a dilute solution? How can we better define the problem?

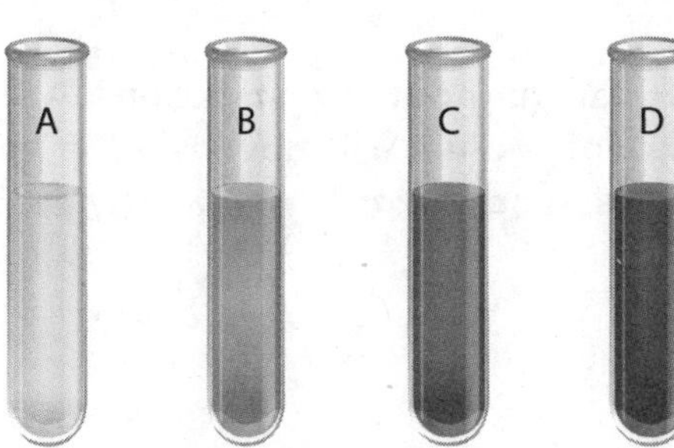

Defining Concentration Quantitatively Molar concentration, called **molarity** (M), is the number of moles of solute dissolved in 1 liter of solution. To calculate the molarity of a solution, divide the number of moles of solute by the volume of the solution in liters.

$$M = \frac{\text{moles of solute}}{\text{liters of solution}}$$

A common error is to use the volume of the solvent in the denominator. The volume of the solution contains both the solute and solvent.

Making a 0.5 *M* Solution Volumetric flasks are used to make specific volumes of solution because they hold a precise amount of liquid. A line on the neck of the flask marks the volume.

Step 1 Start by filling a 1 L volumetric flask halfway with distilled water. Then add 0.5 mol of solute.

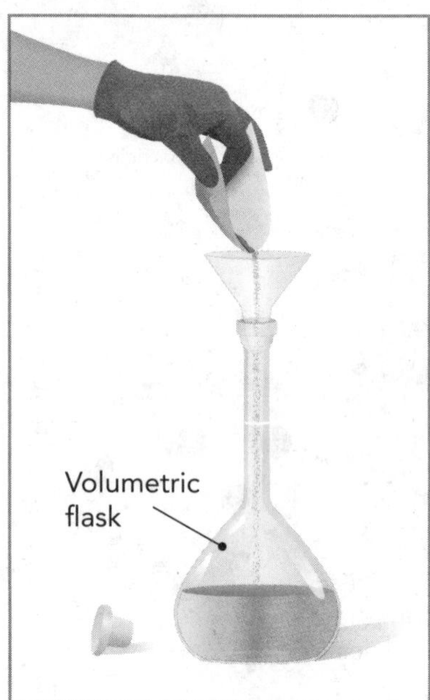

Step 2 Mix the solute and solvent by gently swirling the flask to dissolve the solid solute.

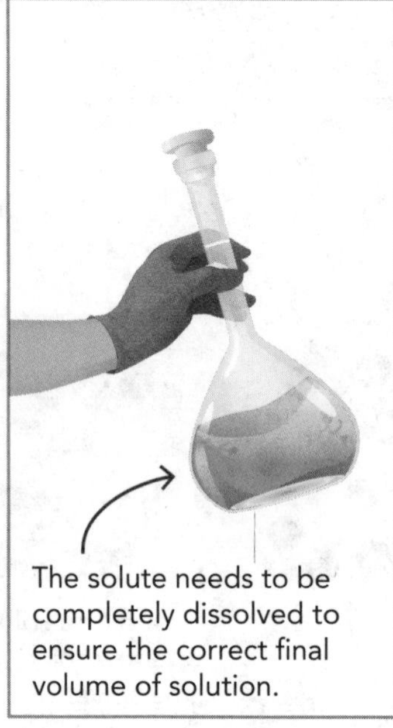

The solute needs to be completely dissolved to ensure the correct final volume of solution.

Step 3 Carefully fill the flask with distilled water to the 1 L mark. Note that you have made 1 L of solution, not added 1 L of solvent.

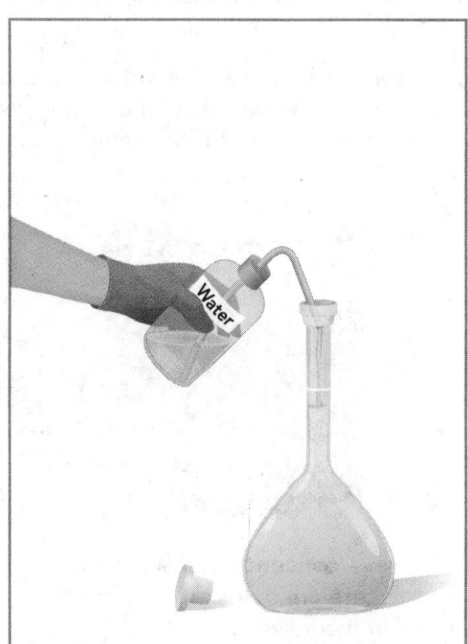

33 **SEP Carrying out Investigations A student adds 1 L of water to 1 mol of sodium chloride. Will the result be a 1 *M* solution of sodium chloride and water? Why or why not?**

SAMPLE PROBLEM

Calculating Molarity

Intravenous saline solutions are often administered to patients in the hospital. One saline solution contains 0.90 g NaCl in exactly 100 mL of solution. What is the molarity of the solution?

ANALYZE **List the knowns and the unknown.**

Knowns	Unknown
solution concentration = 0.90 g NaCl/100 mL	solution concentration = ? *M*
molar mass of NaCl = 58.5 g/mol	

CALCULATE **Solve for the unknown.**

Identify the steps to convert concentration from g/100 mL to mol/L.

g/100 mL → mol/100 mL → mol/L

Use the molar mass to convert g NaCl/100 mL to mol NaCl/100 mL. Convert the volume units from mL to L.

solution concentration =

$$\frac{0.90\ \text{g NaCl}}{100\ \text{mL}} \times \frac{1\ \text{mol NaCl}}{58.5\ \text{g NaCl}} \times \frac{1000\ \text{mL}}{1\ \text{L}} =$$

$$0.15\ \frac{\text{mol}}{\text{L}} = 0.15\ M$$

The relationship 1 L = 1000 mL gives you the conversion factor 1000 mL/1 L.

EVALUATE **Does the result make sense?**

The answer should be less than 1 *M* because 0.90 g/100 mL is the same concentration as 9.0 g/L, and 9.0 g is less than 1 mol of NaCl. The answer is correctly expressed to two significant figures.

34 SEP Use Mathematics **A solution has a volume of 2.0 L and contains 36.0 g of glucose ($C_6H_{12}O_6$). If the molar mass of glucose is 180 g/mol, what is the molarity of the solution?**

35 SEP Use Mathematics **A solution has a volume of 250 mL and contains 0.70 mol NaCl. What is its molarity?**

GO ONLINE for more practice problems.

SAMPLE PROBLEM

Calculating Moles of Solute in Solution

Household laundry bleach is a dilute aqueous solution of sodium hypochlorite (NaClO). How many moles of solute are present in 1.5 L of 0.70 *M* NaClO?

ANALYZE List the knowns and the unknown.

Knowns	Unknown
volume of solution = 1.5 L	moles solute = ? mol
solution concentration = 0.70 *M* NaClO	

CALCULATE Solve for the unknown.

Identify the steps to convert volume to moles using molarity as a conversion factor.

volume of solution → moles of solute

Multiply the given volume by the molarity expressed in mol/L.

$$\text{moles solute} = 1.5\ \cancel{\text{L}} \times \frac{0.70\ \text{mol NaClO}}{1\ \cancel{\text{L}}} = 1.1\ \text{mol NaClO}$$

EVALUATE Does the result make sense?

The answer should be greater than 1 mol but less than 1.5 mol because the solution concentration is less than 0.75 mol/L and the volume is less than 2 L. The answer is correctly expressed to two significant figures.

(36) **SEP Use Mathematics** How many moles of ammonium nitrate are in 335 mL of 0.425 *M* NH_4NO_3?

(37) **SEP Use Mathematics** How many moles of solute are in 250 mL of 2.0 *M* $CaCl_2$?

GO ONLINE for more practice problems.

Dilutions

Diluting a Solution You dilute a solution by adding more solvent to it. During dilution, the total number of moles of solute does not change. However, the number of moles of the solvent does change.

Therefore, diluting a solution reduces the number of moles of solute per unit volume but not the total number of moles of solute.

Diluting a Solution More solvent is added to the solution. No new solute particles are added as the solution volume increases. This decreases the molarity, which is a measure of solute concentration.

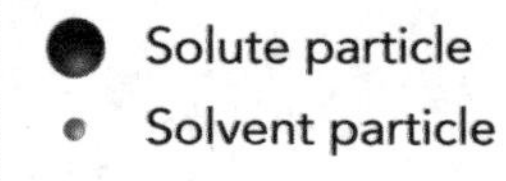

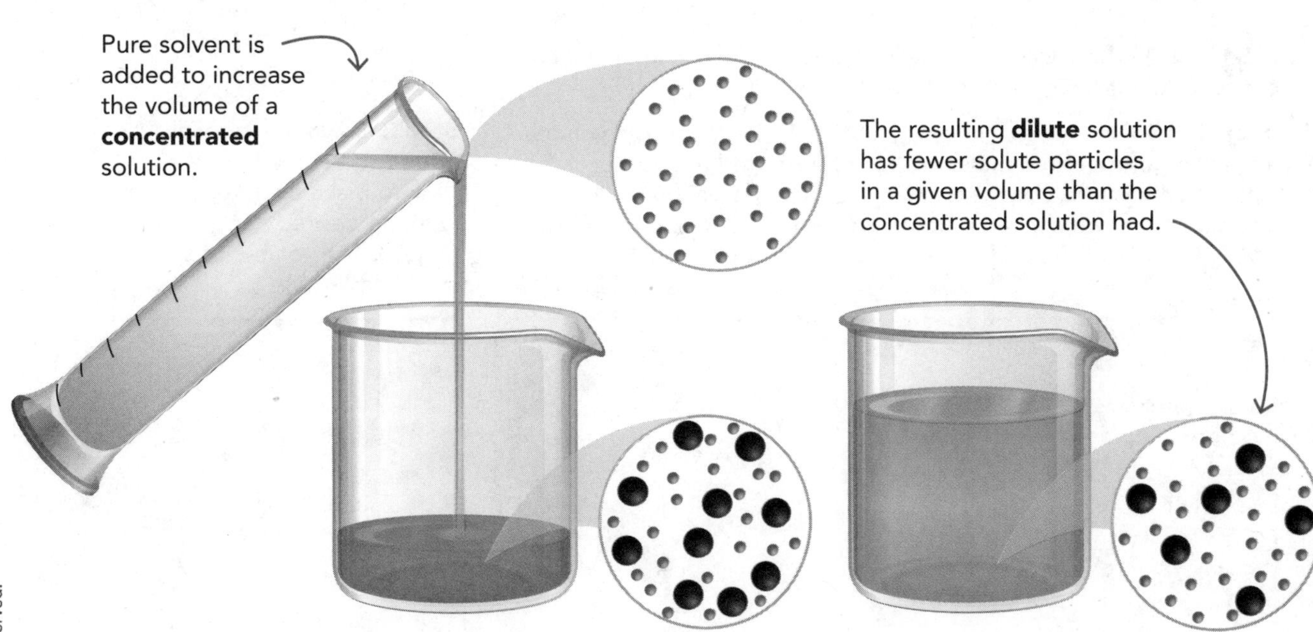

Pure solvent is added to increase the volume of a **concentrated** solution.
The resulting **dilute** solution has fewer solute particles in a given volume than the concentrated solution had.

38 **SEP Develop a Model** Imagine you have a box and a set of red and green balls. The red balls represent solute particles, and the green balls represent solvent particles. Sketch a model showing how the number of red balls doesn't change as more green balls are added. Use your model to show how the percent by count of red balls to total balls decreases.

Making a Dilution The number of moles of solute is related to the molarity (M) and volume (V) of a solution by the following equation:

$$\text{moles of solute} = M \times V$$

A stock solution is a concentrated solution of known molarity that is diluted to make less concentrated solutions. Because the molarity is known, a defined volume of the stock can be measured to make a dilution with the desired molarity. Since the total number of moles of solute does not change during a dilution, we can write the following expression:

$$\text{moles of solute} = M_{stock} \times V_{stock} = M_{dilute} \times V_{dilute}$$

Molarity of the stock solution (M_{stock}); Volume of the stock solution (V_{stock}); Molarity of the dilute solution (M_{dilute}); Volume of the dilute solution (V_{dilute})

Making a Dilution Dilutions often require making a solution with a precise concentration from a small amount of stock solution.

Step 1 A volume (V_{stock}) containing the desired moles of solute is measured from a stock solution of known concentration (M_{stock}).

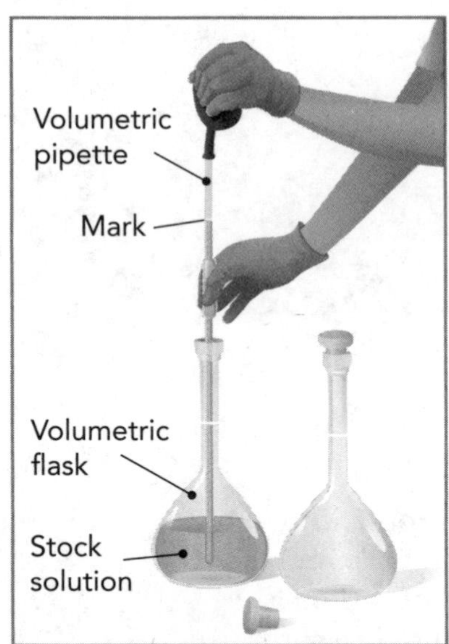

Step 2 The measured volume is transferred to another volumetric flask that will measure the desired amount of dilute solution.

Step 3 Solvent is carefully added to the mark on the flask to make a dilute solution with the desired concentration (M_{dilute}). The volume of solution in the flask is V_{dilute}.

39 SEP Interpret Data **The table shows the volume (V_{stock}) of a 2.0 M $MgSO_4$ stock solution needed to make several different 1 L dilutions at the molarities (M_{dilute}) shown. Complete the table by determining how much stock solution you should measure out to make 1 L of Dilution 3.**

Dilutions From a 2.0 *M* Stock Solution

Dilution	V_{stock} (L)	$M \times V$ (mol)	M_{dilute} (mol/L)	V_{dilute} (L)
Dilution 1	0.5	1	1	1
Dilution 2	0.375	0.75	0.75	1
Dilution 3			0.5	1

SAMPLE PROBLEM

Preparing a Dilute Solution

You have a stock solution of aqueous 2.00 M $MgSO_4$. How many milliliters must be diluted with water to prepare 100.0 mL of aqueous 0.400 M $MgSO_4$?

ANALYZE List the knowns and the unknown.

Knowns	Unknown
$M_{stock} \times V_{stock} = M_{dilute} \times V_{dilute}$	V_{stock} = ? mL of 2.00 M $MgSO_4$
M_{stock} = 2.00 M $MgSO_4$	
M_{dilute} = 0.400 M $MgSO_4$	
V_{dilute} = 100.0 mL of 0.400 M $MgSO_4$	

CALCULATE Solve for the unknown.

Rearrange the equation to solve for V_{stock}.

$$V_{stock} = \frac{M_{dilute} \times V_{dilute}}{M_{stock}}$$

Substitute known values into the equation.

$$V_{stock} = \frac{0.400\ \cancel{M} \times 100.0\ \text{mL}}{2.00\ \cancel{M}} = 20.0\ \text{mL}$$

EVALUATE Does the result make sense?

The initial concentration is five times larger than the dilute concentration. Because the number of moles of solute does not change, the initial volume of solution should be one fifth the final volume of the diluted solution.

40 SEP Design a Solution **How could you prepare 250 mL of 0.20 M NaCl using only a solution of 1.0 M NaCl and water?**

....

....

....

....

....

GO ONLINE for more practice problems.

Percent Solution

If both the solute and solvent are liquids, a convenient way to make a solution is to measure the volumes of the solute and solution. **Percent by volume** of a solution is the ratio of the volumes of solute to solution.

$$\text{Percent by volume } [\% \text{ (v/v)}] = \frac{\text{volume of solute}}{\text{volume of solution}} \times 100\%$$

The **percent by mass** of a solution is the ratio of the masses of the solute and solution.

$$\text{Percent by mass } [\% \text{ (m/m)}] = \frac{\text{mass of solute}}{\text{mass of solution}} \times 100\%$$

Percent by Volume Isopropyl alcohol is sold as a 70% solution by volume. The concentration is written as 70% by volume or 70% (v/v).

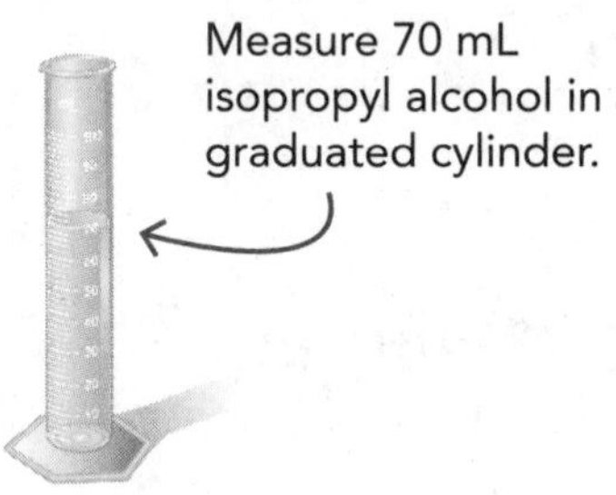

Pure isopropyl alcohol

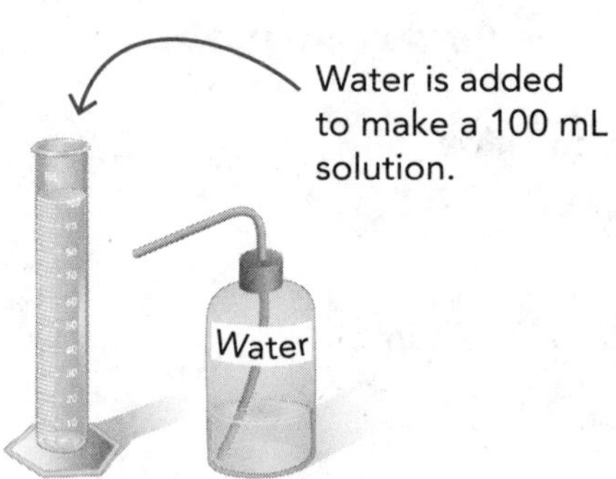

Water is added to make a 100 mL solution.
Water

The percent by volume of the solution is

$$\frac{\text{70 mL isopropyl alcohol}}{\text{100 mL solution}} \times 100 = 70\% \text{ isopropyl alcohol (v/v).}$$

Percent by Mass A brine solution consists of 8.0 g NaCl in 100 g of solution and has 8.0% sodium chloride by mass. The concentration is written as 8.0% by mass or 8.0% (m/m).

The percent by mass of the solution is

$$\frac{\text{8.0 g sodium chloride}}{\text{100 g solution}} \times 100 = 8.0\% \text{ NaCl (m/m).}$$

(41) **SEP Design a Solution** Professional car detailers use a 50% (v/v) solution of isopropyl rubbing alcohol to remove old wax from the car surface. Design a procedure to make a 50% (v/v) solution from store-bought rubbing alcohol, which is 70% (v/v), that fills a 1-L spray bottle.

SAMPLE PROBLEM

Calculating Percent by Volume

What is the percent by volume of ethanol (C_2H_6O, or ethyl alcohol) in the final solution when 85 mL of ethanol is diluted to a volume of 250 mL with water?

ANALYZE List the knowns and the unknown.

Knowns	Unknown
volume of solute = 85 mL ethanol	percent by volume = ?% ethanol (v/v)
volume of solution = 250 mL ethanol	

CALCULATE Solve for the unknown.

Write the equation for percent by volume.

$$\text{Percent by volume [\% (v/v)]} = \frac{\text{volume of solute}}{\text{volume of solution}} \times 100\%$$

Substitute known values into the equation.

$$\text{\% (v/v)} = \frac{85 \text{ mL ethanol}}{250 \text{ mL}} \times 100\% = 34\% \text{ ethanol (v/v)}$$

EVALUATE Does the result make sense?

The volume of the solute is about one third the volume of the solution, so the answer is reasonable. The answer is correctly expressed to two significant figures.

(42) **SEP Design a Solution** A bottle of hydrogen peroxide (H_2O_2) is labeled 3.0% (v/v). How many mL H_2O_2 are in a 400.0-mL bottle?

GO ONLINE for more practice problems.

Revisit

INVESTIGATIVE PHENOMENON

GO ONLINE to Elaborate on and Evaluate your knowledge of solution concentration by completing the discussion and data analysis activities.

In the CER worksheet you completed at the beginning of the investigation, you drafted an explanation for the ways in which matter is quantified. With a partner, reevaluate your arguments.

43 **SEP Plan an Investigation** You make a pitcher of 2 L lemonade following a recipe, but you find that it tastes too sweet. Plan an investigation where you dilute the lemonade into different dilutions with varying concentrations of sugar. Once you have determined your ideal dilution, describe how and why you would adjust the recipe or use the pitcher of lemonade to make a glass of lemonade in the future.

GO ONLINE to Evaluate what you learned about using mathematical representations to quantify matter by using the available assessment resources.

In the Performance-Based Assessment, you collected evidence for determining chemical formulas based on percent composition. Wrap up your analysis by answering the following questions.

44 **SEP Identify Limitations of Models** **Reevaluate your evidence. How can you improve the methodology of collecting the data and the quality of the data collected?**

45 **Revisit the Anchoring Phenomenon** **How does what you learned in this investigation help you understand how the quantification of matter can be used to design better foods?**

INVESTIGATIVE PHENOMENON

GO ONLINE to Engage with real-world phenomena by watching a video and to complete a modeling interactive worksheet.

How is energy obtained from chemical reactions?

Chemical Reactions

When fuel and oxygen chemically react in a rocket engine, a massive amount of energy is released. This energy release propels the rocket and its spacecraft into the sky. Hydrogen fuel cells on a spacecraft use a similar reaction to generate electrical energy that can be used to run the systems, with the only byproduct being water. Once you have viewed the Investigative Phenomenon video and completed the modeling exercise to explain "How is energy obtained from chemical reactions?", answer these reflection questions.

1. **CCC Energy and Matter** When kerosene and oxygen molecules react to form carbon dioxide and water, energy is released. Where do you think the energy comes from?

2. **SEP Engage in Argument from Evidence** Gasoline is composed of a mixture of various hydrocarbons. When hydrocarbons are burned to produce energy, the resulting products are carbon dioxide and water. When hydrogen and oxygen are combined to produce energy, the resulting product is only water. Why are car manufacturers exploring hydrogen fuel cell technology as a possible replacement for gasoline-burning engines? Make a claim and argue from evidence.

EXPERIENCE 1

Modeling Chemical Reactions

GO ONLINE to Explore and Explain how to model chemical reactions.

Word Equations

To represent a chemical reaction, you need to show the substances present before the reaction (the **reactants**) on the left side of the reaction arrow, and the substances present after the reaction (the **products**) on the right side of the reaction arrow. You can model what happens in a chemical reaction using word equations and drawings.

Representing Reactions Using Word Equations Although a sentence describing the reaction can be a perfectly good description, a word equation can be quicker to write and easier to interpret.

Iron and oxygen *react to produce* **iron(III) oxide (rust).**

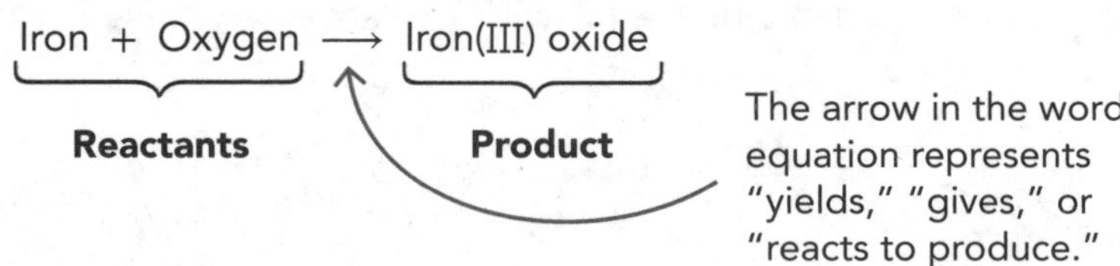

Using Drawings to Explain Word Equations Various ingredients are combined to make a loaf of bread. Though words tell how these ingredients are used to make bread, a picture visually depicts this reaction.

Flour, eggs, milk, salt, baking powder, and oil *react to produce* **bread.**

Flour + eggs + milk + salt + baking powder + oil ⟶ bread

Chemical Equations

Skeleton Equations A chemical equation is a representation of a chemical reaction where we use the chemical symbols instead of words, such as Fe instead of iron. Equations that show just the formulas of the reactants and products are called skeleton equations. A **skeleton equation** is a chemical equation that does not indicate the relative amounts of the reactants and products.

Representing Chemical Reactions

How are **word and skeleton equations** used to represent **chemical reactions?**

Word Equations The full names of elements and compounds are used to describe the reactants and products. The reactants are written on the left side of the arrow, and the products are written on the right side.

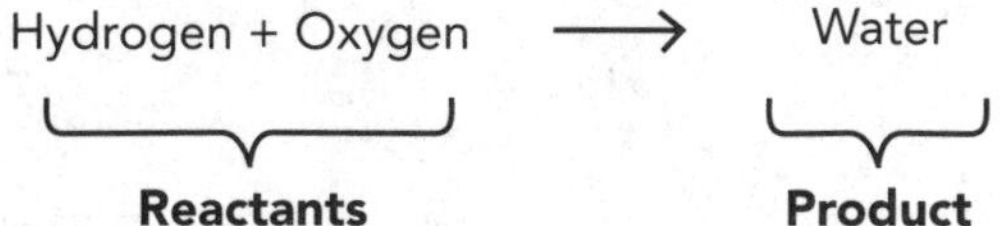

Skeleton Equations Chemical symbols are used to describe the reactants and products in a skeleton equation. A skeleton equation does not indicate the relative amounts of the reactants and products. It's similar to a recipe that lists the ingredients, but does not include measurements.

$H_2 + O_2 \longrightarrow H_2O$

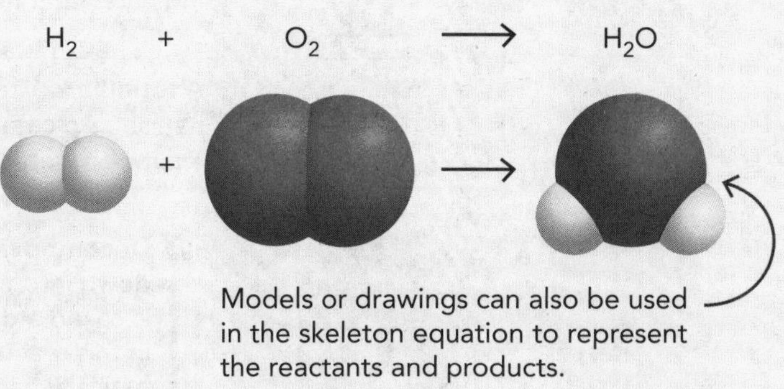

Models or drawings can also be used in the skeleton equation to represent the reactants and products.

Material State Reactants and products can be represented as solids (*s*), gases (*g*), liquids (*l*), or aqueous solutions (*aq*).

$H_2(g) + O_2(g) \longrightarrow H_2O(l)$

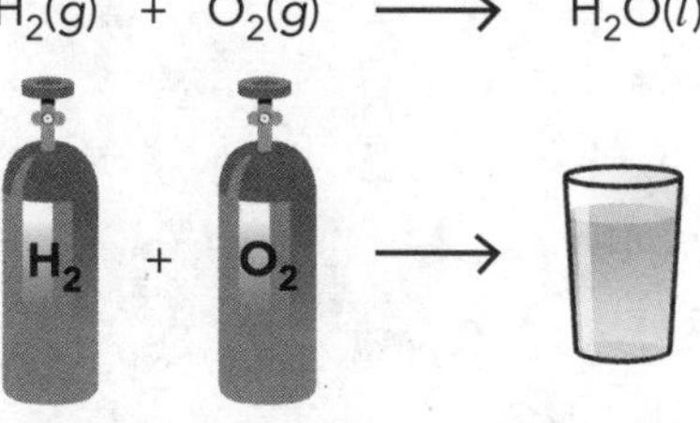

(3) **SEP Develop a Model** Write the skeleton equation for the reaction of iron and diatomic oxygen gas to form iron(III) oxide (Fe_2O_3). Sketch a molecular model of the reactants and products in the reaction.

Symbols Used in Chemical Equations Math equations make it easier to represent a relationship between variables. Similarly, a chemical equation makes it easier to represent what is going on in a chemical reaction. The symbols used in the equation serve as shorthand representations of information about the physical properties and actions.

Symbols Used in Chemical Equations	
Symbol	**Explanation**
+	Separates two reactants or two products
$\longrightarrow$	"Yields"; separates reactants from products
$\rightleftharpoons$	Shows that the reaction is reversible and can go in either direction
(*s*), (*l*), (*g*)	Designates a reactant or product in the solid state, liquid state, or gaseous state; placed after the formula
(*aq*)	Designates an aqueous solution; the substance is dissolved in water; placed after the formula
$\xrightarrow{\Delta}$ or $\xrightarrow{\text{heat}}$	Indicates that heat is supplied to the reaction
$\xrightarrow{\text{Pt}}$	A formula written above or below the yield sign indicates its use as a catalyst, which speeds up a reaction (in this example, platinum [Pt])

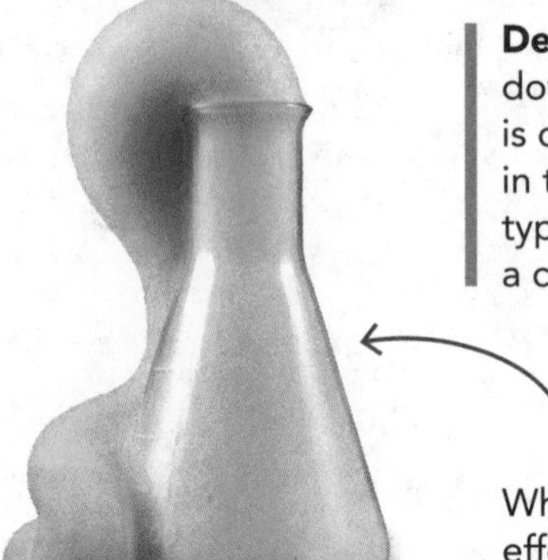

Decomposition Reaction Hydrogen peroxide breaks down into water and oxygen molecules through what is called a decomposition reaction. The only reactant in this reaction is hydrogen peroxide, and the reaction typically happens slowly. Potassium iodide is used as a catalyst.

$$H_2O_2 \xrightarrow{\text{KI}} H_2O + O_2$$

When liquid soap is added for a dramatic effect in this reaction, the foam coming out of the flask is called elephant's toothpaste.

4 **SEP Obtain and Communicate Information Manganese(IV) oxide can also be used as a catalyst that significantly speeds up the decomposition of hydrogen peroxide. Look up what a catalyst does and why it isn't considered a reactant. Communicate the information you obtained in a few short sentences.**

SAMPLE PROBLEM

Writing a Skeleton Equation

Solid sodium hydrogen carbonate reacts with aqueous hydrochloric acid. The products formed are aqueous sodium chloride, water, and carbon dioxide gas. Write a skeleton equation for this chemical reaction.

ANALYZE Identify the relevant concepts.

Write the correct formula for each substance in the reaction. Indicate the state of each substance. Separate the reactants from the products with an arrow. Use plus signs to separate the two reactants and each of the three products.

SOLVE Apply concepts to this problem.

	Reactants	Products
Start with the names of reactants and products. Include their physical states.	sodium hydrogen carbonate (solid) hydrochloric acid (aqueous)	sodium chloride (aqueous) water (liquid) carbon dioxide (gas)
Write the correct formula for each reactant and each product.	$NaHCO_3(s)$ $HCl(aq)$	$NaCl(aq)$ $H_2O(l)$ $CO_2(g)$

Use plus signs to separate reactants. Place an arrow between reactants and products. Use plus signs to separate products.

$$NaHCO_3(s) + HCl(aq) \longrightarrow NaCl(aq) + H_2O(l) + CO_2(g)$$

5 **SEP Use a Model** Sulfur burns in oxygen to form sulfur dioxide. Write a skeleton equation for this chemical reaction.

GO ONLINE for more practice problems.

Balancing Equations

Balancing Word Equations The law of conservation of mass is a fundamental law of nature that states that matter is conserved, which means that during any chemical reaction, the mass of the products is always equal to the mass of the reactants. In any chemical change, the atoms in the products are the same atoms that were in the reactants—they are just rearranged.

Skeleton Equation A skeleton equation does not indicate the quantity of reactants (parts) to make the product (bicycle).

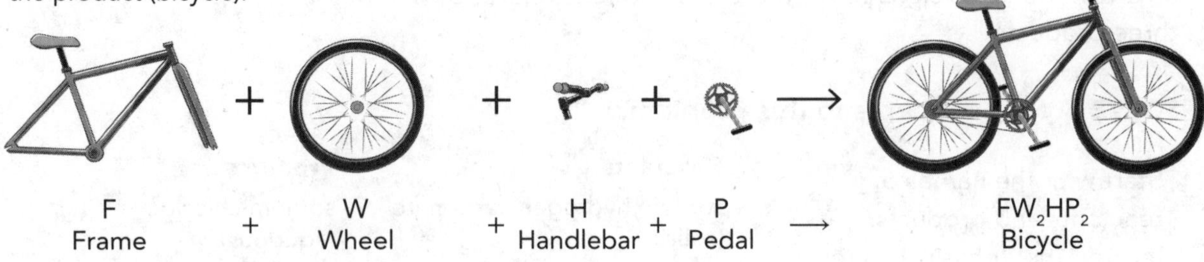

Balanced Equation To balance an equation, the same number of components are required on both sides.

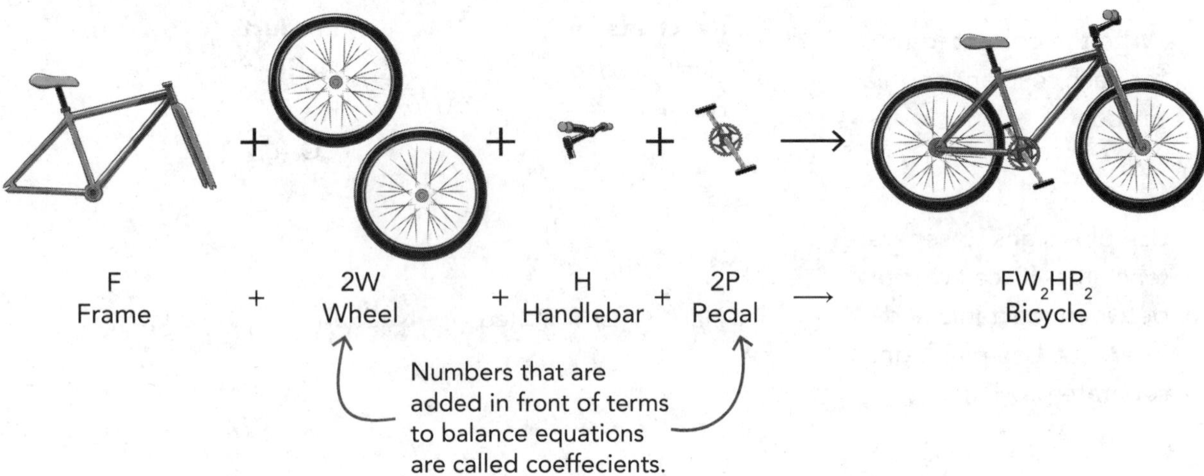

SEP Develop a Model A ham and cheese sandwich is composed of two slices of bread, three slices of ham, and a slice of cheese. Sketch the reactants and products for the sandwich "reaction" in both skeleton and balanced form.

Balancing Chemical Equations To write a balanced chemical equation, first write the skeleton equation. Numbers in front of terms are called **coefficients,** and are used to balance the equation so that it obeys the law of conservation of mass.

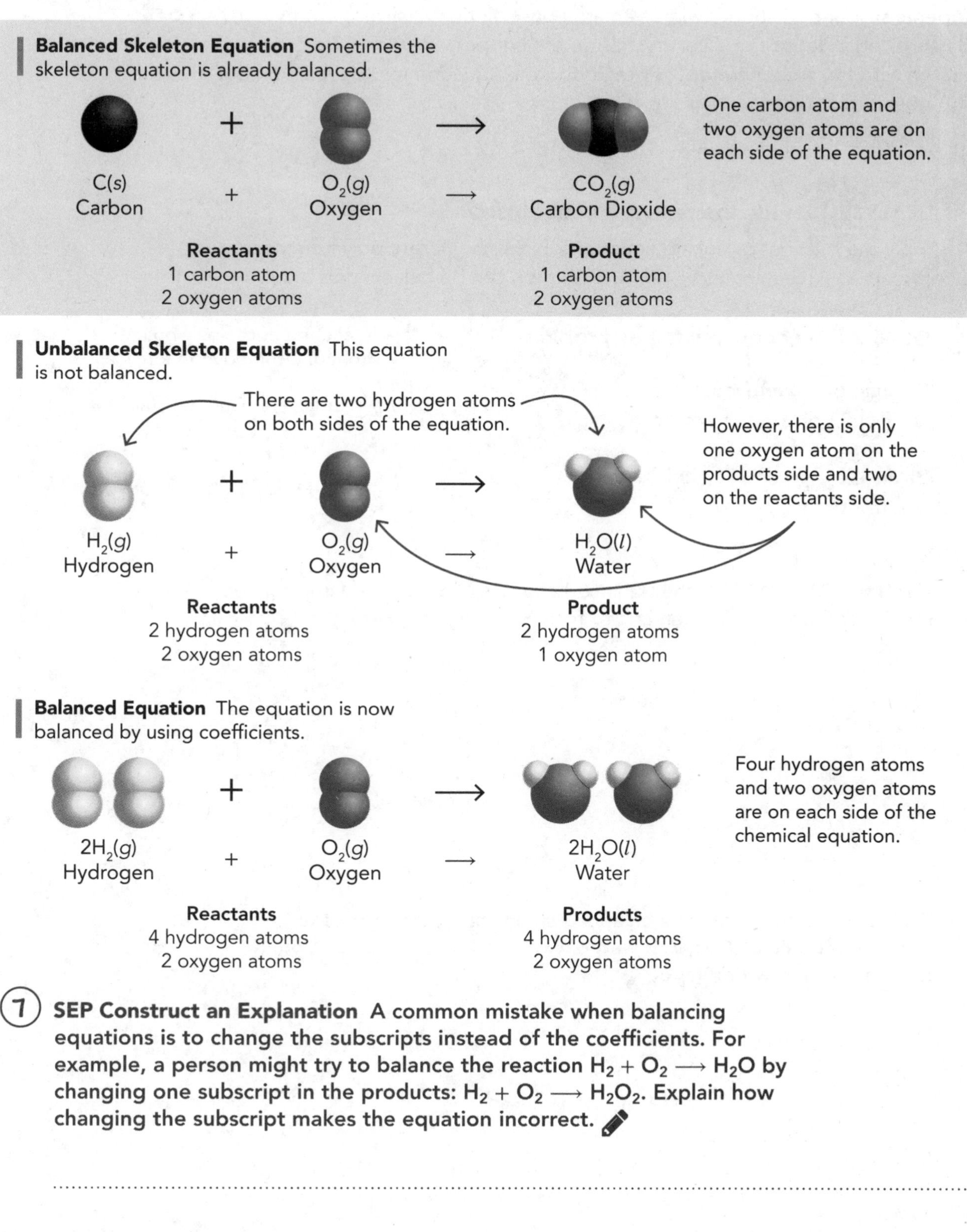

Balanced Skeleton Equation Sometimes the skeleton equation is already balanced.
One carbon atom and two oxygen atoms are on each side of the equation.
$C(s)$ + $O_2(g)$ ⟶ $CO_2(g)$
Carbon
Oxygen
Carbon Dioxide
Reactants
1 carbon atom
2 oxygen atoms
Product
1 carbon atom
2 oxygen atoms
Unbalanced Skeleton Equation This equation is not balanced.
There are two hydrogen atoms on both sides of the equation.
However, there is only one oxygen atom on the products side and two on the reactants side.
$H_2(g)$ + $O_2(g)$ ⟶ $H_2O(l)$
Hydrogen
Oxygen
Water
Reactants
2 hydrogen atoms
2 oxygen atoms
Product
2 hydrogen atoms
1 oxygen atom
Balanced Equation The equation is now balanced by using coefficients.
Four hydrogen atoms and two oxygen atoms are on each side of the chemical equation.
$2H_2(g)$ + $O_2(g)$ ⟶ $2H_2O(l)$
Hydrogen
Oxygen
Water
Reactants
4 hydrogen atoms
2 oxygen atoms
Products
4 hydrogen atoms
2 oxygen atoms

7 SEP Construct an Explanation A common mistake when balancing equations is to change the subscripts instead of the coefficients. For example, a person might try to balance the reaction $H_2 + O_2 \longrightarrow H_2O$ by changing one subscript in the products: $H_2 + O_2 \longrightarrow H_2O_2$. Explain how changing the subscript makes the equation incorrect.

SAMPLE PROBLEM

Balancing a Chemical Equation

Students suspended copper wire in an aqueous solution of silver nitrate. They noticed a deposit of silver crystals on the copper wire when the copper reacted with the silver nitrate. They recorded the equation for this reaction but didn't balance it. Balance their equation.

$AgNO_3(aq) + Cu(s) \longrightarrow Cu(NO_3)_2(aq) + Ag(s)$

ANALYZE Identify the relevant concepts.

Apply the rules for balancing equations. Since the nitrate polyatomic ion appears as a reactant and a product, this ion can be balanced as a unit.

SOLVE Apply concepts to this problem.

A coefficient can only go in front of a compound's formula.

Balance the nitrate ion. Put a coefficient of 2 in front of $AgNO_3(aq)$.

$2AgNO_3(aq) + Cu(s) \longrightarrow Cu(NO_3)_2(aq) + Ag(s)$

Balance the silver. Put a coefficient of 2 in front of $Ag(s)$.

$2AgNO_3(aq) + Cu(s) \longrightarrow Cu(NO_3)_2(aq) + 2Ag(s)$

8 **SEP Use a Model Write the balanced chemical equation for the reaction of solid carbon with oxygen gas to form carbon monoxide gas.**

9 **SEP Use a Model Write the balanced chemical equation for the reaction of glucose ($C_6H_{12}O_6$) with oxygen gas to produce carbon dioxide gas and water vapor.**

GO ONLINE for more practice problems.

Energy of Reactions

Breaking and Forming Chemical Bonds The energy stored in the chemical bonds of a substance is called **chemical potential energy.** The kinds of atoms and the arrangement of the atoms in a substance determine the amount of energy stored in the substance. During a chemical reaction, bonds are broken and re-formed in different ways. It takes energy to break bonds, and energy is released when bonds are formed.

Generation of Hydrogen Iodide One H—H bond and one I—I bond must be broken on the reactants side. Two H—I bonds must be formed on the products side.

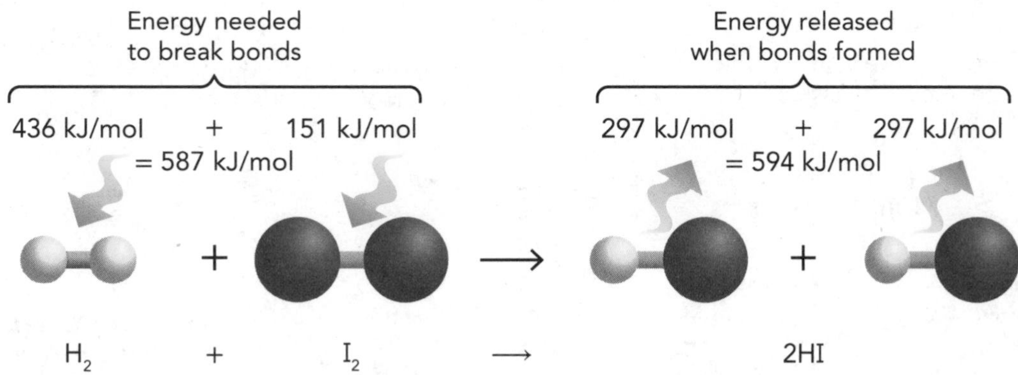

$H_2 + I_2 \longrightarrow 2HI$

The **law of conservation of energy** states that in any chemical reaction, energy is neither created nor destroyed. Therefore, if more energy is required to break bonds than is released in the formation of new bonds, then energy will need to be absorbed from the surroundings to balance the total energy. If more energy is released during bonding than required for breaking bonds, then net energy will be released to the surroundings.

Average Bond Energies Average bond energies are used to estimate the net energy absorbed or released during a reaction.

Average Bond Energies

Bond	Energy (kJ/mol)
H—H	436
O—H	467
H—I	297
I—I	151
N≡N	945
N═O	607
O═O	498

(10) **SEP Use Mathematics Using the table of average bond energies, estimate the energy needed to break the bonds of the reactants and the energy released when the products form for the reaction $N_2 + O_2 \rightarrow 2NO$. Note: N_2 has a triple bond and O_2 and NO have double bonds.**

Exothermic and Endothermic Reactions Chemical reactions will either release energy to the surroundings as heat or light or absorb energy from the surroundings. Reactions that release net energy to the surroundings are called **exothermic.** Reactions that absorb energy from the surroundings are called **endothermic.**

Exothermic Reactions Because more energy is released when two H—I bonds are formed than it takes to break the H—H and I—I bonds, a net –7 kJ/mol of energy is released to the surroundings.

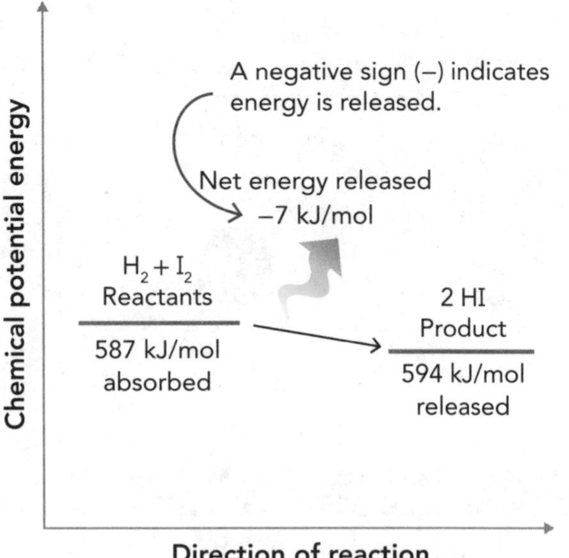

Endothermic Reactions Because more energy is required to break N≡N and O=O bonds than is released during the formation of two N=O bonds, a net +229 kJ/mol of energy must be absorbed from the surroundings.

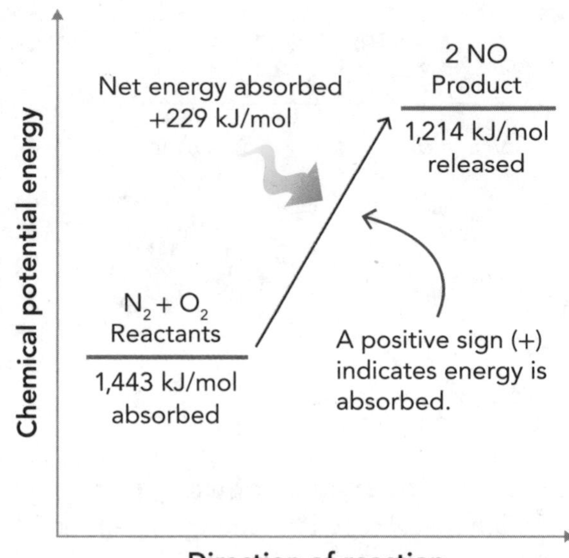

11 **SEP Construct an Explanation Air-activated hand warmers consist of an iron powder contained in a porous pouch. When the pouch is removed from its air-tight packaging, oxygen from the air enters the pouch and reacts with the iron to produce iron(III) oxide. Construct an explanation for why the pouch gets hot based on changes in total bond energy.**

What Causes Reactions?

Reactions happen when bonds are broken and the atoms of the reactants are rearranged. The **collision theory** states that bonds are broken when molecules collide with enough energy. The speed at which reactants become products is called the **reaction rate.** The reaction rate increases with an increased number of collisions and/or increased kinetic energy of the collisions.

Collision Theory For a reaction to take place, the particles must collide with each other. The particles must have enough kinetic energy to break the bonds.

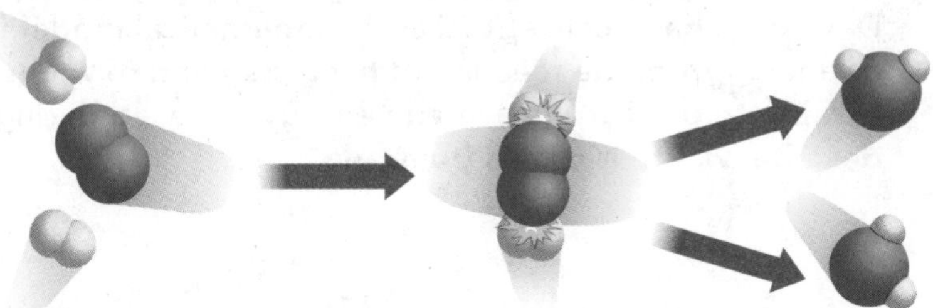

Reaction Rates and Temperature The number and energy of collisions between molecules in a container determines the reaction rate.

As **temperature increases,** the number and energy of the collisions increase, which is also seen by an **increase in the reaction rate.**

(12) **SEP Analyze and Interpret Data The table shows the reaction rate at various temperatures for the decomposition of nitrogen dioxide (NO_2). Graph the reaction rate as a function of the temperature. Describe the pattern in the data (increasing/decreasing, linear/exponential, etc.).**

Reaction Rate of NO_2 with Temperature

T(K)	Reaction Rate $\left(\frac{mol}{L \cdot s}\right)$
< 592	0.522
603	0.755
627	1.70
651	4.02
656	5.03

Revisit

INVESTIGATIVE PHENOMENON

GO ONLINE to Elaborate on and Evaluate your knowledge of modeling chemical reactions by completing the peer review and data analysis activities.

13 **SEP Develop a Model** Generating energy requires exothermic reactions. Develop a basic conceptual and mathematical model for the generation of energy from the reaction of hydrogen and oxygen. Your model should be able to predict the average energy released during the reaction and describe where it comes from.

EXPERIENCE 2

Predicting Outcomes of Chemical Reactions

GO ONLINE to Explore and Explain how to predict outcomes of chemical reactions.

Types of Reactions

By classifying reactions, you can construct a model that can be used to predict what products are likely to form with a given set of reactants. The simple classification system we will use to model reactions identifies five general reaction types. Not all chemical reactions fit uniquely into one of five categories; therefore, like any model, the one we describe here is not complete.

General Types of Chemical Reactions When you learn the patterns for the reactions shown here, you will be able to predict products of a large number of reactions.

In **combination reactions**, two substances "combine" to make one.

→

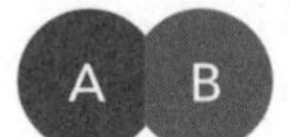

In **decomposition reactions**, one substance "breaks down" to make two.

→ A + B

During a **single-replacement reaction**, two elements are exchanged as one element on the reactant side replaces another element on the product side.

AB + C → A + CB

During a **double-replacement reaction**, two elements on the reactant side are swapped between the two substances that form on the product side.

AB + CD → AD + CB

The form of the reactants and products varies in **combustion reactions.** However, they always involve oxygen and are exothermic.

The reaction of the hydrocarbon CH_4 with oxygen is an example of a combustion reaction.

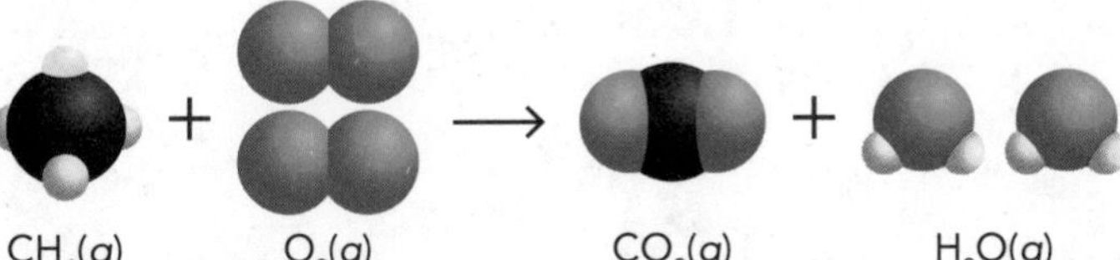

Combination Reactions

A **combination reaction** is a chemical change in which two or more substances react to form a single new substance. Combination reactions are also called synthesis reactions. Many combination reactions are exothermic since they release large amounts of energy. Combination reactions that occur between alkali metals and halogens form common binary ionic compounds such as KCl and NaCl. Two nonmetals, sulfur and oxygen, can react in a combination reaction to form more than one product: sulfur dioxide and sulfur trioxide.

Combination When magnesium ribbon is ignited, magnesium atoms combine with oxygen molecules in the air to form magnesium oxide. Magnesium oxide is a white solid.

This is an exothermic reaction since there is a net release of energy (light and heat).

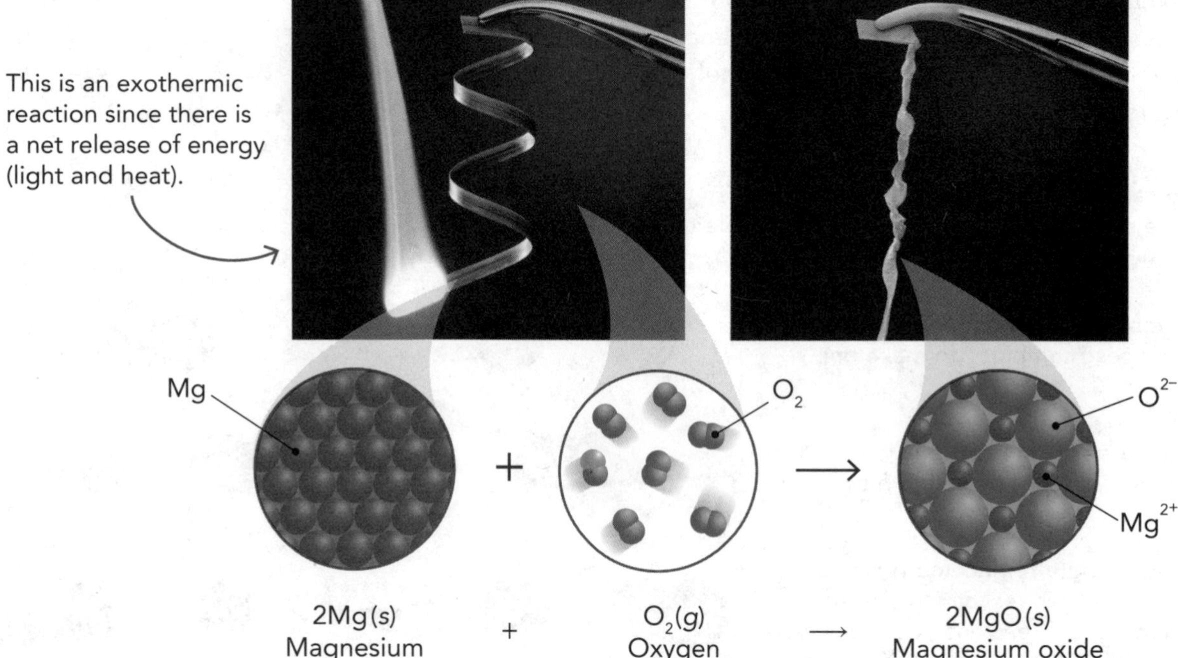

$$2Mg(s) + O_2(g) \longrightarrow 2MgO(s)$$

Magnesium + Oxygen → Magnesium oxide

14 **SEP Interpret Data** **The table shows several combination reactions and the estimated reaction energy based on bond breaking and forming energies. What pattern do you notice concerning the energy for combination reactions?**

Combination Reaction	Reaction Energy (kJ/mol)
$S(s) + O_2(g) \longrightarrow SO_2(g)$	–550
$2K(s) + Cl_2(g) \longrightarrow 2KCl(s)$	–430
$H_2(g) + I_2(s) \longrightarrow 2HI(g)$	–7

Decomposition Reactions

A **decomposition reaction** is a chemical change in which a single compound breaks down into two or more products. The products can be any combination of elements and compounds. Because of this, it can be difficult to predict the products of decomposition reactions.

Decomposition One reactant decomposes into two or more products. When orange-colored mercury(II) oxide is heated, it decomposes into its constituent elements: liquid mercury and gaseous oxygen.

This is an endothermic reaction since there is a net absorption of energy (heat).

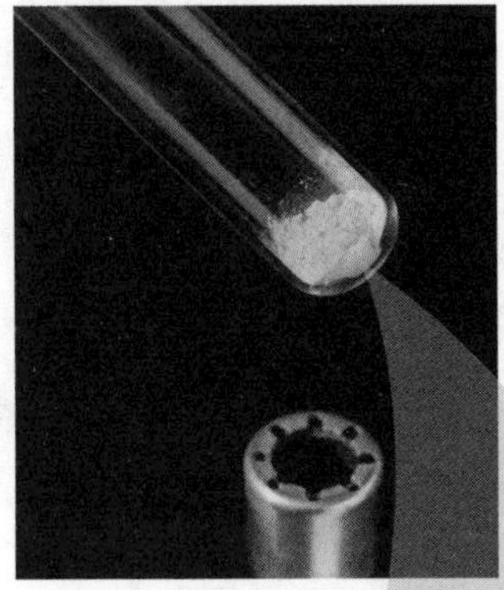

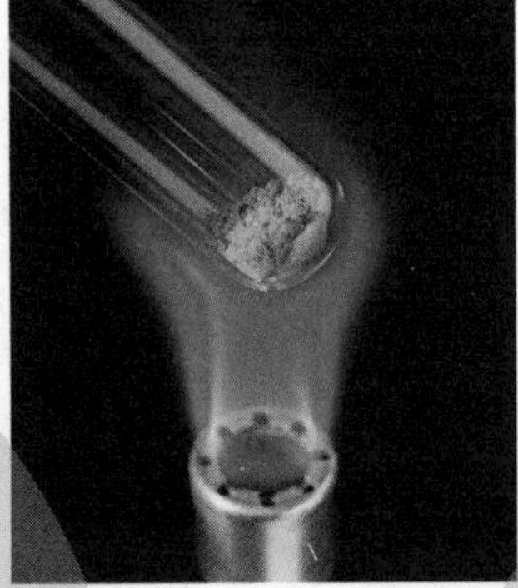

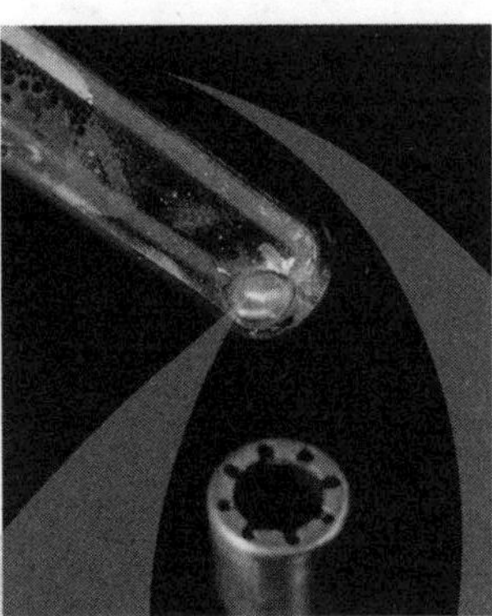

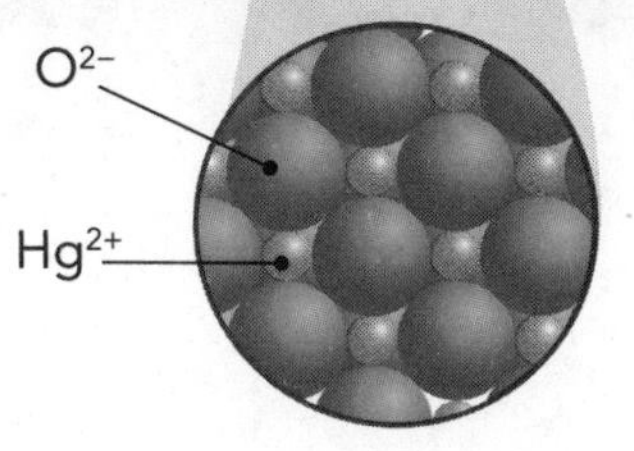

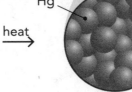

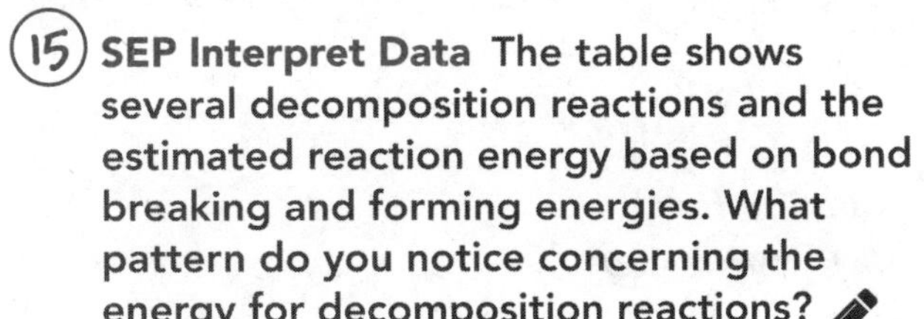

15 **SEP Interpret Data** The table shows several decomposition reactions and the estimated reaction energy based on bond breaking and forming energies. What pattern do you notice concerning the energy for decomposition reactions?

Decomposition Reaction	Reaction Energy (kJ/mol)
$2H_2O(l) \longrightarrow 2H_2(g) + O_2(g)$	+498
$SO_2(g) \longrightarrow S(s) + O_2(g)$	+550
$2HI(g) \longrightarrow H_2(g) + I_2(s)$	+7

SAMPLE PROBLEM

Writing Chemical Equations for Combination and Decomposition Reactions

Write a balanced equation for each of the following reactions.

a. Combination of calcium oxide and water:

$CaO(s) + H_2O(l) \longrightarrow$

b. Decomposition of water:

$H_2O(l) \xrightarrow{\text{electricity}}$

ANALYZE Identify the relevant concepts.

Some metallic oxides react with water to form a compound containing hydroxide ions. Ionic charges can be used to derive the formula for the product. The products of the decomposition of water are the elements that make up the compound.

SOLVE Apply concepts to this problem.

Write the formula for the product(s) in each reaction.	**a.** $Ca(OH)_2$	**b.** $H_2(g)$ $O_2(g)$
Write a skeleton equation for each reaction.	$CaO(s) + H_2O(l) \longrightarrow Ca(OH)_2(aq)$	$H_2O(l) \xrightarrow{\text{electricity}} H_2(g) + O_2(g)$
If the skeleton equation is not balanced then apply the rules for balancing equations.	The skeleton equation is already balanced. $CaO(s) + H_2O(l) \longrightarrow Ca(OH)_2(aq)$	$2H_2O(l) \xrightarrow{\text{electricity}} H_2(g) + O_2(g)$ $2H_2O(l) \xrightarrow{\text{electricity}} 2H_2(g) + O_2(g)$

16 **SEP Develop a Model** **Write and balance the equation for the formation of magnesium nitride (Mg_3N_2) from its elements.**

17 **SEP Develop a Model** **Write two balanced reactions for the combination reactions between copper(I and II) and sulfur.**

GO ONLINE for more practice problems.

Single-Replacement Reactions

A **single-replacement reaction** is a chemical change in which one element replaces a second element in a compound. You can identify a single-replacement reaction by noting that both the reactants and the products consist of an element and a compound.

Elements and Compounds If you drop a piece of potassium into a beaker of water, the reaction will produce potassium hydroxide and hydrogen gas. Notice how there is an element and a compound in both the reactants and the products of this single-replacement reaction.

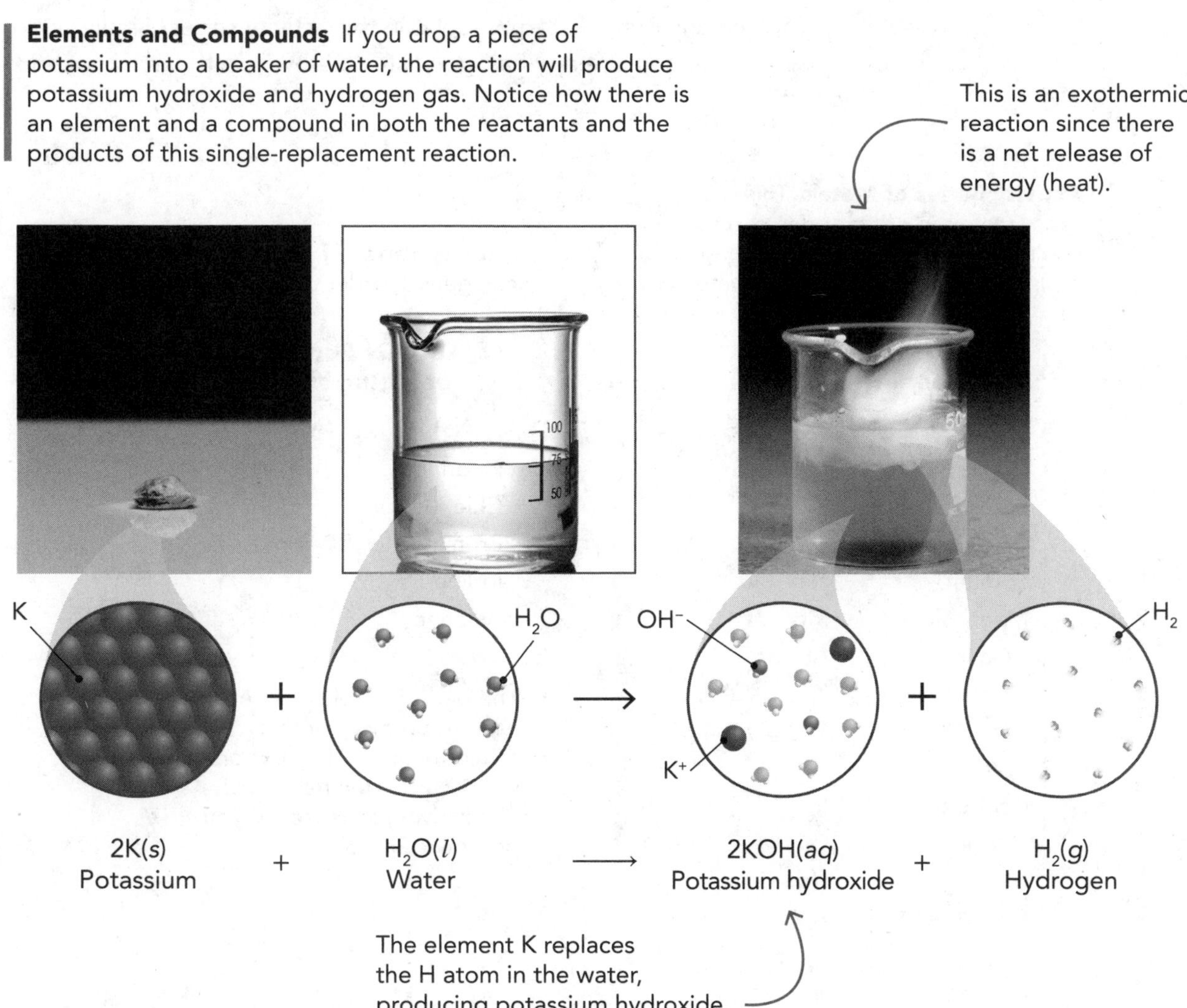

This is an exothermic reaction since there is a net release of energy (heat).
K
H_2O
OH^-
K^+
H_2

$2K(s)$ Potassium + $H_2O(l)$ Water ⟶ $2KOH(aq)$ Potassium hydroxide + $H_2(g)$ Hydrogen

The element K replaces the H atom in the water, producing potassium hydroxide.

(18) **SEP Develop a Model A single-replacement reaction can be compared to switching cases on a cell phone. Sketch what this process looks like and describe how it is analogous to a single-replacement reaction.**

Activity Series

In a single-replacement reaction, whether one element will displace another element from a compound depends upon the relative reactivities of the two elements. The **activity series** lists the relative reactivities of elements within groups, such as metals and halogens. The activity series is a useful empirical tool that is used to predict products in various chemical reactions. A reactive metal will replace any metal listed below it in the activity series. Similarly, a reactive halogen will replace any halogen listed below it in the activity series of halogens.

Activity Series of Metals This is a list of metals in order of decreasing reactivity. Some metals will also replace hydrogen in acids and water.

Activity Series of Metals

Name	Symbol
Lithium	Li
Potassium	K
Calcium	Ca
Sodium	Na
Magnesium	Mg
Aluminum	Al
Zinc	Zn
Iron	Fe
Lead	Pb
(Hydrogen)	(H)*
Copper	Cu
Mercury	Hg
Silver	Ag

*Metals from Li to Na will replace H from acids and water; from Mg to Pb, they will replace H from acids only.

Decreasing reactivity

Activity Series of Halogens This is a list of halogens in order of decreasing reactivity.

Activity Series of Halogens

Name	Symbol
Fluorine	F
Chlorine	Cl
Bromine	Br
Iodine	I
Astatine	At

17
7A
F
Cl
Br
I
At

The periodic table can be used to predict whether single-replacement reactions will occur for the halogens. The activity decreases as you go down Group 7A.

Zinc is added to an aqueous solution that contains a lead compound.

$$\textbf{Zn}(s) + \textbf{Pb}(NO_3)_2(aq) \longrightarrow \textbf{Zn}(NO_3)_2(aq) + \textbf{Pb}(s)$$

Zinc is higher in the activity series than lead. A **reaction** occurs because zinc is more reactive than lead.

Copper is added to an aqueous solution containing iron.

$$\textbf{Cu}(s) + \textbf{Fe}SO_4(aq) \longrightarrow \text{no reaction}$$

Copper is lower in the activity series than iron. **No reaction** occurs because copper is less reactive than iron.

SAMPLE PROBLEM

Writing Chemical Equations for Single-Replacement Reactions

Write a balanced equation for the single-replacement reaction.

$Cl_2(aq) + NaBr(aq) \longrightarrow$

ANALYZE Identify the relevant concepts.

Since the activity of halogens decreases down Group 7A, chlorine displaces bromine.

SOLVE Apply concepts to this problem.

Write the skeleton equation.

$Cl_2(aq) + NaBr(aq) \longrightarrow NaCl(aq) + Br_2(aq)$

Note that the number of reactants and products are not equal in the skeleton equation.

Reactants	Products
2 chlorine atoms	1 chlorine atom
1 sodium atom	1 sodium atom
1 bromine atom	2 bromine atoms

Apply the rules for balancing equations.

$Cl_2(aq) + 2NaBr(aq) \longrightarrow 2NaCl(aq) + Br_2(aq)$

19 **SEP Develop a Model Complete the equations for these single-replacement reactions in aqueous solutions. Balance each equation. Write "no reaction" if a reaction would not occur.**

a. $Fe(s) + Pb(NO_3)_2(aq) \longrightarrow$

b. $Cl_2(aq) + 2NaI(aq) \longrightarrow$

c. $Ca(s) + 2H_2O(l) \longrightarrow$

d. $Br_2(aq) + NaCl(aq) \longrightarrow$

GO ONLINE for more practice problems.

Double-Replacement Reactions

A **double-replacement reaction** is a chemical change involving an exchange of positive ions between two compounds. These reactions generally take place in ionic aqueous solutions and often form a precipitate, a gas, or a molecular compound such as water. Double-replacement reactions are also referred to as double-displacement reactions.

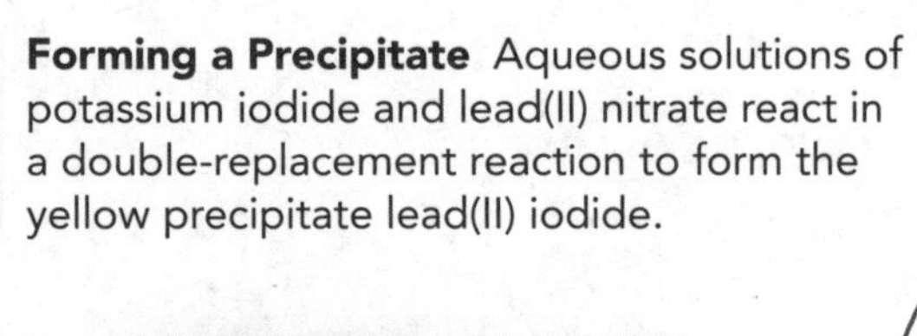

Forming a Precipitate Aqueous solutions of potassium iodide and lead(II) nitrate react in a double-replacement reaction to form the yellow precipitate lead(II) iodide.

The lead iodide precipitate forms due to the strong attractive forces between the Pb^{2+} cations and the I^- anions. The other product, potassium nitrate, is a water-soluble salt.

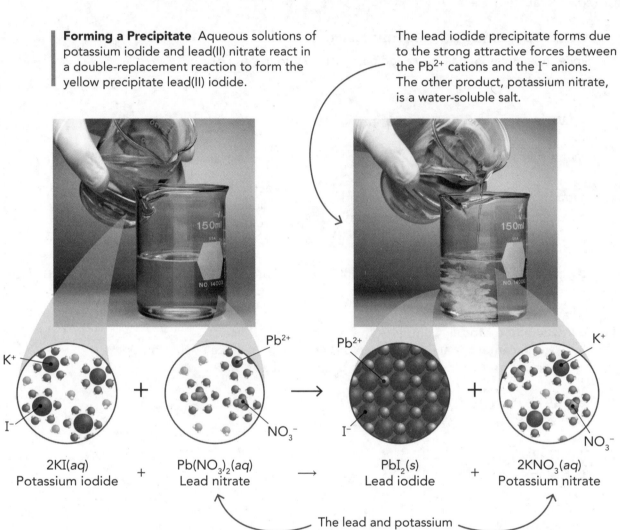

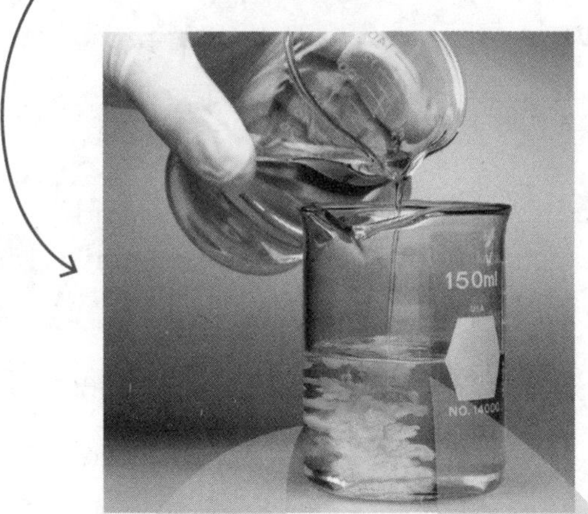

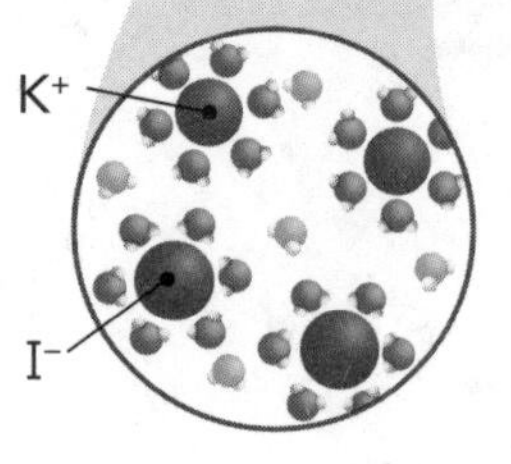

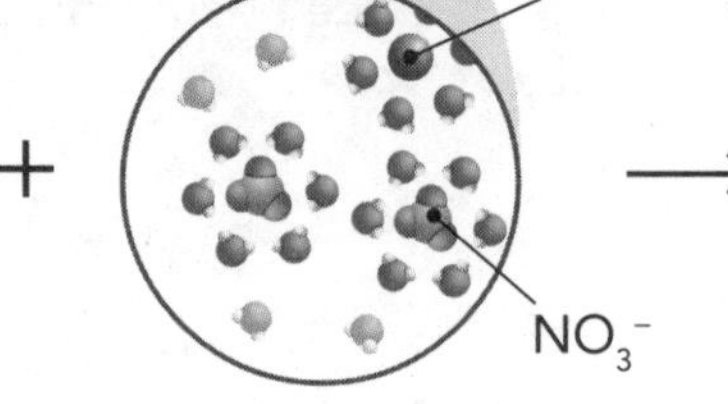

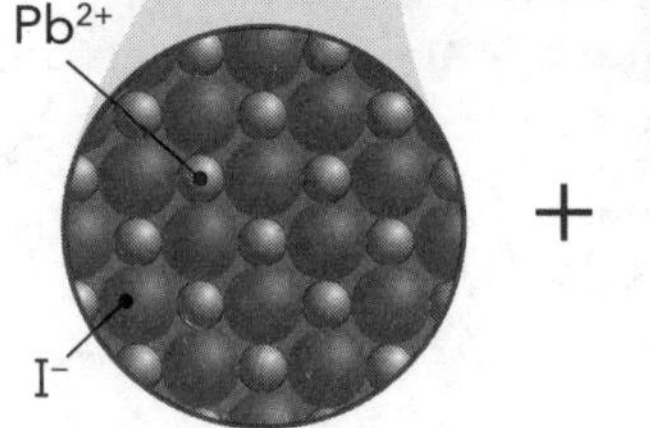

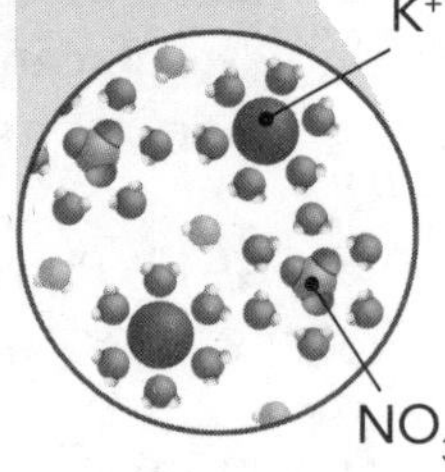

$2KI(aq)$ + $Pb(NO_3)_2(aq)$ → $PbI_2(s)$ + $2KNO_3(aq)$

Potassium iodide + Lead nitrate → Lead iodide + Potassium nitrate

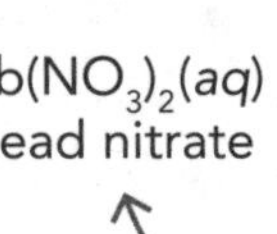

The lead and potassium swap places.

(20) **SEP Use a Model** **Use the model for double-replacement reactions to predict the products for the following reactants. Circle the ionic solution and underline the other compound.**

$Ca(OH)_2(aq) + 2HCl(aq) \longrightarrow$

SAMPLE PROBLEM

Writing Chemical Equations for Double-Replacement Reactions

A precipitate of barium carbonate is formed when an aqueous solution of potassium carbonate reacts with aqueous barium chloride. Write a balanced chemical equation for the double-replacement reaction.

$K_2CO_3(aq) + BaCl_2(aq) \longrightarrow$

ANALYZE Identify the relevant concepts.

The driving force behind the reaction is the formation of a precipitate. Write the correct formulas of the products using ionic charges. Then, balance the equation.

SOLVE Apply concepts to this problem.

Write the skeleton equation. Since this is a double-replacement reaction, potassium and barium switch places.

$K_2CO_3(aq) + BaCl_2(aq) \longrightarrow KCl(aq) + BaCO_3(s)$

Apply the rules for balancing equations.

$K_2CO_3(aq) + BaCl_2(aq) \longrightarrow 2KCl(aq) + BaCO_3(s)$

21 **SEP Develop a Model** **Write a balanced equation for each reaction.**

a. $KOH(aq) + H_3PO_4(aq) \longrightarrow$ (Water is formed.)

b. $AgNO_3(aq) + NaCl(s) \longrightarrow$ (Silver chloride is a precipitate.)

c. $Ca(OH)_2(aq) + H_3PO_4(aq) \longrightarrow$ (Water is formed.)

d. $FeS(s) + HCl(aq) \longrightarrow$ (A gas is formed.)

GO ONLINE for more practice problems.

Combustion Reactions

A **combustion reaction** is a chemical change in which an element or a compound reacts with oxygen, often producing energy in the form of heat and light. A combustion reaction always involves oxygen as a reactant. Often the other reactant is a **hydrocarbon,** which is a compound composed of hydrogen and carbon.

Burning Methane In this combustion reaction, methane gas reacts with oxygen from the surrounding air to produce carbon dioxide and water vapor.

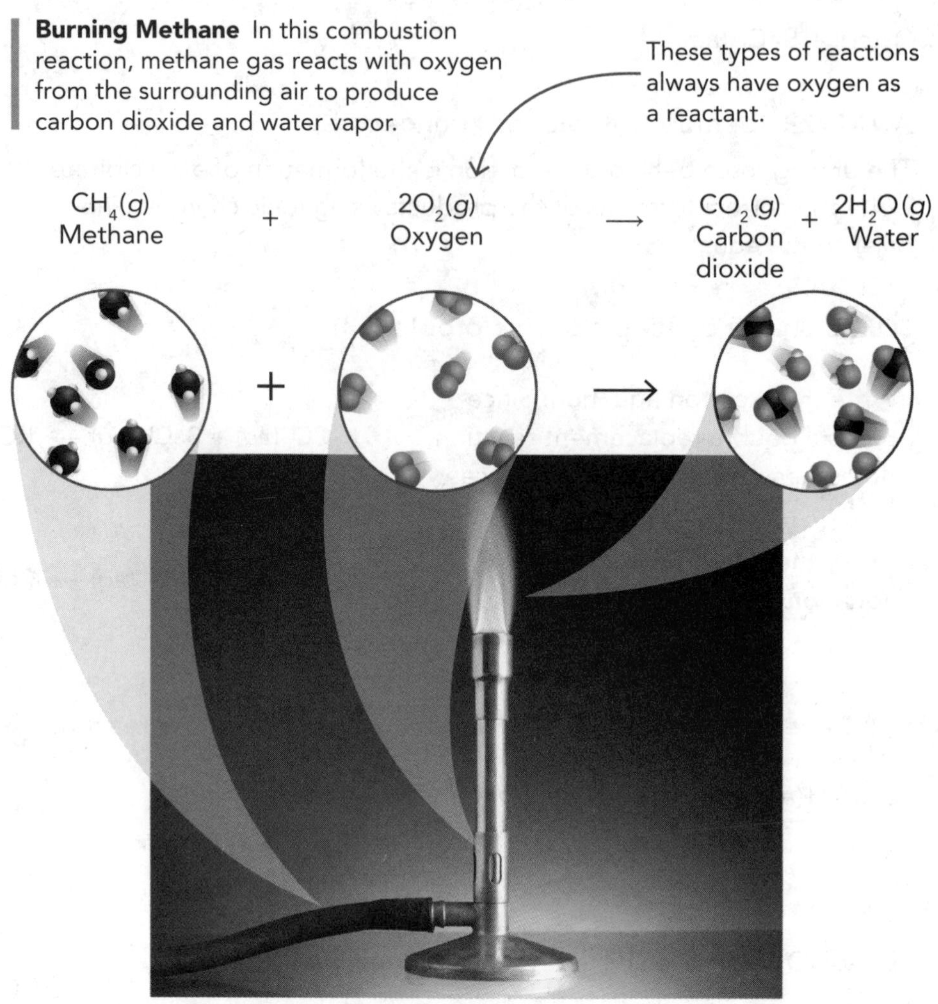
These types of reactions always have oxygen as a reactant.
$CH_4(g)$ Methane + $2O_2(g)$ Oxygen → $CO_2(g)$ Carbon dioxide + $2H_2O(g)$ Water
+
→

22 **SEP Engage in Argument from Evidence** **It is claimed that combustion reactions should always take place in well-ventilated areas. Use evidence from both the reactants and products side of a typical combustion reaction to argue for or against this claim.**

....

....

....

SAMPLE PROBLEM

Writing Chemical Equations for Combustion Reactions

An alcohol lamp often uses ethanol as its fuel. Write a balanced equation for the complete combustion of ethanol ($C_2H_6O(l)$).

ANALYZE Identify the relevant concepts.

Oxygen is the other reactant in a combustion reaction. The products are CO_2 and H_2O.

SOLVE Apply concepts to this problem.

Write the skeleton equation.	$C_2H_6O(l) + O_2(g) \longrightarrow CO_2(g) + H_2O(g)$
Apply the rules for balancing equations.	$C_2H_6O(l) + 3O_2(g) \longrightarrow 2CO_2(g) + 3H_2O(g)$

23 **SEP Develop a Model** Write a balanced equation for the complete combustion of each compound.

a. formaldehyde ($CH_2O(g)$)

b. heptane ($C_7H_{16}(l)$)

c. benzene ($C_6H_6(l)$)

d. hydrogen ($H_2(g)$)

GO ONLINE for more practice problems.

Predicting the Products of Reactions

Now that you have learned about the basic chemical reaction types, you can predict the products of many reactions. By looking at the number and form of reactants, you can determine the probable reaction type. For these first four reactions, general equations are used as representations, with a sample reaction shown underneath.

Combination Reaction

Reactants Generally, two elements, or two compounds (where at least one compound is a molecular compound)

Probable Products A single compound

$$A + B \longrightarrow AB$$

$$2Mg(s) + O_2(g) \longrightarrow 2MgO(s)$$

Decomposition Reaction

Reactants Generally, a single binary compound or a compound with a polyatomic ion

Probable Products Two elements (for a binary compound), or two or more elements and/or compounds (for a compound with a polyatomic ion)

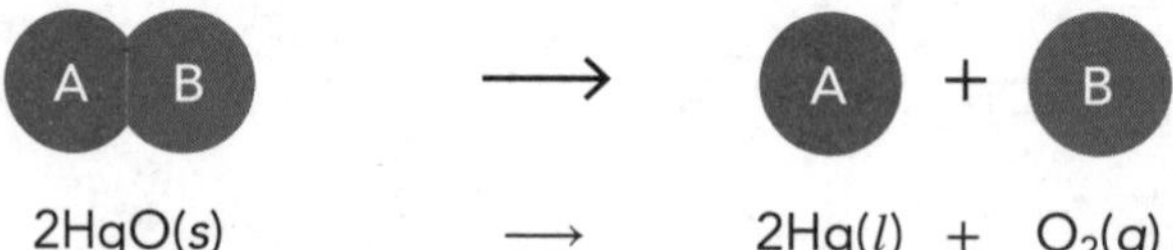

$$2HgO(s) \longrightarrow 2Hg(l) + O_2(g)$$

Single-Replacement Reaction

Reactants An element and a compound. In a single-replacement reaction, an element replaces another element from a compound in aqueous solution. For a single-replacement reaction to occur, the element that is replaced must be less active than the element that is doing the replacing.

Probable Products A different element and a new compound

$$AB + C \longrightarrow A + CB$$

$$2HCl(aq) + Mg(s) \longrightarrow H_2(g) + MgCl_2(aq)$$

Double-Replacement Reaction

Reactants Two ionic compounds. In a double-replacement reaction, two ionic compounds react by exchanging cations to form two different compounds.

Probable Products Two new compounds. Double-replacement reactions are driven by the formation of a precipitate, a gaseous product, or water.

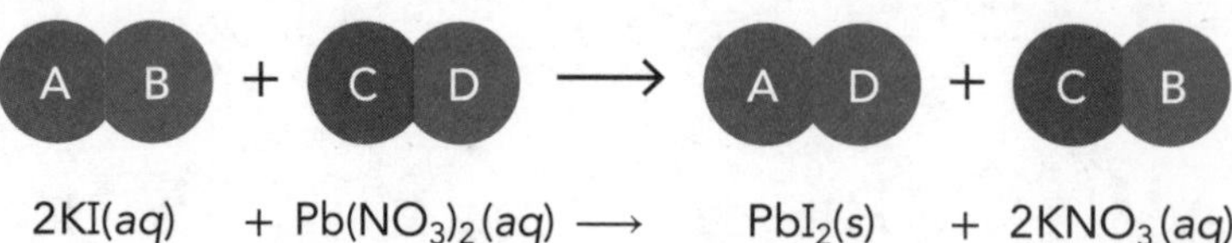

$$2KI(aq) + Pb(NO_3)_2(aq) \longrightarrow PbI_2(s) + 2KNO_3(aq)$$

Combustion reactions vary in their constituents, so general equations are not possible. These reactions rapidly produce energy (heat) and a flame, which is usually visible. Combustion reactions often consist of a hydrocarbon, hydrogen gas, or carbon. Various hydrocarbons include methane gas that is used to heat homes, gasoline that is used to fuel cars, and kerosene that is used as a rocket fuel. Liquid hydrogen is used in cars and also as rocket fuel. Coal contains carbon, and it is used in power plants to produce electricity.

Combustion Reaction

Reactants Oxygen and a compound of C, H, (O). When oxygen reacts with an element or compound, combustion may occur.

Probable Products CO_2 and H_2O. With incomplete combustion, C and CO may also be products.

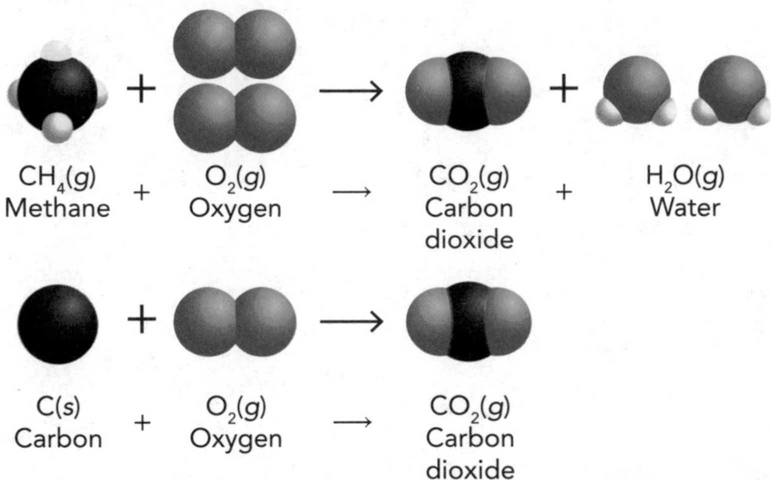

24 SEP Use a Model **You find an old laboratory notebook where you have clearly listed the products of several reactions. However, you do not remember the reactants from the reactions, and you failed to write them down. Use the model for predicting products of reactions to instead predict the probable reactants and complete the table.**

Product	Reaction Type	Probable Reactants
HCN, Na_2SO_4		
Mg_3N_2		
CO_2, H_2O		
Cu, $Zn(NO_3)_2$		
Na, N_2		

Revisit

INVESTIGATIVE PHENOMENON

GO ONLINE to Elaborate on and Evaluate your knowledge of outcomes of chemical reactions by completing the class discussion and writing activities.

25 **SEP Construct an Explanation** Alkaline fuel cells were used by NASA on the space shuttle to convert hydrogen and oxygen gas into electricity, heat, and drinkable water for the astronauts. An alkaline fuel cell uses potassium hydroxide (KOH) as an electrolyte. Because of this, pure oxygen must be used since CO_2 from regular air can "poison" the KOH cell due to the reaction's production of a solid precipitate that blocks the electrode. Construct an explanation for the outcome of the KOH/CO_2 reaction. Predict the reaction type and final product(s).

Reactions in Aqueous Solution

GO ONLINE to Explore and Explain the nature of chemical reactions that occur in aqueous solution.

Ions in Aqueous Solution

Solvation in Solution Many important chemical reactions take place in water—that is, in aqueous solution. Ionic compounds are not made of molecules. Instead, ionic compounds consist of formula units of a positive and negative ion. When sodium chloride and silver nitrate are placed in aqueous solution, the water molecules collide with the ions at the crystal surface. The polar H_2O molecules attract and surround the solute ions (Na^+, Cl^-, Ag^+, NO_3^-). The chemical equation for the reaction is as follows:

$$AgNO_3(aq) + NaCl(aq) \longrightarrow AgCl(s) + NaNO_3(aq)$$

This equation shows a double-replacement reaction, but it does not show the dissociation into cations and anions.

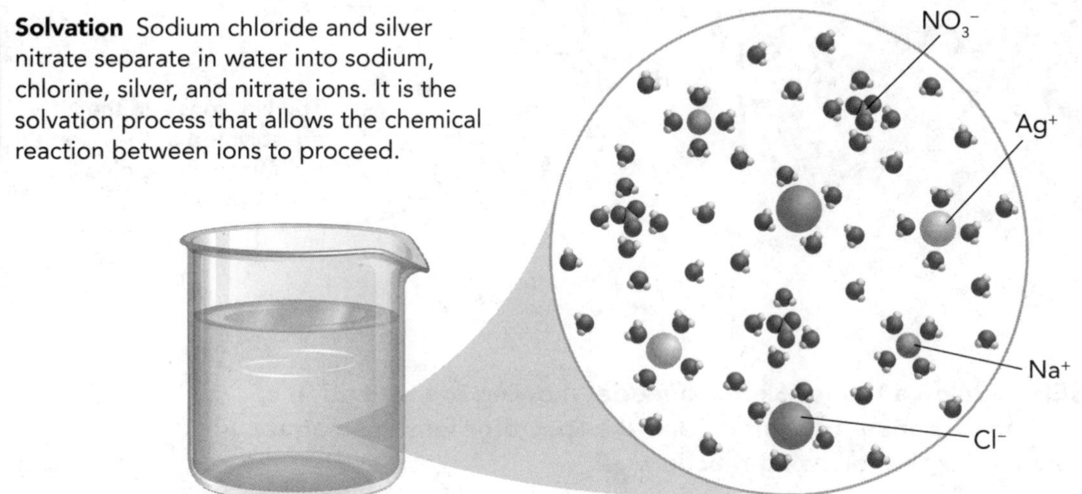

Solvation Sodium chloride and silver nitrate separate in water into sodium, chlorine, silver, and nitrate ions. It is the solvation process that allows the chemical reaction between ions to proceed.

26 **SEP Engage in Argument from Evidence** Do you think this reaction would take place if you placed solid sodium chloride on top of a solid piece of silver nitrate?

Net Ionic Equation The **complete ionic equation** shows dissolved ionic compounds as dissociated free ions. For example, the complete ionic equation for the reaction of aqueous sodium chloride and silver nitrate is as follows:

$$Ag^+(aq) + NO_3^-(aq) + Na^+(aq) + Cl^-(aq) \longrightarrow AgCl(s) + Na^+(aq) + NO_3^-(aq)$$

The nitrate and sodium ions appear unchanged on both sides of the equation. An ion that appears on both sides of an equation and is not directly involved in the reaction is called a **spectator ion.** Similar to spectators at a sporting event, these ions do not participate in the game. The equation can be simplified to eliminate these spectators. The result is what is called the net ionic equation:

$$Ag^+(aq) + Cl^-(aq) \longrightarrow AgCl(s)$$

The **net ionic equation** is an equation for a reaction in solution that shows only those particles that are directly involved in the chemical change.

Formation of a Precipitate The sodium and nitrate ions remain in aqueous solution, while the silver and chlorine ions form a solid precipitate.

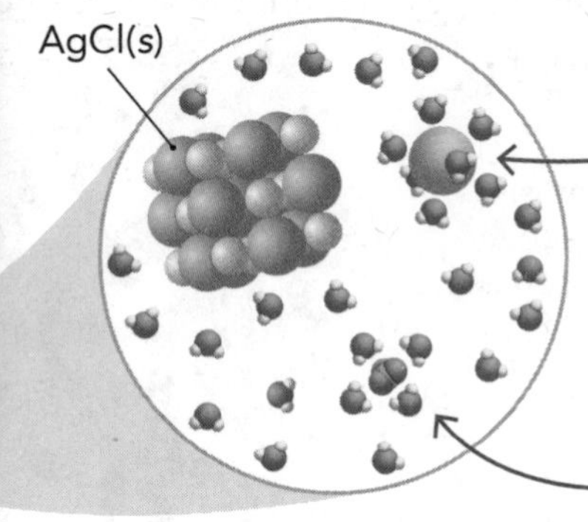

The chemical equation for the reaction of sodium chloride with silver nitrate has $NaNO_3(aq)$ as a product, but that simply means sodium and nitrate ions are spectator ions that are surrounded by water molecules.

The Na^+ ions and the NO_3^- ions are solvated as they are surrounded by polar water molecules.

27 SEP Develop a Model Sketch a model showing the formation of calcium carbonate precipitate and the spectator ions in an aqueous solution for the following reaction.

$Na_2CO_3(aq) + CaCl_2(aq) \longrightarrow CaCO_3(s) + 2NaCl(aq)$

SAMPLE PROBLEM

Writing and Balancing Net Ionic Equations

Aqueous solutions of iron(III) chloride and potassium hydroxide are mixed. A precipitate of iron(III) hydroxide forms. Identify the spectator ions and write a balanced net ionic equation for the reaction.

ANALYZE Identify the relevant concepts.

Write the complete ionic equation. Eliminate aqueous ions that appear in both the reactants and products. Then balance the equation with respect to both mass and charge.

SOLVE Apply concepts to this problem.

Write the skeleton equation for the reaction.

$FeCl_3(aq) + KOH(aq) \longrightarrow Fe(OH)_3(s) + KCl(aq)$

Write the complete ionic equation for the reaction, showing any soluble ionic compounds as individual ions.

$Fe^{3+}(aq) + 3Cl^-(aq) + 3K^+(aq) + 3OH^-(aq) \longrightarrow Fe(OH)_3(s) + 3K^+(aq) + 3Cl^-(aq)$

Eliminate aqueous ions that appear as both reactants and products. The spectator ions are K^+ and Cl^-.

$Fe^{3+}(aq) + \cancel{3Cl^-}(aq) + \cancel{3K^+}(aq) + 3OH^-(aq) \longrightarrow Fe(OH)_3(s) + \cancel{3K^+}(aq) + \cancel{3Cl^-}(aq)$

Balance the net ionic equation.

$Fe^{3+}(aq) + 3OH^-(aq) \longrightarrow Fe(OH)_3(s)$

28 **SEP Develop a Model Write a balanced net ionic equation for the following two reactions.**

a. $Pb(NO_3)_2(aq) + H_2SO_4(aq) \longrightarrow PbSO_4(s) + HNO_3(aq)$

b. $Na_3PO_4(aq) + FeCl_3(aq) \longrightarrow NaCl(aq) + FePO_4(s)$

GO ONLINE for more practice problems.

Solubility and Strength of Intermolecular Forces and Bonds

The strength of intermolecular forces between water molecules and a substance's ions in solution affect the solubility of a substance. A substance is soluble to the extent that the intermolecular forces between the water molecules and individual ions are stronger overall than the bonds between the ions. Otherwise, the bonds would re-form. Hydrogen bonds, the intermolecular forces between water and individual ions, are weaker than ionic bonds, so it isn't obvious that solvation should occur at all. However, a solvation shell forms when a solvent surrounds a solute species (ions) in a solution. A **solvation shell** is a sphere of solvent particles that surrounds a solute.

Solvation Shell Sodium and chlorine ions are surrounded by a "shell" of water molecules that can be several molecules thick.

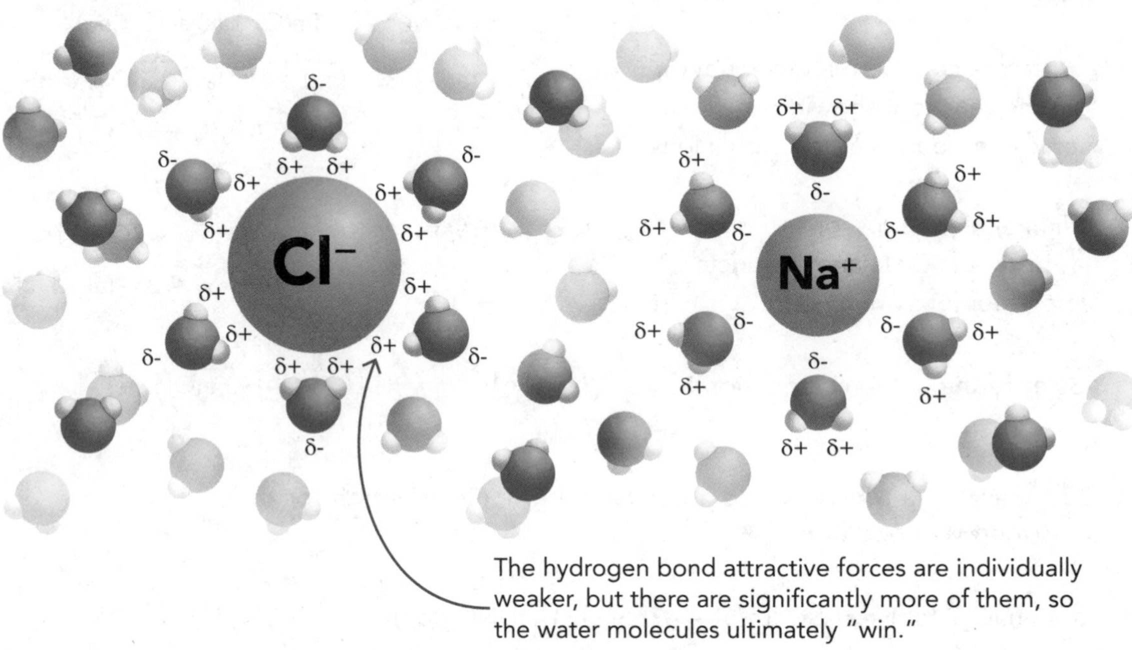

Cl^-
Na^+
δ-
δ+
The hydrogen bond attractive forces are individually weaker, but there are significantly more of them, so the water molecules ultimately "win."

(29) **SEP Construct an Explanation If you keep adding sodium chloride to the solution, eventually the solution will become saturated. Based on the concept of the solvation shell and intermolecular forces, construct an explanation for why only a certain amount of sodium chloride can be dissolved. (Hint: What happens if more sodium and chloride ions were added to the figure above without adding more water?)**

Strong Bonds Make Insoluble Substances The bond between silver and chlorine ions is unusually strong compared to a sodium-chlorine ionic bond. Therefore, silver chloride is insoluble in water. This strong attraction pulls the silver and chlorine ions through the water molecules to form a solid silver chloride precipitate.

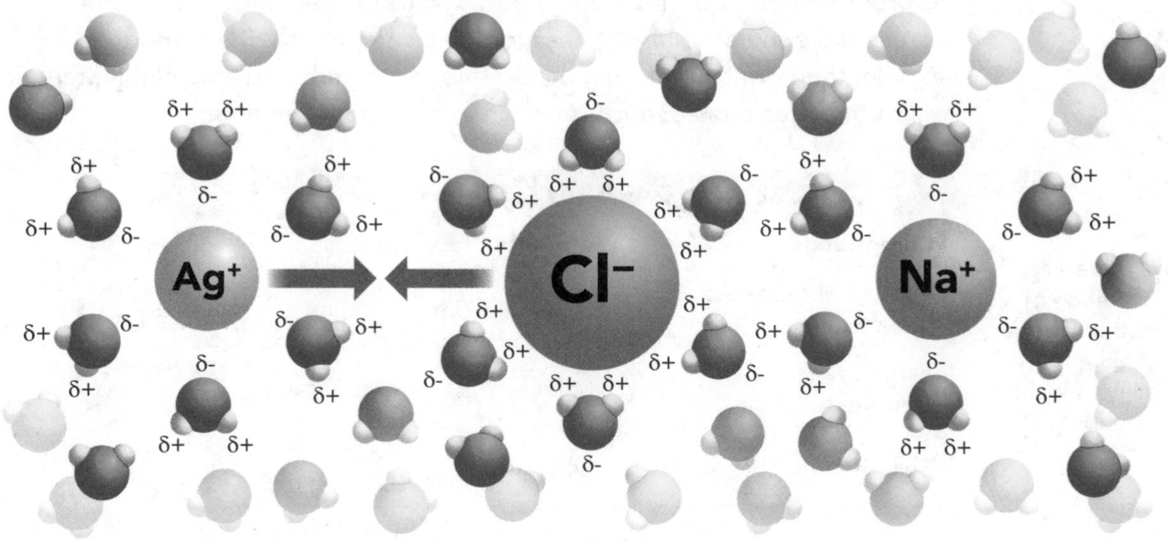

Formation of a Precipitate

Why do some combinations of ions result in the formation of a solid precipitate and some combinations do not? For example, during the reaction of aqueous silver nitrate and sodium chloride, nitrate and sodium ions remain in solution, surrounded by water molecules. The silver and chloride ions push through the water molecules to combine and form silver chloride. Insoluble substances form precipitates. Soluble substances remain in solution.

(30) **SEP Interpret Data The table shows several substances, the type of substance, and the solubility. Determine whether each substance will or will not form a precipitate to complete the table.**

Substance	Type	Solubility (mg/L)	Precipitate?
$Al_2(SO_4)_3$	sulfate	860,000	
KNO_3	nitrate	350,000	
NaCl	chloride salt	100	No
AgCl	chloride salt	2	Yes
$CaCO_3$	carbonate	0.015	

Predicting the Formation of a Precipitate

To predict whether or not a precipitate will form in an aqueous solution, we use the general solubility rules for ionic compounds. If a compound is soluble, then it will not form a precipitate. If a compound is insoluble, then it will form a precipitate, which is shown in a net ionic equation.

You can predict the formation of a precipitate by using the general rules for solubility of ionic compounds.

Solubility Rules for Ionic Compounds

Compounds	Solubility	Exceptions
Salts of alkali metals and ammonia	Soluble	Some lithium compounds
Nitrate salts and chlorate salts	Soluble	Few exceptions
Sulfate salts	Soluble	Compounds of Pb, Ag, Hg, Ba, Sr, and Ca
Chloride salts	Soluble	Compounds of Ag and some compounds of Hg and Pb
Carbonates, phosphates, chromates, sulfides, and hydroxides	Most are insoluble	Compounds of alkali metals and of ammonia

When aqueous solutions of Na_2CO_3 and $Ba(NO_3)_2$ are mixed, what are the possible products?

$$2Na^+(aq) + CO_3^{2-}(aq) + Ba^{2+}(aq) + 2NO_3^-(aq) \longrightarrow$$

Possible Precipitates:
$BaCO_3$ and $NaNO_3$

Sodium is an alkali metal, and nitrate salts are soluble. Therefore, sodium nitrate will not form a precipitate. Carbonates are insoluble, and barium is not in the exceptions list. Therefore, barium carbonate will precipitate.

$$Ba^{2+}(aq) + CO_3^{2-}(aq) \longrightarrow BaCO_3(s)$$

31 **SEP Construct an Explanation** **"Hard water" is the result of a high concentration of dissolved calcium found in some tap water. The calcium ions can react with carbonate ions to form a solid precipitate known as "scale." Write the net ionic equation for the formation of calcium carbonate and construct an explanation for why a precipitate forms. Would scale form if you replaced the calcium ions with sodium ions?**

SAMPLE PROBLEM

Writing and Balancing Net Ionic Equations

Aqueous potassium carbonate reacts with aqueous strontium nitrate. Identify the precipitate formed and write the net ionic equation for the reaction.

ANALYZE Identify the relevant concepts.

Write the reactants. Look at possible new pairings of cation and anion that give an insoluble substance. Eliminate the spectator ions.

SOLVE Apply concepts to this problem.

Use the solubility rules for ionic compounds to identify the precipitate formed.

Write the reactants, showing each as dissociated free ions.	$2K^{+}(aq) + CO_3^{2-}(aq) + Sr^{2+}(aq) + 2NO_3^{-}(aq) \longrightarrow ?$
Look at possible pairings of cations and anions. Use the solubility rules to identify which pair gives an insoluble substance.	Of the two possible combinations, KNO_3 is soluble and $SrCO_3$ is insoluble.
Eliminate the spectator ions and write the net ionic equation.	$CO_3^{2-}(aq) + Sr^{2+}(aq) \longrightarrow SrCO_3(s)$

32 **SEP Use a Model Identify the precipitate formed and write the net ionic equation for the reaction of aqueous solutions of iron(III) nitrate and sodium hydroxide.**

33 **SEP Use a Model Identify the precipitate formed when solutions of these compounds are mixed. Write the net ionic equation.**

$NH_4Cl(aq) + Pb(NO_3)_2(aq) \longrightarrow$

GO ONLINE for more practice problems.

Revisit

INVESTIGATIVE PHENOMENON

GO ONLINE to Elaborate on and Evaluate your knowledge of chemical reactions in aqueous solutions by completing the class discussion and engineering design activities.

In the CER worksheet, you drafted a scientific argument about how to determine the precipitate(s) in a chemical reaction involving ionic compounds. You also defended your argument with evidence. With a partner, re-evaluate the evidence cited in your arguments.

34 **SEP Define a Problem** **The electrolyte in an alkaline fuel cell is an aqueous solution of potassium hydroxide (KOH). Imagine you work in a lab where alkaline fuel cells are manufactured. One day, a new colleague produces a batch of electrolytes that are used in the production of several fuel cells. Unfortunately, these new fuel cells begin to malfunction due to a build-up of what appears to be calcium hydroxide on the electrodes. What might have happened and why?**

ASSESSMENT

GO ONLINE to Evaluate what you learned about patterns observed in chemical reactions by using the available assessment resources.

In the Performance-Based Assessment, you collected evidence for determining when chemical reactions occur. Wrap up your analysis by answering the following questions.

35. **SEP Plan an Investigation** **Suppose you are planning an investigation to determine whether a chemical reaction occurs between two reactants. What factors should you consider to ensure evidence of a chemical reaction can be observed?**

36. **Revisit the Anchoring Phenomenon** **How does what you learned in this investigation help you understand how the mechanisms of chemical reactions can be used to design better foods?**

INVESTIGATIVE PHENOMENON

GO ONLINE to Engage with real-world phenomena by watching a video and to complete a CER interactive worksheet.

What can make a recipe fail?

INVESTIGATION 10

Stoichiometry

To avoid gluten, some amateur bakers often make the mistake of simply replacing the wheat flour with the same weight of a gluten-free flour, such as almond flour. The results can be disastrous. Once you have viewed the Investigative Phenomenon video and worked on a first draft of a Claim-Evidence-Reasoning exercise to explain "What can make a recipe fail?", answer these reflection questions.

1. **CCC Structure and Function Yeast breads rise because yeast breaks down sucrose ($C_{12}H_{22}O_{11}$), or table sugar, during the process of cellular respiration and releases carbon dioxide. Steviol ($C_{20}H_{30}O_3$) is a zero-calorie sweetener. The chemical formulas are similar, with each being made up of carbon, hydrogen, and oxygen. Why can't you replace table sugar with an equal amount of steviol sweetener when baking bread?**

2. **SEP Construct an Explanation You baked whole wheat muffins using a recipe, but they were too sweet. For the second batch, you cut the amount of sugar in half. The second batch was dry, dense, and crumbly. Construct an explanation for why this happened.**

EXPERIENCE 1

Quantifying Reactants and Products

GO ONLINE to Explore and Explain how the amounts of reactants and products are related to each other.

Equations as a Recipe

When making a product, how do you determine how much starting material you need? Whenever you make something, you need ingredients or parts, and you need them in the correct ratios to get the desired product.

Balanced equations are like recipes. They tell you the ingredients that you need and the proper ratios.

Equations Making tricycles is a job that requires quantitative information to create the final product.

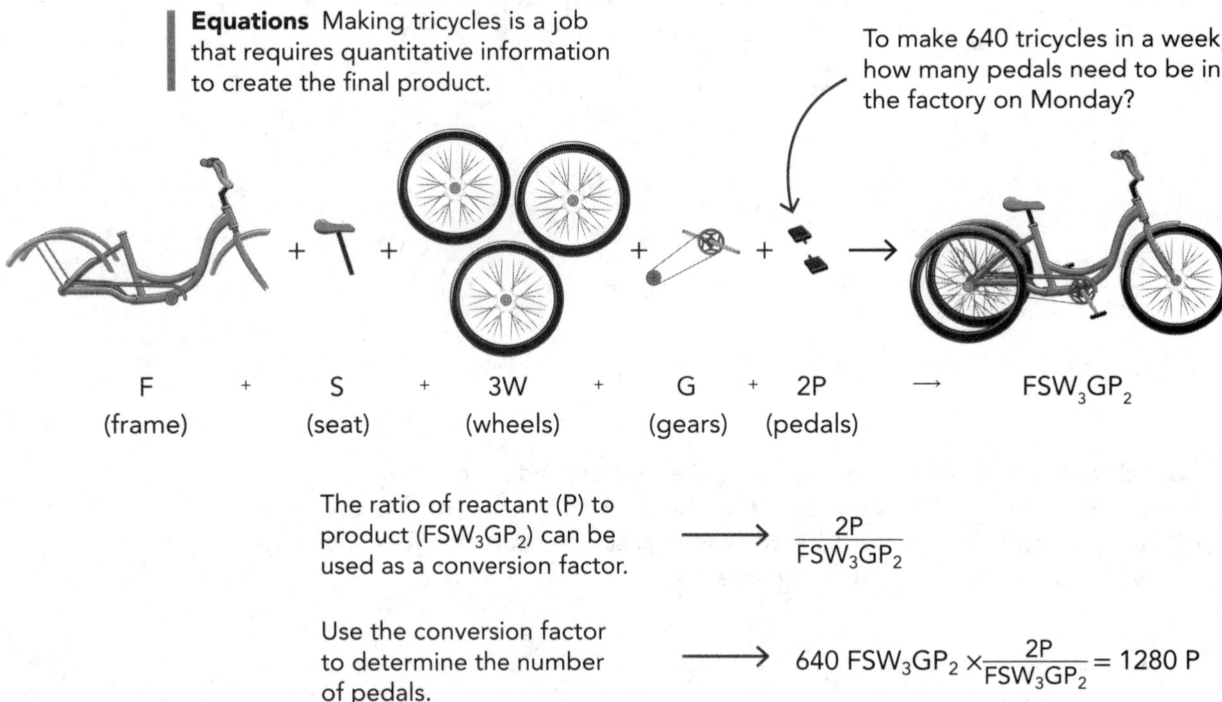

To make 640 tricycles in a week, how many pedals need to be in the factory on Monday?
+
+
+
+
→

$$F + S + 3W + G + 2P \rightarrow FSW_3GP_2$$

(frame) (seat) (wheels) (gears) (pedals)

The ratio of reactant (P) to product (FSW_3GP_2) can be used as a conversion factor. $\longrightarrow$ $\frac{2P}{FSW_3GP_2}$

Use the conversion factor to determine the number of pedals. $\longrightarrow$ $640\ FSW_3GP_2 \times \frac{2P}{FSW_3GP_2} = 1280\ P$

3 **SEP Use Mathematics** If the supplier sends only 500 pedals one week, then how many tricycles would you be able to manufacture? Assume that none of the other parts will run out before using all the pedals.

SAMPLE PROBLEM

Using a Balanced Equation as a Recipe

In a five-day workweek, a tricycle manufacturing facility is scheduled to make 640 tricycles. How many wheels should be in the plant on Monday morning to make these tricycles?

ANALYZE **List the knowns and unknown.**

Knowns	Unknowns
number of tricycles = 640 FSW_3GP_2	Number of wheels = ? W
$F + S + 3W + G + 2P \rightarrow FSW_3GP_2$	

CALCULATE **Solve for the unknown.**

Write the two possible conversion factors relating wheels (W) to tricycles (FSW_3GP_2).

$$\frac{3\ W}{1\ FSW_3GP_2} \text{ and } \frac{1\ FSW_3GP_2}{3\ W}$$

Identify the conversion factor that gives the desired unit (W).

$$\frac{3\ W}{1\ FSW_3GP_2}$$

Multiply the number of tricycles by the conversion factor.

$$640\ \cancel{FSW_3GP_2} \times \frac{3\ W}{1\ \cancel{FSW_3GP_2}} = 1920\ W$$

EVALUATE **Does the result make sense?**

If three wheels are required for each tricycle and more than 600 tricycles are being made, then a number of wheels in excess of 1,800 is a logical answer. The unit of the known (FSW_3GP_2) cancels, and the answer has the correct unit (W).

4 **SEP Apply Mathematical Concepts** **The tricycle manufacturing facility has decided to make 288 tricycles each day. How many tricycle seats, wheels, and pedals are needed for each day?**

GO ONLINE for more practice problems.

Interpreting Chemical Equations

Ammonia is used to make many fertilizers. It is produced industrially by the reaction:

$$N_2(g) + 3H_2(g) \rightarrow 2NH_3(g)$$

This balanced chemical equation gives the relative amounts of reactants and products in the reaction. You can quantify the reactants and products in terms of moles, mass, volume, and number of atoms or molecules. The calculation of quantities in chemical reactions is a subject called **stoichiometry.**

Quantifying Reactants and Products

In terms of what quantities can you interpret **balanced chemical equations?**

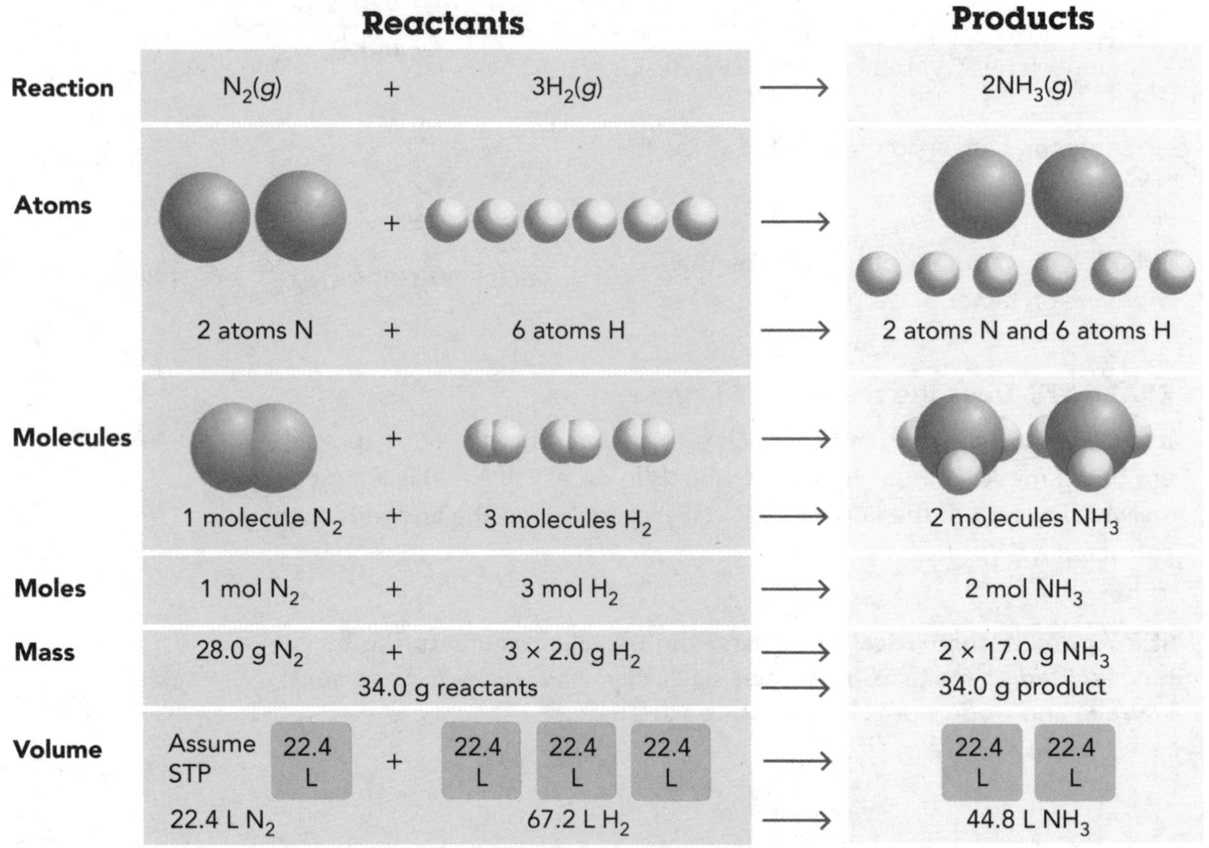

	Reactants				Products
Reaction	$N_2(g)$	+	$3H_2(g)$	$\longrightarrow$	$2NH_3(g)$
Atoms	2 atoms N	+	6 atoms H	$\longrightarrow$	2 atoms N and 6 atoms H
Molecules	1 molecule N_2	+	3 molecules H_2	$\longrightarrow$	2 molecules NH_3
Moles	1 mol N_2	+	3 mol H_2	$\longrightarrow$	2 mol NH_3
Mass	28.0 g N_2	+	3 × 2.0 g H_2	$\longrightarrow$	2 × 17.0 g NH_3
	34.0 g reactants			$\longrightarrow$	34.0 g product
Volume	Assume STP 22.4 L	+	22.4 L 22.4 L 22.4 L	$\longrightarrow$	22.4 L 22.4 L
	22.4 L N_2		67.2 L H_2	$\longrightarrow$	44.8 L NH_3

(5) **CCC Patterns** **Of the five ways to quantify reactants and products for ammonia, which have the same amount on the reactants side and the products side?**

SAMPLE PROBLEM

Interpreting a Balanced Chemical Equation

Hydrogen sulfide, which smells like rotten eggs, is found in volcanic gases. The balanced equation for the burning of hydrogen sulfide is

$$2H_2S(g) + 3O_2(g) \rightarrow 2SO_2(g) + 2H_2O(g)$$

Interpret this equation in terms of

a. numbers of representative particles and moles.

b. masses of reactants and products.

ANALYZE Identify the relevant concepts.

The coefficients in the balanced equation give the relative number of representative particles and moles of reactants and products. A balanced chemical equation obeys the law of conservation of mass.

SOLVE Apply the concepts to the situation.

Use the coefficients in the balanced equation to identify the number of representative particles and moles.

a. 2 molecules H_2S + 3 molecules O_2 → 2 molecules SO_2 + 2 molecules H_2O, or
2 mol H_2S + 3 mol O_2 → 2 mol SO_2 + 2 mol H_2O

Use the periodic table to determine the molar mass of each substance.

b. 1 mol H_2S = 34.1 g H_2S, 1 mol O_2 = 32.0 g O_2, 1 mol SO_2 = 64.1 g SO_2, 1 mol H_2O = 18.0 g H_2O

Multiply the number of moles of each reactant and product by its molar mass.

2 mol H_2S + 3 mol O_2 → 2 mol SO_2 + 2 mol H_2O

$$\left(2\ \cancel{mol} \times 34.1\ \frac{g}{\cancel{mol}}\right) + \left(3\ \cancel{mol} \times 32.0\ \frac{g}{\cancel{mol}}\right) \rightarrow \left(2\ \cancel{mol} \times 64.1\ \frac{g}{\cancel{mol}}\right) + \left(2\ \cancel{mol} \times 18.0\ \frac{g}{\cancel{mol}}\right)$$

Add the masses on the reactants side and on the products side.

68.2 g H_2S + 96.0 g O_2 → 128.2 g SO_2 + 36.0 g H_2O

164.2 g = 164.2 g

6 **CCC Energy and Matter Interpret the equation for the formation of water from its elements in terms of numbers of molecules, moles, and volumes of gases at STP.**

$$2H_2(g) + O_2(g) \rightarrow 2H_2O(g)$$

....

....

GO ONLINE for more practice problems.

What Is Conserved?

In 1789, Antoine Lavoisier discovered that mass is neither created nor destroyed in a chemical reaction. This is known as the **law of conservation of mass**. In modern terms, it means that atoms are neither created nor destroyed in a chemical reaction. Atoms are rearranged to form new molecules during a reaction. However, the number of atoms and the total mass of the reactants and products are always the same.

Burning Charcoal The burning of charcoal can be modeled as the simple combustion of carbon.
$C(s) + O_2(g) \rightarrow CO_2(g)$

Conservation of Mass The molar masses of carbon and oxygen can be used to determine the total mass of the reactants. The molar mass of CO_2 can be used to determine the mass of the product. The mass of CO_2 equals the total mass of C and O_2.

7 **CCC Energy and Matter The charcoal that was burned in a grill left only a fine, light ash. The ash weighs significantly less than the charcoal before being burned. What happened to the extra mass?**

....

....

Proportionality of Reactants and Products

Balanced equations are like recipes. They tell you the ingredients that you need and their proper ratios. In a chemical equation, the chemical symbols provide the ingredients, and the coefficients provide the proper ratios. Stoichiometry tells you how to calculate the moles, mass, volume, or number of atoms or molecules of products or reactants using balanced chemical equations. This is possible because the reactants and products are proportional to each other.

For example, the number of moles of ammonia produced is proportional to the number of moles of nitrogen that reacted. The mass of ammonia produced in the reaction is also proportional to the mass of nitrogen. This information is provided by the chemical equation for the production of ammonia:

$$N_2(g) + 3H_2(g) \rightarrow 2NH_3(g)$$

The equation shows that two moles of ammonia are produced when one mole of nitrogen and three moles of hydrogen react.

Ammonia vs. Nitrogen (Moles) To make two moles of ammonia it takes one mole of nitrogen, a ratio of 2 NH_3:1 N_2. This mole ratio is given by the slope of this graph, which can be determined from the coefficients in the chemical equation.

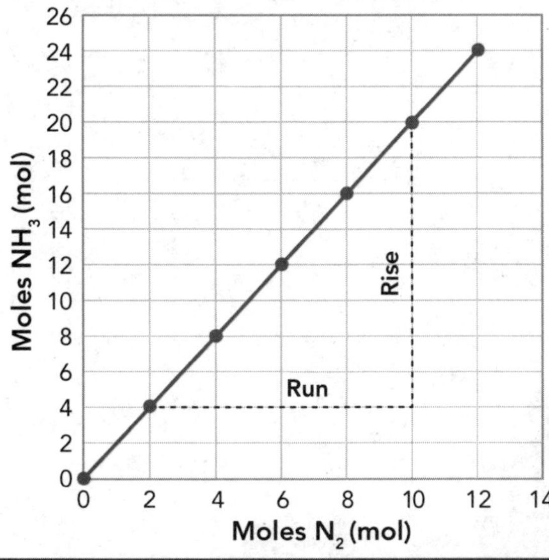

Ammonia vs. Nitrogen (Mass) The slope of this graph gives the mass ratio. It is 1.21 NH_3:1 N_2, not 2 NH_3:1 N_2. Coefficients tell us the mole proportionality, not the mass proportionality.

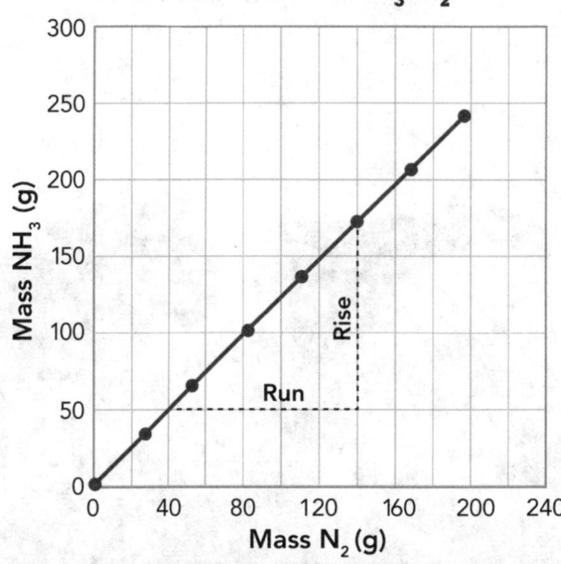

8 **SEP Use Mathematics** Using the data from the graph, predict the mass of nitrogen needed to produce 300 g of ammonia.

Revisit

INVESTIGATIVE PHENOMENON

GO ONLINE to Elaborate on and Evaluate your knowledge of the proportionality of reactants and products by completing the peer review and writing activities.

In the CER worksheet you completed at the beginning of the investigation, you drafted an explanation for why a recipe can fail. With a partner, reevaluate your arguments.

9 **CCC Scale, Proportion, and Quantity** **A simple bread recipe calls for 400 g of flour, 8 g of salt (NaCl), 1 g of yeast, and 0.3 L of water (H_2O). The recipe produces 1 loaf of bread. How much of each ingredient would you need to produce 3 loaves of bread?**

EXPERIENCE 2

Chemical Calculations

GO ONLINE to Explore and Explain stoichiometric calculations.

Mole Ratios

A **mole ratio** is a conversion factor derived from the coefficients of a balanced chemical equation interpreted in terms of moles. In chemical calculations, mole ratios are used to convert between a given number of moles of reactant or product to moles of a different reactant or product. For example, mole ratios can be determined from the balanced chemical equation for ammonia production: $N_2(g) + 3H_2(g) \rightarrow 2NH_3(g)$.

Mole-Mole Graph The number of moles of NH_3 is graphed as a function of the number of moles of N_2 and H_2. The coefficients in the chemical equation provide the proportionality between individual reactants and/or products.

Mole Ratio The coefficients in the chemical equation can also be used to write the mole ratio between any of the reactants and/or products.

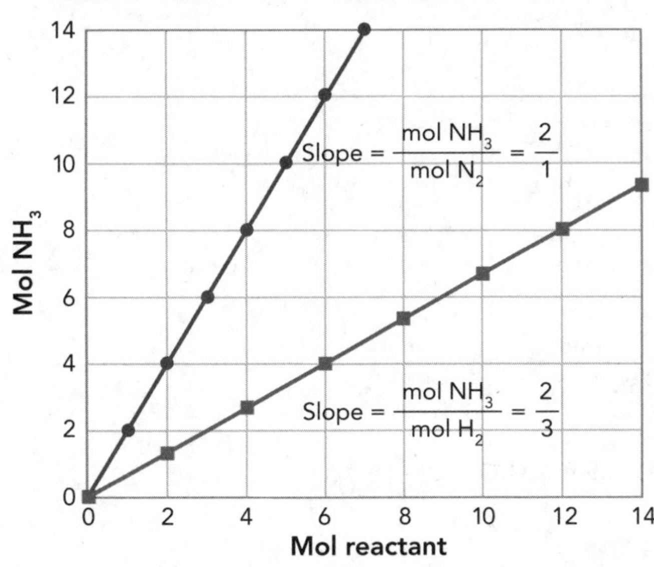

$$\frac{1 \text{ mol } N_2}{3 \text{ mol } H_2}$$

$$\frac{2 \text{ mol } NH_3}{1 \text{ mol } N_2}$$

$$\frac{2 \text{ mol } NH_3}{3 \text{ mol } H_2}$$

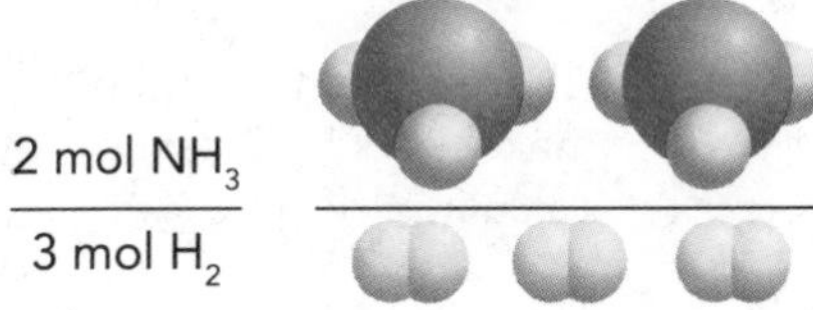

(10) **SEP Develop a Model What would the slopes of the lines be for a graph of the moles of product versus mole of each reactant for the reaction $2H_2 + O_2 \rightarrow 2H_2O$?**

Mole-Mole Calculations

Mole ratios can be used in a mole-mole calculation, which is a conversion between a given number of moles of one reactant or product and moles of another reactant or product. If you're given the number of moles of one of the substances, *G*, then you can use the appropriate mole ratio to calculate the moles of the wanted substance, *W*. To choose the correct mole ratio, make sure the moles of the wanted substance are in the numerator.

Mole-Mole Flowchart Multiply the given number of moles by the appropriate mole ratio to calculate the moles of the wanted quantity.

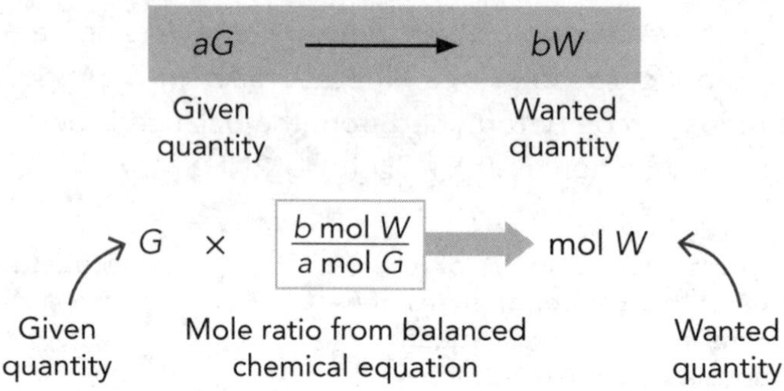

Applying the Mole-Mole Flowchart
How many moles of O_2 would you need to produce 25 mol H_2O from the reaction of H_2 and O_2?

Write the balanced equation. ⟶ $2H_2 + O_2 \rightarrow 2H_2O$

Develop a concept map for the calculation. ⟶ *a* mol H_2O × [Mole ratio] → *b* mol O_2 (Given quantity → Wanted quantity)

Use the coefficients from the equation to write the mole ratios that include H_2O and O_2. ⟶ $\frac{2 \text{ mol } H_2O}{1 \text{ mol } O_2}$ $\frac{1 \text{ mol } O_2}{2 \text{ mol } H_2O}$

Choose the mole ratio that makes mol H_2O cancel out and calculate mol O_2. ⟶ $25 \cancel{\text{mol } H_2O} \times \frac{1 \text{ mol } O_2}{2 \cancel{\text{mol } H_2O}} = 12.5 \text{ mol } O_2$

11 **SEP Use Mathematics How many moles of hydrogen gas would be required to produce 25 moles of H_2O?**

SAMPLE PROBLEM

Calculating Moles of a Product

How many moles of NH_3 are produced when 0.60 mol of nitrogen react with hydrogen?

ANALYZE **List the knowns and unknown.**

Knowns	Unknown
moles of nitrogen = 0.60 mol N_2	moles of ammonia = ? mol NH_3

CALCULATE **Solve for the unknown.**

Write the balanced chemical equation for the formation of ammonia.

$N_2 + H_2 \rightarrow NH_3$ (unbalanced)

$N_2 + 3H_2 \rightarrow 2NH_3$ (balanced)

Write the mole ratio that will allow you to convert from moles N_2 to moles NH_3.

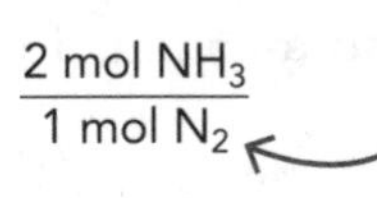

Remember that the mole ratio must have N_2 on the bottom so that the mol N_2 in the mole ratio will cancel with mol N_2 in the known.

Multiply the given quantity of N_2 by the mole ratio in order to find the moles of NH_3.

$$0.60 \text{ mol } N_2 \times \frac{2 \text{ mol } NH_3}{1 \text{ mol } N_2} = 1.2 \text{ mol } NH_3$$

EVALUATE **Does the result make sense?**

The ratio of 1.2 mol NH_3 to 0.60 mol N_2 is 2:1, as predicted by the balanced equation.

(12) **SEP Apply Mathematical Concepts** **This equation shows the formation of aluminum oxide, which is found on the surface of aluminum objects exposed to the air.**

$$4Al(s) + 3O_2(g) \rightarrow 2Al_2O_3(s)$$

a. Write the six mole ratios that can be derived from this equation.

b. How many moles of aluminum are needed to form 3.7 mol Al_2O_3?

GO ONLINE for more practice problems.

Mass-Mass Calculations

Laboratory balances measure mass and cannot measure substances directly in moles. A mass-mass calculation is a conversion between a given mass of one reactant or product to the mass of another reactant or product.

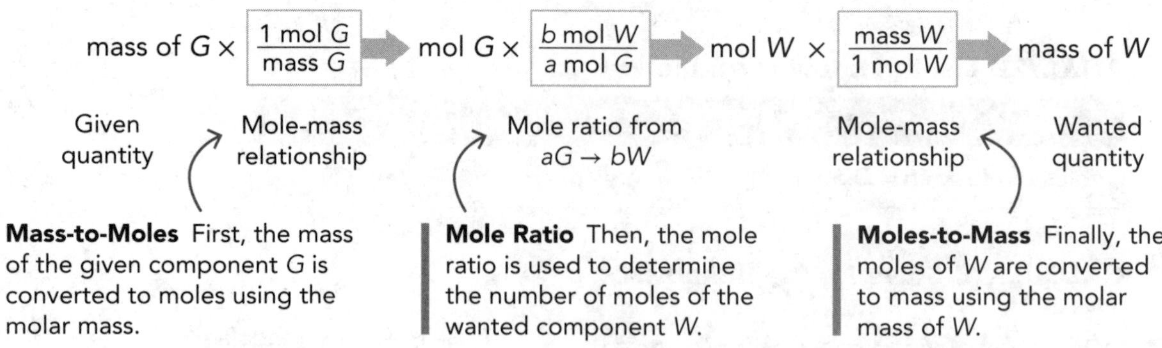

Mass-to-Moles First, the mass of the given component *G* is converted to moles using the molar mass.

Mole Ratio Then, the mole ratio is used to determine the number of moles of the wanted component *W*.

Moles-to-Mass Finally, the moles of *W* are converted to mass using the molar mass of *W*.

This method can be used to determine the mass of ammonia produced in the following reaction, if we start with 100 g of nitrogen.

$$N_2 + 3H_2 \rightarrow 2NH_3$$

$$100 \text{ g } N_2 \times \frac{1 \text{ mol } N_2}{28.0 \; N_2} \rightarrow 3.57 \text{ mol } N_2 \times \frac{2 \text{ mol } NH_3}{1 \text{ mol } N_2} \rightarrow 7.14 \text{ mol } NH_3 \times \frac{17.0 \text{ g } NH_3}{1 \text{ mol } NH_3} \rightarrow = 121 \text{ g } NH_3$$

Mass Ratio of Ammonia Reaction Two moles of ammonia are made when one mole of nitrogen reacts. However, the mass ratio is about 1.21 NH_3:1 N_2 because the molar masses are 17 g/mol and 28 g/mol, respectively.

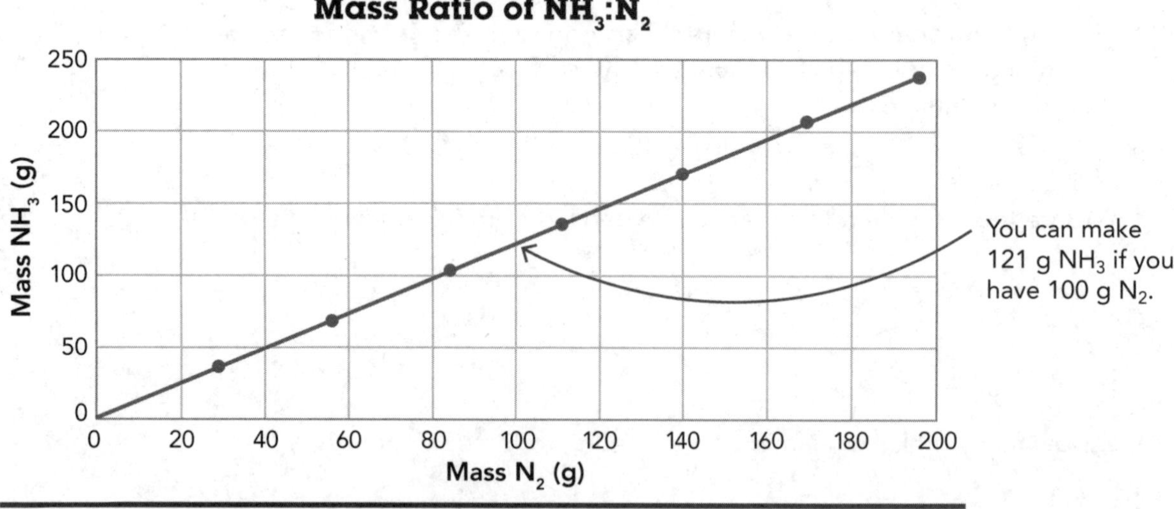

13 **SEP Develop a Model** What are the mole ratio and the mass ratio for H_2O to O_2 in the reaction $2H_2 + O_2 \rightarrow 2H_2O$?

SAMPLE PROBLEM

Calculating the Mass of a Product

Calculate the number of grams of NH_3 produced when 5.40 g H_2 react with an excess of N_2. The balanced equation is $N_2(g) + 3H_2(g) \rightarrow 2NH_3(g)$.

ANALYZE **List the knowns and unknown.**

Knowns	Unknown
mass of hydrogen = 5.40 g H_2	mass of ammonia = ? g NH_3
1 mol H_2 = 2.0 g H_2	
1 mol NH_3 = 17.0 g NH_3	

CALCULATE **Solve for the unknown.**

Identify the steps needed to determine the mass of ammonia.

$$\text{g } H_2 \rightarrow \text{mol } H_2 \rightarrow \text{mol } NH_3 \rightarrow \text{g } NH_3$$

Convert the given mass to moles.

$$5.40 \text{ g } H_2 \times \frac{1 \text{ mol } H_2}{2.0 \text{ g } H_2}$$

Convert from moles of the given reactant to moles of wanted product by using the correct mole ratio.

$$5.40 \text{ g } H_2 \times \frac{1 \text{ mol } H_2}{2.0 \text{ g } H_2} \times \frac{2 \text{ mol } NH_3}{3 \text{ mol } H_2}$$

Don't forget to cancel the units at each step.

Finish by converting moles to grams. Use the molar mass of NH_3.

$$5.40 \text{ g } H_2 \times \frac{1 \text{ mol } H_2}{2.0 \text{ g } H_2} \times \frac{2 \text{ mol } NH_3}{3 \text{ mol } H_2} \times \frac{17.0 \text{ g } NH_3}{1 \text{ mol } NH_3} = 31 \text{ g } NH_3$$

Given quantity | Change given unit to moles | Mole ratio | Change moles to grams

EVALUATE **Does the result make sense?**

Multiple conversion factors make it difficult to evaluate the result, but the molar mass of NH_3 is much greater than that of H_2, which means the answer was likely to have a larger value than the given mass.

14 **SEP Apply Mathematical Concepts** **Acetylene gas (C_2H_2) is produced by adding water to calcium carbide (CaC_2).**

$$CaC_2(s) + 2H_2O(l) \rightarrow C_2H_2(g) + Ca(OH)_2(aq)$$

How many grams of C_2H_2 are produced when water is added (in excess) to 5.00 g CaC_2?

GO ONLINE for more practice problems.

Volume-Volume Calculations

So far, you've learned how to use the molar mass to convert between moles and mass, and how to use the mole ratio to complete the stoichiometric calculation. The mole can also be related to other quantities, such as volume. A volume-volume calculation is a conversion between a given volume of one reactant or product and the volume of another reactant or product. Volume-volume calculations only apply to gases at STP because the molar volume is used as a conversion factor.

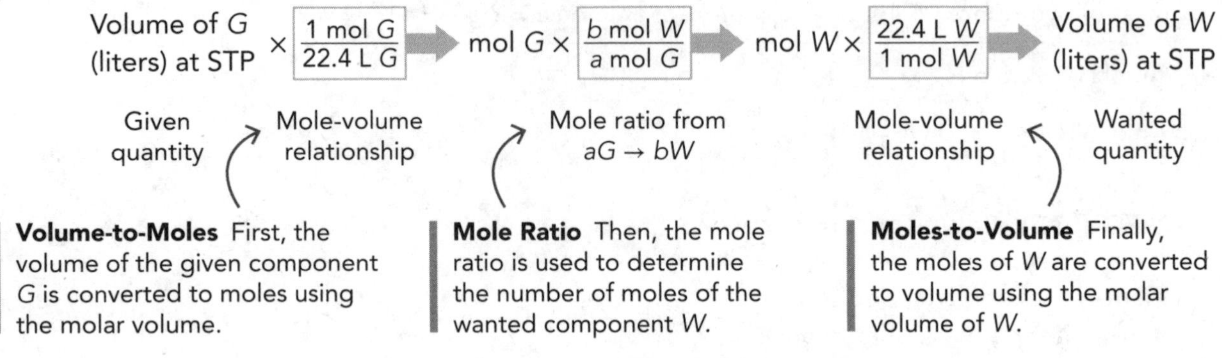

Volume of G (liters) at STP $\times \frac{1 \text{ mol } G}{22.4 \text{ L } G}$ → mol G × $\frac{b \text{ mol } W}{a \text{ mol } G}$ → mol W × $\frac{22.4 \text{ L } W}{1 \text{ mol } W}$ → Volume of W (liters) at STP
Given quantity
Mole-volume relationship
Mole ratio from $aG \rightarrow bW$
Mole-volume relationship
Wanted quantity

Volume-to-Moles First, the volume of the given component *G* is converted to moles using the molar volume.

Mole Ratio Then, the mole ratio is used to determine the number of moles of the wanted component *W*.

Moles-to-Volume Finally, the moles of *W* are converted to volume using the molar volume of *W*.

$$2CO(g) + O_2(g) \rightarrow 2CO_2(g)$$

$$1 \text{ L } O_2 \times \frac{1 \text{ mol } O_2}{22.4 \text{ L } O_2} \rightarrow \text{mol } O_2 \times \frac{2 \text{ mol } CO_2}{1 \text{ mol } O_2} \rightarrow \text{mol } CO_2 \times \frac{22.4 \text{ L } CO_2}{1 \text{ mol } CO_2} = 2 \text{ L } CO_2$$

Combustion of Carbon Monoxide To make 2 L of carbon dioxide, you need 1 L of oxygen. The volume ratio is 2 L CO_2:1 L O_2. Because of Avogadro's law, the mole ratio is also 2 mol CO_2:1 mol O_2.

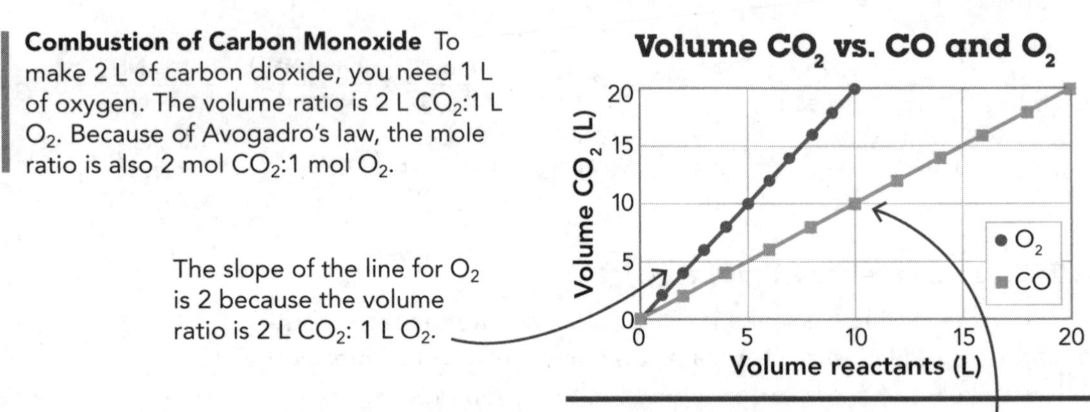

The slope of the line for O_2 is 2 because the volume ratio is 2 L CO_2: 1 L O_2.

The slope of the line for CO is 1 because the volume ratio is 1 L CO_2: 1 L CO.

15 **SEP Develop a Model** What are the slopes of the lines on a graph of the volume of the product versus volume of the reactants for the reaction represented by $2NO(g) + O_2(g) \rightarrow 2NO_2(g)$?

SAMPLE PROBLEM

Calculating the Volume of a Product

Nitrogen monoxide (NO) and oxygen gas combine to form the brown gas nitrogen dioxide (NO_2), which contributes to photochemical smog. How many liters of NO_2 are produced when 34 L O_2 react with an excess of NO at STP? The balanced equation is $2NO(g) + O_2(g) \rightarrow 2NO_2(g)$.

ANALYZE **List the knowns and unknown.**

Knowns	Unknown
volume of oxygen = 34 L O_2	volume of nitrogen dioxide = ? L NO_2
1 mol O_2 = 22.4 L O_2 (at STP)	
1 mol NO_2 = 22.4 L NO_2 (at STP)	

CALCULATE **Solve for the unknown.**

Identify the steps needed to determine the unknown.

$$\text{L } O_2 \rightarrow \text{mol } O_2 \rightarrow \text{mol } NO_2 \rightarrow \text{L } NO_2$$

Convert the given volume to moles using the mole-volume ratio.

$$34\ \cancel{\text{L } O_2} \times \frac{1 \text{ mol } O_2}{22.4\ \cancel{\text{L } O_2}}$$

Then, convert from moles of given reactant to moles of wanted product by using the correct mole ratio.

$$34\ \cancel{\text{L } O_2} \times \frac{1\ \cancel{\text{mol } O_2}}{22.4\ \cancel{\text{L } O_2}} \times \frac{2 \text{ mol } NO_2}{1\ \cancel{\text{mol } O_2}}$$

Finish by using the molar volume of NO_2 to convert from moles to liters.

$$\underset{\text{Given quantity}}{34\ \cancel{\text{L } O_2}} \times \underset{\text{Change to moles}}{\frac{1\ \cancel{\text{mol } O_2}}{22.4\ \cancel{\text{L } O_2}}} \times \underset{\text{Mole ratio}}{\frac{2\ \cancel{\text{mol } NO_2}}{1\ \cancel{\text{mol } O_2}}} \times \underset{\text{Change to liters}}{\frac{22.4 \text{ L } NO_2}{1\ \cancel{\text{mol } NO_2}}} = 68 \text{ L } NO_2$$

EVALUATE **Does the result make sense?**

Because 2 mol NO_2 are produced for each 1 mol O_2 that reacts, the volume of NO_2 should be twice the given volume of O_2. The answer should have two significant figures.

16 **SEP Apply Mathematical Concepts** How many liters of oxygen are required to burn 3.86 L of carbon monoxide?

$$2CO(g) + O_2(g) \rightarrow 2CO_2(g)$$

GO ONLINE for more practice problems.

A Roadmap for Solving Stoichiometric Problems

Mass can be measured easily for solids and liquids, and volume can be measured easily for gases. What happens when a chemical reaction involves a combination of solids and gases? Combining the processes discussed so far provides a general framework that you can use to complete mass-volume, particle-mass, and volume-particle calculations.

Mass-Volume The dashed arrows show the process for calculating the volume of a gas needed in a reaction when given the mass of another substance.

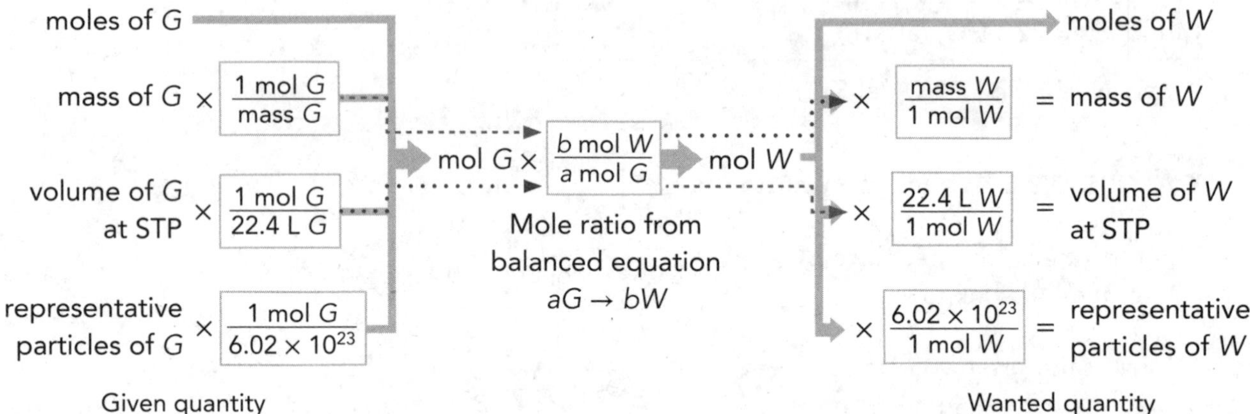

Volume-Mass The dotted arrows show the process for calculating the mass of a substance needed in a reaction when given the volume of a gas.

17 **SEP Computational Thinking** Sketch a flowchart for determining the number of representative particles of *W* needed if given the mass of *G*.

SAMPLE PROBLEM

Calculating Molecules of a Product

How many molecules of oxygen are produced when 29.2 g of water are decomposed by electrolysis according to this balanced equation?

$$2H_2O(l) \xrightarrow{\text{electricity}} 2H_2(g) + O_2(g)$$

ANALYZE **List the knowns and unknown.**

Knowns	Unknown
mass of water = 29.2 g H_2O	molecules of oxygen = ? molecules of O_2
1 mol H_2O = 18.0 g H_2O	
1 mol O_2 = 6.02×10^{23} molecules O_2	

CALCULATE **Solve for the unknown.**

Identify the steps needed to determine the unknown.

$$\text{g } H_2O \rightarrow \text{mol } H_2O \rightarrow \text{mol } O_2 \rightarrow \text{molecules } O_2$$

Convert the given mass to moles.

$$29.2 \cancel{\text{g } H_2O} \times \frac{1 \text{ mol } H_2O}{18.0 \cancel{\text{g } H_2O}}$$

Convert from moles of reactant to moles of wanted product.

$$29.2 \cancel{\text{g } H_2O} \times \frac{1 \cancel{\text{mol } H_2O}}{18.0 \cancel{\text{g } H_2O}} \times \frac{1 \text{ mol } O_2}{2 \cancel{\text{mol } H_2O}}$$

Finally, convert the wanted product from moles to molecules using Avogadro's number.

$$29.2 \cancel{\text{g } H_2O} \times \frac{1 \cancel{\text{mol } H_2O}}{18.0 \cancel{\text{g } H_2O}} \times \frac{1 \cancel{\text{mol } O_2}}{2 \cancel{\text{mol } H_2O}} \times \frac{6.02 \times 10^{23} \text{ molecules } O_2}{1 \cancel{\text{mol } O_2}}$$

Given quantity | Change to moles | Mole ratio | Change to molecules

$$= 4.88 \times 10^{23} \text{ molecules } O_2$$

EVALUATE **Does the result make sense?**

The given mass of water should produce a little less than 1 mole of oxygen, which is a little less than Avogadro's number of molecules. The answer has the right number of significant figures.

18 **SEP Apply Mathematical Concepts** **How many molecules of oxygen are produced when 6.54 g of potassium chlorate ($KClO_3$) decompose?**

$$2KClO_3(s) \rightarrow 2KCl(s) + 3O_2(g)$$

GO ONLINE for more practice problems.

Revisit

INVESTIGATIVE PHENOMENON

GO ONLINE to Elaborate on and Evaluate your knowledge of stoichiometric calculations by completing the peer review and writing activities.

In the CER worksheet you completed at the beginning of the investigation, you drafted an explanation for why a recipe can fail. With a partner, reevaluate your arguments.

19 **SEP Use Mathematics When dough bakes in the oven, baking soda, also known as sodium bicarbonate ($NaHCO_3$), decomposes into sodium carbonate (Na_2CO_3), water, and carbon dioxide. If your recipe calls for 2.0 grams of baking soda, what mass of carbon dioxide will be released during the reaction? Write a balanced chemical equation and use the molar masses in the table.**

Molar Masses of Reactants and Products

Substance	Molar mass (g/mol)
$NaHCO_3$	84
Na_2CO_3	106
H_2O	18
CO_2	44

EXPERIENCE 3

Limiting Reagent and Percent Yield

GO ONLINE to Explore and Explain limiting reagents and reaction yields.

Limiting Ingredients

In any recipe, an insufficient amount of any of the ingredients will limit the amount of product you can make. The amount of product is determined by the amount of the limiting ingredient. No matter how much of the other ingredients you have, you can only make as much product as allowed by the limiting ingredient. For example, the limiting ingredient determines how many tacos you can make, even if you have more of every other ingredient.

You could make more than two tacos with these ingredients. They are excess ingredients.

Cilantro

Salsa

Lime

Shredded cabbage

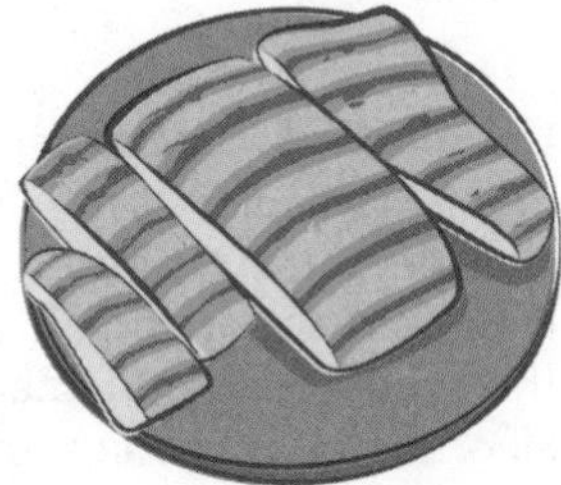

Grilled fish

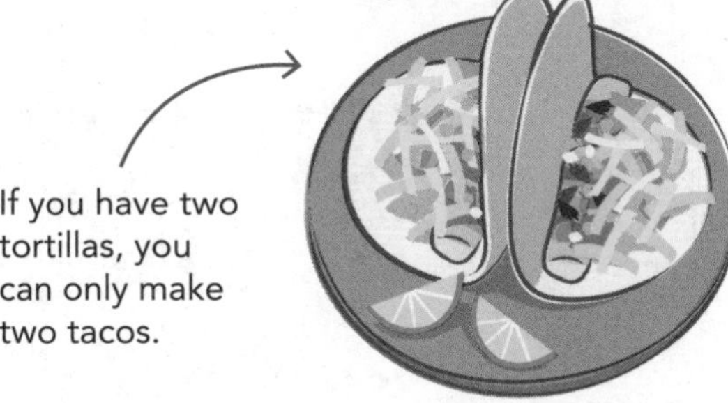

If you have two tortillas, you can only make two tacos.

Fish tacos

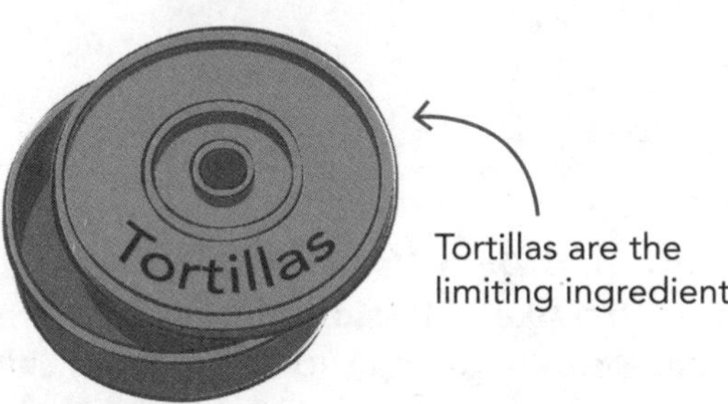

Tortilla warmer

Tortillas are the limiting ingredient.

Limiting and Excess Ingredients Combining a tortilla, fish, cabbage, cilantro, salsa, and a splash of lime produces a delicious taco. If you use up the tortillas before the other ingredients, they are the limiting ingredient.

20 **SEP Use a Model Write a balanced equation for the production of sausage sandwiches. Assume that sausages only come in packs of five and buns in packs of eight. How many sandwiches can you make if you have one pack of each ingredient?**

Limiting and Excess Reagents

In a chemical reaction, an insufficient amount of any of the reactants will limit the amount of product that forms. The reactant that determines the amount of product that can be formed is called the **limiting reagent.** The reaction stops after the limiting reagent is used up, even though some amount of the other reactant(s) remains. Any reactant that is not used up in a reaction is called the **excess reagent.**

Balanced Reactants The chemical equation for the production of ammonia is a precise "recipe" that calls for three molecules of hydrogen (H_2) for every one molecule of nitrogen (N_2). The product is two molecules of ammonia (NH_3), with no leftover reagents.

Reactants **Products**

$N_2(g) + 3H_2(g) \longrightarrow 2NH_3(g)$

1 molecule N_2 + 3 molecules $H_2 \longrightarrow$ 2 molecules NH_3

Unbalanced Reactants In this particular experiment, H_2 is the limiting reagent and N_2 is the excess reagent. After all of the H_2 is used up to make NH_3, there is still some N_2 left over.

Before Reaction **After Reaction**

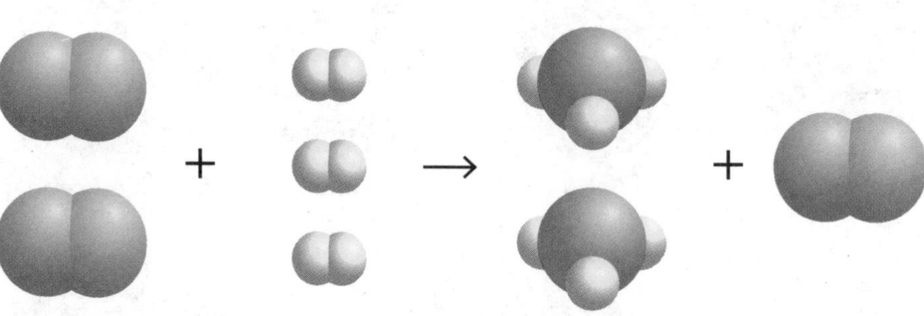

2 molecules N_2 + 3 molecules $H_2 \longrightarrow$ 2 molecules NH_3 + 1 molecule N_2

(21) **SEP Interpret Data Varying masses of sodium metal react with a fixed mass of chlorine. The graph shows the masses of sodium used and sodium chloride produced. Explain the general shape of the graph and identify the limiting and excess reagents.**

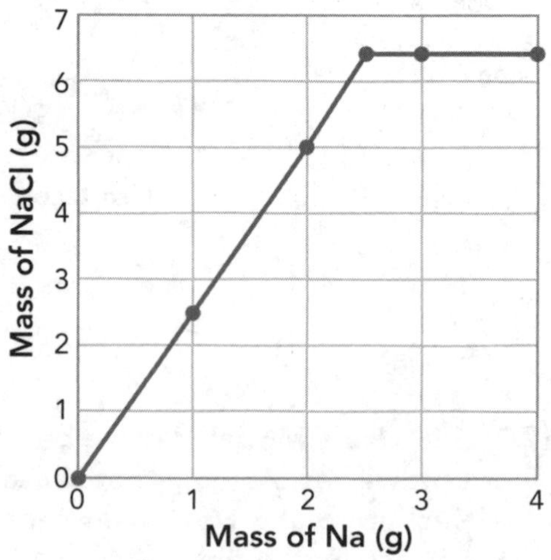

....

....

....

....

....

Mass of Products and Reactants

Often in stoichiometric problems, the given quantities of reactants are expressed in units other than moles, such as mass. The amount of each reactant first has to be converted from mass to moles before the mole ratio is applied to determine the limiting reagent. Then, the limiting reagent can be used to determine the mass of the products.

Determining the Limiting Reagent The mole ratio is used to determine the number of moles of one of the reactants needed to complete the reaction. If you do not have enough, then this is the limiting reagent.

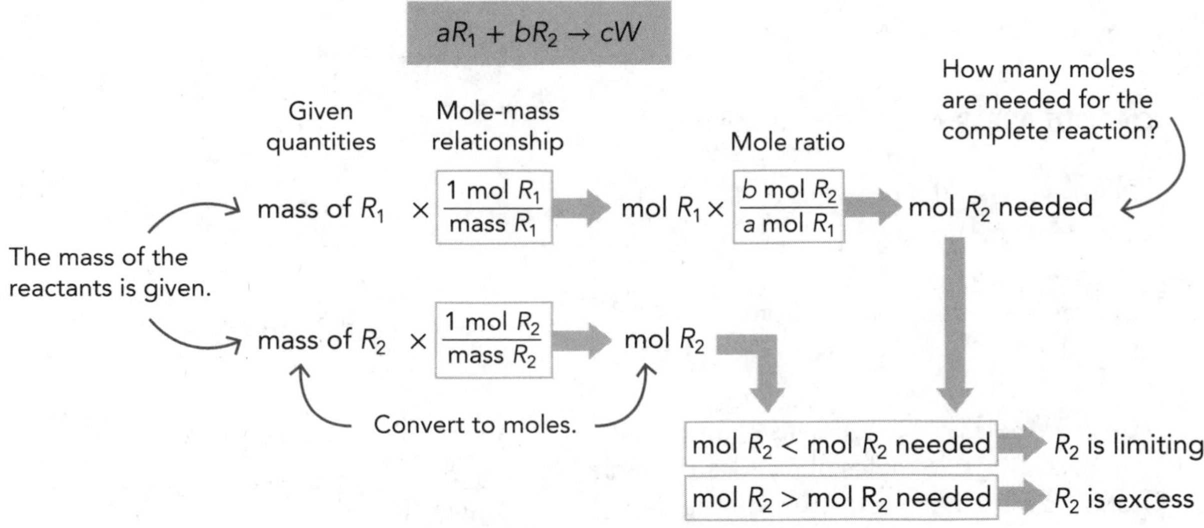

Determining Mass from the Limiting Reagent The limiting reagent limits the reaction. It is used in a mole-mass calculation with the mole ratio to determine the mass of the product.

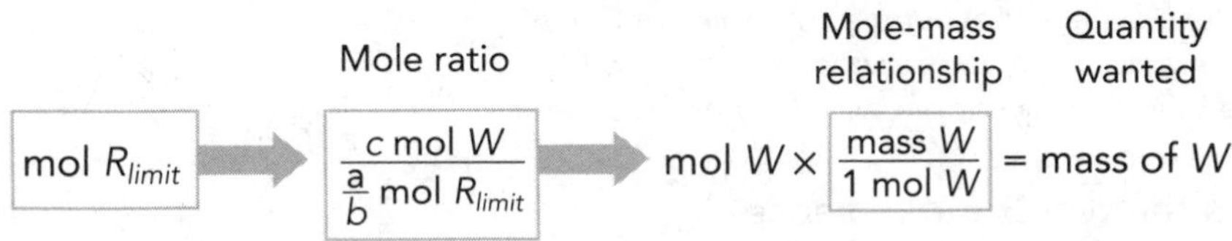

Mole ratio
Mole-mass relationship
Quantity wanted
mol R_{limit}
$\frac{c \text{ mol } W}{\frac{a}{b} \text{ mol } R_{limit}}$
mol W × $\frac{\text{mass } W}{1 \text{ mol } W}$ = mass of W

22 SEP Analyze Data The table shows the masses of sodium used and sodium chloride produced when varying masses of sodium react with a fixed mass of chlorine. From the data, estimate the total mass of chlorine that was available for each trial.

$Na(g) + Cl_2(g)$ Reaction Data

Mass Na (g)	Mass NaCl (g)
1	2.5
2	5
2.5	6.5
4	6.5

SAMPLE PROBLEM

Determining the Limiting Reagent

Copper reacts with sulfur to form copper(I) sulfide according to the following balanced equation: $2Cu(s) + S(s) \rightarrow Cu_2S(s)$. What is the limiting reagent when 80.0 g Cu reacts with 25.0 g S?

ANALYZE **List the knowns and unknown.**

Knowns	Unknown
mass of copper = 80.0 g Cu	limiting reagent = ?
mass of sulfur = 25.0 g S	

CALCULATE **Solve for the unknown.**

Choose one of the reactants and convert from mass to moles.

$$80.0\ \cancel{g\ Cu} \times \frac{1\ mol\ Cu}{63.5\ \cancel{g\ Cu}} = 1.26\ mol\ Cu$$

Convert the other reactant from mass to moles.

$$25.0\ \cancel{g\ S} \times \frac{1\ mol\ S}{32.1\ \cancel{g\ S}} = 0.779\ mol\ S$$

Convert moles of Cu to moles of S needed to react with 1.26 moles of Cu. Use the mole ratio from the balanced equation.

$$1.26\ \cancel{mol\ Cu} \times \frac{1\ mol\ S}{2\ \cancel{mol\ Cu}} = 0.630\ mol\ S$$

Given quantity | Mole ratio | Needed amount

Compare the amount of sulfur needed with the given amount of sulfur.

0.630 mol S (amount needed) $<$ 0.779 mol S (given amount). Sulfur is in excess. Therefore, copper is the limiting reagent.

If you used the actual number of moles of S to find the amount of copper needed, then you would still identify copper as the limiting reagent.

EVALUATE **Does the result make sense?**

Since the ratio of the given moles of Cu to moles of S was less than the ratio (2:1) from the balanced equation, copper should be the limiting reagent.

23 **SEP Apply Mathematical Concepts The equation for the combustion of ethene (C_2H_4) is $C_2H_4(g) + 3O_2(g) \rightarrow 2CO_2(g) + 2H_2O(g)$. If 2.70 mol C_2H_4 reacts with 6.30 mol O_2, identify the limiting reagent.**

GO ONLINE for more practice problems.

SAMPLE PROBLEM

Using the Limiting Reagent to Find the Quantity of a Product

What is the maximum number of grams of Cu_2S that can be formed when 80.0 g Cu react with 25.0 g S?

$$2Cu(s) + S(s) \rightarrow Cu_2S(s)$$

ANALYZE List the knowns and unknown.

Knowns	Unknown
limiting reagent = 1.26 mol Cu	yield = ? g Cu_2S
1 mol Cu_2S = 159.1 g Cu_2S	

CALCULATE Solve for the unknown.

Identify the steps needed to determine the mass of product.

mol Cu → mol Cu_2S → g Cu_2S

Convert moles of limiting reagent to moles of product.

$$1.26 \text{ mol Cu} \times \frac{1 \text{ mol } Cu_2S}{2 \text{ mol Cu}}$$

Use the mole ratio from the balanced equation.

Finish by converting from moles to mass of product.

$$1.26 \text{ mol Cu} \times \frac{1 \text{ mol } Cu_2S}{2 \text{ mol Cu}} \times \frac{159.1 \text{ g } Cu_2S}{1 \text{ mol } Cu_2S} = 1.00 \times 10^2 \text{ g } Cu_2S$$

EVALUATE Does the result make sense?

Copper is the limiting reagent. The maximum number of grams of Cu_2S produced should be more than the amount of Cu that reacted because Cu and S combine. However, the mass of Cu_2S produced should be less than the total mass of the reactants (105.0 g) because S was in excess.

24 SEP Apply Mathematical Concepts **The incomplete combustion of ethene is given by the equation $C_2H_4(g) + 2O_2(g) \rightarrow 2CO(g) + 2H_2O(g)$.**

If 2.70 mol C_2H_4 is reacted with 6.30 mol O_2,

a. identify the limiting reagent.

b. calculate the moles of water produced.

GO ONLINE for more practice problems.

Percent Yield

Success Stats In the average professional hockey game, a team will make thirty shots at the goal. Theoretically, every shot could result in a score. However, this outcome does not occur. The average professional team scores fewer than two goals per game. The success percentage is the ratio of the actual score to the theoretical score expressed as a percent:

$$\text{Percent Success} = \frac{\text{actual score}}{\text{theoretical score}} \times 100\%$$

Percent Success A hockey team may score on less than 7% of the shots that they make on the goal.

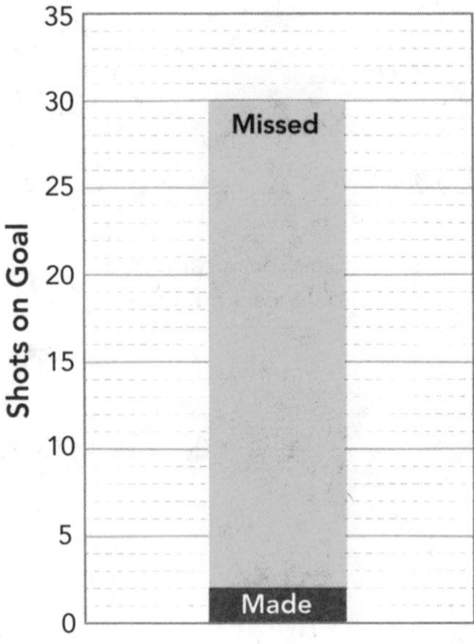

Improving the Score To improve, the team could either try to make more shots on the goal during a game or increase their percent success by making more of the shots they attempt.

25 **SEP Define a Problem** Grades on tests can also be thought of as a success statistic. How would you define the actual score and theoretical score on an exam, and how would you calculate the percent success?

Percent Yield in Reactions When a balanced chemical equation is used to calculate the amount of product of a reaction, the calculated value represents the **theoretical yield**. It is the maximum amount of product that can be formed. The actual amount of product made during a real reaction is called the **actual yield**. You can measure the mass of the product of a laboratory experiment to find the actual yield. The **percent yield** is the ratio of the actual to the theoretical yield expressed as a percent, and represents the efficiency of a reaction:

$$\text{Percent Yield} = \frac{\text{actual yield}}{\text{theoretical yield}} \times 100\%$$

Theoretical Yield The balanced chemical equation for the formation of ammonia can be used to determine the theoretical yield. Theoretical yield assumes that all of the reactants are used to make the product.

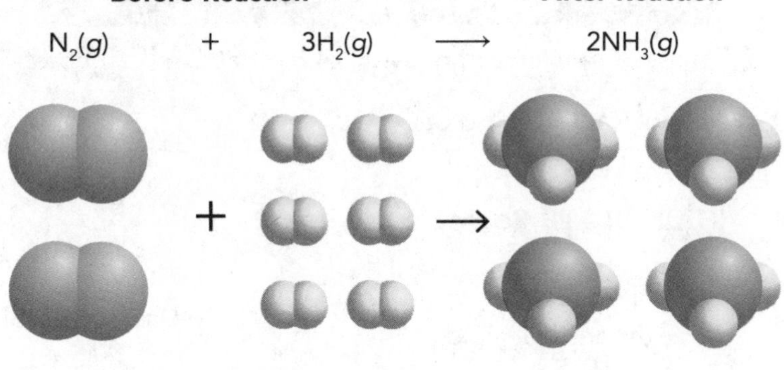

Side Reactions and Actual Yield Often, side reactions reduce the yield of a reaction. In this case, only 50% of the possible ammonia was produced because oxygen caused a side reaction. The oxygen may have been introduced from an impure gas source.

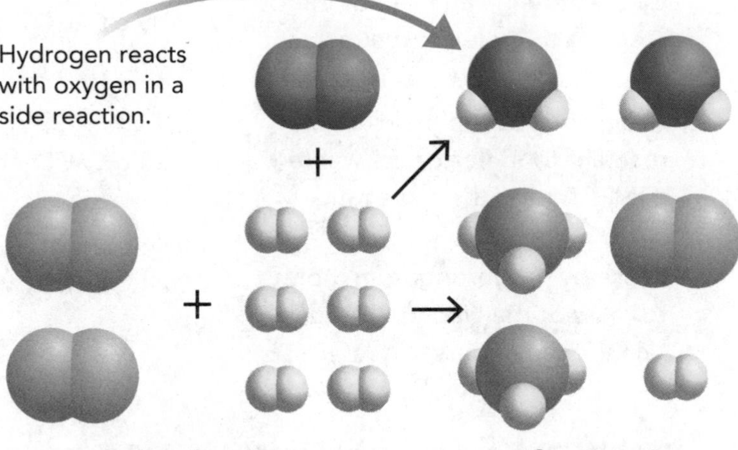

26 **SEP Construct an Explanation** **Imagine you are a chemical engineer at a chemical plant. One day the air conditioning in the plant stops working, resulting in high humidity. The percent yield for a chemical you produce drops significantly. Construct an explanation for the decrease in yield.**

....

....

....

SAMPLE PROBLEM

Calculating the Theoretical Yield

Calcium carbonate, which is found in seashells, is decomposed by heating. The balanced equation for this reaction is

$$CaCO_3(s) \xrightarrow{\Delta} CaO(s) + CO_2(g)$$

What is the theoretical yield of CaO if 24.8 g $CaCO_3$ is heated?

ANALYZE **List the knowns and unknown.**

Knowns	Unknown
mass of calcium carbonate = 24.8 g $CaCO_3$	theoretical yield = ? g CaO
1 mol CaO = 56.1 g CaO	

CALCULATE **Solve for the unknown.**

Identify the steps to determine the theoretical yield.

Theoretical yield is a mass-mass calculation.

$$\text{g } CaCO_3 \rightarrow \text{mol } CaCO_3 \rightarrow \text{mol CaO} \rightarrow \text{g CaO}$$

Convert the given mass of the reactant to moles of the reactant.

$$24.8 \text{ g } CaCO_3 \times \frac{1 \text{ mol } CaCO_3}{100.1 \text{ g } CaCO_3}$$

Then, convert the moles of the reactant to moles of the wanted product using the mole ratio.

$$24.8 \text{ g } CaCO_3 \times \frac{1 \text{ mol } CaCO_3}{100.1 \text{ g } CaCO_3} \times \frac{1 \text{ mol CaO}}{1 \text{ mol } CaCO_3}$$

Finish by converting from moles to mass of the wanted product. Use the molar mass of CaO.

$$24.8 \text{ g } CaCO_3 \times \frac{1 \text{ mol } CaCO_3}{100.1 \text{ g } CaCO_3} \times \frac{1 \text{ mol CaO}}{1 \text{ mol } CaCO_3} \times \frac{56.1 \text{ g CaO}}{1 \text{ mol CaO}}$$

$$= 13.9 \text{ g CaO}$$

EVALUATE **Does the result make sense?**

The mole ratio of CaO to $CaCO_3$ is 1:1. The ratio of their masses in the reaction should be the same as the ratio of their molar masses, which is slightly greater than 1:2. The result of the calculations shows that the mass of CaO is slightly greater than half the mass of $CaCO_3$.

27 **SEP Apply Mathematical Concepts** **When 84.8 g of iron(III) oxide react with an excess of carbon monoxide, iron is produced. What is the theoretical yield of iron?**

$$Fe_2O_3(s) + 3CO(g) \rightarrow 2Fe(s) + 3CO_2(g)$$

GO ONLINE for more practice problems.

SAMPLE PROBLEM

Calculating the Percent Yield

What is the percent yield if 13.1 g CaO are actually produced when 24.8 g $CaCO_3$ are heated?

$$CaCO_3(s) \xrightarrow{\Delta} CaO(s) + CO_2(g)$$

ANALYZE List the knowns and unknown.

Knowns	Unknown
actual yield = 13.1 g CaO	percent yield = ? %
theoretical yield = 13.9 g CaO	

CALCULATE Solve for the unknown.

Substitute the values for actual yield and theoretical yield into the equation for percent yield.

$$\text{percent yield} = \frac{\text{actual yield}}{\text{theoretical yield}} \times 100\%$$

$$\text{percent yield} = \frac{13.1 \text{ g } \cancel{CaO}}{13.9 \text{ g } \cancel{CaO}} \times 100\% = 94.2\%$$

EVALUATE Does the result make sense?

In this example, the actual yield is slightly less than the theoretical yield. Therefore, the percent yield should be slightly less than 100 percent.

28 **SEP Apply Mathematical Concepts** **If 50.0 g of silicon dioxide are heated with an excess of carbon, 27.9 g of silicon carbide are produced.**

$$SiO_2(s) + 3C(s) \xrightarrow{\Delta} SiC(s) + 2CO(g)$$

What is the percent yield of this reaction?

29 **SEP Apply Mathematical Concepts** **If 15.0 g of nitrogen react with 15.0 g of hydrogen, 10.5 g of ammonia are produced. What is the theoretical yield and percent yield of this reaction?**

GO ONLINE for more practice problems.

Revisit

INVESTIGATIVE PHENOMENON

GO ONLINE to Elaborate on and Evaluate your knowledge of percent yield, actual yield, and theoretical yield by completing the discussion and engineering design activities.

In the CER worksheet you completed at the beginning of the investigation, you drafted an explanation for why a recipe can fail. With a partner, reevaluate your arguments.

30 SEP Analyze and Interpret Data **A simple bread recipe calls for 400 g of flour, 8 g of salt, 1 g of yeast, and 0.3 L of water. The recipe produces 1 loaf of bread. The data table shows the amounts of each ingredient you have. Identify the limiting reagent. What is the theoretical yield, assuming you could make partial loaves? How many whole loaves of bread can you actually make? What is the percent yield? How much of each ingredient do you have left over?**

Available Ingredients

Ingredients	Amount (g)
Flour	1,350
Salt	450
Yeast	7
Water	unlimited

GO ONLINE to Evaluate what you learned about the consistent proportions of reactants and products in chemical reactions by using the available assessment resources.

In the Performance-Based Assessment, you used different amounts of reagents to collect, analyze, and interpret data in order to understand limiting and excess reagents. Wrap up your analysis by answering the following questions.

31 **SEP Use Mathematics** **During a demonstration, 2.0 L of 1.5 *M* acetic acid (CH_3COOH) is mixed with a 454 g box of baking soda ($NaHCO_3$). What is the limiting reactant?**

32 **CCC Consistency in Natural Systems** **When an asteroid enters Jupiter's atmosphere at great speed, it becomes extremely hot. Jupiter's atmosphere is rich in flammable gases, such as hydrogen and methane, but falling asteroids never start planet-wide fires on Jupiter. Use what you know about combustion and limiting reagents to provide a possible explanation.**

33 **Revisit the Anchoring Phenomenon** **How does what you learned in this investigation help you explain why chefs measure the amount of ingredients they need before preparing foods?**

INVESTIGATIVE PHENOMENON

GO ONLINE to Engage with real-world phenomena by watching a video and completing a modeling interactive worksheet.

Why do you get hot when you exercise?

INVESTIGATION 11

Thermochemistry

During exercise, many chemical reactions are happening within your body. Carbohydrates and fats are transformed to produce energy. To produce the energy needed to contract, your muscles break down a chemical called adenosine triphosphate. Your heart rate increases, you get hot, and you begin to sweat. Once you have viewed the Investigative Phenomenon video and completed the modeling exercise to help explain the phenomenon you observed, answer these reflection questions about how heat flows into and out of systems.

1. **SEP Develop a Model** **Your body gets energy from many sources, and it releases energy in many ways. Develop a model of the energy gain and loss by sketching the various flows of heat into and out of your body.**

2. **CCC Energy and Matter** **A classroom will get several degrees warmer when it is filled with students. Where does the energy come from to produce that temperature change?**

EXPERIENCE 1

Energy in Chemical Bonds

GO ONLINE to Explore and Explain how a model of colliding particles helps with understanding chemical reactions.

Collisions in Reactions

Reactions happen when bonds are broken and the atoms of the reactants are rearranged. **Collision theory** states that bonds are broken and/or formed when reactant particles collide with enough energy and with the correct orientation. The **activated complex** is an unstable cluster of atoms that exists during the transition from reactants to products.

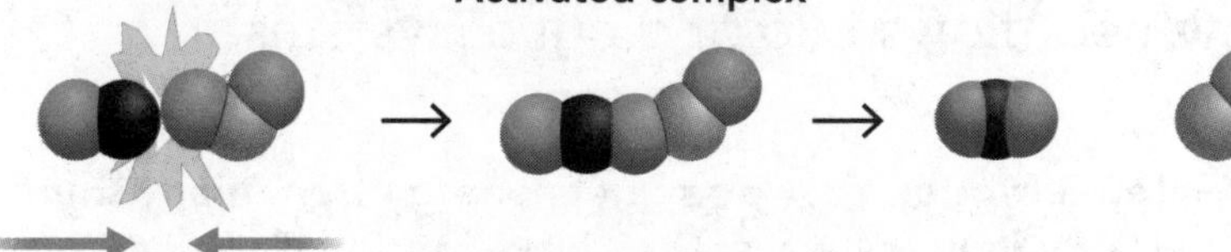

Successful Reaction When the reactants CO and NO_2 have enough energy and collide with the correct orientation, the reaction is successful. It forms the products CO_2 and NO.

Insufficient energy

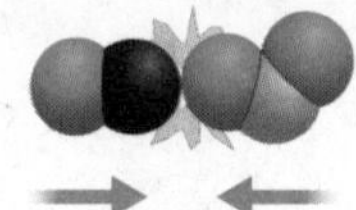

Unsuccessful Reactions If the reactants do not have enough energy, or their orientation during the collision is incorrect, then the reaction will be unsuccessful.

Incorrect orientation

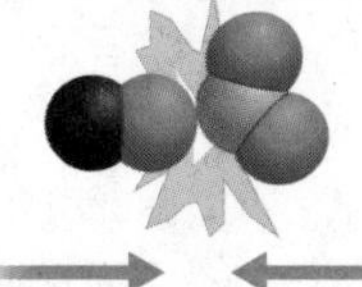

3 **SEP Use a Model The collision that forms an activated complex is like the passing of a baton in a relay race. The complex has partial bonds between atoms in the reactants and products. Relate electron sharing in an activated complex to the passing of a baton.**

Systems and Surroundings

A **system** is defined as a part of the universe on which you focus your attention. Everything else in the universe makes up the **surroundings.** Energy that moves from one object to another due to a temperature difference is **heat.** The transfer of energy happens through radiation or the collision of particles, with heat always flowing from warmer objects to cooler objects.

Conservation of Energy During any chemical or physical process, the energy of the universe remains the same. If the energy of a system increases, then that energy must have come from its surroundings.

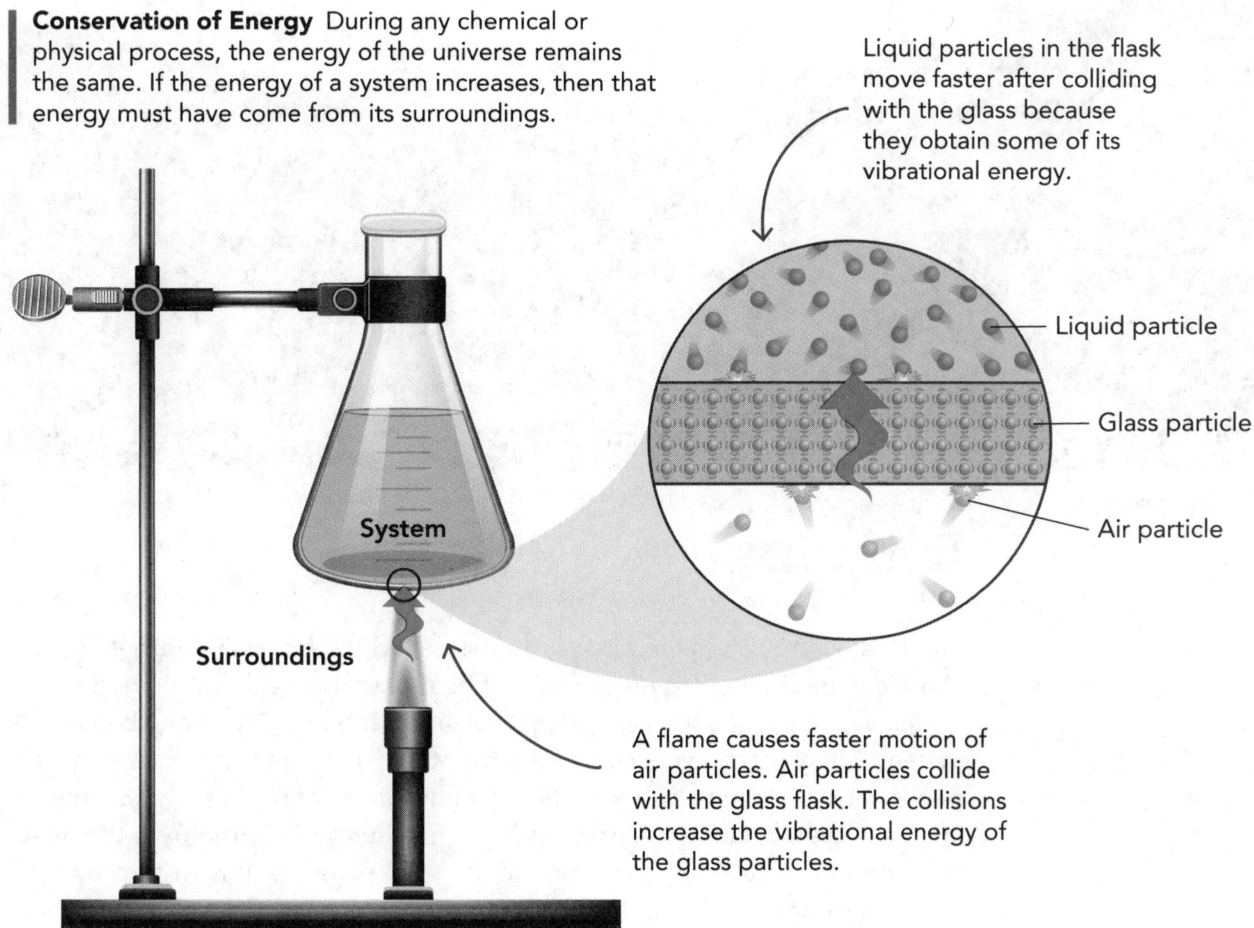

Liquid particles in the flask move faster after colliding with the glass because they obtain some of its vibrational energy.
Liquid particle
Glass particle
Air particle
System
Surroundings
A flame causes faster motion of air particles. Air particles collide with the glass flask. The collisions increase the vibrational energy of the glass particles.

4 **SEP Develop a Model When ice is dropped into warm water, it begins to melt. Define the system as the ice, and the surroundings as the warm water. Sketch a model similar to the figure, showing the flow of energy between ice and water. Include a molecular model showing how energy is transferred.**

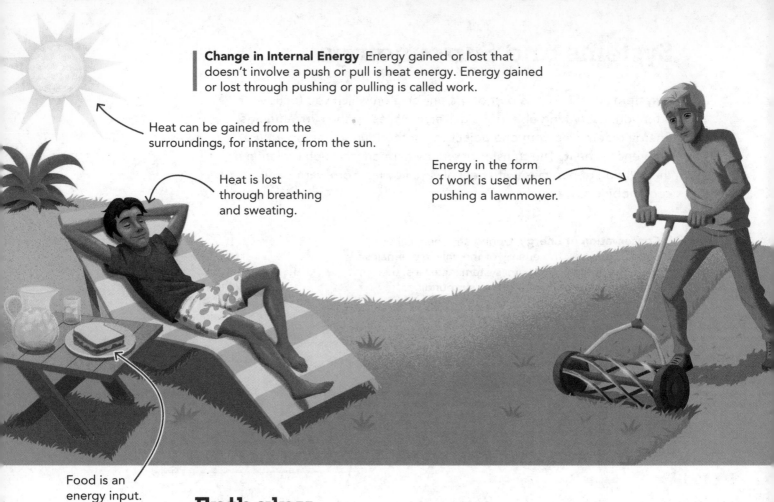

Change in Internal Energy Energy gained or lost that doesn't involve a push or pull is heat energy. Energy gained or lost through pushing or pulling is called work.

Heat can be gained from the surroundings, for instance, from the sun.

Heat is lost through breathing and sweating.

Energy in the form of work is used when pushing a lawnmower.

Food is an energy input.

Enthalpy

The total energy contained in a system is called the **internal energy.** The change in internal energy is the sum of heat absorbed and any work done on the system minus the sum of heat released and any work done by the system. Many reactions occur in systems at constant pressure, such as a beaker at atmospheric pressure. To account for heat flow in such systems, chemists use a quantity called enthalpy. The **change in enthalpy** is the heat absorbed or released by a reaction at constant pressure. It is written with the symbol ΔH.

5 CCC Energy and Matter **Similar to a beaker, an open pitcher of cold lemonade is a system at constant pressure. On the figure, label the system and the surroundings. Then sketch the flow of energy into and out of the system on a warm day.**

Bond Enthalpy

Energy in Bonds The amount of energy needed to break the bonds of one mole of a substance is called **bond enthalpy.** The changes in enthalpy can be shown in an **enthalpy diagram,** which is a representation of the relative enthalpy of a system undergoing a chemical change.

Energy is absorbed from the surroundings when a bond is broken. Energy is released to the surroundings when a bond is formed.

Energy absorbed by a system cools the surroundings. Energy released by a system warms the surroundings.

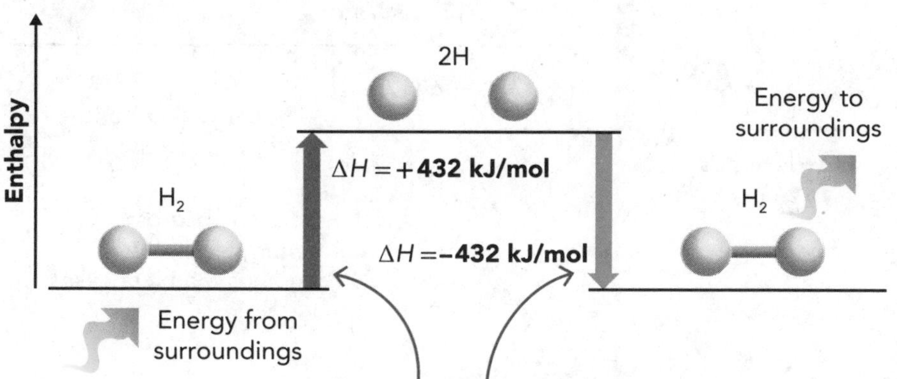

The same 432 kJ of energy required to break the bonds of one mole of hydrogen gas is released when those bonds form.

Breaking and Forming Bonds Breaking a bond is endothermic, with positive ΔH. Forming a bond is exothermic, with negative ΔH.

Average Bond Enthalpies

Bond	Enthalpy (kJ/mol)	Bond	Enthalpy (kJ/mol)	Bond	Enthalpy (kJ/mol)
H—H	432	H—I	295	N=N	418
H—F	565	I—I	151	N=O	607
O—H	467	N≡N	945	O=O	498

Bond Enthalpies The average bond enthalpies for some bonds are listed in the table. More extensive tables of average bond enthalpies can be found online. Actual bond enthalpy depends on the specific molecule in which the bond is found, but the tabulated values are good estimates.

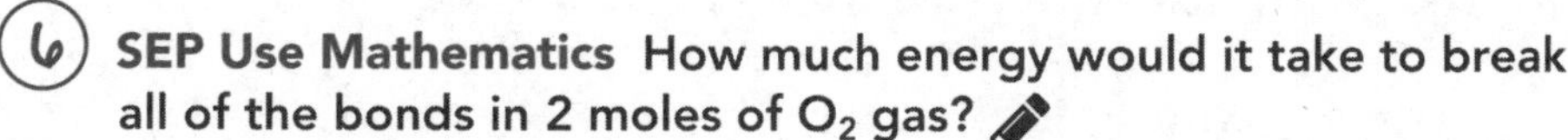

SEP Use Mathematics How much energy would it take to break all of the bonds in 2 moles of O_2 gas?

Using Bond Enthalpy to Estimate Reaction Enthalpy During a chemical reaction, bonds are broken and reformed in different ways. Since energy in reactions comes from the breaking and forming of bonds, you can use the average bond enthalpies to estimate the total change in energy for a reaction, which is called the **enthalpy of reaction.**

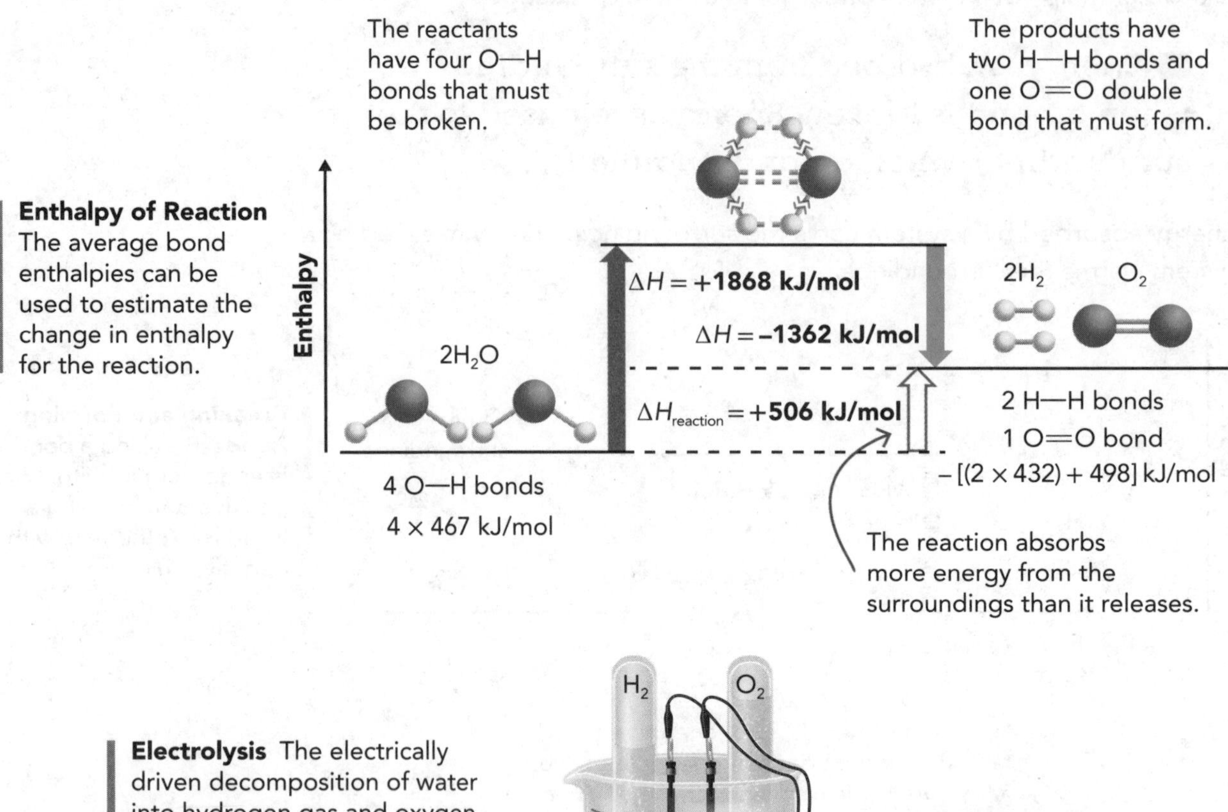

The reactants have four O—H bonds that must be broken.
The products have two H—H bonds and one O=O double bond that must form.
Enthalpy
2H2O
ΔH = +1868 kJ/mol
ΔH = –1362 kJ/mol
ΔHreaction = +506 kJ/mol
2H2
O2
4 O—H bonds
4 × 467 kJ/mol
2 H—H bonds
1 O=O bond
– [(2 × 432) + 498] kJ/mol
The reaction absorbs more energy from the surroundings than it releases.

Enthalpy of Reaction The average bond enthalpies can be used to estimate the change in enthalpy for the reaction.

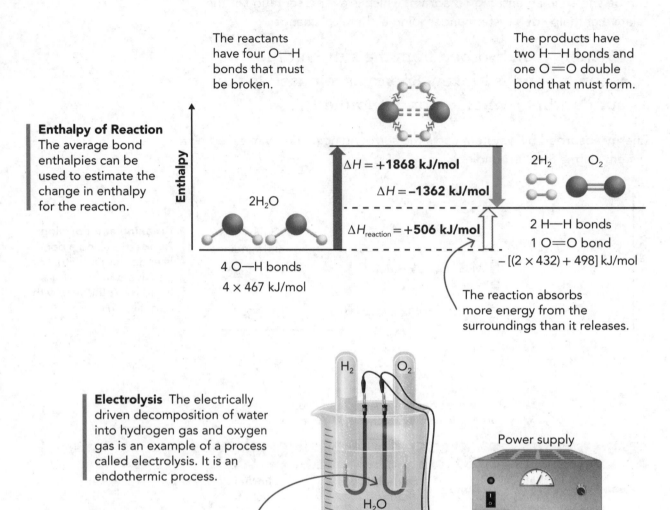

H_2

O_2

Power supply

H_2O (electrolyte solution)

Electrolysis The electrically driven decomposition of water into hydrogen gas and oxygen gas is an example of a process called electrolysis. It is an endothermic process.

The water (system) absorbs electrical energy through the electrodes (surroundings).

7 **SEP Use a Model Sketch an enthalpy diagram like the one shown, but for the reaction $N_2 + O_2 \rightarrow 2NO$. Use the bond enthalpy values on the previous page to estimate the change in enthalpy for the reaction.**

Activation Energy

The minimum energy that colliding particles must have in order to react is called the **activation energy.** The activation energy is the barrier that reactants must overcome before products can form. It is usually not necessary to break all the bonds in the reactants in order to form products, so the activation energy is less than the sum of the bond energies of the reactants.

Enthalpy Diagram for Combustion of Methane The combustion of methane is an exothermic reaction. The energy of the products is lower than the energy of the reactants. However, methane does not spontaneously ignite.

It takes energy to break bonds in the reactants before the reaction can proceed. That energy is typically supplied by a spark or match.

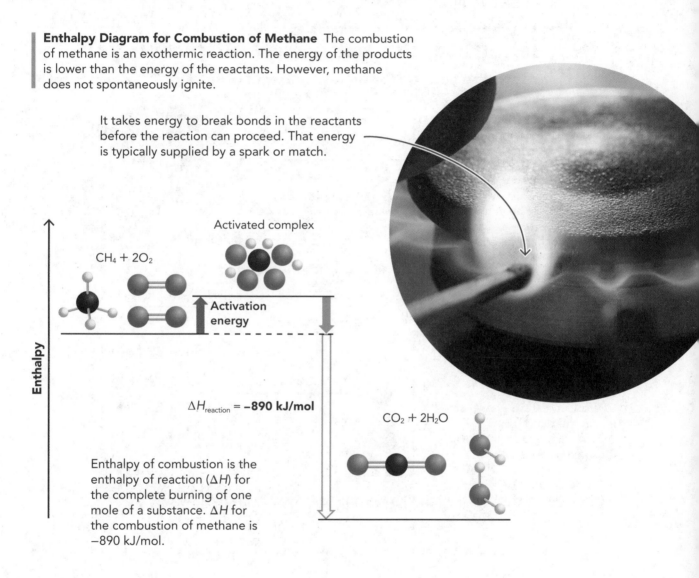

Activated complex

$CH_4 + 2O_2$

Activation energy

Enthalpy

$\Delta H_{reaction}$ = **−890 kJ/mol**

$CO_2 + 2H_2O$

Enthalpy of combustion is the enthalpy of reaction (ΔH) for the complete burning of one mole of a substance. ΔH for the combustion of methane is −890 kJ/mol.

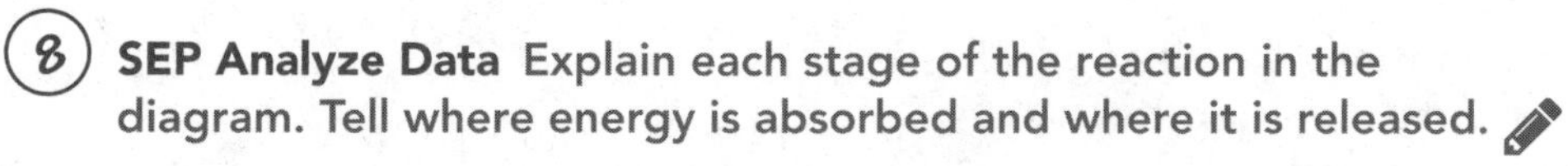

(8) **SEP Analyze Data Explain each stage of the reaction in the diagram. Tell where energy is absorbed and where it is released.**

Representations of Enthalpy

Enthalpy diagrams can be used to visually represent the changes in enthalpy for reactions. Another way to represent an enthalpy change is by writing it as part of a chemical equation. Such an expression is a **thermochemical equation,** with the enthalpy written as a product or a reactant. You can also write the enthalpy change as a separate algebraic equation to the side of the chemical equation.

Representing Enthalpy in Multiple Ways

How can you **model the enthalpy** of a reaction?

Exothermic Reaction
Calcium oxide, an ingredient of cement, gets hot when mixed with water. The **energy released** in such a reaction can be shown as a down arrow in an enthalpy diagram or written as part of a thermochemical equation.

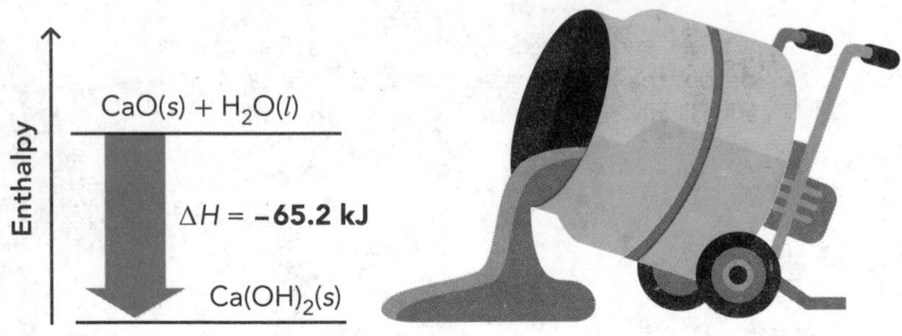

$CaO(s) + H_2O(l) \rightarrow Ca(OH)_2(s) + \mathbf{65.2\ kJ}$

$CaO(s) + H_2O(l) \rightarrow Ca(OH)_2(s)$ $\quad$ **$\Delta H = -65.2$ kJ**

Endothermic Reaction
Sodium bicarbonate, used in muffin batter, requires energy (heating in an oven) to produce the CO_2 gas that makes the batter rise. When **energy is absorbed,** it can be shown as an up arrow in an enthalpy diagram or written as part of a thermochemical equation.

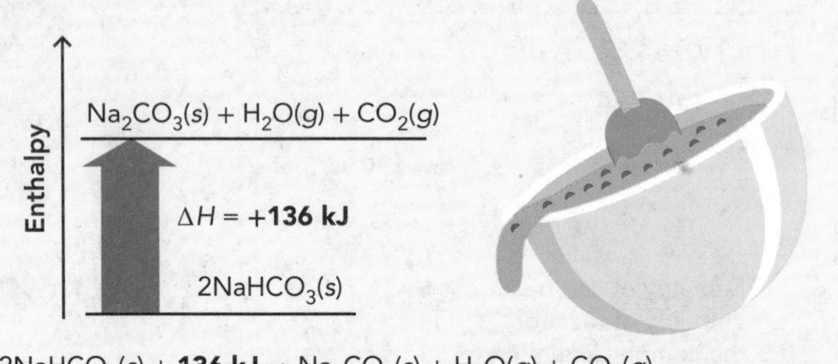

$2NaHCO_3(s) + \mathbf{136\ kJ} \rightarrow Na_2CO_3(s) + H_2O(g) + CO_2(g)$

$2NaHCO_3(s) \rightarrow Na_2CO_3(s) + H_2O(g) + CO_2(g)$ $\quad$ **$\Delta H = +136$ kJ**

9 **SEP Communicate Information** Sketch an enthalpy diagram and write a thermochemical equation for the following reaction:

$4FeO(s) + O_2(g) \rightarrow 2Fe_2O_3(s)$, $\Delta H = -561$ kJ

SAMPLE PROBLEM

Using Enthalpy of Reaction to Calculate Enthalpy Change

Calculate the amount of heat (in kJ) required to decompose 2.24 mol of $NaHCO_3(g)$.

$$2NaHCO_3(s) + 136\ kJ \rightarrow Na_2CO_3(s) + H_2O(g) + CO_2(g)$$

ANALYZE **List the knowns and the unknown.**

Knowns	Unknown
amount of $NaHCO_3$ = 2.24 mol	ΔH = ? kJ for 2.24 mol $NaHCO_3$
ΔH = 136 kJ for 2 mol $NaHCO_3$	

CALCULATE **Solve for the unknown.**

Use the thermochemical equation to determine the conversion factor relating kJ of heat and moles of $NaHCO_3$.

$$\frac{136\ kJ}{2\ mol\ NaHCO_3}$$

Using dimensional analysis, solve for ΔH.

$$\Delta H = 2.24\ \cancel{mol\ NaHCO_3} \times \frac{136\ kJ}{2\ \cancel{mol\ NaHCO_3}}$$

$$= 152\ kJ$$

EVALUATE **Does the result make sense?**

The 136 kJ in the thermochemical equation refers to the decomposition of 2 mol $NaHCO_3(s)$. Therefore, the decomposition of 2.24 mol should absorb more heat than 136 kJ. The answer of 152 kJ is consistent with the estimate. In addition, the heat is shown on the reactant side of the equation, which indicates an endothermic reaction. The answer should be positive for an endothermic reaction (heat absorption), and it is.

10 **The production of iron and carbon dioxide from iron(III) oxide and carbon monoxide is an exothermic reaction. How many kJ of heat are produced when 3.40 mol Fe_2O_3 reacts with an excess of CO?**

$$Fe_2O_3(s) + 3CO(g) \rightarrow 2Fe(s) + 3CO_2(g) + 26.3\ kJ$$

GO ONLINE for more practice problems.

Revisit

INVESTIGATIVE PHENOMENON

GO ONLINE to Elaborate on and Evaluate what you learned about colliding reactant particles and energy in chemical bonds by completing the class discussion and engineering design activities.

In the modeling worksheet you completed at the beginning of the investigation, you constructed a model for the flow of heat in a given scenario. With a partner, reevaluate your models.

(11) **CCC Energy and Matter During exercise, your body obtains energy from the carbohydrate glucose ($C_6H_{12}O_6$). The reaction has products CO_2 and H_2O. Formulate a balanced chemical equation for the combustion of glucose. Then sketch a qualitative enthalpy diagram for the release of energy from the reaction and how it depends on the changes in total bond energy.**

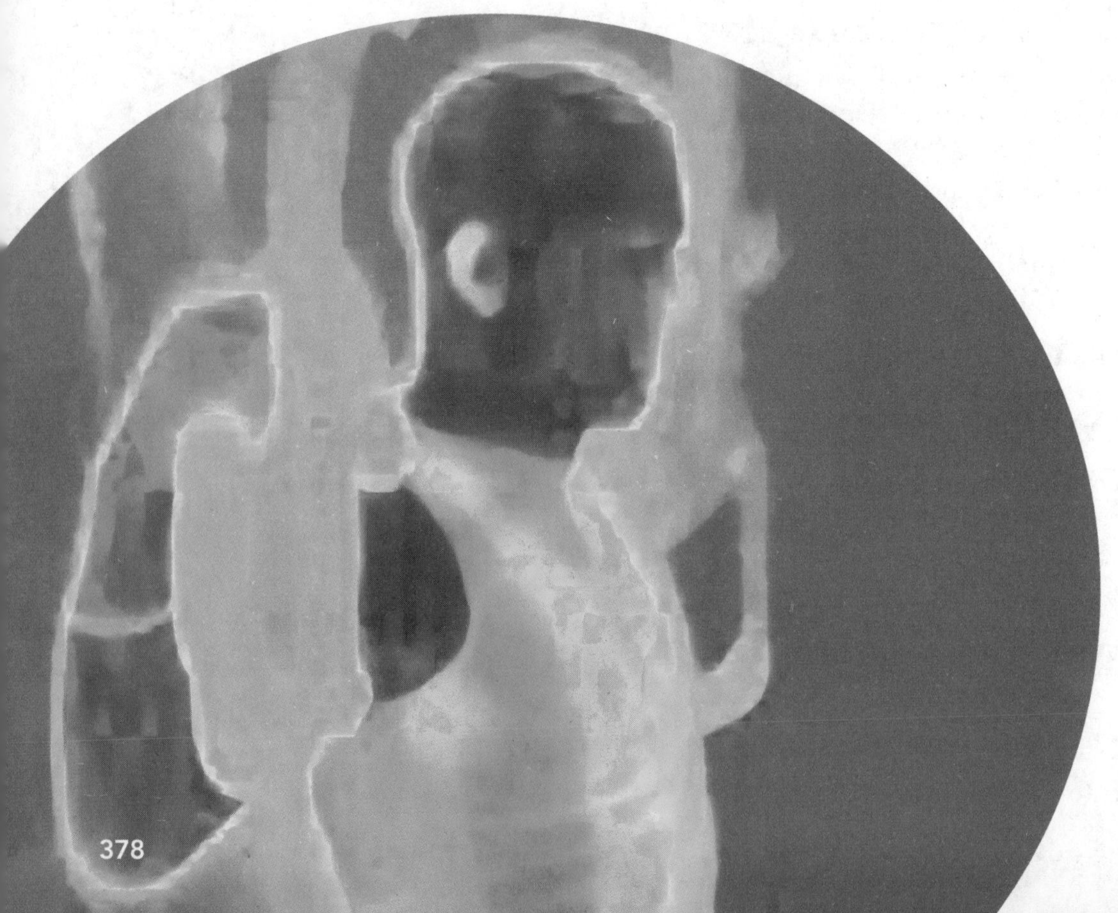

Enthalpies of Formation and Reaction

GO ONLINE to Explore and Explain the enthalpy changes involved in various chemical processes.

Hess's Law

Russian chemist Germain Hess determined in 1840 that the change in enthalpy for a chemical change is independent of the path the reaction takes. The path independence of the energy in reactions is referred to as Hess's law. Converting reactants A directly into products B results in an enthalpy change ΔH_{AB}.

If reactants A change to intermediate C, which then changes into products B, then the enthalpy change will still be ΔH_{AB}.

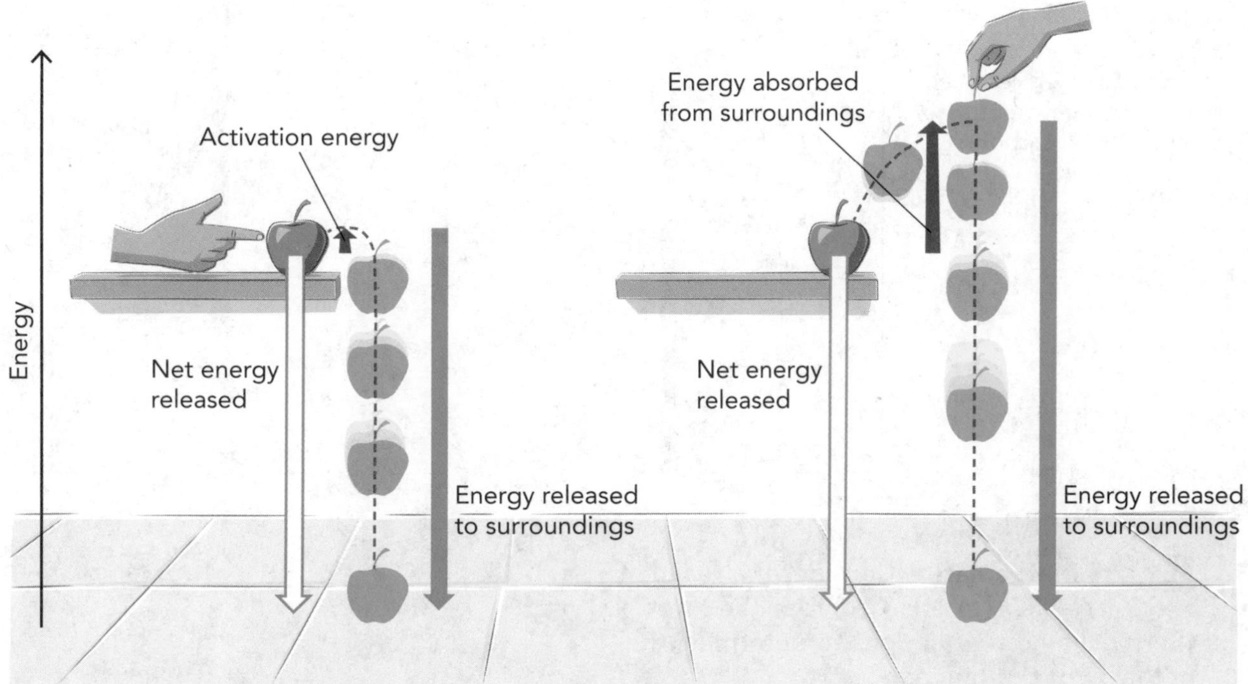

Direct Path Suppose an apple (the system) falls from a shelf to the floor. It hits the floor and releases a certain amount of energy.

Indirect Path If you lift the apple above the shelf and then drop it, it will hit the floor with greater energy. The net energy released is the same in both cases when you account for the extra energy the apple absorbed as you lifted it.

Heat Summation

Hess's law of heat summation states that if you add two or more thermochemical equations to give an overall equation, you can also add the enthalpies of reaction to give the overall enthalpy of reaction. The law allows you to determine the enthalpy of reaction indirectly by using the known enthalpies of reaction of two or more thermochemical equations. For example, carbon and water vapor react to form carbon dioxide and hydrogen. However, the reaction includes an intermediate step. The complete reaction can be represented as the sum of two reactions. If you add the two thermochemical equations, you get the equation for the carbon-and-water reaction, with the oxygen gas canceling because it's on both sides of the equation. You get the enthalpy of reaction by adding the enthalpies for the two reactions.

$$C(s) + 2H_2O(g) \rightarrow CO_2(g) + 2H_2(g)$$

$$2H_2O(g) \rightarrow 2H_2(g) + O_2(g) \qquad \Delta H = +483.6 \text{ kJ/mol}$$

$$+\ C(s) + O_2(g) \rightarrow CO_2(g) \qquad +\ \Delta H = -393.5 \text{ kJ/mol}$$

$$C(s) + \cancel{O_2(g)} + 2H_2O(g) \rightarrow CO_2(g) + 2H_2(g) + \cancel{O_2(g)} \qquad \Delta H = +90.1 \text{ kJ/mol}$$

Summing Two Reactions
In the first step of the reaction, water dissociates into hydrogen gas and oxygen gas. The hydrogen becomes a product for the overall reaction. Oxygen gas is an intermediate reactant that combines with carbon.

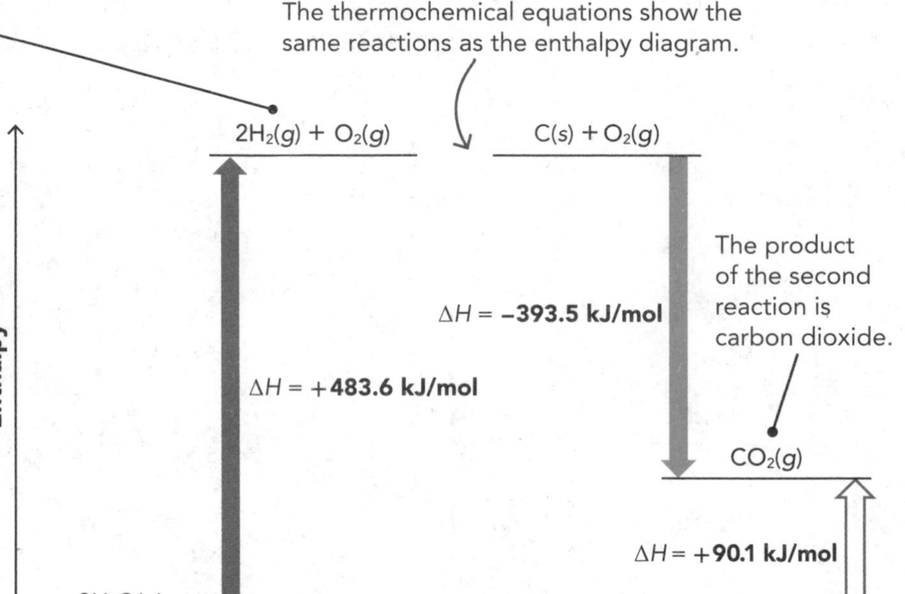

(12) **SEP Use Mathematics Consider the reaction $H_2SO_4(l) \rightarrow SO_3(g) + H_2O(g)$. Use the three thermochemical equations to determine the enthalpy of the reaction.**

$H_2SO_4(l) \rightarrow H_2S(g) + 2O_2(g)$ $\quad \Delta H = 235.5$ kJ/mol

$H_2S(g) + 2O_2(g) \rightarrow SO_3(g) + H_2O(l)$ $\quad \Delta H = -207.0$ kJ/mol

$H_2O(l) \rightarrow H_2O(g)$ $\quad \Delta H = 44.0$ kJ/mol

Standard Enthalpy of Formation

The **standard enthalpy of formation** ($\Delta H_f°$) of a compound is the change in enthalpy when one mole of the compound is formed from its elements, with all substances in their standard states. The **standard state** is the stable form of a substance at a temperature of 25°C and a pressure of 100 kPa, which may be a solid, liquid, or gas. The standard enthalpy of formation for a free element in its standard state is set at zero.

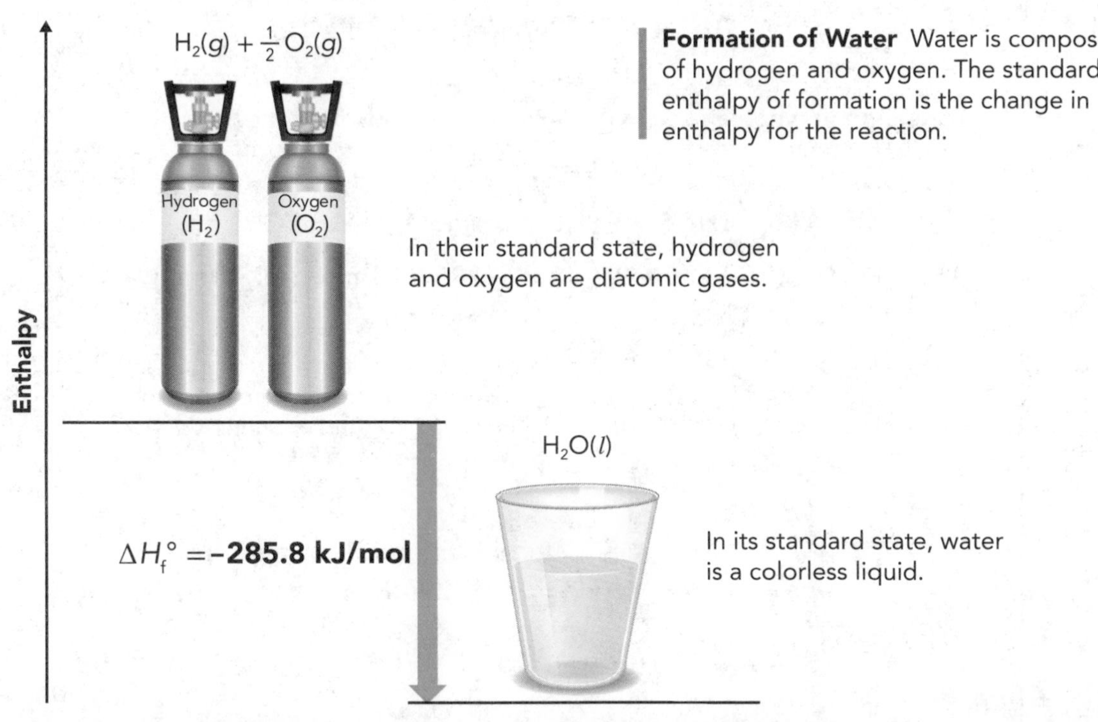

Formation of Water Water is composed of hydrogen and oxygen. The standard enthalpy of formation is the change in enthalpy for the reaction.

In their standard state, hydrogen and oxygen are diatomic gases.

In its standard state, water is a colorless liquid.

Standard Enthalpies of Formation at 25°C and 101.3 kPa

Substance	$\Delta H_f°$ (kJ/mol)	Substance	$\Delta H_f°$ (kJ/mol)	Substance	$\Delta H_f°$ (kJ/mol)
$H_2(g)$	0.0	C(s, graphite)	0.0	$SO_2(g)$	−296.8
$O_2(g)$	0.0	C(s, diamond)	1.9	$SO_3(g)$	−395.7
$H_2O(l)$	**−285.8**	$CO(g)$	−110.5	$NO(g)$	90.37
$H_2O(g)$	−241.8	$CO_2(g)$	−393.5	$NO_2(g)$	33.85

Standard Enthalpies of Formation The values for water and several other common substances are listed in the table.

13 **SEP Develop a Model** **Identify the standard states of the elements that make up CO_2, and then sketch an enthalpy diagram for its formation. Use the table to find the standard enthalpy of formation.**

Standard Enthalpy of Reaction

For a reaction that occurs at 25°C and 100 kPa, you can calculate the enthalpy of reaction by using the standard enthalpies of formation. The change in enthalpy when one mole of matter undergoes a chemical reaction at standard conditions is called the **standard enthalpy of reaction** ($\Delta H°$). The standard enthalpy of reaction is the difference between the standard enthalpies of formation of all the products and all the reactants:

$$\Delta H° = \Delta H_f°(\text{products}) - \Delta H_f°(\text{reactants})$$

For example, you can calculate $\Delta H°$ for the following reaction:

$$2SO_2(g) + O_2(g) \rightarrow 2SO_3(g)$$

$$\Delta H° = [2 \times \Delta H_f°(SO_3)] - [2 \times \Delta H_f°(SO_2) + \Delta H_f°(O_2)]$$

$$\Delta H° = [2 \times (-395.7 \text{ kJ/mol})] - [2 \times (-296.8 \text{ kJ/mol}) - 0 \text{ kJ/mol}]$$

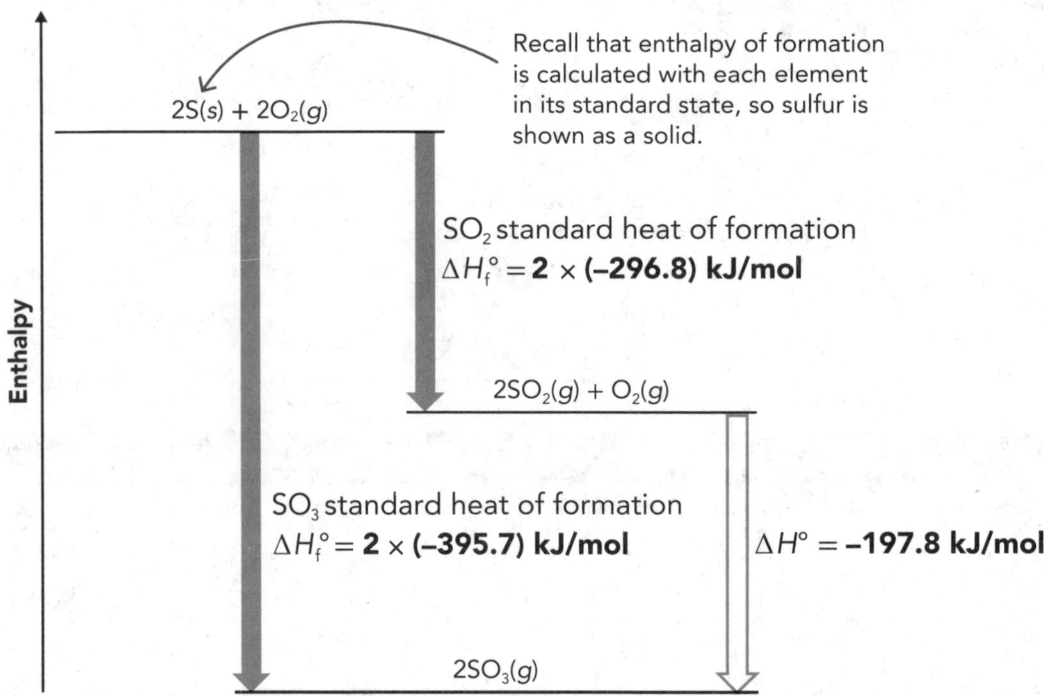

Overall Enthalpy The standard enthalpies of formation for sulfur dioxide, sulfur trioxide, and oxygen are used to calculate the standard enthalpy of the reaction.

(14) **SEP Construct an Explanation** **Look at the enthalpy diagram and construct an explanation for why $\Delta H_f°$ for both SO_3 and SO_2 is multiplied by two. Also, explain why $\Delta H_f°$ for O_2 is not shown.**

SAMPLE PROBLEM

Calculating the Standard Enthalpy of Reaction

What is the standard enthalpy of reaction ($\Delta H°$) for the reaction of $CO(g)$ with $O_2(g)$ to form $CO_2(g)$?

ANALYZE List the knowns and the unknown.

Knowns	Unknown
$\Delta H_f° CO(g) = -110.5$ kJ/mol	$\Delta H° = ?$ kJ
$\Delta H_f° O_2(g) = 0.0$ kJ/mol	
$\Delta H_f° CO_2(g) = -393.5$ kJ/mol	

CALCULATE Solve for the unknown.

Write a balanced chemical equation.

$$2CO(g) + O_2(g) \rightarrow 2CO_2(g)$$

Add $\Delta H_f°$ of all of the reactants.

$$\Delta H_f°(\text{reactants}) = \begin{cases} 2\ \cancel{\text{mol } CO(g)} \times \dfrac{-110.5\text{ kJ}}{1\ \cancel{\text{mol } CO(g)}} + \\ 1\ \cancel{\text{mol } O_2(g)} \times \dfrac{0.0\text{ kJ}}{1\ \cancel{\text{mol } O_2(g)}} \end{cases}$$

$$= -221.0\text{ kJ}$$

Add $\Delta H_f°$ of all of the products.

$$\Delta H_f°(\text{products}) = 2\ \cancel{\text{mol } CO_2(g)} \times \frac{-393.5\text{ kJ}}{1\ \cancel{\text{mol } CO_2(g)}}$$

$$= -787.0\text{ kJ}$$

Calculate $\Delta H°$ for the reaction using the formula.

$$\Delta H° = \Delta H_f°(\text{products}) - \Delta H_f°(\text{reactants})$$

$$= (-787.0\text{ kJ}) - (-221.0\text{ kJ})$$

$$= -566.0\text{ kJ}$$

EVALUATE Does the result make sense?

The $\Delta H°$ is negative, so the reaction is exothermic. The outcome makes sense, because combustion reactions always release heat.

What is the standard enthalpy of reaction ($\Delta H°$) for the formation of $NO_2(g)$ from $NO(g)$ and $O_2(g)$?

15

GO ONLINE for more practice problems.

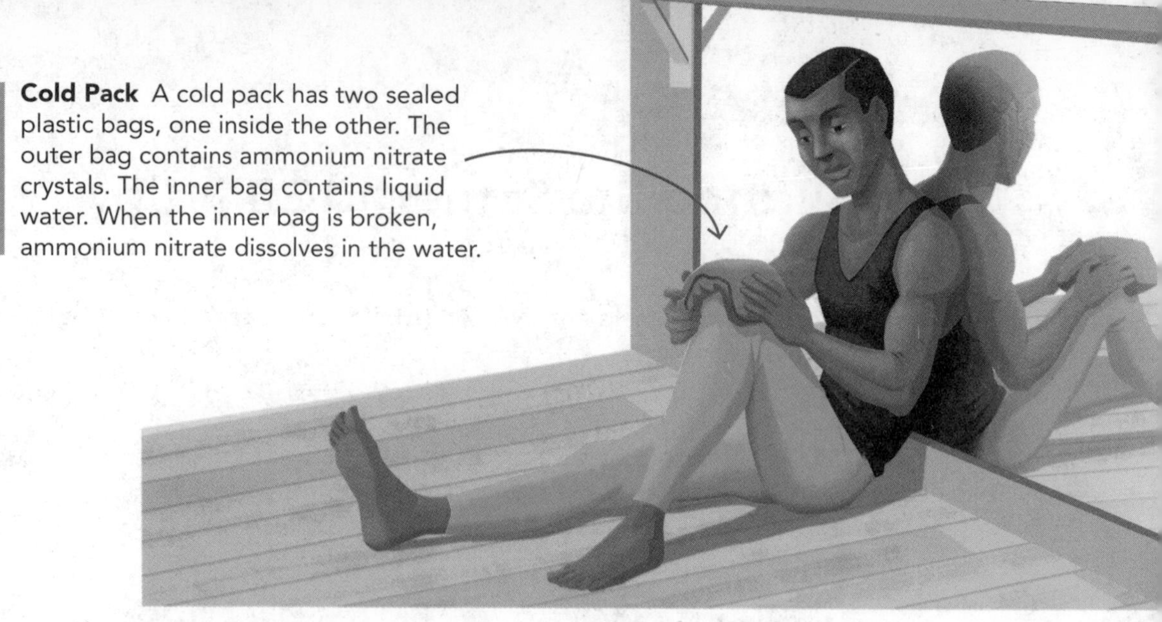

Cold Pack A cold pack has two sealed plastic bags, one inside the other. The outer bag contains ammonium nitrate crystals. The inner bag contains liquid water. When the inner bag is broken, ammonium nitrate dissolves in the water.

Enthalpy of Solution

During the formation of a solution, heat is either released or absorbed. The enthalpy change caused by the dissolution of one mole of substance is called the **molar enthalpy of solution** (ΔH_{soln}). Water molecules are polar, so there are dipole interactions between the partially positive and negative ends of neighboring molecules. These forces attract water molecules to one another, and they are also effective in breaking the bonds of solids with ionic structure. Whether a solid has an ionic structure or a molecular structure, attractive forces must be overcome to dissolve it. Breaking up those attractive forces is an endothermic process. Forming solvation shells, or surrounding the solute with water molecules, is an exothermic process. The enthalpy of solution is the difference in enthalpy between breaking up attractive forces and forming solvation shells.

Solution Formation Energy is absorbed to overcome intermolecular forces in molecular solids and to break bonds in ionic solids. Energy is released when solvation shells are formed. Depending on the difference between those two quantities, a solution-forming process can be either endothermic or exothermic.

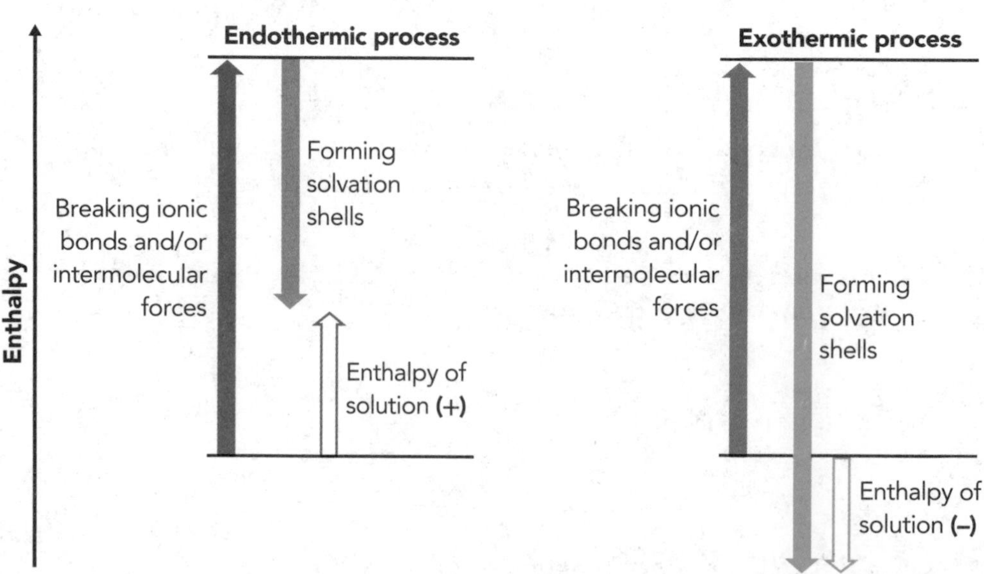

16 **SEP Design a Solution** Suppose you are designing an instant heat pack. Would you select a compound with a positive value or a negative value of ΔH_{soln} in water?

SAMPLE PROBLEM

Calculating the Enthalpy Change in Solution Formation

When 1 mol of NaOH(*s*) is dissolved in water, 44.5 kJ of heat are released. How much heat is released when 2.50 mol of NaOH(*s*) is dissolved in water?

ANALYZE List the knowns and the unknown.

Knowns	Unknown
$\Delta H_{soln} = -44.5$ kJ/mol	$\Delta H = ?$ kJ
amount of NaOH(*s*) dissolved = 2.50 mol	

CALCULATE Solve for the unknown.

Write the known ΔH_{soln} as a conversion factor.

$$\frac{-44.5 \text{ kJ}}{1 \text{ mol NaOH}(s)}$$

Multiply the number of moles by the conversion factor.

$$\Delta H = 2.50 \cancel{\text{mol NaOH}(s)} \times \frac{-44.5 \text{ kJ}}{1 \cancel{\text{mol NaOH}(s)}} = -111 \text{ kJ}$$

EVALUATE Does the result make sense?

ΔH is 2.5 times greater than ΔH_{soln}, as it should be. Also, ΔH should be negative because the dissolution of NaOH(*s*) in water is exothermic.

17 How many moles of $NH_4NO_3(s)$ must be dissolved in water so that 88.0 kJ of heat is absorbed from the water? ΔH_{soln} for the dissolution of $NH_4NO_3(s)$ in water is 25.7 kJ/mol.

GO ONLINE for more practice problems.

Revisit

INVESTIGATIVE PHENOMENON

GO ONLINE to Elaborate on and Evaluate what you learned about energy changes in chemical processes by completing the class discussion and writing activities.

In the modeling worksheet you completed at the beginning of the investigation, you constructed a model for the flow of heat in a given scenario. With a partner, reevaluate your models.

18 **SEP Use Mathematics The table shows the standard enthalpies of formation for the reactants and products involved in the reaction for the combustion of glucose ($C_6H_{12}O_6$). Use the data to calculate the standard enthalpy for this combustion reaction.**

Compound	$\Delta H_f°$ (kJ/mol)
$C_6H_{12}O_6(s)$	−1271
$O_2(g)$	0
$CO_2(g)$	−393.5
$H_2O(l)$	−285.8

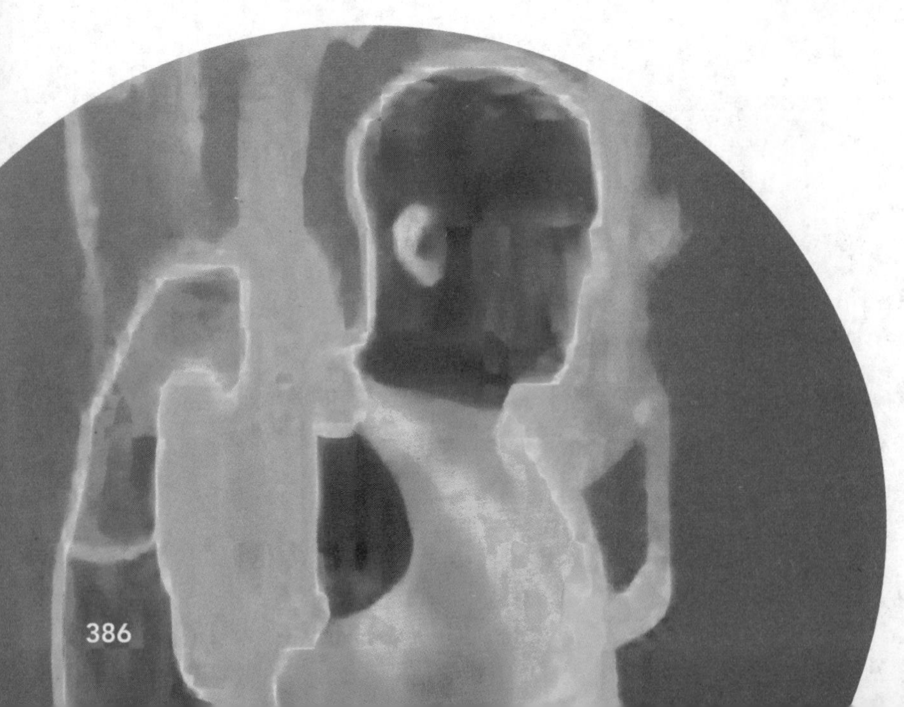

EXPERIENCE 3

Enthalpy in Changes of State

GO ONLINE to Explore and Explain the enthalpy changes involved in changes of state.

Heat During Phase Changes

As you add heat to a material, the temperature of the material changes. However, there is a certain point where the temperature stops increasing as you add energy. That happens because the material is undergoing a phase change. A phase change occurs when adding or removing heat changes how the particles are arranged in a substance.

Unlike a chemical reaction, a phase change involves no forming or breaking of chemical bonds within molecules, or other changes to constituent particles. In the example shown, ice, liquid water, and water vapor are composed of the same H_2O molecules. Hydrogen bonding gives water higher melting and boiling points than other compounds of similar molecular weight. When water undergoes a phase change, it is these hydrogen bonds that break, not the intramolecular chemical bonds.

Heating Curve The graph shows the enthalpy changes that happen during two phase changes for water. The temperature stops rising because all the added energy goes into changing water's intermolecular structure instead of increasing the kinetic energy of the molecules.

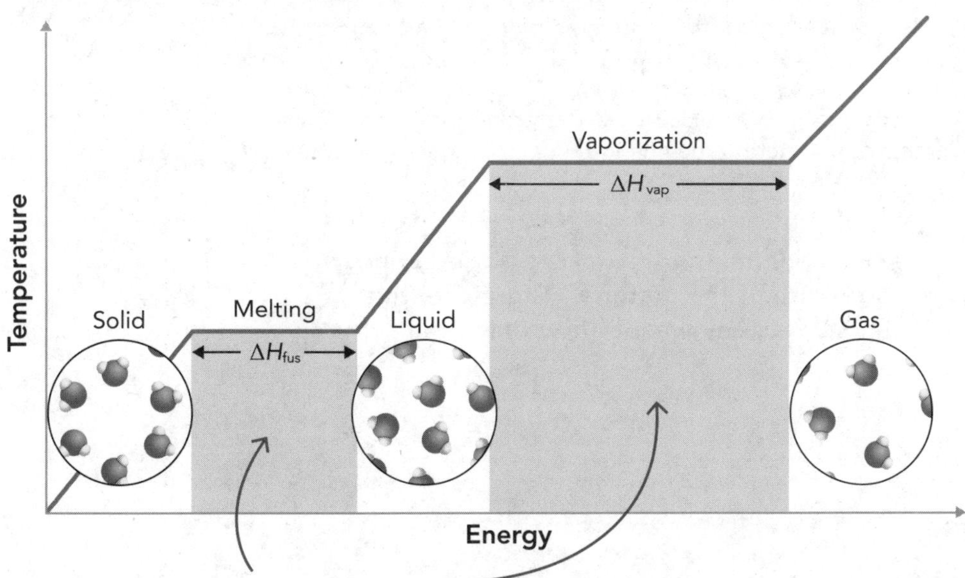

ΔH_{fus} is less than ΔH_{vap} because less energy is required to disrupt the hexagonal structure of ice than to separate the molecules of water.

Enthalpy of Fusion and Solidification

The heat absorbed by one mole of a solid substance as it melts to a liquid at constant temperature is called the **molar enthalpy of fusion** (ΔH_{fus}). The **molar enthalpy of solidification** (ΔH_{solid}) is the heat lost when one mole of a liquid substance solidifies at constant temperature. The heat absorbed by a melting solid is the same as the heat released by the liquid solidifying:

$$\Delta H_{fus} = -\Delta H_{solid}$$

Freezing Water Converting one mole of liquid water to one mole of ice releases 6.01 kJ of heat. The highly-organized hexagonal arrangement of molecules in the solid state is lower in energy.

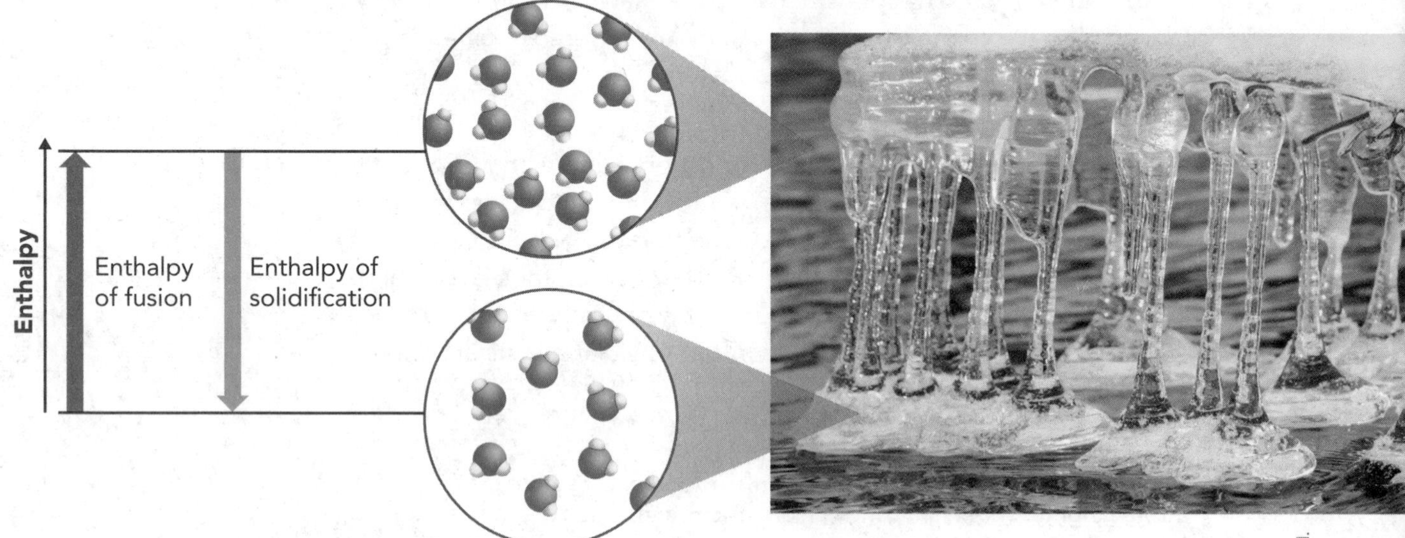

Melting Ice Converting one mole of ice to one mole of liquid water requires the absorption of 6.01 kJ of heat. The energy is used to change the structure of the system instead of the kinetic energy of the particles. Therefore, the temperature remains 0°C during the change.

19 **SEP Plan an Investigation** **During melting, all of the added energy goes into changing the structure of the material. Therefore, the temperature doesn't change. Plan an investigation that would test that claim.**

SAMPLE PROBLEM

Using the Heat of Fusion in Phase-Change Calculations

How many grams of ice at 0°C will melt if 2.25 kJ of heat is added?

ANALYZE **List the knowns and the unknown.**

Knowns	Unknown
$\Delta H_{fus} = 6.01$ kJ/mol	$m_{ice} = ?$ g
$\Delta H = 2.25$ kJ	

CALCULATE **Solve for the unknown.**

Write the known ΔH_{fus} as a conversion factor.

$$\frac{1 \text{ mol } H_2O(s)}{6.01 \text{ kJ}}$$

Write the molar mass of ice as a conversion factor.

$$\frac{18 \text{ g } H_2O(s)}{1 \text{ mol } H_2O(s)}$$

Multiply the known enthalpy change by the conversion factors.

$$m_{ice} = 2.25 \cancel{\text{kJ}} \times \frac{1 \cancel{\text{mol } H_2O(s)}}{6.01 \cancel{\text{kJ}}} \times \frac{18 \text{ g } H_2O(s)}{1 \cancel{\text{mol } H_2O(s)}}$$

$$= 6.74 \text{ g } H_2O(s)$$

EVALUATE **Does the result make sense?**

To melt one mole of ice, 6.01 kJ of energy is required. The added 2.25 kJ of heat is about one third the amount of heat needed to melt one mole of ice, so only about one third of a mole of ice, or 18.0 g ÷ 3 = 6 g, should melt. That estimate is close to the calculated answer.

20 **How many kJ of heat are required to melt a 50.0-g popsicle at 0°C? Assume the popsicle has the same molar mass and enthalpy of fusion as water.**

GO ONLINE for more practice problems.

Enthalpy of Vaporization and Condensation

The heat absorbed by one mole of a liquid substance as it vaporizes at constant temperature is called the **molar enthalpy of vaporization** (ΔH_{vap}). The heat lost by one mole of a gas substance as it condenses at its normal boiling point is the **molar enthalpy of condensation** (ΔH_{cond}). The heat absorbed by a vaporizing liquid is the same as the heat released by a condensing gas:

$$\Delta H_{vap} = -\Delta H_{cond}$$

Condensing Steam Converting one mole of water vapor to one mole of liquid water releases 40.7 kJ of heat. The release of energy comes from the formation of hydrogen bonds in the liquid phase of water.

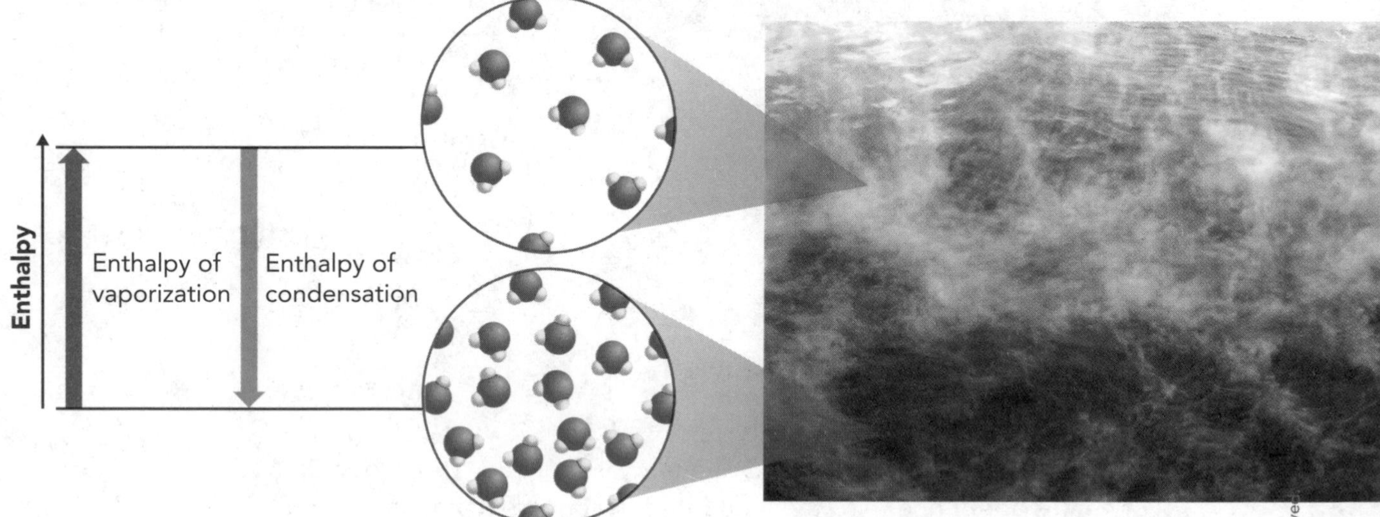

Vaporizing Water Converting one mole of liquid water to one mole of water vapor requires the absorption of 40.7 kJ of heat. The energy is used to break the hydrogen bonds between molecules instead of increasing the kinetic energy of the particles.

21 **SEP Develop a Model** **The structure of diethyl ether ($C_4H_{10}O$) is shown. Sketch a model that shows four $C_4H_{10}O$ molecules in the liquid state and four in the gas state. Include intermolecular forces in your model.**

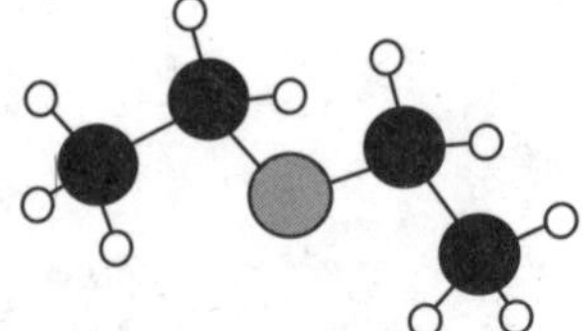

SAMPLE PROBLEM

Using the Heat of Vaporization in Phase-Change Calculations

How much heat (in kJ) is absorbed when 24.8 g $H_2O(l)$ at 100°C is converted to $H_2O(g)$ at 100°C?

ANALYZE List the knowns and the unknown.

Knowns	Unknown
mass of liquid water converted to vapor = 24.8 g	$\Delta H = ?$ kJ
$\Delta H_{vap} = 40.7$ kJ/mol	

CALCULATE Solve for the unknown.

Write the known ΔH_{vap} as a conversion factor.

$$\frac{40.7\text{ kJ}}{1\text{ mol }H_2O(l)}$$

Write the molar mass of water as a conversion factor.

$$\frac{1\text{ mol }H_2O(l)}{18\text{ g }H_2O(l)}$$

Multiply the mass of water in grams by the conversion factors.

$$\Delta H = 24.8\text{ g }H_2O(l) \times \frac{40.7\text{ kJ}}{1\text{ mol }H_2O(l)} \times \frac{1\text{ mol }H_2O(l)}{18\text{ g }H_2O(l)}$$

$$= 56.1\text{ kJ}$$

EVALUATE Does the result make sense?

Knowing the molar mass of water is 18.0 g/mol, you can estimate that 24.8 g $H_2O(l)$ is somewhat less than 1.5 mol H_2O. The calculated enthalpy change should be a little less than 1.5 mol × 40 kJ/mol = 60 kJ, and it is.

22 **How many kJ of heat are absorbed when 0.46 g of chloroethane (C_2H_5Cl) vaporizes at its boiling point? The molar heat of vaporization of chloroethane is 24.7 kJ/mol.**

GO ONLINE for more practice problems.

Structure and Changes of State

Unlike with chemical reactions, the molecules or other representative particles remain the same in a change of state. Since the molecules do not change, no chemical bonds are broken or formed. However, the way the molecules are structured and how they are connected through intermolecular forces does change.

Therefore, the strengths of intermolecular forces and the sizes of particles can be used to predict the relative amount of energy required to change the phase of a substance.

Enthalpy of Vaporization

How can you **predict relative values of enthalpy** of vaporization?

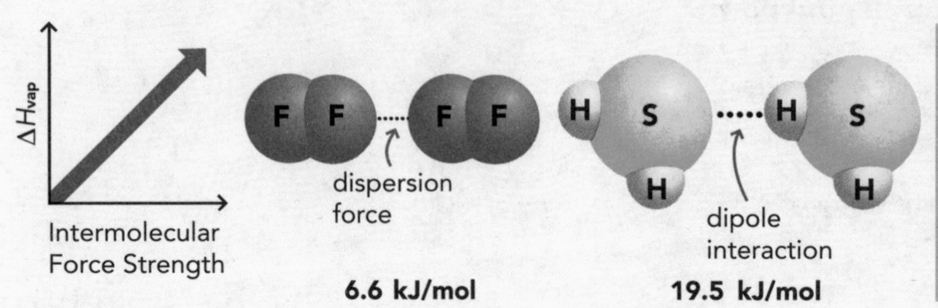

Intermolecular Force It takes more energy to vaporize a substance that is held together more strongly. **The stronger the intermolecular force, the greater is the value of ΔH_{vap}.**

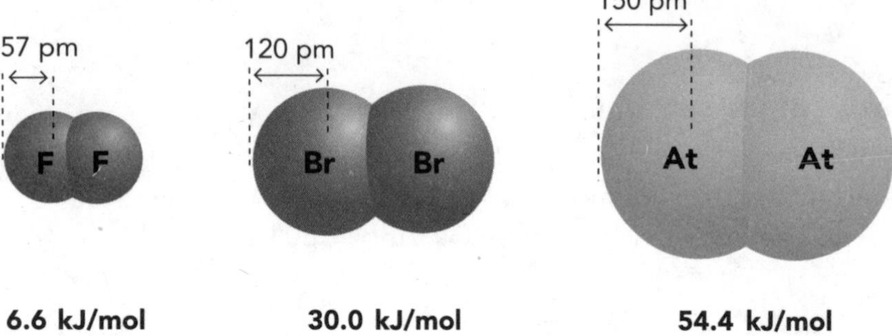

Size Atomic radii increase as you go down the halogen column on the periodic table. **The values for ΔH_{vap} increase with increasing atomic radius.**

(23) **CCC Patterns** Graph the size versus ΔH_{vap} data shown in the figure. Use your graph to estimate ΔH_{vap} for the remaining halogens, diatomic chlorine (102 pm) and iodine (139 pm).

Evaporation Water molecules evaporate at the surface of a lake, but the lake, of course is not boiling.

Evaporation

A liquid doesn't have to be boiling for vaporization to occur. Below the boiling point, most of the particles don't have enough energy to overcome the intermolecular forces and escape into the gaseous state. However, since the individual kinetic energies of particles fall within a wide distribution, some particles at the surface of a liquid do have enough energy to break free. The process is called evaporation.

Kinetic Energy Distribution There is not a single value that characterizes the kinetic energies of particles in a substance. Instead, kinetic energies of particles have a wide range.

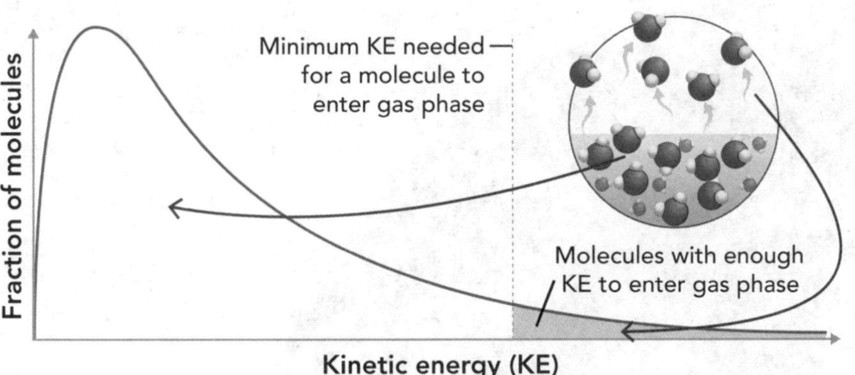

If a particle has enough energy to escape intermolecular forces and a free path to do so, then it will go into the gas phase. The free-path requirement means that evaporation happens only at surfaces.

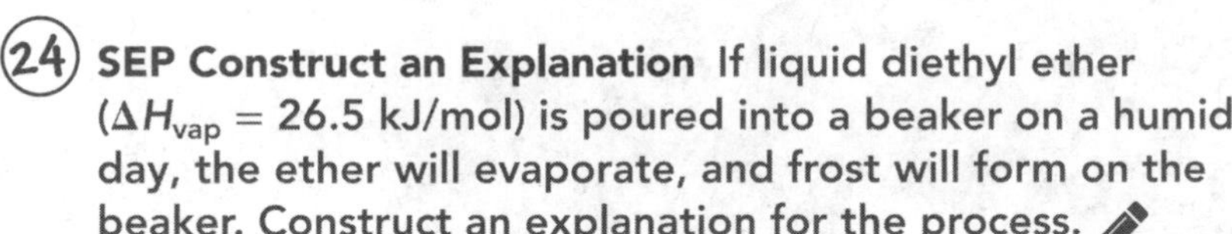

24 SEP Construct an Explanation If liquid diethyl ether (ΔH_{vap} = 26.5 kJ/mol) is poured into a beaker on a humid day, the ether will evaporate, and frost will form on the beaker. Construct an explanation for the process.

Revisit

INVESTIGATIVE PHENOMENON

GO ONLINE to Elaborate on and Evaluate what you learned about energy changes in changes of state by completing the peer review and writing activities.

In the modeling worksheet you completed at the beginning of the investigation, you constructed a model for the flow of heat in a given scenario. With a partner, reevaluate your models.

25 **SEP Construct an Explanation When you exercise, your body produces perspiration, which then evaporates from the surface of your skin. Construct an explanation for how perspiring can help cool the body during exercise.**

....

....

....

....

....

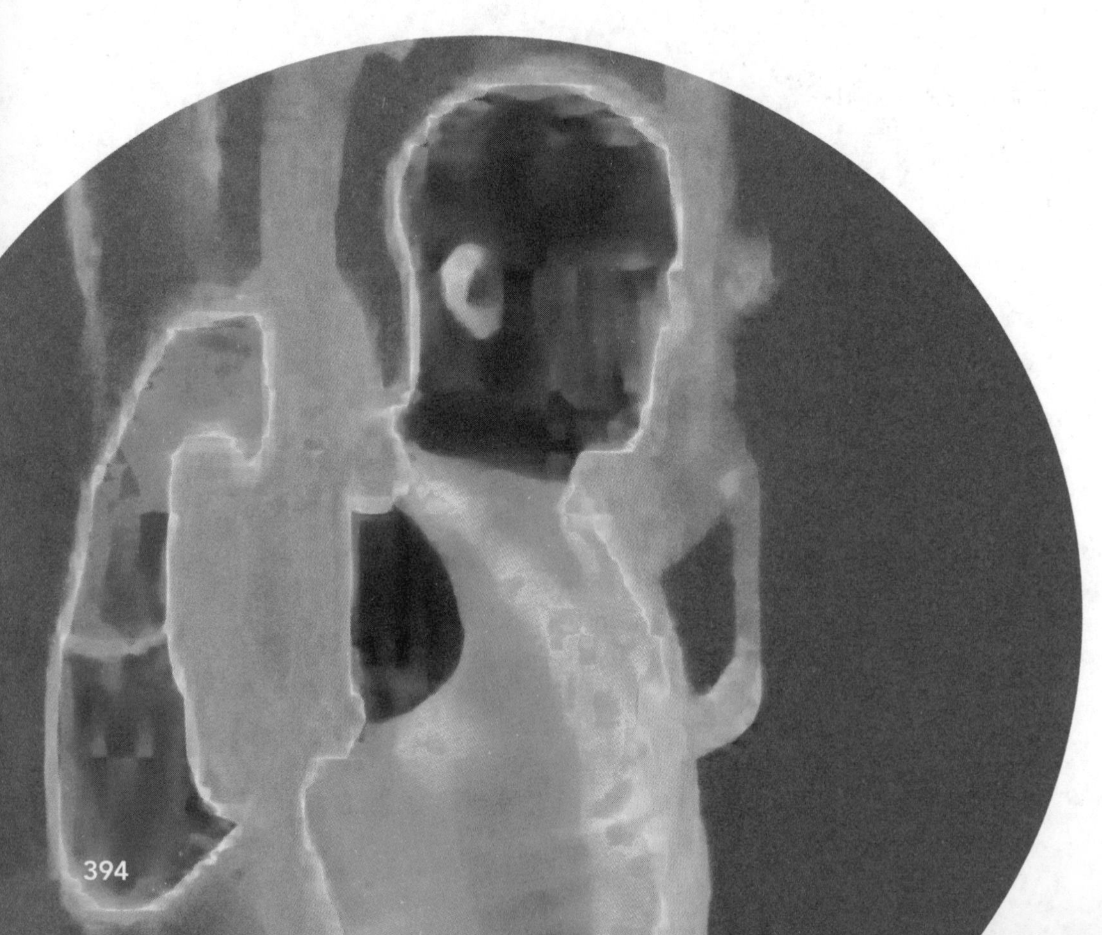

GO ONLINE to Evaluate what you learned about thermochemistry by using the available assessment resources.

In the Performance-Based Assessment, you investigated and analyzed the energy changes involved in a particular reaction between an acid and a base. Wrap up your analysis by answering the following question.

26 **SEP Energy and Matter You carried out the exothermic neutralization reaction NaOH(*aq*) + HCl(*aq*) → NaCl(*aq*) + H_2O(*l*). What bonds were broken and what bonds were formed that resulted in a net release of energy?**

Revisit

ANCHORING PHENOMENON

27 **Apply what you learned in Instructional Segment 3 to answer the Anchoring Phenomenon question "How can we produce better foods?"**

GO ONLINE for a **problem-based learning** activity that you can tackle after completing Instructional Segment 3.

End-of-Book Resources

APPENDIX A REFERENCE TABLES

TABLE A.1	
PHYSICAL CONSTANTS	
Atomic mass unit	1 amu = 1.6605×10^{-24} g
Avogadro's number	$N = 6.02 \times 10^{23}$ particles/mol
Gas constant	$R = 8.31$ L•kPa/K•mol
Ideal gas molar volume	$V_m = 22.4$ L/mol
Masses of subatomic particles	
Electron (e^-)	$m_e = 0.000549$ amu $= 9.1094 \times 10^{-28}$ g
Proton (p^+)	$m_p = 1.00728$ amu $= 1.67262 \times 10^{-24}$ g
Neutron (n^0)	$m_n = 1.00867$ amu $= 1.67493 \times 10^{-24}$ g
Speed of light in a vacuum	$c = 3.00 \times 10^8$ m/s

TABLE A.2					
COMMON SYMBOLS AND ABBREVIATIONS					
α	alpha rays	GWP	global warming potential	mm	millimeter
β	beta rays	H	enthalpy	mol	mole
γ	gamma rays	ΔH_f	heat of formation	mp	melting point
Δ	change in	h	hour	n^0	neutron
δ+, δ−	partial ionic charge	h	Planck's constant	n	number of moles
λ	wavelength	Hz	hertz	n	principal quantum number
π	pi bond	J	joule		
σ	sigma bond	K	kelvin	P	pressure
ν	frequency	K_a	acid dissociation constant	p^+	proton
amu	atomic mass unit	K_b	base dissociation constant	Pa	pascal
(*aq*)	aqueous solution	K_{eq}	equilibrium constant	R	ideal gas constant
atm	atmosphere	K_w	ion product constant for water	S	entropy
bp	boiling point			s	second
°C	degree Celsius	kcal	kilocalorie	(*s*)	solid
c	speed of light in a vacuum	kg	kilogram	STP	standard temperature and pressure
cm	centimeter	kPa	kilopascal		
E	energy	L	liter		
e^-	electron	(*l*)	liquid	T	temperature
EFM	empirical formula mass	M	molarity	$t_{1/2}$	half-life
fp	freezing point	m	meter	V	volume
G	Gibbs free energy	m	mass	v	velocity
g	gram	m	molality	Z_{eff}	effective nuclear charge
(*g*)	gas	mL	milliliter		

TABLE A.3

SOME PROPERTIES OF THE ELEMENTS

Element	Symbol	Atomic number	Atomic mass	Melting point (°C)	Boiling point (°C)	Density (g/cm³) (gases at STP)	Oxidation numbers
Actinium	Ac	89	(227)	1050	3200	10.07	+3
Aluminum	Al	13	26.98154	660.37	2467	2.6989	+3
Americium	Am	95	243	994	2607	13.67	+3, +4, +5, +6
Antimony	Sb	51	121.75	630.74	1587	6.691	−3, +3, +5
Argon	Ar	18	39.948	−189.2	−185.7	0.0017837	
Arsenic	As	33	74.9216	817	613	5.73	−3, +3, +5
Astatine	At	85	(210)	302	337	—	
Barium	Ba	56	137.33	725	1640	3.5	+2
Berkelium	Bk	97	(247)	986	—	14.78	
Beryllium	Be	4	9.01218	1278	2970	1.848	+2
Bismuth	Bi	83	208.9804	271.3	1560	9.747	+3, +5
Bohrium	Bh	107	(264)	—	—	—	
Boron	B	5	10.81	2075	3675	2.34	+3
Bromine	Br	35	79.904	−7.2	58.78	3.12	−1, +1, +5
Cadmium	Cd	48	112.41	320.9	765	8.65	+2
Calcium	Ca	20	40.08	839	1484	1.55	+2
Californium	Cf	98	(251)	900	—	14	
Carbon	C	6	12.011	3550	4827	2.267	−4, +2, +4
Cerium	Ce	58	140.12	799	3426	6.657	+3, +4
Cesium	Cs	55	132.9054	28.40	669.3	1.873	+1
Chlorine	Cl	17	35.453	−100.98	−34.6	0.003214	−1, +1, +5, +7
Chromium	Cr	24	51.996	1907	2672	7.18	+2, +3, +6
Cobalt	Co	27	58.9332	1495	2870	8.9	+2, +3
Copernicium	Cn	112	(277)	—	—	—	
Copper	Cu	29	63.546	1083.4	2567	8.96	+1, +2
Curium	Cm	96	(247)	1340	—	13.51	+3
Darmstadtium	Ds	110	(269)	—	—	—	
Dubnium	Db	105	(262)	—	—	—	
Dysprosium	Dy	66	162.50	1412	2562	8.550	+3
Einsteinium	Es	99	(252)	—	—	—	
Erbium	Er	68	167.26	159	2863	9.066	+3
Europium	Eu	63	151.96	822	1597	5.243	+2, +3
Fermium	Fm	100	(257)	—	—	—	
Flerovium	Fl	114	(289)	—	—	—	
Fluorine	F	9	18.998403	−219.62	−188.54	0.00181	−1
Francium	Fr	87	(223)	27	677	—	+1
Gadolinium	Gd	64	157.25	1313	3266	7.9004	+3
Gallium	Ga	31	69.72	29.78	2204	5.904	+3
Germanium	Ge	32	72.59	937.4	2830	5.323	+2, +4
Gold	Au	79	196.9665	1064.43	2856	19.3	+1, +3
Hafnium	Hf	72	178.49	2227	4602	13.31	+4
Hassium	Hs	108	(265)	—	—	—	
Helium	He	2	4.00260	−272.2	−268.934	0.0001785	
Holmium	Ho	67	164.9304	1474	2695	8.795	+3
Hydrogen	H	1	1.00794	−259.14	−252.87	0.00008988	−1, +1
Indium	In	49	114.82	156.61	2080	7.31	+1, +3
Iodine	I	53	126.9045	113.5	184.35	4.93	−1, +1, +5, +7
Iridium	Ir	77	192.22	2410	4130	22.42	+3, +4
Iron	Fe	26	55.847	1535	2750	7.874	+2, +3
Krypton	Kr	36	83.80	−156.6	−152.30	0.003733	
Lanthanum	La	57	138.9055	921	3457	6.145	+3
Lawrencium	Lr	103	(262)	—	—	—	+3
Lead	Pb	82	207.2	327.502	1740	11.35	+2, +4
Lithium	Li	3	6.941	180.54	1342	0.534	+1
Livermorium	Lv	116	(293)	—	—	—	
Lutetium	Lu	71	174.967	1663	3395	9.840	+3
Magnesium	Mg	12	24.305	648.8	1107	1.738	+2
Manganese	Mn	25	54.9380	1244	1962	7.32	+2, +3, +4, +7

TABLE A.3 (cont.)

SOME PROPERTIES OF THE ELEMENTS

Element	Symbol	Atomic number	Atomic mass	Melting point (°C)	Boiling point (°C)	Density (g/cm^3) (gases at STP)	Oxidation numbers
Meitnerium	Mt	109	(278)	—	—	—	
Mendelevium	Md	101	257	—	—	—	+2, +3
Mercury	Hg	80	200.59	−38.842	356.58	13.55	+1, +2
Molybdenum	Mo	42	95.94	2617	4612	10.22	+6
Moscovium	Mc	115	(289)	—	—	—	
Neodymium	Nd	60	144.24	1021	3068	6.90	+3
Neon	Ne	10	20.179	−248.67	−246.048	0.0008999	
Neptunium	Np	93	(237)	640	3902	20.25	+3, +4, +5, +6
Nickel	Ni	28	58.69	1453	2732	8.902	+2, +3
Nihonium	Nh	113	(286)	—	—	—	
Niobium	Nb	41	92.9064	2468	4742	8.57	+3, +5
Nitrogen	N	7	14.0067	−209.86	−195.8	0.0012506	−3, +3, +5
Nobelium	No	102	(259)	—	—	—	+2, +3
Oganesson	Og	118	(294)	—	—	—	
Osmium	Os	76	190.2	3045	5027	22.57	+3, +4
Oxygen	O	8	15.9994	−218.4	−182.962	0.001429	−2
Palladium	Pd	46	106.42	1554	2970	12.02	+2, +4
Phosphorus	P	15	30.97376	44.1	280	1.82	−3, +3, +5
Platinum	Pt	78	195.08	1772	3627	21.45	+2, +4
Plutonium	Pu	94	(244)	641	3232	19.84	+3, +4, +5, +6
Polonium	Po	84	(209)	254	962	9.32	+2, +4
Potassium	K	19	39.0982	63.25	760	0.862	+1
Praseodymium	Pr	59	140.9077	931	3512	6.64	+3
Promethium	Pm	61	(145)	1168	2460	7.22	+3
Protactinium	Pa	91	231.0359	1560	4027	15.37	+4, +5
Radium	Ra	88	(226)	700	1140	5.5	+2
Radon	Rn	86	(222)	−71	−61.8	0.00973	
Rhenium	Re	75	186.207	3180	5627	21.02	+4, +6, +7
Rhodium	Rh	45	102.9055	1966	3727	12.41	+3
Roentgenium	Rg	111	(272)	—	—	—	
Rubidium	Rb	37	85.4678	38.89	686	1.532	+1
Ruthenium	Ru	44	101.07	2310	3900	12.41	+3
Rutherfordium	Rf	104	(261)	—	—	—	
Samarium	Sm	62	150.36	1077	1791	7.520	+2, +3
Scandium	Sc	21	44.9559	1541	2831	2.989	+3
Seaborgium	Sg	106	(263)	—	—	—	
Selenium	Se	34	78.96	217	684.9	4.79	−2, +4, +6
Silicon	Si	14	28.0855	1410	2355	2.33	−4, +2, +4
Silver	Ag	47	107.8682	961.93	2212	10.50	+1
Sodium	Na	11	22.98977	97.81	882.9	0.971	+1
Strontium	Sr	38	87.62	769	1381	2.63	+2
Sulfur	S	16	32.06	112.8	444.7	2.07	−2, +4, +6
Tantalum	Ta	73	180.9479	2996	5425	16.654	+5
Technetium	Tc	43	(98)	2172	4877	11.50	+4, +6, +7
Tellurium	Te	52	127.60	449.5	989.8	6.24	−2, +4, +6
Tennessine	Ts	117	(294)	—	—	—	
Terbium	Tb	65	158.9254	1356	3123	8.229	+3
Thallium	Tl	81	204.383	303.5	1457	11.85	+1, +3
Thorium	Th	90	232.0381	1750	4790	11.72	+4
Thulium	Tm	69	168.9342	1545	1947	9.321	+3
Tin	Sn	50	118.69	231.968	2270	7.31	+2, +4
Titanium	Ti	22	47.88	1660	3287	4.54	+2, +3, +4
Tungsten	W	74	183.85	3410	5660	19.3	+6
Uranium	U	92	238.0289	1132.3	3818	18.95	+3, +4, +5, +6
Vanadium	V	23	50.9415	1890	3380	6.11	+2, +3, +4, +5
Xenon	Xe	54	131.29	−111.9	−107.1	0.005887	
Ytterbium	Yb	70	173.04	819	1194	6.965	+2, +3
Yttrium	Y	39	88.9059	1522	3338	4.469	+3
Zinc	Zn	30	65.38	419.58	907	7.133	+2
Zirconium	Zr	40	91.22	1852	4377	6.506	+4

TABLE A.4

ELECTRON CONFIGURATION OF THE ELEMENTS

Element		Sublevels																		
		1*s*	2*s*	2*p*	3*s*	3*p*	3*d*	4*s*	4*p*	4*d*	4*f*	5*s*	5*p*	5*d*	5*f*	6*s*	6*p*	6*d*	7*s*	7*p*
1	Hydrogen	1																		
2	Helium	2																		
3	Lithium	2	1																	
4	Beryllium	2	2																	
5	Boron	2	2	1																
6	Carbon	2	2	2																
7	Nitrogen	2	2	3																
8	Oxygen	2	2	4																
9	Fluorine	2	2	5																
10	Neon	2	2	6																
11	Sodium	2	2	6	1															
12	Magnesium	2	2	6	2															
13	Aluminum	2	2	6	2	1														
14	Silicon	2	2	6	2	2														
15	Phosphorus	2	2	6	2	3														
16	Sulfur	2	2	6	2	4														
17	Chlorine	2	2	6	2	5														
18	Argon	2	2	6	2	6														
19	Potassium	2	2	6	2	6		1												
20	Calcium	2	2	6	2	6		2												
21	Scandium	2	2	6	2	6	1	2												
22	Titanium	2	2	6	2	6	2	2												
23	Vanadium	2	2	6	2	6	3	2												
24	Chromium	2	2	6	2	6	5	1												
25	Manganese	2	2	6	2	6	5	2												
26	Iron	2	2	6	2	6	6	2												
27	Cobalt	2	2	6	2	6	7	2												
28	Nickel	2	2	6	2	6	8	2												
29	Copper	2	2	6	2	6	10	1												
30	Zinc	2	2	6	2	6	10	2												
31	Gallium	2	2	6	2	6	10	2	1											
32	Germanium	2	2	6	2	6	10	2	2											
33	Arsenic	2	2	6	2	6	10	2	3											
34	Selenium	2	2	6	2	6	10	2	4											
35	Bromine	2	2	6	2	6	10	2	5											
36	Krypton	2	2	6	2	6	10	2	6											
37	Rubidium	2	2	6	2	6	10	2	6			1								
38	Strontium	2	2	6	2	6	10	2	6			2								
39	Yttrium	2	2	6	2	6	10	2	6	1		2								
40	Zirconium	2	2	6	2	6	10	2	6	2		2								
41	Niobium	2	2	6	2	6	10	2	6	4		1								
42	Molybdenum	2	2	6	2	6	10	2	6	5		1								
43	Technetium	2	2	6	2	6	10	2	6	5		2								
44	Ruthenium	2	2	6	2	6	10	2	6	7		1								
45	Rhodium	2	2	6	2	6	10	2	6	8		1								
46	Palladium	2	2	6	2	6	10	2	6	10										
47	Silver	2	2	6	2	6	10	2	6	10		1								
48	Cadmium	2	2	6	2	6	10	2	6	10		2								
49	Indium	2	2	6	2	6	10	2	6	10		2	1							
50	Tin	2	2	6	2	6	10	2	6	10		2	2							
51	Antimony	2	2	6	2	6	10	2	6	10		2	3							
52	Tellurium	2	2	6	2	6	10	2	6	10		2	4							
53	Iodine	2	2	6	2	6	10	2	6	10		2	5							
54	Xenon	2	2	6	2	6	10	2	6	10		2	6							
55	Cesium	2	2	6	2	6	10	2	6	10		2	6			1				
56	Barium	2	2	6	2	6	10	2	6	10		2	6			2				
57	Lanthanum	2	2	6	2	6	10	2	6	10		2	6	1		2				
58	Cerium	2	2	6	2	6	10	2	6	10	1	2	6	1		2				
59	Praseodymium	2	2	6	2	6	10	2	6	10	3	2	6			2				

TABLE A.4 *(cont.)*

ELECTRON CONFIGURATION OF THE ELEMENTS

	Element	Sublevels																		
		1*s*	2*s*	2*p*	3*s*	3*p*	3*d*	4*s*	4*p*	4*d*	4*f*	5*s*	5*p*	5*d*	5*f*	6*s*	6*p*	6*d*	7*s*	7*p*
60	Neodymium	2	2	6	2	6	10	2	6	10	4	2	6			2				
61	Promethium	2	2	6	2	6	10	2	6	10	5	2	6			2				
62	Samarium	2	2	6	2	6	10	2	6	10	6	2	6			2				
63	Europium	2	2	6	2	6	10	2	6	10	7	2	6			2				
64	Gadolinium	2	2	6	2	6	10	2	6	10	7	2	6	1		2				
65	Terbium	2	2	6	2	6	10	2	6	10	9	2	6			2				
66	Dysprosium	2	2	6	2	6	10	2	6	10	10	2	6			2				
67	Holmium	2	2	6	2	6	10	2	6	10	11	2	6			2				
68	Erbium	2	2	6	2	6	10	2	6	10	12	2	6			2				
69	Thulium	2	2	6	2	6	10	2	6	10	13	2	6			2				
70	Ytterbium	2	2	6	2	6	10	2	6	10	14	2	6			2				
71	Lutetium	2	2	6	2	6	10	2	6	10	14	2	6	1		2				
72	Hafnium	2	2	6	2	6	10	2	6	10	14	2	6	2		2				
73	Tantalum	2	2	6	2	6	10	2	6	10	14	2	6	3		2				
74	Tungsten	2	2	6	2	6	10	2	6	10	14	2	6	4		2				
75	Rhenium	2	2	6	2	6	10	2	6	10	14	2	6	5		2				
76	Osmium	2	2	6	2	6	10	2	6	10	14	2	6	6		2				
77	Iridium	2	2	6	2	6	10	2	6	10	14	2	6	7		2				
78	Platinum	2	2	6	2	6	10	2	6	10	14	2	6	9		1				
79	Gold	2	2	6	2	6	10	2	6	10	14	2	6	10		1				
80	Mercury	2	2	6	2	6	10	2	6	10	14	2	6	10		2				
81	Thallium	2	2	6	2	6	10	2	6	10	14	2	6	10		2	1			
82	Lead	2	2	6	2	6	10	2	6	10	14	2	6	10		2	2			
83	Bismuth	2	2	6	2	6	10	2	6	10	14	2	6	10		2	3			
84	Polonium	2	2	6	2	6	10	2	6	10	14	2	6	10		2	4			
85	Astatine	2	2	6	2	6	10	2	6	10	14	2	6	10		2	5			
86	Radon	2	2	6	2	6	10	2	6	10	14	2	6	10		2	6			
87	Francium	2	2	6	2	6	10	2	6	10	14	2	6	10		2	6		1	
88	Radium	2	2	6	2	6	10	2	6	10	14	2	6	10		2	6		2	
89	Actinium	2	2	6	2	6	10	2	6	10	14	2	6	10		2	6	1	2	
90	Thorium	2	2	6	2	6	10	2	6	10	14	2	6	10		2	6	2	2	
91	Protactinium	2	2	6	2	6	10	2	6	10	14	2	6	10	2	2	6	1	2	
92	Uranium	2	2	6	2	6	10	2	6	10	14	2	6	10	3	2	6	1	2	
93	Neptunium	2	2	6	2	6	10	2	6	10	14	2	6	10	4	2	6	1	2	
94	Plutonium	2	2	6	2	6	10	2	6	10	14	2	6	10	6	2	6		2	
95	Americium	2	2	6	2	6	10	2	6	10	14	2	6	10	7	2	6		2	
96	Curium	2	2	6	2	6	10	2	6	10	14	2	6	10	7	2	6	1	2	
97	Berkelium	2	2	6	2	6	10	2	6	10	14	2	6	10	9	2	6		2	
98	Californium	2	2	6	2	6	10	2	6	10	14	2	6	10	10	2	6		2	
99	Einsteinium	2	2	6	2	6	10	2	6	10	14	2	6	10	11	2	6		2	
100	Fermium	2	2	6	2	6	10	2	6	10	14	2	6	10	12	2	6		2	
101	Mendelevium	2	2	6	2	6	10	2	6	10	14	2	6	10	13	2	6		2	
102	Nobelium	2	2	6	2	6	10	2	6	10	14	2	6	10	14	2	6		2	
103	Lawrencium	2	2	6	2	6	10	2	6	10	14	2	6	10	14	2	6	1	2	
104	Rutherfordium	2	2	6	2	6	10	2	6	10	14	2	6	10	14	2	6	2	2	
105	Dubnium	2	2	6	2	6	10	2	6	10	14	2	6	10	14	2	6	3	2	
106	Seaborgium	2	2	6	2	6	10	2	6	10	14	2	6	10	14	2	6	4	2	
107	Bohrium	2	2	6	2	6	10	2	6	10	14	2	6	10	14	2	6	5	2	
108	Hassium	2	2	6	2	6	10	2	6	10	14	2	6	10	14	2	6	6	2	
109	Meitnerium	2	2	6	2	6	10	2	6	10	14	2	6	10	14	2	6	7	2	
110	Darmstadium	2	2	6	2	6	10	2	6	10	14	2	6	10	14	2	6	9	1	
111	Roentgenium	2	2	6	2	6	10	2	6	10	14	2	6	10	14	2	6	10	1	
112	Copernicium	2	2	6	2	6	10	2	6	10	14	2	6	10	14	2	6	10	2	
113	Nihonium	2	2	6	2	6	10	2	6	10	14	2	6	10	14	2	6	10	2	1
114	Flerovium	2	2	6	2	6	10	2	6	10	14	2	6	10	14	2	6	10	2	2
115	Moscovium	2	2	6	2	6	10	2	6	10	14	2	6	10	14	2	6	10	2	3
116	Livermorium	2	2	6	2	6	10	2	6	10	14	2	6	10	14	2	6	10	2	4
117	Tennessine	2	2	6	2	6	10	2	6	10	14	2	6	10	14	2	6	10	2	5
118	Oganesson	2	2	6	2	6	10	2	6	10	14	2	6	10	14	2	6	10	2	6

TABLE A.5

COMMON POLYATOMIC IONS

Charge	Name	Formula	Charge	Name	Formula
1–	Chlorate	ClO_3^-	2–	Carbonate	CO_3^{2-}
	Chlorite	ClO_2^-		Chromate	CrO_4^{2-}
	Cyanide	CN^-		Dichromate	$Cr_2O_7^{2-}$
	Dihydrogen phosphate	$H_2PO_4^-$		Oxalate	$C_2O_4^{2-}$
	Ethanoate	CH_3COO^-		Peroxide	O_2^{2-}
	Hydroxide	OH^-		Silicate	SiO_3^{2-}
	Hydrogen carbonate	HCO_3^-		Sulfate	SO_4^{2-}
	Hydrogen sulfate	HSO_4^-		Sulfite	SO_3^{2-}
	Hydrogen sulfite	HSO_3^-		Thiosulfate	$S_2O_3^{2-}$
	Hypochlorite	ClO^-			
	Nitrate	NO_3^-	3–	Phosphate	PO_4^{3-}
	Nitrite	NO_2^-		Phosphite	PO_3^{3-}
	Perchlorate	ClO_4^-			
	Permanganate	MnO_4^-	1+	Ammonium	NH_4^+
	Thiocyanate	SCN^-			

TABLE A.6

SOLUBILITIES OF COMPOUNDS AT 25°C

	ethanoate	bromide	carbonate	chlorate	chloride	hydroxide	iodide	nitrate	oxide	perchlorate	phosphate	sulfate	sulfide
aluminum	S	S	X	S	S	I	S	S	I	S	I	S	d
ammonium	S	S	S	S	S	X	S	S	X	S	S	S	S
barium	S	S	I	S	S	S	S	S	sS	S	I	I	d
calcium	S	S	I	S	S	S	S	S	sS	S	I	sS	I
copper(II)	S	S	X	S	S	I	S	S	I	S	I	S	I
iron(II)	S	S	I	S	S	I	S	S	I	S	I	S	I
iron(III)	S	S	X	S	S	I	S	S	I	S	I	sS	d
lithium	S	S	sS	S	S	S	S	S	S	S	sS	S	S
magnesium	S	S	I	S	S	I	S	S	I	S	I	S	d
potassium	S	S	S	S	S	S	S	S	S	S	S	S	S
silver	sS	I	I	S	I	X	I	S	I	S	I	sS	I
sodium	S	S	S	S	S	S	S	S	S	S	S	S	S
strontium	S	S	I	S	S	S	S	S	S	S	I	I	I
zinc	S	S	I	S	S	I	S	S	I	S	I	S	I

Key: S = soluble; sS = slightly soluble; I = insoluble; d = decomposes in water; X = no such compound

TABLE A.7

SI UNITS AND EQUIVALENTS

Quantity	SI unit	Common equivalents
Length	meter (m)	1 meter = 1.0936 yards 1 centimeter = 0.39370 inch 1 inch = 2.54 centimeters 1 mile = 5280 feet = 1.6093 kilometers
Volume	cubic meter (m^3)	1 liter = 10^{-3} m^3 = 1.0567 quarts 1 gallon = 4 quarts = 8 pints = 3.7854 liters 1 quart = 32 fluid ounces = 0.94635 liter
Temperature	kelvin (K)	1 kelvin = 1 degree Celsius °C = $\frac{5}{9}$ (F − 32) K = °C + 273.15
Mass	kilogram (kg)	1 kilogram = 1000 grams = mass weighing 2.2046 pounds 1 amu = 1.66057×10^{-27} kilograms
Time	second (s)	1 hour = 60 minutes 1 hour = 3600 seconds
Energy	joule (J)	1 joule = 1 $kg \cdot m^2/s^2$ (exact) 1 joule = 0.2390 calorie 1 calorie = 4.184 joules
Pressure	pascal (Pa)	1 atmosphere = 101.3 kilopascals = 760 mm Hg (Torr) = 14.70 pounds per square inch

The experiments in this program have been carefully designed to minimize the risk of injury. However, safety is also your responsibility. The following rules are essential for keeping you safe in the laboratory. The rules address pre-lab preparation, proper laboratory practices, and post-lab procedures.

Pre-Lab Preparation

1. Read the entire procedure before you begin. Listen to all of your teacher's instructions. When in doubt about a procedure, ask your teacher.
2. Do only the assigned experiments. Only do experiments when your teacher is present and has given you permission to work.
3. Know the location and operation of the following safety equipment: fire extinguisher, fire blanket, emergency shower, and eye wash station.
4. Know the location of emergency exits and escape routes. To make it easy to exit quickly, do not block walkways with furniture. Keep your work area orderly and free of personal belongings, such as coats and backpacks.
5. Protect your clothing and hair from chemicals and sources of heat. Tie back long hair and roll up loose sleeves when working in the laboratory. Avoid wearing bulky or loose-fitting clothing. Remove dangling jewelry. Wear closed-toe shoes at all times in the laboratory.

Proper Laboratory Practices

6. Even with well-designed and tested laboratory procedures, an accident may occur while you are working in the lab. Report any accident, no matter how minor, to your teacher.
7. Wear chemical splash goggles at all times when working in the laboratory. These goggles are designed to protect your eyes from injury. While working in the lab, do not rub your eyes, because chemicals are easily transferred from your hands to your eyes.

   ⚠ If, despite these precautions, a chemical gets in your eye, remove any contact lenses and immediately wash your eye with a continuous stream of lukewarm water for at least 15 minutes.
8. Always use the minimal amounts of chemicals specified for an experiment to reduce danger, waste, and cleanup.
9. Never taste any chemical used in the laboratory, including food products that are the subject of an investigation. Treat all items as though they are contaminated with unknown chemicals that may be toxic. Keep all food and drink that is not part of an experiment out of the laboratory. Do not eat, drink, or chew gum in the laboratory.

   ⚠ If you accidentally ingest a substance, notify your teacher immediately.
10. Don't use chipped or cracked glassware. Don't handle broken glass. If glassware breaks, tell your teacher and nearby classmates. Discard broken glass as instructed by your teacher.

    ⚠ If, despite these precautions, you receive a minor cut, allow it to bleed for a short time. Wash the injured area under cold, running water and notify your teacher. More serious cuts or puncture wounds require immediate medical attention.
11. Do not handle hot glassware or equipment. You can prevent burns by being aware that hot and cold equipment can look exactly the same.

    ⚠ If you are burned, immediately run cold water over the burned area for several minutes until the pain is reduced. Cooling helps the burn heal. Ask a classmate to notify your teacher.
12. Recognize that the danger of an electrical shock is greater in the presence of water. Keep electrical appliances away from sinks and faucets to minimize the risk of electrical shock. Be careful not to spill water or other liquids in the vicinity of an electrical appliance.

▲ If, despite these precautions, you spill water near an electrical appliance, stand back, notify your teacher, and warn other students in the area.

13. Report any chemical spills immediately to your teacher. Follow your teacher's instructions for cleaning up spills. Warn other students about the identity and location of spilled chemicals.

▲ If, despite these precautions, a corrosive chemical gets on your skin or clothing, notify your teacher. Then wash the affected area with cold running water for several minutes.

Post-Lab Procedures

14. Dispose of chemicals in a way that protects you, your classmates, and the environment. Always follow your teacher's directions for cleanup and disposal. Clean your small-scale reaction surface by draining the contents onto a paper towel. Then wipe the surface with a damp paper towel and dry the surface completely. Dispose of the paper towels in the waste bin.

15. Wash your hands thoroughly with soap and water before leaving the laboratory.

A Materials Safety Data Sheet (MSDS) for a chemical describes any safety issues. A diagram summarizes risks related to flammability, health, and reactivity. A number scale indicates the level of risk.

0 Low
1 Slight
2 Moderate
3 High
4 Extreme

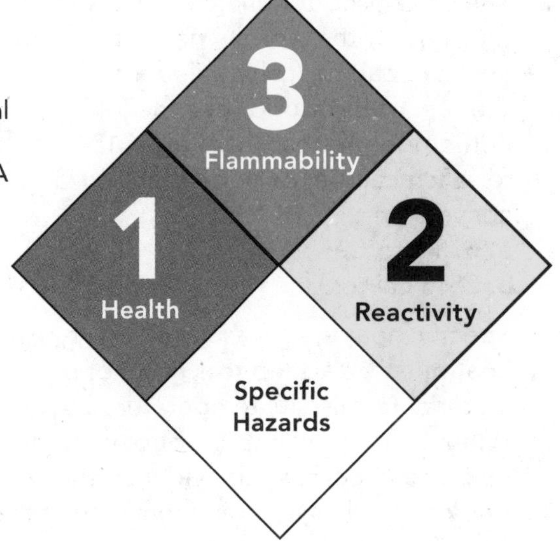

Safety Procedures

Take appropriate precautions when any of the following safety symbols appears in an experiment.

 **Eye Safety** Wear safety goggles.

 **Clothing Protection** Wear a lab coat or apron when using corrosive chemicals or chemicals that can stain clothing.

 **Skin Protection** Wear plastic gloves when using chemicals that can irritate or stain your skin.

 **Broken Glass** Do not use chipped or cracked glassware. Do not heat the bottom of a test tube.

 **Open Flame** Tie back hair and loose clothing. Never reach across a lit burner.

 **Flammable Substance** Do not have a flame near flammable materials.

 **Corrosive Substance** Wear safety goggles, an apron, and gloves when working with corrosive chemicals.

 **Poison** Don't chew gum, drink, or eat in the laboratory. Never taste a chemical in the laboratory.

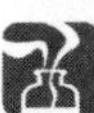 **Fume** Avoid inhaling substances that can irritate your respiratory system. Use a fume hood whenever possible.

 **Thermal Burn** Do not touch hot glassware or equipment.

 **Electrical Equipment** Keep electrical equipment away from water or other liquids.

 **Sharp Object** To avoid a puncture wound, use scissors or other sharp objects only as intended.

 **Disposal** Dispose of chemicals only as directed.

 **Hand Washing** Wash your hands thoroughly with soap and water.

INVESTIGATION 1

1. Using the law of the conservation of energy, suggest what types of energy transformations may occur in each scenario below.
   a. logs burn in a fire
   b. a waterfall turns a turbine to create electricity
   c. a battery is used to power a flashlight
2. The units used for energy (heat) vary throughout the world. The United States uses the calorie (cal), while most of the rest of the world uses the joule (J). Remembering that there are 4.184 J for each calorie, perform the following conversions:
   a. 575 J to cal
   b. 2515 cal to J
3. Specific heat is a measure of how much heat must be added to 1 gram of a material to raise its temperature by 1°C. When heating a copper pot of water for mac and cheese, what evidence shows that copper has a lower specific heat than water?
4. Refer to the heat diagram for water. What occurs while the line is horizontal?

Heating Diagram for Water

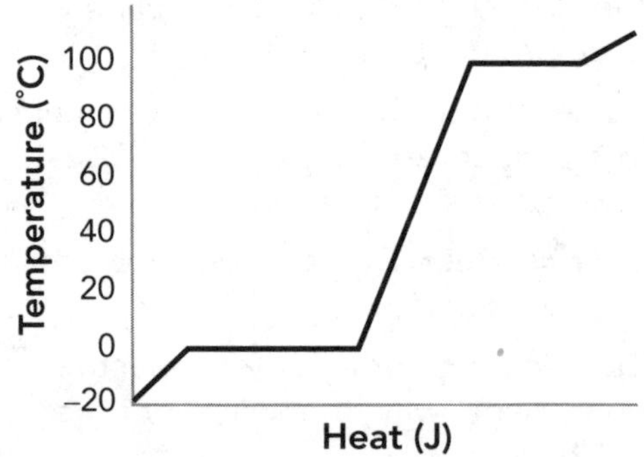

5. Under ordinary circumstances, heat flows from objects with ______ temperatures to objects with ______ temperatures.
6. Eight atoms of carbon react with 18 atoms of hydrogen, forming only one molecule of C_8H_{18}. Is the forming of only one molecule considered a violation of the law of conservation of mass? Explain.
7. Chemists must often identify whether their experiment is taking place in an open or a closed system. In an open system, mass can be added or removed. In a closed system, mass remains constant. Identify whether each system is open or closed.
   a. a fence rusting
   b. food digesting in your stomach
   c. souring of milk in a container
8. The law of conservation of mass states that no mass can be gained or lost during a regular chemical reaction. Based on this, determine the proper coefficients to balance the following reactions so that no atoms are gained or lost.
   a. $\_\ H_2(g) + \_\ O_2(g) \longrightarrow \_\ H_2O(l)$
   b. $\_\ Al(s) + \_\ O_2(g) \longrightarrow \_\ Al_2O_3(s)$
9. When a candle burns, all that remains is soot and a little unburned wax. Explain how the law of conservation of mass was not violated while burning the candle.
10. Suppose 2.02 grams of hydrogen are reacted with 16.00 grams of oxygen. According to the law of conservation of mass, how many grams of water form?

INVESTIGATION 2

1. A student throws a 0.237 kg rock at a velocity of 17 m/s. What is the kinetic energy of the rock in joules? Report the answer to the correct number of significant figures.
2. What is the kinetic energy of an electron moving at 2.2×10^6 m/s? The mass of an electron is considered to be 9.109×10^{-31} kg. Report the answer to the correct number of significant figures.

3. A helium atom has a speed of 1350 m/s at room temperature. What is the mass of the atom if it has 6.06×10^{-21} J of energy? Report the answer to the correct number of significant figures.

4. What power is produced by a circuit with a resistance of 120 ohms and a current of 1.5 amps? Calculate to the proper number of significant figures.

5. What is the resistance of a resistor that can handle 650 W of power at a current of 15 amps? Calculate to the proper number of significant figures.

6. In a circuit, a 0.72 amp current moves through a wire with a resistance of 16 ohm. How much power is produced by the circuit? Calculate to the proper number of significant figures.

7. As the average velocity of particles in a sample increases, the thermal energy of the sample ______.

8. Explain the difference between heat and thermal conduction.

9. Heat will flow naturally from a body with ______ temperature to a body with ______ temperature and never freely in reverse.

10. A beaker containing hot water is being stirred by a glass rod. Identify each part below as being part of the system or part of the surroundings:
    a. beaker
    b. water
    c. air in the room
    d. stirring rod

11. A solid metal barrier has a thermal conductivity value (k) of 67 W/m•K. The thickness of this barrier is 45 mm. Both the length and width of the barrier surface is 1.2 m. One side of the barrier has a temperature of 143°C. The other side of the barrier has a temperature of 78°C. What is the conductive heat transfer value (Q)?

12. Describe what happens when a beaker of water at 85°C is combined with a beaker of 22°C water.

13. There are three different ways heat is transferred through matter. Heat transferred through or between objects in contact is called ______. This type of heat transfer is generally faster through solids than liquids or gases. Heat transferred by the flow of fluid materials is called ______. Heat transferred through radiation is called ______.

14. A metal bridge panel has a thermal conductivity value (k) of 95 W/m•K. Both the length and width of the panel surface is 2.5 m. One side of the panel has a temperature of 157°C. The other side of the panel has a temperature of 85°C. The conductive heat transfer value (Q) is 1.7×10^6 W. What is the thickness of this metal panel?

15. Using the concept of entropy, explain why your bedroom does not clean or organize itself.

16. When a bottle of perfume is dropped in the corner of a room and breaks, what entropy changes are involved?

17. Diffusion is the spreading out of particles over time to make an equal concentration throughout a system. Does diffusion increase, decrease, or keep the same amount of entropy in a system?

18. Explain what occurs when a system has reached thermal equilibrium.

INVESTIGATION 3

1. Investigating the interior of Earth poses an immense challenge for scientists and geologists. Describe how seismic data provide indirect evidence supporting the layered model of Earth.

2. Based on the knowledge of chemical elements, name the **most** abundant elements that comprise Earth's surface and its interior. Which elements are likely to be present in Earth's innermost layers and why?

3. Describe the mechanism of heat transfer in the following layers of Earth.
    a. inner core
    b. outer core
    c. mantle

4. Explain the following phenomena.
   a. geomagnetic reversal
   b. mantle downwelling
   c. mantle upwelling

5. Earth's geological history can be understood through the theory of plate tectonics. Describe what one may observe if the following data from along a mid-ocean ridge are recorded.
   a. water temperature along the mid-ocean ridge
   b. age of the oceanic crust along the mid-ocean ridge
   c. paleomagnetic data from either side of the mid-ocean ridge

6. The samples collected during several drilling explorations suggest that barely any rocks or sediments collected from the seafloor are older than 180 million years. In light of the theory of plate tectonics, why do you think these results are significant? Would you expect all samples of continental crust to be less than 180 million years old?

7. Explain how the following specific geological features were possibly formed on Earth.
   a. the Himalayan Mountain Range
   b. the Mariana Trench
   c. the San Andreas Fault

8. Explain why tectonic plate boundaries may be preferred locations for geologists searching for mineral deposits.

9. The eruptions from volcanoes can take various shapes, giving rise to steeper or flatter volcanoes. Some volcanoes erupt violently, covering the atmosphere with ash for several days. Describe the various factors that determine the shape and nature of these types of volcanoes.

10. Based on the interplay of temperature and pressure inside Earth's interior, predict the physical state of the following.
   a. outer core
   b. inner core

INVESTIGATION 4

1. List the three main subatomic particles. Describe their relative masses and locations within an atom.

2. Complete the table.

Particle	Symbol	Relative charge
Electron		
		1^+
	n^0	

3. Determine the number of electrons and protons for these elements.
   a. Be
   b. Cl
   c. Co

4. What is the difference between matter and element?

5. Determine the atomic number and mass number for these elements.
   a. $^{40}_{20}Ca$
   b. $^{28}_{14}Si$
   c. $^{101}_{44}Ru$

6. Potassium has an atomic number of 19. How many protons and electrons are in a neutral potassium atom?

7. What are isotopes? Do isotopes differ chemically? Why or why not?

8. Calculate the number of protons, electrons, and neutrons for these elements.
   a. $^{23}_{11}Na$
   b. $^{88}_{38}Sr$

9. Magnesium has three isotopes with the following atomic masses and relative abundance: 23.985 amu (78.99%), 24.986 amu (10.00%), and 25.982 amu (11.01%). Calculate the atomic mass of magnesium as a weighted average.

10. Uranium has three naturally occurring isotopes: uranium-238, uranium-235, and uranium-234. The atomic mass for uranium is 238.028 amu. Which of these three isotopes is most abundant? Explain.

11. What is the frequency of radiation with a wavelength of 5×10^{-10} m?

12. What is the wavelength of radiation with a frequency of 5.2×10^{7}/s? Is it closer to red or blue light?

13. What is the frequency of radiation that has a wavelength of 510 nm? What is the energy of a single photon of this light?

14. What is the frequency of radiation that has a wavelength of 750 nm? What is the energy of a single photon of this light?

15. What is the electron configuration for the following?
    a. He
    b. Si
    c. As
    d. Kr

16. Write the electron configuration for the following atoms. How many unpaired electrons are present for each atom?
    a. nitrogen
    b. calcium
    c. sodium

17. Write the electron configuration for iodine (I). Then draw the electron dot structure for iodine.

18. Draw the electron dot structure for each element.
    a. Sr
    b. Sn
    c. Te

INVESTIGATION 5

1. What is the difference in the way Mendeleev ordered the elements in his periodic table and the modern periodic table?

2. Identify the element in each description.
    a. Group 3, row 5
    b. column 6, Period 4
    c. metalloid in row 2
    d. 3rd column of p-block, Period 4

3. Based on their position in the periodic table, state which atom in each pair has the larger atomic radius.
    a. potassium, rubidium
    b. magnesium, aluminium
    c. bromine, iodine
    d. oxygen, nitrogen

4. Choose the species that has the larger atomic radius in the following pairs.
    a. chlorine atom and chloride ion
    b. sodium atom and sodium ion
    c. sodium ion and potassium ion
    d. oxide ion and sulfide ion

5. Element X has 13 protons.
    a. To which group and period does X belong?
    b. Is X a metal, nonmetal, or metalloid?
    c. How many valence electrons does an atom of element X have?
    d. What is the effective nuclear charge experienced by the valence electrons of atom X?

6. The table shows two sets of ionization energies. One set is made up of elements in Group 1A. The other set is made up of elements in Group 7A.
   Explain which set of values may be assigned to which group.

First Ionization Energy (kJ/mol) Set 1	First Ionization Energy (kJ/mol) Set 2
1681	1312
1251	520
1140	496
1008	419

7. Explain how ionization energy and electron affinity are basically measures of energy of opposite processes, but they both generally increase from left to right in a period.

8. Explain the trend that both atomic radius and ionic radius increase going down a group in the periodic table.

9. Explain why the second ionization energy for elements in Group 1 is significantly higher than the second ionization energy for Group 2.

10. Explain why noble gases do not have electronegativity values.

INVESTIGATION 6

1. For each element, write its symbol and charge as an ion.
   a. lithium
   b. chlorine
   c. sulfur
   d. magnesium

2. Draw the electron dot structure for each compound.
   a. KCl
   b. $BaBr_2$
   c. MgO

3. Atoms can gain or lose electrons to become stable ions. How many valence electrons are present in an oxygen atom?

4. Do the following properties apply to ionic compounds?
   a. low melting points
   b. conduct electricity in aqueous solution
   c. form crystalline solids
   d. conduct electricity in solid form

5. Metals such as gold, silver, and copper have high thermal and electrical conductivity. How does the "sea of electrons" model explain these properties?

6. Explain why some covalent bonds contain multiple pairs of shared electrons.

7. Using the terms "share" and "transfer," describe the difference between an ionic and a covalent bond.

8. Based on electronegativity values, are the covalent bonds in each of these compounds polar or nonpolar?
   a. H_2O
   b. O_2
   c. HCl
   d. H_2

9. How many unshared pairs are present in each molecule?
   a. H_2S
   b. NH_3
   c. BF_3
   d. CCl_4

10. Based on their valence electrons, how many atoms of chlorine are expected to bond with each of the following elements?
    a. carbon
    b. nitrogen
    c. aluminum
    d. sulfur

11. Draw the electron dot structure for each of the following compounds.
    a. H_2O
    b. BF_3
    c. CCl_4

12. Considering the intermolecular forces that may be present, predict whether each compound would have a relatively low or relatively high melting point.
    a. H_2O
    b. CO_2
    c. BF_3
    d. NaCl

13. Does each molecule exhibit hydrogen bonding?
    a. H_2O
    b. H_2S
    c. CH_4
    d. NH_3

14. Identify each compound as ionic or molecular.
    a. CaO
    b. CS_2
    c. LiF
    d. PCl_3

15. Name the ionic compounds that form from their ions in these solutions.
   a. Ba^{2+} and Cl^-
   b. Mg^{2+} and O^{2-}
   c. Li^+ and P^{3-}
   d. Be^{2+} and I^-
16. Name the molecular compounds formed when these nonmetals combine.
   a. one atom of carbon and one atom of oxygen
   b. one atom of silicon and four atoms of chlorine
   c. one atom of boron and three atoms of fluorine
   d. two atoms of phosphorus and five atoms of sulfur
17. Write the formula for the ionic compound that forms from
   a. lithium and nitrogen.
   b. strontium and bromine.
   c. aluminum and oxygen.
   d. potassium and fluorine.
18. Write the formula for the covalent compounds.
   a. nitrogen triiodide
   b. sulfur hexafluoride
   c. trinitrogen heptachloride
   d. phosphorus pentabromide

INVESTIGATION 7

1. Solid particles exhibit only ______ motion. As heat is added and the sample becomes a liquid, ______ motion is added, and upon its change to gas, ______ motion is added.
2. The strength of intermolecular forces directly impacts the physical properties of materials. What type of solid is described in each statement?
   a. typically soft; low melting points
   b. charges are present; high melting points
   c. a network of atoms; strong; typically highest of all melting points
   d. properties vary widely; tend to be conductive and malleable
3. In terms of energy and pressure, explain what occurs when gas in a rigid container is heated.
4. Identify each phase change described.
   a. liquid to gas
   b. solid to gas
   c. gas to liquid
   d. solid to liquid
5. Use the phase diagram for water to answer the following questions.

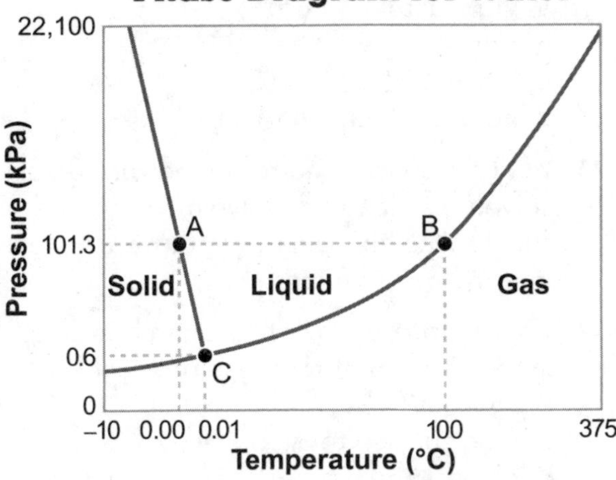

   a. What phase is present at 90°C and 50 kPa?
   b. What process occurs when water at 0.5 kPa and –5°C goes to 10 kPa and 50°C?
   c. What is significant about water at 101.3 kPa and 0°C?
6. Explain the difference between evaporation and boiling in terms of the energy involved.
7. You are provided with two white, crystalline solids. Suggest at least two tests that could be performed to determine which is molecular and which is ionic.
8. Predict whether an ionic or molecular compound forms when the following elements combine:
   a. sodium and bromine
   b. carbon and fluorine
   c. magnesium and oxygen
   d. chlorine and iodine

9. The strength of a bond between two ions increases with the charge on each ion, and decreases as the ions' radii increase. Using this information, predict which compound in each pair should have a higher melting point.
   a. sodium chloride ($NaCl$) vs. potassium chloride (KCl)
   b. sodium chloride ($NaCl$) vs. barium chloride ($BaCl_2$)
10. Identify whether each property describes a metal or a nonmetal.
   a. high luster
   b. brittle
   c. malleable
   d. non-conductive/insulator
11. Water is considered to be the "universal solvent" as it can dissolve many substances. Explain this in terms of intermolecular forces.
12. Can the presence of hydrogen bonding in water account for these physical properties?
   a. high surface tension
   b. color
   c. high boiling point
   d. density as a solid being less than as a liquid
   e. being a non-conductor
13. How does the addition of a surfactant reduce the surface tension of water?
14. What is the difference between a non-electrolyte, a weak electrolyte, and a strong electrolyte?
15. The solubility of barium hydroxide in water is 4.68 g/100 mL at 25°C. If a mixture of 2.50 g barium hydroxide in 100 mL of water is prepared, will it be unsaturated, saturated, or supersaturated?
16. Describe the process of preparing a supersaturated solution.
17. The solubility of a gas in a liquid ______ as the pressure over a solution increases. The solubility of the same gas ______ as the temperature of the solvent increases.
18. Determine whether each of the following is a homogeneous or heterogeneous mixture.
   a. pepperoni pizza
   b. white vinegar
   c. crunchy peanut butter
   d. warm maple syrup
   e. beach sand

INVESTIGATION 8

1. For each pair listed, which has more particles?
   a. 1 mol OCl_2 or 1 mol H_2O
   b. 0.5 mol O_2 or 0.75 mol H_2
   c. 1.5 mol SnO or 3.0 mol SnO_2
   d. 0.33 mol Fe_2O_3 or 0.66 mol FeO
2. Does one mole of sodium, Na, have the same volume as one mole of bromine, Br?
3. How does the concept of the mole help chemists?
4. Explain how a mole of hydrogen peroxide (H_2O_2) and a mole of hydrogen chloride (HCl) are the same but different.
5. If one mole of an unknown substance is 200.59 g/mol, what is the mass of 0.33 mol of the substance?
6. If you had one mole of avocados, then how many avocados would you have?
7. A chemist has 3.45×10^{22} molecules of P_2O_5. How many grams of P_2O_5 does the scientist have?
8. Calculate the number of moles of each substance.
   a. 5.45×10^{26} particles of methane, CH_4
   b. 3.22×10^{23} atoms of xenon, Xe
   c. 9.6×10^{23} formula units of sodium chloride, $NaCl$
9. How many moles of hydrogen atoms are in 7.10 mol of H_2O?
10. How many moles of oxygen atoms are in 3.60 mol of SiO_2?
11. What is the molar mass of molecular oxygen, O_2?
12. What is the molar mass of barium chloride, $BaCl_2$?

13. What is the molar mass of $CaCO_3$?

14. What is the molar mass of SF_6?

15. Calculate the number of moles of each substance.
    a. 6.00 g oxygen, O_2
    b. 450.0 g of iron(III) oxide, Fe_2O_3
    c. 45.5 g of calcium chloride, $CaCl_2$

16. Which has more atoms: 2.5 mol of calcium carbonate, $CaCO_3$, or 3.5 mol of calcium hydroxide, $Ca(OH)_2$?

17. How many grams is 2.50 mol of H_2O?

18. How many atoms is 0.750 mol of Na_3PO_4?

19. How many moles are present in 20.0 g of NO_2?

20. How many formula units are in 171 g of lithium nitride, Li_3N?

21. How many molecules are in 550.0 g of palladium(IV) oxide, PdO_2?

22. How many formula units are in 0.472 mol of iron(III) bromide, $FeBr_3$?

23. How many ions of fluoride are in 410.0 g of uranium(VI) fluoride, UF_6?

24. What is molar volume of a gas?

25. How does the number of particles of nitrogen in a balloon at STP compare to the number of particles of oxygen in a different balloon at STP with the same volume?

26. A compound contains 85.63% carbon and 14.37% hydrogen. What is the empirical formula of the compound?

27. Glucose has the formula $C_6H_{12}O_6$. What is the percent composition of each element?

28. How many moles of sodium fluoride are needed to make 500.0 mL of 3.5*M* solution?

29. How many grams of ethanol, CH_3CH_2OH, are needed to make 1.00 L of a 3.50*M* solution?

30. What is the concentration of the these solutions?
    a. 3.5 mol HBr in 500 mL of water
    b. 0.0750 mol NaCl in 250.0 mL of water
    c. 1.95 mol $AgNO_3$ in 1.2 L of water
    d. 0.500 mol NH_3 in 2.5 L of water

INVESTIGATION 9

1. In the following reactions, what is/are the reactant(s)?
    a. $C_6H_{12}O_2 + 8O_2 \rightarrow 6CO_2 + 6H_2O$
    b. $2H_2O_2 \rightarrow 2H_2O + O_2$
    c. $BaO + H_2O \rightarrow Ba(OH)_2$

2. In the following reaction, what is(are) the product(s)?
    a. $CaCO_3 + 2HCl \rightarrow CO_2 + CaCl_2 + H_2O$
    b. $N_2 + O_2 \rightarrow 2NO$
    c. $2SO_2 + O_2 \rightarrow 2SO_3$

3. In the following reaction, what is(are) the reactant(s)?
    Potassium bromate, $KBrO_4$, decomposes into potassium bromide, KBr, and oxygen, O_2.

4. In the following reaction, what is the solid?
    $AgNO_3(aq) + NaCl(aq) \rightarrow AgCl(s) + NaNO_3(aq)$

5. What is the skeleton equation for these reactions?
    a. magnesium oxide, MgO, and water to produce magnesium hydroxide, $Mg(OH)_2$
    b. aqueous phosphoric acid, H_3PO_4, and aqueous sodium hydroxide, NaOH, to produce aqueous sodium phosphate, Na_3PO_4, and water
    c. methane, CH_4, and oxygen, O_2, to produce carbon dioxide, CO_2, and water, H_2O

6. What is the skeleton equation for the decomposition of aqueous hydrogen peroxide, H_2O_2, into liquid water and gaseous oxygen, O_2, as catalyzed by potassium iodide, KI?

7. What are the coefficients in the following reactions?
    a. __ Fe_2O_3 + __ H_2O → __ $Fe(OH)_3$
    b. __ C_2H_4 + __ O_2 → __ CO_2 + __ H_2O

8. What is the balanced equation for the synthesis of sodium bromate, $NaBrO_3$, from oxygen, O_2, and sodium bromide, NaBr?

9. What is the balanced equation for the combustion of ethanol, C_2H_6O, and oxygen, O_2, to produce carbon dioxide, CO_2, and water?

10. When lithium chloride, LiCl, is dissolved in water, there is a steep rise in the temperature of the water. Based on this evidence, is the dissolution of lithium chloride endothermic, exothermic, or neither? Explain.

11. How much energy is required to break apart one mole of single-bonded oxygen atoms?

12. How much energy is needed to break the necessary bonds in the formation of water based on the following reaction?

$2H_2 + O_2 \rightarrow 2H_2O$

13. How much energy is released or absorbed in the formation of water based on the following reaction?

$2H_2 + O_2 \rightarrow 2H_2O$

14. An emergency ice pack is made of a pouch containing a chemical inside a large pouch containing a different chemical. When the inner pouch is broken, the solution cools drastically. In terms of bond energy, what is happening?

15. This reaction is an example of what type of chemical reaction?

$2KCl + 3O_2 \rightarrow 2KClO_3$

16. This reaction is an example of what type of chemical reaction?

$2B(OH)_3 \rightarrow B_2O_3 + 3H_2O$

17. Write a balanced equation for the synthesis of solid lithium oxide, Li_2O, from solid lithium, Li, and gaseous oxygen, O_2.

18. In this single replacement reaction, why does one sodium replace hydrogen?

$2Na(s) + 2HCl(aq) \rightarrow 2NaCl(aq) + H_2(g)$

19. For each pair listed, which element is the most reactive?
    a. Mg or Li
    b. H or Al
    c. Na or K
    d. Br or Cl

20. A precipitate of iron (III) carbonate, $Fe_2(CO_3)_3$, forms in the reaction of sodium carbonate, Na_2CO_3, and iron (III) chloride, $FeCl_3$. Write a balanced chemical reaction for this reaction.

21. What reactants and/or products do the following reactions have in common?

$CH_4(g) + 2O_2(g) \rightarrow CO_2(g) + 2H_2O(l)$

$2C_2H_6(g) + 7O_2(g) \rightarrow 4CO_2(g) + 6H_2O(l)$

$C_4H_8(g) + 6O_2(g) \rightarrow 4CO_2(g) + 4H_2O(l)$

22. Write the balanced reaction that occurs between solid sodium, Na, and gaseous chlorine, Cl_2.

23. Write the net ionic equation for the reaction between aqueous lead (II) nitrate, $Pb(NO_3)_2$, and aqueous sodium chloride, NaCl, to produce solid lead (II) iodide, PbI_2, and aqueous sodium chloride, NaCl.

24. Some hand warmers use a solution of sodium acetate and water. When triggered, solid sodium acetate forms. Why is some of the sodium acetate not dissolved in the water?

25. Complete the equation.

$Ba(OH)_2(aq) + H_2SO_4(aq) \rightarrow$

26. Complete the equation.

$C_2H_2(g) + O_2(g) \rightarrow$

27. In the net ionic equation for the reaction between aqueous hydrochloric acid, HCl, and aqueous sodium hydroxide, NaOH, what are the spectator ions?

28. Write the net ionic equation for the reaction between aqueous magnesium chloride, $MgCl_2$, and aqueous potassium carbonate, K_2CO_3.

29. Identify which of these ions will combine to form a precipitate.
    a. Pb^+ and Cl^-
    b. Ba^{+2} and OH^-
    c. Na^+ and CO_3^{-2}
    d. Pb^{+2} and I^-

30. Why do precipitate compounds not have a solvation shell?

INVESTIGATION 10

1. Balance the equation.
   $Fe + Cl_2 \longrightarrow FeCl_3$

2. Why is it so important to balance equations? Use a specific law to justify your response.

3. The balanced equation for the formation of water is given:

$2H_2 + O_2 \longrightarrow 2H_2O$

How many moles of water are produced when 4.5 mol of O_2 fully react?

4. Reinterpret the following equation in terms of volumes of each gas at STP.

$2N_2(g) + O_2(g) \longrightarrow 2N_2O(g)$

5. What is a mole ratio? Why is it important?

6. In order to produce 40 mol of NO_2 gas, how many moles of oxygen gas are needed? The balanced equation is given.

$2NO(g) + O_2(g) \longrightarrow 2NO_2(g)$

7. The unbalanced equation for the combustion of propane gas is given.

$C_3H_8 + O_2 \longrightarrow CO_2 + H_2O$

Balance the equation and determine the mole ratio of oxygen gas to carbon dioxide.

8. Using the equation for the combustion of propane, determine the number of molecules of CO_2 produced if the reaction uses and fully consumes 3.4 mol of C_3H_8?

$C_3H_8 + O_2 \longrightarrow CO_2 + H_2O$

9. Your friend's favorite superhero is a man that is able to change shape. In one episode, the hero turns into a very large dinosaur. Explain, using conservation of mass, why this super power is possible or not.

10. The reaction for the formation of ammonia (NH_3) is shown:

$N_2 + 3H_2 \longrightarrow 2NH_3$

Suppose you start with 2 mol of N_2 at 300.0 K and 0.70 atm. Your classmate tries to determine the amount of ammonia gas produced and comes up with 89.6 L of ammonia. Is this calculation correct? Explain your answer.

11. This is the equation for the formation of sodium hydroxide:

$Na_2O(s) + H_2O(l) \longrightarrow 2NaOH(aq)$

How many moles of H_2O are needed to produce 4.5 L of NaOH?

12. Would you ever need more than two conversion factors to convert between volume, mass, and/or factors representative? Explain your answer.

13. The equation for the formation of calcium nitrate is given. Assume that you have 30.1 g of HNO_3.

$Ca(OH)_2(aq) + 2HNO_3(aq) \longrightarrow 2H_2O(l) + Ca(NO_3)_2(aq)$

a. How many grams of $Ca(OH)_2$ are needed to fully react with the HNO_3?
b. Assuming that both reactants are fully consumed and there is no excess left, how many liters of H_2O are produced in this reaction?

14. The unbalanced equation that results in the formation of aluminum sulfate is given.

$Al(OH)_3 + H_2SO_4 \longrightarrow Al_2(SO_4)_3 + H_2O$

a. Balance the equation.
b. Determine mole ratio of H_2O to $Al_2(SO_4)_3$.
c. If 50.6 g of H_2O was produced during this reaction, how many grams of aluminum sulfate was produced?

15. How many representative particles of NF_3 are formed when 30 L of N_2 at STP is consumed in the following reaction?

$N_2 + 2F_3 \rightarrow 2NF_3$

16. Magnesium oxide is produced from magnesium and oxygen gas. The unbalanced equation is given.

$Mg(s) + O_2(g) \longrightarrow MgO(s)$

a. Balance the equation.
b. How many grams of MgO are produced if a total of 40.5 L of oxygen gas at STP reacts with magnesium?

17. The balanced equation for the reaction of sodium carbonate and hydrochloric acid is given.

$Na_2CO_3 + 2HCl \longrightarrow CO_2 + H_2O + 2NaCl$

Assume that you start with 30.0 g of Na_2CO_3.

a. How many grams of NaCl can be produced?
b. At STP, how many liters of CO_2 are produced?
c. How many molecules of H_2O are produced?
d. What is the minimum mass of HCl needed in order for all of the Na_2CO_3 to be fully consumed?

18. Carbon monoxide reacts with nitrogen monoxide to form carbon dioxide and nitrogen.

$2NO(g) + 2CO(g) \longrightarrow 2CO_2(g) + N_2(g)$

Suppose you start with 3.6 g of NO and perform the reaction at STP conditions. How many liters of N_2 are produced from this reaction?

19. The density of nitric oxide, a highly corrosive mineral acid, is 1.51 g/cm^3. It is involved in the following reaction:

$4NO + O_2 + 2H_2O \longrightarrow 4HNO_2$

Suppose you start with 13.3 L of liquid nitric oxide.

a. How many grams of NO do you have?
b. How many moles of HNO_2 can be produced if all of the NO reacts?

20. Decomposition of hydrogen peroxide results in water and oxygen gas. How many grams of hydrogen peroxide are needed to produce 1.20×10^{24} molecules of oxygen gas? The unbalanced equation is provided.

$H_2O_2(l) \longrightarrow H_2O(l) + O_2(g)$

21. Water vapor reacts with potassium superoxide to form oxygen and potassium hydroxide.

$4KO_2(s) + 2H_2O(g) \longrightarrow 3O_2(g) + 4KOH(s)$

How many grams of potassium superoxide were consumed in the reaction if 34.0 L of oxygen gas is produced at STP from this reaction?

22. The conservation of mass states that matter is conserved in chemical reactions. Does having a percent yield <100% violate this law? Explain your answer.

23. Consider this equation.

$2A + 3B \longrightarrow 5C$

What is the limiting reactant if you have 20 moles of compound A and 25 moles of compound B?

24. A reaction predicted to make 94.5 g of HCN actually produced about 87.4 g of HCN. What is the percent yield?

25. In a reaction, compounds A and B react to form compound C. You are given 100 g of both compounds. Compound A has a molar mass of 100 g/mol, while compound B has a molar mass of 200 g/mol. Is it possible to determine which one is the limiting reagent from the information given? Explain your answer.

$3A + B \longrightarrow C$

26. In a reaction, 24.0 g of diboron hexahydride reacts with 40.0 L of oxygen to form diboron trioxide at STP. The balanced equation is shown.

$B_2H_6(g) + 3O_2(g) \longrightarrow 3H_2O(l) + B_2O_3(s)$

a. Which reagent is the limiting reagent?
b. Assume that the reaction produces 37.6 g of B_2O_3. What is the percent yield?

27. In a reaction, 233.0 g of n-heptane (C_7H_{16}) is combusted with 540.0 g of oxygen. The skeletal equation is shown.

$C_7H_{16}(l) + O_2(g) \longrightarrow CO_2(g) + H_2O(g)$

a. What is the balanced equation?
b. What is the limiting reagent?
c. How many grams of water are produced?

28. In a reaction, 30.5 g of sulfuric acid reacts with 51.6 g of calcium fluoride to form hydrogen fluoride and calcium sulfate. The balanced equation is shown.

$H_2SO_4(l) + CaF_2(s) \longrightarrow 2HF(g) + CaSO_4(s)$

a. What is the limiting reagent?
b. What is the percent yield if 39.0 g of $CaSO_4$ is produced?

29. In a reaction at STP, 58.6 L of chlorine gas reacts with 89.5 g of sodium hydroxide to form laundry bleach (NaClO) as shown in the equation.

$Cl_2(g) + 2NaOH(aq) \longrightarrow NaClO(aq) + NaCl(aq) + H_2O(l)$

a. Which is the limiting reagent?
b. How many grams of NaClO are produced?

30. Suppose that the actual yield of NaClO from the given equation is only 56.3 g. What is the percent yield?

$Cl_2(g) + 2NaOH(aq) \longrightarrow NaClO(aq) + NaCl(aq) + H_2O(l)$

31. A sample of 7.40 g of aluminum oxide was prepared. Assuming all of the starting reagents were consumed, how many grams of aluminum were needed to create this compound? An unbalanced equation is provided.

$Al + O_2 \longrightarrow Al_2O_3$

INVESTIGATION 11

1. Explain why the rate of a reaction increases when the temperature increases.
2. Why is activation energy required even when the enthalpy of the reaction is negative?
3. What is an activated complex? How does it relate to the activation energy?
4. Your friend argues that when sunlight is absorbed by trees, the trees reduce some of the energy present in the universe. Using the concept of a system and its surroundings, how would you correct your friend?
5. When energy is absorbed by a system, what happens to the surrounding temperature? What happens when energy is released?
6. Suppose that reactant A reacts to form product B and releases –300 kJ of heat. However, it is later discovered that there is an intermediate C that is formed before product B. The enthalpy change from A to C is –150 kJ of heat. Does the discovery of this intermediate require us to determine a new heat of reaction for $A \longrightarrow B$?
7. Compare the chemical potential energy of the reactants and the products:
   a. exothermic reaction
   b. endothermic reaction
8. Identify each of the reactions as exothermic or endothermic.
   a. combustion of propane to produce carbon dioxide and water
   b. decomposition of sodium hydrogen carbonate by applying heat
   c. synthesis of salt (NaCl) through the combination of sodium and chlorine
9. Suppose a combustion reaction of propane was performed with excess oxygen. How many kcal of energy are produced when 36.2 g of C_3H_8 is burned?

   $C_3H_8(g) + 5O_2(g) \longrightarrow 3CO_2(g) + 4H_2O(g) + 526\ kcal$
10. Suppose that sulfuric acid is dissolved in water. The reaction is shown.

    $H_2SO_4(aq) \longrightarrow H^+(aq) + HSO_4^-(aq)$

    $\Delta H_{soln} = -71.76\ kJ/mol$

    How does this reaction change the temperature of the water?
11. Describe Hess's law. What does it allow us to determine?
12. The heat of fusion of aluminum is 10.79 kJ/mol. How much heat is released when 13.3 g Al changes from a liquid state to a solid state at the freezing point?
13. At 0°C, does H_2O exist as solid ice, liquid water, or both?
14. Calculate the amount of heat required to change 75.0 g of liquid mercury to a gas. The heat of vaporization of mercury is 55.229 kJ/mol.

15. Calculate the quantity of energy gained or lost in the following reactions.
    a. 5.66 mol of water condensing at 100°C
    b. 0.90 mol of water freezing at 0°C

16. A cold pack contains two sealed bags. When the cold pack is squeezed, these bags break and their compounds intermix, leading to a chemical reaction. Would you expect this reaction to be exothermic or endothermic? How about for a hot pack?

17. The heat of vaporization of water is 40.7 kJ/mol while the heat of vaporization of acetone is 31.3 kJ/mol. Explain what these values mean about the structure of these molecules and what would happen if the surroundings of these chemicals were heated up.

18. The enthalpy of a solution for sodium hydroxide is –44.5 kJ/mol. If this compound is dissolved in water, how will the temperature of the water change?

19. What is the amount of heat required to vaporize 30.0 g of these compounds?
    a. water (ΔH_{vap}40.1 kJ/mol)
    b. ethanol C_2H_6O (ΔH_{vap}38.6 kJ/mol)
    c. nitrogen N_2 (ΔH_{vap}2.79 kJ/mol)

20. How much heat is lost when 109.5 g of water freezes to form solid ice? The heat of fusion of water is –6.01 kJ/mol.

21. How much heat is released during the decomposition of 6.5 mol of H_2O_2? Enthalpy of reaction is –196.4 kJ.

    $2H_2O_2 \longrightarrow 2H_2O + O_2$

22. How much energy is required to turn 45 g of liquid nitrogen into a gas? The heat of vaporization of liquid nitrogen (N_2) is 6.1 kJ/mol.

23. Calculate the heat absorbed when 3.6 mol of $CaCl_2$ is dissolved in water. The heat of solution is –80 kJ/mol. Is this reaction exothermic or endothermic?

24. Consider these equations:

    $2A + 2B \longrightarrow 3C$ –200 kJ/mol

    $C + E \longrightarrow F$ –150 kJ/mol

    Calculate the enthalpy of the combined reaction using Hess's law.

25. What are the conditions of the surroundings required to define the standard enthalpy of a system?

26. Describe the relative values of enthalpy of vaporization of chlorine (Cl_2), oxygen (O_2), and hydrogen (H_2). Explain your answer.

27. How much heat must be added to a 1,000-kg piece of ice in order for it to melt? Assume that the temperature is at 0°C exactly. The heat of fusion of water is 6.01 kJ/mol.

28. The equation for the formulation of HCN is shown.

    $CH_4(g) + NH_3(g) \longrightarrow HCN(g) + 3H_2(g)$

    Given the equations, calculate the total ΔH for the following reaction to form HCN.

    $N_2(g) + 3H_2(g) \longrightarrow 2NH_3(g)$
    $\Delta H = -91.8$ kJ

    $C(s) + 2H_2(g) \longrightarrow CH_4(g)$
    $\Delta H = -74.9$ kJ

    $2C(s) + H_2(g) + N_2(g) \longrightarrow 2HCN(g)$
    $\Delta H = 270.3$ kJ

29. Which is greater: the quantity of heat absorbed by a vaporizing liquid, or the quantity of heat released when the vapor condenses?

30. When isopropyl alcohol is placed on the skin, the alcohol evaporates and there is a cooling sensation on the skin. Skin has an average temperature of 37°C and the boiling point of isopropyl alcohol is 82.5°C. The heat of vaporization of isopropyl alcohol is 45.2 kJ/mol. Explain this phenomenon in terms of the heat of vaporization.

A

activated complex: an unstable cluster of atoms that exists during the transition from reactants to products (370)

activation energy: the minimum energy colliding particles must have in order to react (19)

activity series: a list of elements in order of decreasing activity (320)

actual yield: the amount of product that forms when a reaction is carried out in the laboratory (363)

allotropes: different molecular forms of an element in the same physical state; graphite and diamond are allotropes of the element carbon (227)

amorphous solid: a solid that lacks an ordered internal structure; rubber, plastic, and asphalt are examples (210)

anion: any atom or group of atoms with a negative charge (146)

aqueous solution: a solution in which water is the solvent (242)

atom: the smallest particle of an element that retains its identity in a chemical reaction (100)

atomic emission spectrum: the pattern formed when light passes through a prism or diffraction grating to separate it into the different frequencies of light it contains (110)

atomic mass: the weighted average of the masses of the isotopes of an element (106)

atomic number: the number of protons in the nucleus of an atom of an element (101)

atomic orbital: a mathematical expression describing the probability of finding an electron at various locations; usually represented by the region of space around the nucleus where there is a high probability of finding an electron (116)

atomic radius: one half the distance between the nuclei of two atoms of the same element when the atoms are joined (144)

Avogadro's hypothesis: any two samples of gas with an equal number of particles will have the same volume when they are held at the same pressure and temperature (275)

Avogadro's number: the number of representative particles contained in one mole of a substance; equal to 6.02×10^{23} (264)

B

binary compound: a compound composed of only two elements (187)

black-body radiation: the radiation emitted by a heated object; exhibits a continuous, temperature-dependent frequency distribution (52)

bond enthalpy: the amount of energy needed to break the bonds of one mole of a substance (373)

C

cation: any atom or group of atoms with a positive charge (146)

change of enthalpy (ΔH): the heat absorbed or released by a reaction at constant pressure (372)

chemical formula: an expression that indicates the number and type of atoms present in the smallest representative unit of a substance (187)

chemical potential energy: energy stored in the chemical bonds of a substance (7, 311)

chemical symbol: a one- or two-letter representation of an element (102)

coefficients: whole numbers that appear in front of formulas in a balanced chemical equation (309)

collision theory: a theory that states that bonds are broken when molecules collide with enough energy to break bonds in reactants and with the correct orientation to form bonds that make products (313)

colloid: a heterogeneous mixture containing particles, called the dispersed phase, that are spread throughout another substance, called the dispersion medium (256)

combination reaction: a chemical change in which two or more substances react to form a single new substance (316)

combustion reaction: a chemical change in which an element or a compound reacts with oxygen, often producing energy in the form of heat and light (324)

complete ionic equation: an equation that shows dissolved ionic compounds as dissociated free ions (330)

concentrated solution: a solution that contains a large amount of solute (291)

concentration: measure of the amount of solute that is dissolved in a given quantity of solvent, usually expressed in moles/L or molarity (291)

condensation: the changing from a gas to a liquid (214)

conduction: the diffusion of thermal energy through a material or between adjacent materials (42)

convection: the cycling of fluid materials driven by differences in density (45)

covalent bond: a bond formed by the sharing of electrons between atoms (169)

covalent network solids: solids consisting of networks of atoms held together by covalent bonds; they are very hard and tend to have the highest melting points of all solids (209)

crystal: a solid consisting of particles arranged in an orderly, repeating, three-dimensional pattern called a crystal lattice (210)

crystal lattice: an orderly, repeating, three-dimensional pattern of many ions, atoms, or molecules (160)

current: the flow of electrons measured in amperes or amps (39)

D

decomposition reaction: a chemical change in which a single compound breaks down into two or more products (317)

density: the ratio of the mass of an object to its volume (67)

deposition: the changing from a gas directly to a solid without passing through the liquid state (214)

dilute solution: a solution with a small amount of solute (291)

dipole interactions: the intermolecular attractions between oppositely charged regions of polar molecules (180)

dislocation: a defect or irregularity within a crystal structure (234)

dispersion forces: attractions between molecules caused by the electron motion on one molecule affecting the electron motion on the other through electrical forces; these are the weakest interactions between molecules (179)

dissolution rate: the rate at which a solute dissolves (249)

double covalent bond: a bond made by two shared pairs of electrons (172)

double-replacement reaction: a chemical change involving an exchange of positive ions between two compounds (322)

ductility: the ability to be drawn into wires (230)

E

effective nuclear charge (Z_{eff}): the net positive nuclear charge experienced by an electron in an atom (141)

efflorescence: the loss of water by a hydrate (246)

electrical conductivity: the ability of a material to conduct electricity (231)

electricity: a form of energy involving electrically-charged particles (39)

electrolyte: a compound that conducts electric current when dissolved in an aqueous solution or in the molten state (244)

electron: a negatively charged subatomic particle (100)

electron affinity: the energy change when an atom gains an electron (149)

electron configurations: the arrangement of electrons of an atom in its ground state into various orbitals around the nuclei of atoms (121)

electron dot structure: a notation that depicts valence electrons as dots around the atomic symbol of the element (127)

electronegativity: a measure of the ability of an atom to attract electrons when the atom is in a compound (174)

element: the simplest form of matter that has a unique set of properties; an element cannot be broken down into simpler substances by chemical means (101)

empirical formula: the chemical formula of a compound that gives the lowest whole-number ratio of the atoms or moles of elements in a compound (286)

endothermic: a term describing processes that absorb energy from the surroundings (312)

endothermic reaction: a chemical reaction that absorbs heat from the surroundings; the reaction products are at a higher energy than the reactants (18)

energy: the capacity for doing work or producing heat (7)

energy levels: the specific energies an electron in an atom or other system can have (112)

enthalpy diagram: a representation of the relative internal energy of a system undergoing a chemical change (373)

enthalpy of reaction: the total change in energy for a reaction (374)

entropy: a measure of the disorder of a system; systems tend to go from a state of order (low entropy) to a state of maximum disorder (high entropy) (55)

evaporation: vaporization that occurs at the surface of a liquid that is not boiling (216)

excess reagent: any reactant that is not used up in a reaction (358)

exothermic: a term describing processes that release net energy to the surroundings (312)

exothermic reaction: a chemical reaction that releases heat to the surroundings; the reaction products are at a lower energy than the reactants (18)

F

fluid: any substance that flows; both liquids and gases are fluids (206)

G

gas pressure: the result of forces between the molecules of a gas with each other and a container's walls (202)

group: a vertical column of elements in the periodic table; the constituent elements of a group have similar chemical and physical properties (134)

H

heat: the energy transferred from one object to another because of a temperature difference between the objects (9)

heat flow: the rate at which heat moves from one object to another (10)

Henry's law: at a given temperature, the solubility of a gas in a liquid is directly proportional to the pressure of the gas above the liquid (254)

Hess's law of heat summation: if you add two or more thermochemical equations to give a final equation, you can also add the enthalpies of reaction to give the final enthalpy of reaction (380)

heterogeneous mixtures: mixtures that do not have uniform composition (256)

homogeneous mixtures: mixtures that have a uniform appearance and composition (256)

hydrate: a solid, typically crystalline compound that contains water molecules as an integral part of its structure (246)

hydrocarbon: a compound composed of hydrogen and carbon (324)

hydrogen bonds: intermolecular forces in which a hydrogen covalently bonded to a very electronegative atom is also weakly bonded to an unshared electron pair of another electronegative atom from a second molecule (181)

hypoxic zones: areas in the ocean where the oxygen concentration is so low that animal life suffocates (252)

I

insulators: materials with very low thermal conductivities (42)

internal energy: the total energy contained in a system (372)

ion: an atom or group of atoms that has a positive or negative charge (146)

ionic bond: an electrostatic attraction that holds oppositely charged ions together (158)

ionic compound: an electrically neutral compound made of cations and anions (158)

ionic solids: solids that consist of positively and negatively charged ions held together by ionic bonds with relatively strong attractions and resulting in high melting points and hardness (209)

ionization energy: the energy required to remove an electron from an atom in its gaseous state (147)

isostasy: the equilibrium between upward and downward forces in the lithosphere (89)

isotopes: atoms of the same element that have the same atomic number but different atomic masses due to a different number of neutrons (104)

K

kinetic energy: the energy of an object's motion (7)

kinetic theory: a theory explaining the states of matter, based on the concept that all matter consists of tiny particles that are in constant motion (200)

L

law of conservation of energy: in any chemical or physical process, energy is neither created nor destroyed (11, 311)

law of conservation of mass: in any chemical reaction, the mass of the products is always equal to the mass of the reactants (308)

law of constant composition: any sample of a compound will be made up of the same elements in the same ratio (282)

law of definite proportions: a compound contains its component elements in a fixed ratio by mass (280)

limiting reagent: the reactant that determines the amount of product that can be formed (358)

luster: the way light interacts with a material's surface (231)

M

main group elements: elements in groups 1, 2, and 13 to 18 of the periodic table that display a wide range of physical and chemical properties (136)

malleability: the ability to be hammered or pressed into shapes (230)

mass number: the total number of protons and neutrons in the nucleus of an atom (103)

melting point: the temperature at which a solid becomes a liquid (220)

metal: one of a class of elements that are good conductors of heat and electric current; metals tend to be ductile, malleable, and shiny (135)

metallic bond: the electrostatic attraction between the free-floating valence electrons and the positively charged metal cations (165)

metallic solids: solids formed via strong metallic bonds and having highly variable properties dependent on electron arrangement (209)

metalloid: an element that tends to have properties that are similar to those of metals and nonmetals (135)

molar enthalpy of condensation: the heat released by one mole of a gaseous substance as it condenses at its normal boiling point (390)

molar enthalpy of fusion: the heat absorbed by one mole of a solid substance as it melts to a liquid at constant temperature (388)

molar enthalpy of solidification: the heat released by one mole of a liquid substance as it solidifies at constant temperature (388)

molar enthalpy of solution: the enthalpy change caused by the dissolution of one mole of a substance (384)

molar enthalpy of vaporization: the heat absorbed by one mole of a liquid substance as it vaporizes at constant temperature (390)

molar mass: the mass of one mole of a substance (266)

molar volume: the volume of one mole of a gas at STP; 22.4 L/mol for any ideal gas (275)

molarity: molar concentration; the number of moles of solute dissolved in one liter of solution (292)

mole: the amount of a substance that contains 6.02×10^{23} representative particles of that substance (264)

mole ratio: a conversion factor derived from the coefficients of a balanced chemical equation interpreted in terms of moles (347)

molecular formula: the chemical formula of a compound that is either the same as its experimentally determined empirical formula or a simple whole-number multiple of its empirical formula (288)

molecular solids: solids held together by the relatively weak dipole-dipole intermolecular forces; tend to be soft and have low melting points (209)

molecule: a neutral group of atoms held together by one or more covalent bonds (169)

momentum: a vector with both magnitude and direction equal to the mass of an object times its velocity (36)

monoatomic ion: a single atom with a positive or negative charge (185)

N

net ionic equation: an equation for a reaction in solution that shows only the particles directly involved in a chemical change (330)

neutron: a subatomic particle with no charge and a mass of 1 amu; found in the nucleus of an atom (100)

nonelectrolyte: a compound that does not conduct electric current when dissolved in an aqueous solution or in the molten state (244)

nonmetal: an element that tends to be a poor conductor of heat and electric current; nonmetals generally have properties opposite to those of metals (135)

nonpolar covalent bond: a bond in which the electrons are shared equally (175)

nucleus: the tiny, dense central portion of an atom, composed of protons and neutrons (100)

O

octet rule: a general rule that atoms tend to form bonds so that each atom has eight electrons in its valence shell (156)

P

paleomagnetic data: information gathered from remnant magnetic fields retained in the structure of iron-rich minerals when rock forms (82)

percent by mass: the ratio of the masses of solute to solution, expressed as a percentage (298)

percent by volume: the ratio of the volumes of solute to solution, expressed as a percentage (298)

percent composition: the percent by mass of each element in a compound (280)

percent yield: the ratio of the actual yield to the theoretical yield for a chemical reaction expressed as a percentage; a measure of the efficiency of a reaction (363)

period: a horizontal row of elements in the periodic table (134)

periodic law: when the elements are arranged in order of increasing atomic number, there is a periodic repetition of their physical and chemical properties (134)

periodic table: an arrangement of elements in which the elements are separated into groups based on a set of repeating properties (102)

phase change: the changing from one state of matter to another (213)

phase diagram: a graph that describes the conditions of temperature and pressure at which a substance exists as a solid, liquid, or gas (222)

plate boundaries: the area between tectonic plates; the location of most geologic activity (85)

plate tectonics: the theory that Earth's lithosphere is broken into large rigid pieces that move very slowly across Earth's surface due to convection currents in the mantle (80)

point defect: a defect or irregularity within a crystal that occurs at a point in the lattice (233)

polar covalent bond: a bond in which electrons are not shared equally between the atoms (175)

polyatomic ion: a group of atoms that is covalently bonded together and has a positive or negative charge (186)

potential energy: the energy stored in a system (7)

power: the rate of energy flow measured in watts (W) (10)

products: substances produced in a chemical reaction (304)

proton: a positively-charged subatomic particle found in the nucleus of an atom (100)

Q

quantum: the amount of energy needed to move an electron from one energy level to another (112)

quantum mechanical model: the modern description, primarily mathematical, of the behavior of electrons in atoms (116)

R

reactants: substances present at the start of a reaction (304)

reaction rate: the speed at which reactants become products (313)

representative particle: the species present in a substance; usually atoms, molecules, or formula units (264)

resistance: the counteraction to the flow of current through a circuit, measured in ohms (39)

rotation: the movement of a body in a circular path around a fixed point (205)

S

saturated solution: a solution that contains the maximum amount of solute for a given quantity of solvent at a constant temperature and pressure (250)

seafloor spreading: the continuous process of new seafloor formation and the expansion of an ocean basin (87)

single covalent bond: a bond made by one shared pair of electrons (172)

single-replacement reaction: a chemical change in which one element replaces a second element in a compound (319)

skeleton equation: a chemical equation that does not indicate the relative amounts of the reactants and products (305)

solubility: the amount of solute that dissolves in a given quantity of a solvent at a specified temperature and pressure to produce a saturated solution (250)

solubility curve: a graph of solubility as a function of temperature (251)

solute: the dissolved particles; usually ions, but also polar molecules (242)

solvation: the process of ion capture by a solvent (242)

solvation shell: a layer of solvent particles surrounding a solute species (ions) in a solution (332)

solvent: the dissolving medium in any solution (242)

specific heat: the amount of energy needed to increase the temperature of 1 kg of a substance by 1 K (13)

spectator ion: an ion that is not directly involved in a reaction (330)

spin: a quantum mechanical property of electrons that may be thought of as clockwise or counterclockwise orientation (122)

standard enthalpy of formation: the change in enthalpy that accompanies the formation of one mole of the compound from its elements, with all substances in their standard states (381)

standard enthalpy of reaction: the change in enthalpy when one mole of matter undergoes a chemical reaction at standard conditions (382)

standard state: the stable form of a substance at a temperature of 25°C and a pressure of 101.3 kPa, which may be a solid, liquid, or gas (381)

standard temperature and pressure (STP): the standard set of conditions used for comparing properties of different gases; corresponds to a temperature of 0°C and approximately atmospheric pressure at sea level (101.3 kPa) (201)

stoichiometry: the calculation of quantities in chemical reactions (342)

subduction zones: areas where parts of oceanic plates sink into the mantle and beneath other plates (90)

sublimation: the changing from a solid directly to a gas without passing through the liquid state (214)

supercontinents: large continents formed from the collision and merger of smaller continents (84)

supersaturated solution: a solution that contains more solute than it can theoretically hold at a given temperature (253)

surface tension: an inward force that tends to minimize the surface area of a liquid; it causes the surface to behave as if it were a thin skin (237)

surfactant: a substance that reduces surface tension (238)

surroundings: everything in the universe outside of the system (371)

suspension: a heterogeneous mixture from which particles settle out upon standing (256)

system: a part of the universe on which you focus your attention (371)

T

temperature: a measure of the average kinetic energy of particles in matter (12)

theoretical yield: the amount of product that could form during a reaction calculated from a balanced chemical equation; it represents the maximum amount of product that could be formed from a given amount of reactant (363)

thermal boundary layer: the boundary between fluid layers where heat enters or leaves a convection cell via conduction (50)

thermal conductivity: the ability of a material to conduct heat (42, 231)

thermal energy: the kinetic energy of the atoms of a substance (37)

thermal equilibrium: the state in which heat is no longer flowing in or out of a system (56)

thermal expansion: the expansion of a material when heated (47)

thermochemical equation: a chemical equation that includes the enthalpy change (376)

thermochemistry: the study of changes in energy during chemical reactions and changes in state (9)

translation: the shift of a body from one point in space to another (205)

triple covalent bond: a bond made by three pairs of shared electrons (172)

V

valence electron: an electron in the outermost or highest occupied energy level of an atom (126)

van der Waals forces: the two weakest intermolecular attractions—dispersion interactions and dipole forces (179)

vapor pressure: a measure of the force exerted by a gas above a liquid in a sealed container; a dynamic equilibrium exists between the vapor and the liquid (218)

vaporization: the changing from a liquid to a gas (214)

vibration: the rapid back-and-forth movement of an object in a fixed place (205)

viscosity: the resistance of a material to flow, measured in pascal-seconds (46)

VSEPR theory (valence-shell electron-pair repulsion theory): a theory that states that bonding pairs of electrons and unshared valence electron pairs repel each other and push each other as far away as possible to minimize the electrostatic repulsion between them; these repulsions result in specific three-dimensional shapes (176)

The page on which a term is defined is indicated in **boldface** type. Page numbers for appendices begin with *R*.

A

B

C

D

E

F

G

J

K

L

M

N

O

P

Q

R

S

T

U

V

W

Y

CREDITS

PHOTOGRAPHY
Photo locators denoted as follows: Top (T), Center (C), Bottom (B), Left (L), Right (R), Background (Bkgd)

Cover: Sebastian Janicki/Shutterstock; Bkgd: Sylverarts Vectors/Shutterstock

FRONT MATTER
ii: Sebastian Janicki/Shutterstock; **iii** (TC): Up Late Creative; (B): Kai Kiefer; **iv**: Tanya Katovich; **vi** (A): Igor Sasin/AFP/Getty Images; (B): Paolo Lo Pinto/RealyEasyStar/Alamy Stock Photo; (C): Mint Images RF/Getty Images; (D): Eddtoro/Shutterstock; (E): Hendrik Holler/Look-foto/Getty Images

INSTRUCTIONAL SEGMENTS
2: Igor Sasin/AFP/Getty Images; **3** (TL): Josh Edelson/AFP/Getty Images; (TC): Inga Spence/Alamy Stock Photo; (TR): Philip Wallick/Age fotostock/Getty Images; **96**: Paolo Lo Pinto/RealyEasyStar/Alamy Stock Photo; **97** (TL): Lilyling1982/Shutterstock; (TC): B.O'Kane/Alamy Stock Photo; (TC Inset): The Granger Collection Ltd.; (TR): Berkay/iStock/Getty Images; **196**: Mint Images RF/Getty Images; (TR): Adie Bush/Cultura Creative (RF)/Alamy Stock Photo; **197** (TL): Noel Hendrickson/Getty Images; (TCL): Thom Baur/TPX Images of the Day/Reuters; (TCR): Stockcreations/Shutterstock; (TR): Joseph Giacomin/Cultura/Getty Images

INVESTIGATION 1
4: Josh Edelson/AFP/Getty Images; **10** (L): Wollertz/Shutterstock; (R): Kip Evans/Alamy Stock Photo; **11**: Thomas Barrat/Shutterstock; **13**: Josh Edelson/AFP/Getty Images; **15**: Gaertner/Alamy Stock Photo; **19**: Alexandre Dotta/Science Source; **20**: Elxeneize/Shutterstock; **23**: Josh Edelson/AFP/Getty Images; **27**: Hunter Walker/EyeEm/Getty Images; **29**: ZUMA Press, Inc./Alamy Stock Photo; **32**: Josh Edelson/AFP/Getty Images

INVESTIGATION 2
34: Inga spence/Alamy Stock Photo; **39**: GIPhotoStock/Science Source; **40**: Inga spence/Alamy Stock Photo; **41**: 123RF; **42**: DOE/Science Source; **43**: Rubberball/Erik Isakson/Getty Images; **44**: Pindyurin Vasily/Shutterstock; **46** (T): Stacy Pospelova/Getty Images; (B): Stockcam/E+/Getty Images; **47**: Vladyslav Danilin/Shutterstock; **51**: BSIP/Getty Images; **54**: Inga spence/Alamy Stock Photo; **56**: Valery Rizzo/Stockimo/Alamy Stock Photo; **58**: Dorling Kindersley/Alamy Stock Photo; **61** (L): Kichigin/Shutterstock; (R): Shawn Hempel/Alamy Stock Photo; **62**: Inga spence/Alamy Stock Photo

INVESTIGATION 3
64: Philip Wallick/Age fotostock/Getty Images; **73**: Weisen Shen; **74** (L): Republished with permission of Nature Publishing Group from *Vertical mantle flow associated with a lithospheric drip beneath the Great Basin*, 2009; permission conveyed through Copyright Clearance Center, Inc.; (BR): Michael Wysession; **75**: Mark D. Behn; **77**: Dr. J. Huw Davies; **78**: Tjlsfinland/123RF; **79**: Philip Wallick/Age fotostock/Getty Images; **83**: R.D. Müller/M. Sdrolias/C. Gaina/W.R. Roest/NOAA; **86**: Lingxiao Xie/Moment/Getty Images; **88**: Kevin Schafer/Avalon/Photoshot License/Alamy Stock Photo; **94**: Philip Wallick/Age fotostock/Getty Images; **95**: Igor Sasin/AFP/Getty Images

INVESTIGATION 4
98: Lilyling1982/Shutterstock; **100**: James Brey/E+/Getty Images; **101** (L): iStock/Getty Images; (R): Timofeev Sergey/Shutterstock; **103**: Conrado Tramontini/Moment/Getty Images; **104**: WilleeCole Photography/Shutterstock; **109**: Lilyling1982/Shutterstock; **115**: Lilyling1982/Shutterstock; **116**: Photomatz/Shutterstock; **120**: Lilyling1982/Shutterstock; **123**: PH888/Shutterstock; **128**: Lilyling1982/Shutterstock

INVESTIGATION 5
130: B.O'Kane/Alamy Stock Photo; **136**: © The Granger Collection LTD.; **137**: B.O'Kane/Alamy Stock Photo; **143**: B.O'Kane/Alamy Stock Photo; **152**: B.O'Kane/Alamy Stock Photo

INVESTIGATION 6
154: Berkay/iStock/Getty Images; **160**: Peterhermesfurian/123RF; **162** (L): Cagla Acikgoz/Shutterstock; (R): Universal Images Group North America LLC/DeAgostini/Alamy Stock Photo; **164**: Berkay/iStock/Getty Images; **165**: Jeff J Daly/Alamy Stock Photo; **166**: Saqib Majeed/SOPA Images/LightRocket/Getty Images; **168**: Berkay/iStock/Getty Images; **178**: Berkay/iStock/Getty Images; **183**: David Wall/Alamy Stock Photo; **184**: Berkay/iStock/Getty Images; **189** (T): Maxim Boldyrev/Alamy Stock Photo; (B): Focal Point/Shutterstock; **192**: NASA Photo/Alamy Stock Photo; **194**: Berkay/iStock/Getty Images; **195**: Paolo Lo Pinto/RealyEasyStar/Alamy Stock Photo

INVESTIGATION 7
198: Adie Bush/Cultura Creative (RF)/Alamy Stock Photo; **200**: Shutter Professional/Shutterstock; **205** (L): Monbibi/Shutterstock; (C): Andreykuzmin/Shutterstock; (R): Billion Photos/Shutterstock; **206** (L): Richard Megna/Fundamental Photographs, NYC; (R): Richard Megna/Fundamental Photographs, NYC; **208** (TL): Al1962/Shutterstock; (TR): Sirtravelalot/Shutterstock; (BL): HelloRF Zcool/Shutterstock; (BR): DmitrySt/Shutterstock; **210** (L): Stefano Cavoretto/Shutterstock; (R): Siim Sepp/Shutterstock; **212**: Adie Bush/Cultura Creative (RF)/Alamy Stock Photo; **214**: Gerhard Zwerger-Schoner/ImageBroker/Alamy Stock Photo; **215**: 123RF; **217**: Kwest/Shutterstock; **221**: Jeff J Daly/Alamy Stock Photo; **223**: Adie Bush/Cultura Creative (RF)/Alamy Stock Photo; **224** (T): Nubephoto/Shutterstock; (B): Christopher Elwell/Shutterstock; **226** (L): Jeff J Daly/Alamy Stock Photo; (C): Andreykuzmin/Shutterstock; (R): Sirtravelalot/Shutterstock; **228**: Adie Bush/Cultura Creative (RF)/Alamy Stock Photo; **231**: MarcelClemens/Shutterstock; **233**: PjrStudio/Alamy Stock Photo; **234**: 123RF; **235**: Adie Bush/Cultura Creative (RF)/Alamy Stock Photo; **237**: Allstars/Shutterstock; **241**: Doug Allan/Nature Picture Library/Alamy Stock Photo; **245**: Charles D. Winters/Science Source; **246**: Turtle Rock Scientific/Science Source; **247** (L): Martyn F. Chillmaid/Science Source; (R): Jason Kolenda/Shutterstock; **248**: Adie Bush/Cultura Creative (RF)/Alamy Stock Photo; **252**: Jonathan Alcorn/Zumapress.com/Alamy Live News/Alamy Stock Photo; **253**: Charles D. Winters/Science Source; **258**: Adie Bush/Cultura Creative (RF)/Alamy Stock Photo

INVESTIGATION 8
260: Noel Hendrickson/Getty Images; **266**: Charles D. Winters/Science Source; **270**: Noel Hendrickson/Getty Images; **279**: Noel Hendrickson/Getty Images; **282**: Fotomandm/123RF; **290**: Noel Hendrickson/Getty Images; **300**: Noel Hendrickson/Getty Images

INVESTIGATION 9
302: Thom Baur/TPX Images of the Day/Reuters; **306**: Science Photo Library/Science Source; **314**: Thom Baur/TPX Images of the Day/Reuters; **316**: Richard Megna/Fundamental Photographs, NYC; **317**: Richard Megna/Fundamental Photographs, NYC; **319** (L): Turtle Rock Scientific/Science Source; (C): Totojang1977/Shutterstock; (R): Richard Megna/Fundamental Photographs, NYC; **322**: Richard Megna/Fundamental Photographs, NYC; **324**: Richard Megna/Fundamental Photographs, NYC; **328**: Thom Baur/TPX Images of the Day/Reuters; **330**: Richard Megna/Fundamental Photographs, NYC; **336**: Thom Baur/TPX Images of the Day/Reuters

INVESTIGATION 10
338: Stockcreations/Shutterstock; **346**: Stockcreations/Shutterstock; **356**: Stockcreations/Shutterstock; **366**: Stockcreations/Shutterstock; **362**: Isantilli/Shutterstock

INVESTIGATION 11
368: Joseph Giacomin/Cultura/Getty Images; **375**: Peter de Kievith/Shutterstock; **378**: Joseph Giacomin/Cultura/Getty Images; **386**: Joseph Giacomin/Cultura/Getty Images; **388**: Leonid Ikan/Shutterstock; **390**: Juhku/Shutterstock; **393**: Michael Shake/Shutterstock; **394**: Joseph Giacomin/Cultura/Getty Images; **395**: Mint Images RF/Getty Images.

TEXT ACKNOWLEDGEMENTS
48: *Geophysical Journal International.* Vol.199 (1), 2014:580-603. Fig1. Foley, Bradford J. and David Bercovici. "Scaling laws for convection with temperature-dependent viscosity and grain-damage." Reprinted with permission.

Notes

Notes

Notes

Notes

Notes

Notes

Notes

Notes

Notes

Notes

Notes

Notes

Notes

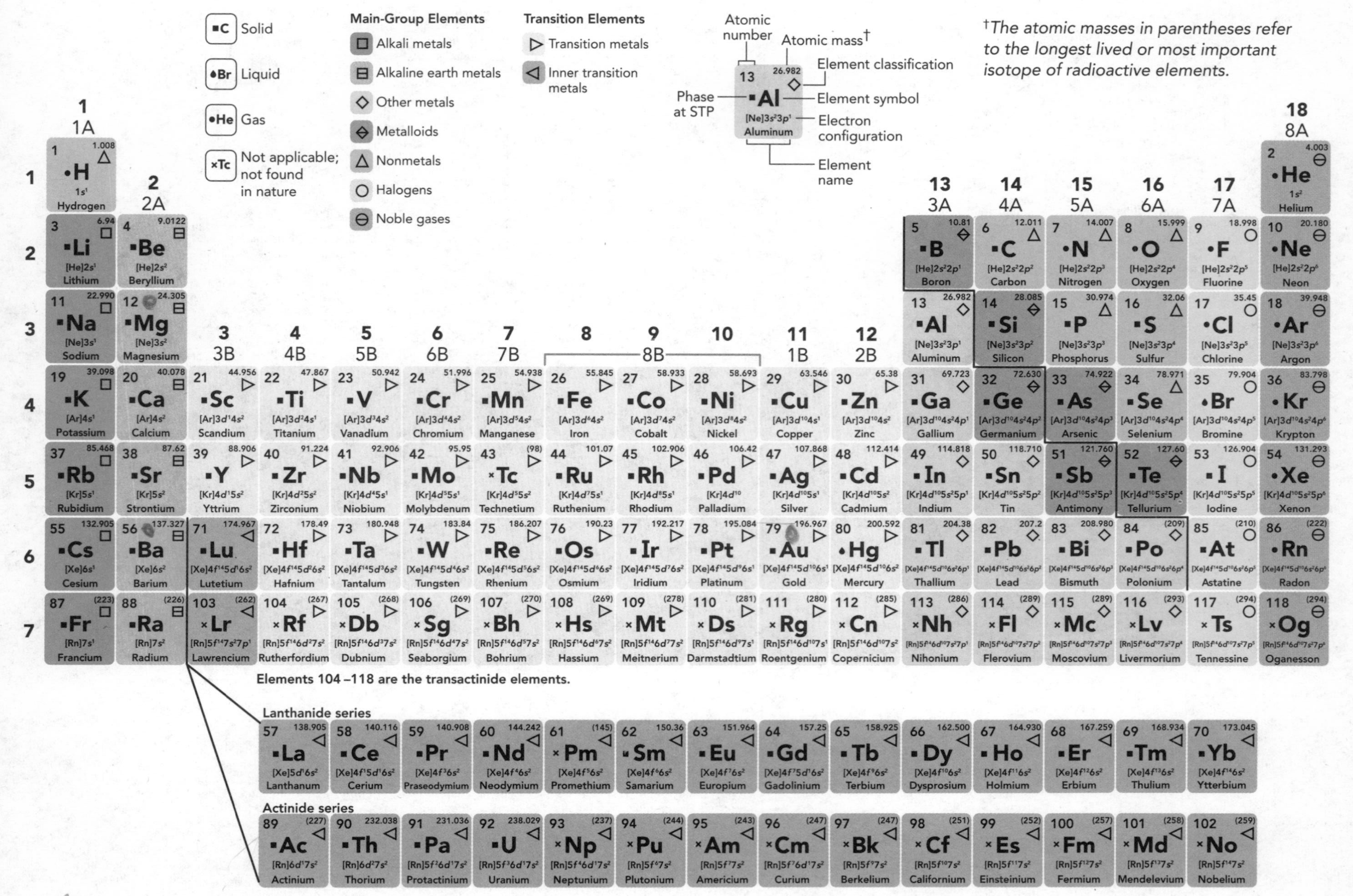

†The atomic masses in parentheses refer to the longest lived or most important isotope of radioactive elements.

	1 1A	2 2A	3 3B	4 4B	5 5B	6 6B	7 7B	8 8B	9 8B	10 8B	11 1B	12 2B	13 3A	14 4A	15 5A	16 6A	17 7A	18 8A
1	1 •H 1.008 $1s^1$ Hydrogen																	2 •He 4.003 $1s^2$ Helium
2	3 ■Li 6.94 $[He]2s^1$ Lithium	4 ■Be 9.0122 $[He]2s^2$ Beryllium											5 ■B 10.81 $[He]2s^22p^1$ Boron	6 ■C 12.011 $[He]2s^22p^2$ Carbon	7 •N 14.007 $[He]2s^22p^3$ Nitrogen	8 •O 15.999 $[He]2s^22p^4$ Oxygen	9 •F 18.998 $[He]2s^22p^5$ Fluorine	10 •Ne 20.180 $[He]2s^22p^6$ Neon
3	11 ■Na 22.990 $[Ne]3s^1$ Sodium	12 ■Mg 24.305 $[Ne]3s^2$ Magnesium											13 ■Al 26.982 $[Ne]3s^23p^1$ Aluminum	14 ■Si 28.085 $[Ne]3s^23p^2$ Silicon	15 ■P 30.974 $[Ne]3s^23p^3$ Phosphorus	16 ■S 32.06 $[Ne]3s^23p^4$ Sulfur	17 •Cl 35.45 $[Ne]3s^23p^5$ Chlorine	18 •Ar 39.948 $[Ne]3s^23p^6$ Argon
4	19 ■K 39.098 $[Ar]4s^1$ Potassium	20 ■Ca 40.078 $[Ar]4s^2$ Calcium	21 ■Sc 44.956 $[Ar]3d^14s^2$ Scandium	22 ■Ti 47.867 $[Ar]3d^24s^2$ Titanium	23 ■V 50.942 $[Ar]3d^34s^2$ Vanadium	24 ■Cr 51.996 $[Ar]3d^54s^1$ Chromium	25 ■Mn 54.938 $[Ar]3d^54s^2$ Manganese	26 ■Fe 55.845 $[Ar]3d^64s^2$ Iron	27 ■Co 58.933 $[Ar]3d^74s^2$ Cobalt	28 ■Ni 58.693 $[Ar]3d^84s^2$ Nickel	29 ■Cu 63.546 $[Ar]3d^{10}4s^1$ Copper	30 ■Zn 65.38 $[Ar]3d^{10}4s^2$ Zinc	31 ■Ga 69.723 $[Ar]3d^{10}4s^24p^1$ Gallium	32 ■Ge 72.630 $[Ar]3d^{10}4s^24p^2$ Germanium	33 ■As 74.922 $[Ar]3d^{10}4s^24p^3$ Arsenic	34 ■Se 78.971 $[Ar]3d^{10}4s^24p^4$ Selenium	35 ●Br 79.904 $[Ar]3d^{10}4s^24p^5$ Bromine	36 •Kr 83.798 $[Ar]3d^{10}4s^24p^6$ Krypton
5	37 ■Rb 85.468 $[Kr]5s^1$ Rubidium	38 ■Sr 87.62 $[Kr]5s^2$ Strontium	39 ■Y 88.906 $[Kr]4d^15s^2$ Yttrium	40 ■Zr 91.224 $[Kr]4d^25s^2$ Zirconium	41 ■Nb 92.906 $[Kr]4d^45s^1$ Niobium	42 ■Mo 95.95 $[Kr]4d^55s^1$ Molybdenum	43 ×Tc (98) $[Kr]4d^55s^2$ Technetium	44 ■Ru 101.07 $[Kr]4d^75s^1$ Ruthenium	45 ■Rh 102.906 $[Kr]4d^85s^1$ Rhodium	46 ■Pd 106.42 $[Kr]4d^{10}$ Palladium	47 ■Ag 107.868 $[Kr]4d^{10}5s^1$ Silver	48 ■Cd 112.414 $[Kr]4d^{10}5s^2$ Cadmium	49 ■In 114.818 $[Kr]4d^{10}5s^25p^1$ Indium	50 ■Sn 118.710 $[Kr]4d^{10}5s^25p^2$ Tin	51 ■Sb 121.760 $[Kr]4d^{10}5s^25p^3$ Antimony	52 ■Te 127.60 $[Kr]4d^{10}5s^25p^4$ Tellurium	53 ■I 126.904 $[Kr]4d^{10}5s^25p^5$ Iodine	54 •Xe 131.293 $[Kr]4d^{10}5s^25p^6$ Xenon
6	55 ■Cs 132.905 $[Xe]6s^1$ Cesium	56 ■Ba 137.327 $[Xe]6s^2$ Barium	71 ■Lu 174.967 $[Xe]4f^{14}5d^16s^2$ Lutetium	72 ■Hf 178.49 $[Xe]4f^{14}5d^26s^2$ Hafnium	73 ■Ta 180.948 $[Xe]4f^{14}5d^36s^2$ Tantalum	74 ■W 183.84 $[Xe]4f^{14}5d^46s^2$ Tungsten	75 ■Re 186.207 $[Xe]4f^{14}5d^56s^2$ Rhenium	76 ■Os 190.23 $[Xe]4f^{14}5d^66s^2$ Osmium	77 ■Ir 192.217 $[Xe]4f^{14}5d^76s^2$ Iridium	78 ■Pt 195.084 $[Xe]4f^{14}5d^96s^1$ Platinum	79 ■Au 196.967 $[Xe]4f^{14}5d^{10}6s^1$ Gold	80 ●Hg 200.592 $[Xe]4f^{14}5d^{10}6s^2$ Mercury	81 ■Tl 204.38 $[Xe]4f^{14}5d^{10}6s^26p^1$ Thallium	82 ■Pb 207.2 $[Xe]4f^{14}5d^{10}6s^26p^2$ Lead	83 ■Bi 208.980 $[Xe]4f^{14}5d^{10}6s^26p^3$ Bismuth	84 ■Po (209) $[Xe]4f^{14}5d^{10}6s^26p^4$ Polonium	85 ■At (210) $[Xe]4f^{14}5d^{10}6s^26p^5$ Astatine	86 •Rn (222) $[Xe]4f^{14}5d^{10}6s^26p^6$ Radon
7	87 ■Fr (223) $[Rn]7s^1$ Francium	88 ■Ra (226) $[Rn]7s^2$ Radium	103 ×Lr (262) $[Rn]5f^{14}7s^27p^1$ Lawrencium	104 ×Rf (267) $[Rn]5f^{14}6d^27s^2$ Rutherfordium	105 ×Db (268) $[Rn]5f^{14}6d^37s^2$ Dubnium	106 ×Sg (269) $[Rn]5f^{14}6d^47s^2$ Seaborgium	107 ×Bh (270) $[Rn]5f^{14}6d^57s^2$ Bohrium	108 ×Hs (269) $[Rn]5f^{14}6d^67s^2$ Hassium	109 ×Mt (278) $[Rn]5f^{14}6d^77s^2$ Meitnerium	110 ×Ds (281) $[Rn]5f^{14}6d^97s^1$ Darmstadtium	111 ×Rg (280) $[Rn]5f^{14}6d^{10}7s^1$ Roentgenium	112 ×Cn (285) $[Rn]5f^{14}6d^{10}7s^2$ Copernicium	113 ×Nh (286) $[Rn]5f^{14}6d^{10}7s^27p^1$ Nihonium	114 ×Fl (289) $[Rn]5f^{14}6d^{10}7s^27p^2$ Flerovium	115 ×Mc (289) $[Rn]5f^{14}6d^{10}7s^27p^3$ Moscovium	116 ×Lv (293) $[Rn]5f^{14}6d^{10}7s^27p^4$ Livermorium	117 ×Ts (294) $[Rn]5f^{14}6d^{10}7s^27p^5$ Tennessine	118 ×Og (294) $[Rn]5f^{14}6d^{10}7s^27p^6$ Oganesson

Elements 104–118 are the transactinide elements.

Lanthanide series

57 ■La 138.905 $[Xe]5d^16s^2$ Lanthanum	58 ■Ce 140.116 $[Xe]4f^15d^16s^2$ Cerium	59 ■Pr 140.908 $[Xe]4f^36s^2$ Praseodymium	60 ■Nd 144.242 $[Xe]4f^46s^2$ Neodymium	61 ×Pm (145) $[Xe]4f^56s^2$ Promethium	62 ■Sm 150.36 $[Xe]4f^66s^2$ Samarium	63 ■Eu 151.964 $[Xe]4f^76s^2$ Europium	64 ■Gd 157.25 $[Xe]4f^75d^16s^2$ Gadolinium	65 ■Tb 158.925 $[Xe]4f^96s^2$ Terbium	66 ■Dy 162.500 $[Xe]4f^{10}6s^2$ Dysprosium	67 ■Ho 164.930 $[Xe]4f^{11}6s^2$ Holmium	68 ■Er 167.259 $[Xe]4f^{12}6s^2$ Erbium	69 ■Tm 168.934 $[Xe]4f^{13}6s^2$ Thulium	70 ■Yb 173.045 $[Xe]4f^{14}6s^2$ Ytterbium

Actinide series

89 ■Ac (227) $[Rn]6d^17s^2$ Actinium	90 ■Th 232.038 $[Rn]6d^27s^2$ Thorium	91 ■Pa 231.036 $[Rn]5f^26d^17s^2$ Protactinium	92 ■U 238.029 $[Rn]5f^36d^17s^2$ Uranium	93 ×Np (237) $[Rn]5f^46d^17s^2$ Neptunium	94 ×Pu (244) $[Rn]5f^67s^2$ Plutonium	95 ×Am (243) $[Rn]5f^77s^2$ Americium	96 ×Cm (247) $[Rn]5f^76d^17s^2$ Curium	97 ×Bk (247) $[Rn]5f^97s^2$ Berkelium	98 ×Cf (251) $[Rn]5f^{10}7s^2$ Californium	99 ×Es (252) $[Rn]5f^{11}7s^2$ Einsteinium	100 ×Fm (257) $[Rn]5f^{12}7s^2$ Fermium	101 ×Md (258) $[Rn]5f^{13}7s^2$ Mendelevium	102 ×No (259) $[Rn]5f^{14}7s^2$ Nobelium